CAMERON
HYDRAULIC DATA

A handy reference on the subject of hydraulics, and steam

Edited by

C. R. Westaway

and

A. W. Loomis

Sixteenth Edition
Third Printing

Price
$10.00

 INGERSOLL-RAND.

Woodcliff Lake, N.J. 07675

INGERSOLL-RAND®

Pump Manufacturing Plants

Phillipsburg, N.J., U.S.A.
Allentown, Pa., U.S.A.
Gateshead, Co. Durham, England
Sherbrooke, Que., Canada
Kitchner/Cambridge, Ontario, Canada
Naucalpan de Juarez, Mexico
Alberton, Transvaal, So. Africa
Coslada, Madrid, Spain

Form 931

CAMERON
HYDRAULIC DATA

Preface to the Sixteenth Edition (2nd Printing)

The Cameron Hydraulic Data Book is an Ingersoll-Rand publication and, as in the previous fifteen editions, is published as an aid to engineers involved with the selection and application of pumping equipment.

The information in the sixteenth edition, has been updated and brought in line with current practice, primarily the data dealing with the flow of liquids through pipes, valves and fittings. Other information which has been expanded on in considerable detail includes: "Weight—Volume Relationships for Cellulose Fiber-Water Suspensions" and the section on conversion factor (metric) data.

Also, minor rearrangements of certain material has been made for more convenient reference; in addition, some additional data on density, specific gravity, specific weight, vapor pressure and viscosity of various liquids that may be of help and interest has been included.

To facilitate locating the desired data, a detailed index has been provided in the rear of this book (Section IX). It should be noted that for convenient reference this index is arranged in two (2) parts; first a General Index with items listed alphabetically, page 9–2 through page 9–10, and secondly, an Index of Liquids arranged alphabetically, page 9–11 through page 9–14.

Frequent reference to this index is suggested for quickly locating the information desired.

WARNING

The misuse or misapplication of data in this book could result in machinery or system failures, severe damage to other property and/or serious injury to persons. Ingersoll-Rand Company does not assume any liability for any losses or damages resulting from the use or application of the materials and data set forth in this book.

INGERSOLL-RAND CAMERON HYDRAULIC DATA

Contents

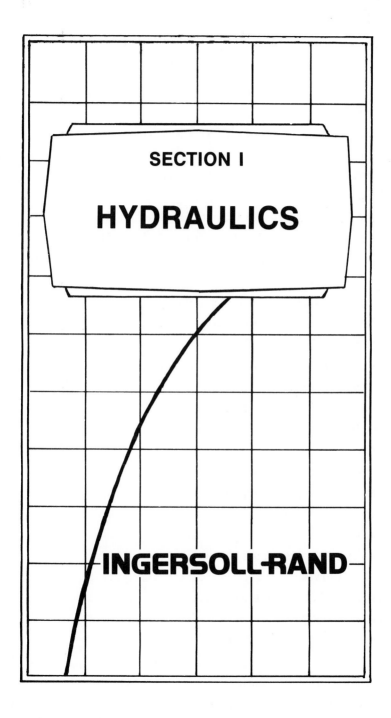

SECTION I

HYDRAULICS

INGERSOLL-RAND

CONTENTS OF SECTION 1
Hydraulics

Introduction

The following outline is offered for those who have a basic understanding and knowledge of hydraulic and fluid dynamic principles, but who would like a convenient reference to various items that must be taken into consideration in the commercial selection and application of pumping equipment. If more detailed information is desired, or to investigate the subject in greater depth, reference is suggested to the many Textbooks, Technical Papers, Engineering Handbooks, Standards and Manuals that are available, some of which are listed in the Bibliography at the conclusion of this section. (Page 1-47)

Liquids

Hydraulics is concerned with the behavior of liquids at rest and in motion. A liquid has a definite volume as contrasted to a gas which will expand or contract depending on changes in temperature and pressure.

Liquids are said to be "practically" incompressible. This is true for most considerations at low pressures but at higher pressures and as temperatures vary, there will be changes in density which must be taken into account.

The pressure existing at any point in a liquid at rest is caused by the atmospheric pressure exerted on the surface, plus the weight of liquid above the point in question. Such pressure is equal in all directions and acts perpendicularly to any surfaces in contact with the liquid.

All liquid pressures can be visualized as being caused by a column of liquid which due to its weight would produce a pressure equivalent to the pressure at the point in question. Such a column of liquid, real or imaginary, is called the "pressure head," or the "static head" and is usually expressed in feet of liquid.

The flow of liquids may be caused by gravity or by mechanical means using one of the many types of pumps that may be available depending on the characteristics of the liquid and the nature of the service conditions.

Since this discussion is primarily concerned with the proper selection and application of centrifugal pumps reference is made to Figure 1 illustrating diagrammatically a simple centrifugal pump; here it will be observed that in its simplest form a centrifugal pump consists of an impeller rotating within a casing. Liquid directed into the center of the rotating impeller is picked up by the impeller vanes and accelerated to a

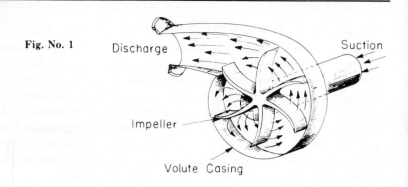

Fig. No. 1   Discharge   Suction

Impeller

Volute Casing

high velocity by the rotation of the impeller and discharged by centrifugal force into the casing and out the discharge. When the liquid in the impeller is forced away from the center of the impeller a reduced pressure is produced and consequently more liquid flows forward. Therefore a steady flow through the impeller is produced unless something happens to break the vacuum at the inlet or disrupt the flow to the center of the impeller or unless the flow at the discharge is restricted by a pressure greater than the pressure head developed by the rotating impeller.

Liquid flow

During passage through a pipe the flow of a liquid is said to be laminar (viscous) or turbulent depending on the liquid velocity, pipe size and liquid viscosity. For any given liquid and pipe size these factors can be expressed in terms of a dimensionless number called the Reynolds number R where:

$$R = \frac{VD}{v}$$

V = Average velocity—ft/sec
D = Average internal diameter—ft
v = Kinematic viscosity of the fluid—ft²/sec (For pure fresh water at 60°F v = 0.000 012 16 ft²/sec)

For values of R less than approximately 2000 the flow is laminar (viscous); i.e., particles of the liquid follow separate non-intersecting paths with little or no eddying or turbulence.

When R is above 4000 turbulent flow is considered to exist.

Values of R between 2000 and 4000 are in the critical zone where the flow is generally considered to be turbulent for the purpose of friction loss or pressure drop calculations; this gives safe results because the friction loss is higher for turbulent flow than for laminar (viscous) flow.

Viscosity (see page 4-23)

In flowing liquids the existence of internal friction or the internal resistance to relative motion of the fluid particles with respect to each other must be considered; this resistance is called viscosity.

The viscosities of most liquids vary appreciably with changes in temperature whereas the influence of pressure change is usually negligible. The viscosities of certain liquids can change depending on the extent to which the liquid may be agitated.

A liquid is said to be a "Newtonian" or "true" fluid if its viscosity is unaffected by the kind and magnitude of motion or agitation to which it may be subjected as long as the temperature remains constant; an example of a "Newtonian" liquid would be water or mineral oil.

A liquid is said to be "thixotropic" if its viscosity decreases as agitation is increased at constant temperature; examples of "thixotropic" liquids would be asphalts, cellulose compounds, glues, greases, molasses, paints and soaps.

A liquid is said to be "dilatant" if the viscosity increases as agitation is increased at constant temperature; examples of "dilatant" liquids are clay slurries and candy compounds.

Pumping

To move a liquid against gravity or to force it into a pressure vessel, or to provide enough head, or pressure head, to overcome pipe friction and other resistance work must be expended. No matter what the service required of a pump, all forms of energy imparted to the liquid both on the suction and discharge sides in performing this service must be accounted for in establishing the duty to be performed.

In centrifugal pump applications in order that all these forms of energy may be algebraically added it is customary to express them all in terms of head expressed in feet of liquid. In reciprocating, rotary, or positive displacement types of pumps it is customary to express the heads in terms of pressure (psi).

The various items that must be taken into account in establishing the total head (based on feet of liquid) including design capacity (volume) are discussed below.

Volume

In this discussion the standard unit of volume will be the U.S. gallon. The rate of flow shall be expressed in gallons per minute (gpm).

The specific weight of water at a temperature of 65°F shall be taken as 62.34 lbs per cubic foot. For other temperatures proper specific weight corrections should be made in calculating the rate of flow particularly if the required delivery is given in pounds per hour; for example:

$$\text{gpm} = \frac{\text{lb per hour}}{*500 \times \text{specific gravity}}$$

System head calculations

The *total head* (H)—formerly called "total dynamic head"—for a specific system is equal to the total discharge head (h_d) minus the total suction head (h_s) or plus the total suction lift.

It is recommended that total head calculations for the suction side be listed separately from those for the discharge side to help avoid the possibility of overlooking a troublesome suction condition.

In this discussion the terms suction head and suction lift (or the equivalent of a lift) are discussed separately to help visualize the suction conditions that may exist.

Suction head

Suction head (h_s) exists when the liquid supply level is above the pump centerline or impeller eye. The *total suction head* is equal to the static height or static submergence in feet that the liquid supply level is above the pump centerline less all suction line losses including entrance loss plus any pressure (a vacuum as in a condenser hotwell being a negative pressure) existing at the suction supply source. *Caution*—even when the liquid supply level is above the pump centerline the equivalent of a lift will exist if the total suction line losses (and vacuum effect) exceed the positive static suction head. This condition can cause problems particularly when handling volatile or viscous liquids.

---

* Note: One gallon of water weighs 8.333 pounds at 65°F; therefore 60 × 8.333 equals 500.

For practical applications the ** specific gravity of water is considered to be equal to 1.00 at normal temperatures (60°F to 70°F); for some purposes it is taken as 1.00 at 39.2°F (4°C) which is its point of maximum density; for most applications which base is selected makes little difference. See pages 2-3 and 4-3.

** Basis specific gravity of 1.00, one psi equals 2.31 ft of water at normal temperatures.

On an existing installation total suction head would be the reading of a gage at the suction flange converted to feet of liquid and corrected to the pump centerline elevation plus the velocity head in feet of liquid at point of gage attachment.

Suction lift

Suction lift (h_s) exists when the liquid supply level or suction source is below the pump centerline or impeller eye. Total suction lift is equal to the static lift in feet plus all friction losses in the suction line including entrance loss.

When the liquid supply level or suction source is above the pump centerline or impeller eye and under a vacuum, as in a condenser hotwell, the equivalent of a suction lift will exist which will be equal to the vacuum effect in feet less the net submergence.

On an existing installation the *total suction lift* is the reading of a mercury column or vacuum gage at the suction flange converted to feet of liquid and corrected to the pump centerline elevation minus the velocity head in feet of liquid at point of gage attachment.

Total discharge head (h_d)—is the sum of: (1) Static discharge head. (2) All piping and friction losses on discharge side including straight runs of pipe, losses at all valves, fittings, strainers, control valves, etc. (3) Pressure in discharge chamber (if a closed vessel). (4) Losses at sudden enlargements (as in a condenser water box). (5) Exit loss at liquid discharge (usually assumed to be equal to one velocity head at discharge velocity) (6) Plus any loss factors that experience indicates may be desirable.

On an existing installation *total discharge head* would be the reading of a pressure gage at the discharge flange converted to feet of liquid and corrected to the pump centerline plus the velocity head (in feet of liquid) at the point of gage attachment.

Velocity head (h_v)—in a pumping system is an energy component that represents the kinetic or "velocity" energy in a moving liquid at the point being considered in the system. It is equivalent to the vertical distance the mass of liquid would have to fall (in a perfect vacuum) to acquire the velocity V and is expressed as:

$$h_v = \frac{V^2}{2g} = 0.0155V^2 = \frac{0.00259(\text{gpm})^2}{d^4} = \frac{0.00127(\text{bph})^2}{d^4}$$

where:

h_v = velocity head in feet of liquid
V = velocity of liquid—ft/sec
d = inside diameter of pipe in inches
g = gravitational constant—32.174 ft/sec^2
gpm = gallons (U.S.) per minute
bph = barrels (42 gallons—U.S.) per hour

The velocity head energy component is used in system head calculations as a basis for establishing entrance losses, losses in valves and fittings, losses at other sudden enlargements and exit losses by applying the appropriate resistance coefficient K to the $V^2/2g$ term (see page 3-110).

In system head calculations for high head pumps the velocity head will be but a small percentage of the total head and is not significant. However, in low head pumps it can be a substantial percentage and must be considered.

When total heads on an existing installation are being determined from gage readings then the velocity head values as calculated must be included; i.e. the *total suction lift* will be the reading of a vacuum gage or mercury column at the suction flange, corrected to the pump centerline elevation minus the velocity head at point of gage attachment. The *total suction head* and *total discharge head* will be the readings of gages at the flanges corrected to the pump centerline elevation plus the velocity heads at the points of gage attachements.

Total system head (H)—formerly total dynamic head—is the total discharge head (h_d) minus the total suction head (h_s) if positive or plus if a suction lift: $H = h_d - h_s$ (head) or $H = h_d + h_s$ (lift). *Note*: For typical suction head calculations, see examples 1, 2, 3, 4 and 5 under NPSH pages 1-11 to 1-15. For total head calculation see example on pages 3-9 and 3-10.

Pump head—Pressure—Specific gravity

In a centrifugal pump the head developed (in feet) is dependent on the velocity of the liquid as it enters the impeller eye and as it leaves the impeller periphery and therefore is independent of the specific gravity of the liquid. The pressure head developed (in psi) will be directly proportional to the specific gravity.

Head and *Pressure* are interchangeable terms provided that they are expressed in their correct units. In English Units to convert from one to the other use:

$$\text{Liquid Head in feet} = \frac{\text{psi} \times 2.31}{\text{sp gr}}$$

or

$$\text{Liquid Head in feet} = \frac{\text{psi} \times 144}{\text{W}}$$

$$\text{Pressure in psi} = \frac{\text{Head in feet} \times \text{sp gr}}{2.31}$$

or

$$\text{Pressure in psi} = \frac{\text{Head in feet} \times \text{W}}{144}$$

Where W = *Specific weight in pounds per cubic foot of liquid being pumped under pumping conditions; For Water W = 62.32 lb per cu ft at 68 degrees F (20°C).

A column of water 2.31 ft high will exert a pressure of one (1) psi based on water at approximately 65°F.*

Figures 2 and 3 are included to help visualize the head-pressure relationships of centrifugal pumps when handling liquids of varying specific gravities.

Fig. 2 illustrates three identical pumps, each pump designed to develop 115.5 ft. of head; when pumping water with a specific gravity of 1.0 (at 68°F) the pressure head will be 50 psi (115.5 ft divided by 2.31); when pumping liquids of other gravities, the head (in feet) will be the same, but the pressure head (psi) will be proportional to the specific gravities as shown; to avoid errors, it is advisable to check one's calculations by using the above formulas.

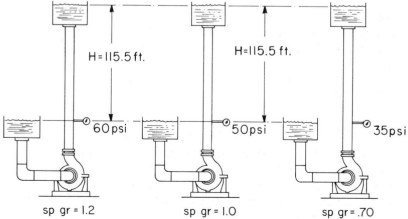

Fig. 2. Pressure—head relationship of identical pumps handling liquids of differing specific gravities.

* For other water temperatures see tables on pages 4-4 and 4-5

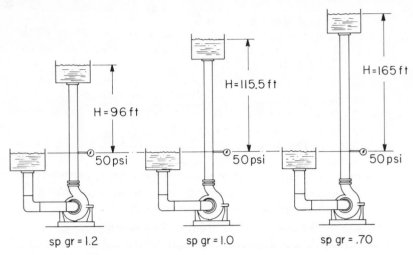

Fig. 3 Pressure-head relationship of pumps delivering same pressure handling liquids of differing specific gravity.

Figure 3 illustrates three pumps, each designed to develop the same pressure head (in psi); consequently the head (in feet of liquid) will be inversely proportional to the specific gravity as shown.

In these illustrations friction losses, etc., have been disregarded.

Net Positive Suction Head

The Net Positive Suction Head (NPSH) is the total suction head in feet of liquid (absolute at the pump centerline or impeller eye) less the absolute vapor pressure (in feet) of the liquid being pumped.

It must always have a positive value and can be calculated by the following equations: To help in visualizing the conditions that exist, two (2) expressions will be used; the *first expression* is basis a suction lift-liquid supply level is below the pump centerline or impeller eye; the *second expression* is basis a positive suction, (flooded), where the liquid supply level is above the pump centerline or impeller eye.

For Suction Lift:

$$NPSH = h_a - h_{vpa} - h_{st} - h_{fs}$$

For Positive (Flooded) Suction:

$$NPSH = h_a - h_{vpa} + h_{st} - h_{fs}$$

where:

h_a = absolute pressure (in feet of liquid) on the surface of the liquid supply level (this will be barometric pressure if suction is from an open tank or sump; or the absolute pressure existing in a closed tank such as a condenser hotwell or deareator).

h_{vpa} = The head in feet corresponding to the vapor pressure of the liquid at the temperature being pumped.

h_{st} = Static height in feet that the liquid supply level is above or below the pump centerline or impeller eye.

h_{fs} = All suction line losses (in feet) including entrance losses and friction losses through pipe, valves and fittings, etc.

Two values of net positive suction head must be considered; i.e. Net Positive Suction Head Required (NPSHR) and Net Positive Suction Head Available (NPSHA).

The NPSHR is determined by the pump manufacturer and will depend on many factors including type of impeller inlet, impeller design, pump flow, rotational speed, nature of liquid, etc. NPSHR is usually plotted on the characteristic pump performance curve supplied by the pump manufacturer. The Net Positive Suction Head Available (NPSHA) depends on the system layout and must always be equal to or greater than the NPSHR.

The vapor pressure of the liquid at the pumping temperature must always be known to calculate the NPSHA. On an existing installation the NPSH available would be the reading of a gage at the suction flange converted to feet of liquid absolute and corrected to the pump centerline elevation less the vapor pressure of the liquid in feet absolute plus the velocity head in feet of liquid at point of gage attachment.

The **following examples** show the importance and influence of vapor pressure. In all cases, for simplicity, the same capacity will be used; also the following suction line losses will be assumed in all cases:

Friction loss through suction pipe and fittings	2.51 ft
*Entrance loss (assume equal to one half velocity head)	0.41
	———
Total losses	2.92 ft

*Note: For more exact entrance losses, refer to pages 3-116 thru 3-118.

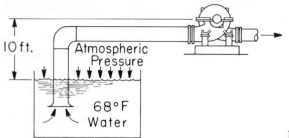

Fig. 4. (Example No 1)

Example No 1 (Fig 4)

Open system, source below pump; 68° F water at sea level. Atmospheric pressures 14.696 psia, 33.96 ft abs. Vapor pressure of liquid 0.339 psia = 0.783 ft abs.

NPSHA = 33.96 − 0.783 − 10.00 − 2.92 = 20.26 ft

Suction Lift = 10.00 + 2.92 = 12.92 ft—this is to be added to discharge head to obtain total head.

Note: No pump can actually lift water on the suction side. In this case, water is forced in by an excess of atmospheric pressure over the vapor pressure less 12.92 ft net static lift.

Example No 2 (Fig 5)

Open system, source above pump; 68° F water at sea level.

NPSHA = 33.96 − 0.783 + 10.00 − 2.92 = 40.26 ft.

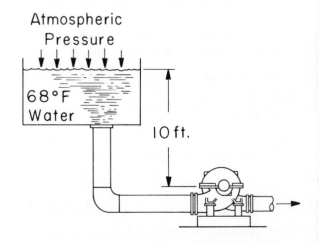

Fig. 5 (Example 2)

Suction Head $-$ $10.00 - 2.92 = 7.08$ ft—this is to be subtracted from discharge head to obtain total head.

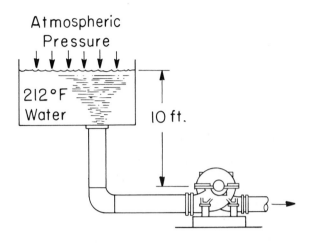

Fig. 6 (Example 3)

Example No. 3 (Fig. 6)

Open system, source above pump; 212° F water at sea level; vapor pressure same as atmospheric since liquid at boiling point.

NPSHA $= 33.96 - 33.96 + 10.00 - 2.92 = 7.08$ ft. In this case, atmospheric pressure does not add to NPSHA since it is required to keep the water in liquid phase.

Suction Head $= 10.00 - 2.92 = 7.08$ ft—this is to be subtracted from discharge head to obtain total head.

Note: In this example it was assumed that pipe friction losses for 212° F

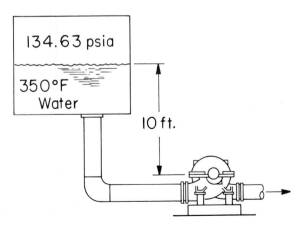

Fig. 7 (Example 4)

water were the same as for 68° F water whereas actually they would be somewhat less, as will also be the case in Example 4.

Example No 4 (Fig 7)

Closed system (under pressure as a feed water deareator) source above pump.

350° F water V.P. = 134.60 psia = 348.76 ft abs (at 350° F sp gr = 0.8904).

NPSHA = 348.76 − 348.76 + 10.00 − 2.92 = 7.08 ft.

Suction Head—(Figure basis gage pressures; i.e., 119.91 psig = 310.69 ft) = 310.69 + 10.00 − 2.92 = 317.77 ft—This to be subtracted from the discharge head to obtain total system head. It is important to note that while the suction head is 317.77 ft (122.64 psig) the NPSHA is still only 7.08 ft.

Example No 5 (Fig. 8)—Closed system (under vacuum as a condenser hotwell) liquid source above pump. Absolute pressure (h_a) = 1.50″ Hg × 1.139 = 1.71 ft. Water at saturation point 91.72°F; therefore vapor pressure (h_{vpa}) = 1.50″ Hg × 1.139 = 1.71 ft.

NPSHA = 1.71 − 1.71 + 10.00 − 2.92 = 7.08 ft.

Suction Condition—In this example the suction condition (head or lift) for the pump can best be visualized by the calculations listed below where it can be seen that we have a suction lift equal to the vacuum effect at the suction source less the net static submergence.

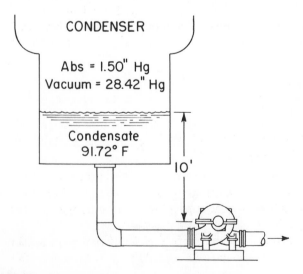

CONDENSER

Abs = 1.50″ Hg
Vacuum = 28.42″ Hg

Condensate
91.72° F

10′

Fig. 8 (Example 5)

28.42″ Hg Vacuum = 28.42 × 1.139 =		32.37 ft
Static submergence	10.00 ft	
Friction and entrance loss	2.92 ft	
	———	
Net static submergence	= 7.08 ft	7.08 ft
		−
		———
Equivalent suction lift = vacuum		
effect less net submergence =		25.29 ft

In this example it is noted that the NPSHA is equal to the static suction head less the friction and entrance losses. Also the equivalent suction lift must be added to the total discharge head to obtain the total system head.

In the foregoing examples standard sea level atmospheric conditions were assumed; for other locations where altitude is a factor proper corrections must be made. These examples (3, 4 and 5) illustrate that if the liquid is in equilibrium (vapor pressure corresponds to saturation temperature) then the NPSH is equal to the difference in elevation between the liquid supply level and the pump centerline elevation (or impeller eye) less the sum of the entrance loss and the friction losses in the suction line.

NPSH reductions—hydrocarbon liquids and hot water

The NPSH requirements of centrifugal pumps are normally determined on the basis of handling water at or near normal room temperatures. However, field experience and laboratory tests have confirmed that pumps handling certain gas free hydrocarbon fluids and water at elevated temperatures will operate satisfactorily with harmless cavitation and less NPSH available than would be required for cold water.

The figure on page 1-46 shows NPSH reductions that may be considered for hot water and certain gas free pure hydrocarbon liquids.

The use and application of this chart is subject to certain limitations some of which are summarized below:

1. The NPSH reductions shown are based on laboratory test data at steady state suction conditions and on the gas free pure hydrocarbon liquids shown; its application to other liquids must be considered experimental and is not recommended.
2. No NPSH reduction should exceed 50% of the NPSH required for cold water or ten feet whichever is smaller.

3. In the absence of test data demonstrating NPSH reductions greater than ten feet the chart has been limited to that extent and extrapolation beyond that point is not recommended.
4. Vapor pressure for the liquid should be determined by the bubble point method—do not use the Reid vapor pressure.
5. Do not use the chart for liquids having entrained air or other non-condensible gases which may be released as the absolute pressure is lowered at the entrance to the impeller, in which case additional NPSH may be required for satisfactory operation.
6. In the use of the chart for high temperature liquids, particularly with water, due consideration must be given to the susceptibility of the suction system to transient changes in temperature and absolute pressure which might require additional NPSH to provide a margin of safety, far exceeding the reduction otherwise permitted for steady state operation.

Subject to the above limitations, which should be reviewed with the Manufacturer, the proceedure in using the chart is as follows: Assume a pump requires 16 feet NPSH on cold water at the design capacity is to handle pure propane at 55 Deg F which has a vapor pressure of approximately 100 psia; the chart shows a reduction of 9.5 feet which is greater than one half the cold water NPSHR. The corrected value of the NPSHR is one half the cold water NPSHR or 8 feet. Assume this same pump has another application to handle propane at 14 Deg F where its vapor pressure is 50 psia. In this case the chart shows a reduction of 6 feet which is less than one half of the cold water NPSH. The corrected value of NPSH is therefore 16 feet less 6 feet or 10 feet. Note in reading the chart follow the sloping lines from left to right.

For a more detailed discussion on the use of this chart and its limitations reference is suggested to the Hydraulic Institute Standards.

NPSH—Reciprocating pumps

The foregoing discussion on NPSH and accompanying calculations was primarily for the benefit of centrifugal pump selections and applications.

NPSH available for a reciprocating pump application is calculated in the same manner as for a centrifugal pump, except in the NPSH required for a reciprocating pump some additional allowance must be made for the reciprocating action of the pump; this *additional* requirement is termed "acceleration head." This is the head required to

1

accelerate the liquid column on each suction stroke so that there will be no separation of this column in the pump or suction line.

If this minimum condition is not met the pump will experience a fluid knock caused when the liquid column, which has a vapor space between it and the plunger, overtakes the receding plunger. This knock occurs approximately two-thirds of the way through the suction stroke. If sufficient acceleration is provided for the liquid to completely follow the motion of the receding face of the plunger, this knock will disappear.

If there is insufficient head to meet minimum acceleration requirements of NPSH, the pump will experience cavitation resulting in loss of volumetric efficiency; also, serious damage can occur to the plungers, pistons, valves and packing due to the forces released in collapsing the gas or vapor bubbles.

Acceleration head—reciprocating pumps

The head required to accelerate the fluid column is a function of the length of the suction line, the average velocity in this line, the rotative speed, the type of pump, and the relative elasticity of the fluid and the pipe and may be calculated as follows:

$$h_a = \frac{LVnC}{Kg}$$

where

h_a = Acceleration head in feet
L = Length of suction line in feet
V = Velocity in suction line in fps
n = Pump speed in rpm
*C = Constant (for the type of pump)
C = 0.200 for duplex single-acting
  = 0.115 for duplex double-acting
  = 0.066 for triplex single or double-acting
  = 0.040 for quintuplex single or double-acting
  = 0.028 for septuplex single or double-acting
  = 0.022 for nonuplex, single or double-acting.

*K = A factor representing the reciprocal of the fraction of the theoretical acceleration head which must be provided to avoid a noticeable disturbance in the suction line: (K = 2.5 for hot

Note: The constant C will vary from these values for unusual ratios of connecting rod length to crank radius.

* Courtesy of Hydraulic Institute.

oil, 2.0 most hydrocarbons, 1.5 amine, glycol, water, 1.4 deareated water, 1.0 urea and liquids with small amounts of entrained gases).

g = Gravitational constant (32.174 ft/sec^2)

A pulsation damper properly installed with a short, full-size connection to the pump or suction pipe can absorb the cyclical flow variation and reduce the pressure fluctuation in the suction pipe to that corresponding to a length of 5 to 15 pipe diameters, if kept properly charged.

There is a similar pressure fluctuation on the discharge side of every power pump, but it cannot be analyzed as readily because of the greater influence of liquid and piping elasticity and the smaller diameter and much greater length of the discharge line in most applications. However, a pulsation damper can be just as effective in absorbing the flow variation on the discharge side of the pump, as on the suction side, and should be used if pressure-fluctuation and piping vibration is a problem.

Example: Given a 2" × 5" triplex pump running at 360 rpm and displacing 73 gpm of water with a suction pipe made up of 4 feet of 4-inch pipe and 20 feet of 6-inch pipe:

Average velocity in 4-inch pipe

$$V_4 = \frac{0.321 \times 73}{12.73} = 1.84 \text{ fps}$$

Average velocity in 6-inch pipe

$$V_6 = \frac{0.321 \times 73}{28.89} = 0.811 \text{ fps}$$

Acceleration head in 4-inch pipe

$$h_{a4} = \frac{4 \times 1.84 \times 360 \times 0.066}{1.4 \times 32.2} = 3.88 \text{ ft}$$

Acceleration head in 6-inch pipe

$$h_{a6} = \frac{20 \times .811 \times 360 \times 0.066}{1.4 \times 32.2} = 8.55 \text{ ft}$$

Total acceleration head

$$h_a = 3.88 + 8.55 = 12.4 \text{ ft}$$

Note: h_a is added to the NPSHR by the pump.

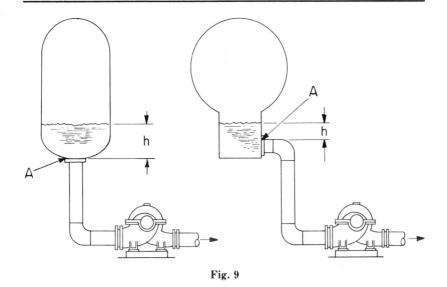

Fig. 9

Entrance losses

Special mention is made of entrance loss considerations because failure to appreciate and provide for this problem is one of the major causes of faulty pump performance, particularly when handling liquids that are in equilibrium such as light hydrocarbons from a vacuum tower or condensate from a condenser hotwell.

Reference to Figure 9 illustrates that when taking suction from the bottom of a tower, or a side outlet from a condenser hotwell, sufficient static height (h) must be provided to account for the entrance loss and velocity head at point "A" plus any additional submergence that may be required to prevent vortices from entering the suction line. The submergence required to control vortices may be reduced by using suitable baffles or other anti-swirl devices.

Specific speed

In the intelligent consideration of centrifugal pumps it is helpful to have an understanding of specific speed to determine if the pump design being proposed is within certain established limits for the service conditions under which it will operate.

In Specific Speed terminology there are two considerations: (1) First—Impeller specific speed and (2) Secondly—suction specific speed; Impeller specific speed will be discussed first.

Impeller specific speed (N_s)

This is an index of hydraulic design; it is defined as the speed at which an impeller, geometrically similar to the one under consideration, would run if it were reduced in size to deliver one gpm at one foot head.

Mathematically it is expressed as:

$$N_s = \frac{\text{rpm} \sqrt{\text{gpm}}}{H^{3/4}}$$

where:

      rpm = Pump speed.
      gpm = Design capacity at best efficiency point.
      H = Total head per stage in feet at best efficiency point.

Impeller specific speed is an index as to the type of impeller when the factors in the above formula correspond to its performance at optimum (or best) efficiency point. It is a useful tool for the Hydraulic Designer in the designing of impellers to meet varying conditions of head, capacity (and shape of curve), suction conditions and speed. Impellers for high heads and low net positive suction head required usually have low specific speeds, whereas, impellers for low heads and high NPSHR usually have high specific speeds. Depending on the type of impeller specific speeds can range between 400 to 20,000 for commerical designs. According to specific speed values impellers and pumps can be classified roughly as follows:

      Below 4200-Centrifugal or Radial type;
      Between 4200 and 9000-Mixed Flow;
      Above 9000-Axial Flow.

The charts and illustrations included herewith—pages 1-36 to 1-37 show typical impeller types for various specific speed ranges; also the variations in head—capacity performance characteristics for various specific speed are illustrated.

Specific speed is also a very valuable criterion in determining the permissable safe maximum suction lift or the minimum net positive suction head required for various conditions of capacity, head and speed.

The Hydraulic Institute has established suggested specific speed limitations with respect to suction conditions for various types of pumps. These suggested limitations are expressed graphically on charts (pages 1-38 to 1-46) reproduced herein with permission of the Hydraulic Institute. For a more detailed discussion of these charts and their application reference should be made to the Hydraulic Institute Standards.

Suction specific speed (S)

Suction specific speed (S) like Impeller specific speed (N_s) is a parameter, or index of hydraulic design except here it is essentially an index descriptive of the suction capabilities and characteristics of a given first stage impeller. It is expressed as:

$$S = \frac{rpm \sqrt{gpm}}{(NPSHR)^{3/4}}$$

where

    rpm = Pump speed.

    gpm = Design capacity at best efficiency point for single suction first stage impellers, or one half the design capacity in gpm for double suction first stage impellers (at maximum diameter).

  NPSHR = Net positive suction head required in feet (at best efficiency point).

By selecting reasonable values for S which have been determined by experience and can be considered conservative, the Engineer concerned in making a suction line layout can estimate what NPSH must be provided to handle a certain flow (gpm); i.e.

$$(NPSHR)^{3/4} = \frac{rpm \sqrt{gpm}}{S}$$

$$NPSHR = \left(\frac{rpm \sqrt{gpm}}{S} \right)^{1.33}$$

Suction specific speeds (S) can range between 3000 and 20,000 depending on impeller design, speed, capacity, nature of liquid and conditions of service and degree of cavitation.

From experience, reasonable values of S for estimating purposes have been found to be in the range of 7000 to 12,000 for water, depending on the pump speed and type of service under which the pump is to operate. Pumps handling hydrocarbons may operate satisfactorily with values of S ranging up to 15,000 or higher.

A high suction specific speed may indicate the impeller eye is somewhat larger than normal and consequently the efficiency may be compromised to obtain a low NPSHR. Higher values of S may also require special designs and may also operate with some degree of cavitation; to avoid marginal designs on the suction side it is desirable for the user or systems engineer to consult with the Pump Manufacturer for suggested design criteria, and to make certain that the suction conditions finally established will meet the requirements of the pump selected.

Submergence

Submergence must not be confused with NPSH regardless of whether the suction is negative (lift) or positive (flooded). Usually submergence is a term used to relate liquid level to the setting of a vertical immersed wet pit type pump with a free air surface at the liquid supply level.

In the case of a conventional horizontal pump operating with a suction lift, or a large dry pit type pump, with a flooded suction, some submergence or liquid level, in addition to the NPSHR, may be necessary to prevent vortex formation on the liquid supply surface and thus preclude or retard the possibility of air being drawn in the pump suction intake. The amount of submergence will depend to some extent on the design of the suction intake; i.e. a bell or cone shaped entrance should require less than a straight pipe intake.

Intake design

In addition to providing sufficient submergence for vertical wet pit immersed pumps it is imperative that the sump and intake structure be of proper proportions—and that pump arrangements be such as to preclude uneven velocity distributions in the approach to the pump or around the suction bell.

Uneven velocity distributions particularly when accompanied by insufficient submergence can result in the formation of vortices which will introduce air in the pump suction causing a reduction in capacity, unbalance and rough operation resulting in rapid deterioration of equipment and costly outages. Also, underwater vortices can form, causing uneven flow into the impeller resulting in rough operation. Providing additional submergence will not compensate for an improperly designed intake and therefore careful consideration must be given to pump arrangement and location of intake and sump dimensions.

Vertical wet pit pumps

Referring to Figure 10 and using the pump suction bell diameter* (D) as a reference:

1. Back wall distance to centerline of pump is 0.75D.
2. Side wall distance to centerline of pump is 1.00D.
3. Bottom clearance (approximate) is 0.30D.
4. Location of the intake screen can vary depending on the particular design, but usually should be in the range of 3D to 4D minimum from inside face of screen to centerline of pump.
5. Intake tunnel velocity should be less than 2 to 3 ft/sec.
6. No restrictions or sharp turns should occur less than 6D or 3 times the channel width in front of the pump, whichever is greater.
7. Provide water depth (submergence) over the pump suction bell in accordance with the "Capacity vs Submergence" chart—Fig. No. 14.

* Check Manufacturer for dimensions.

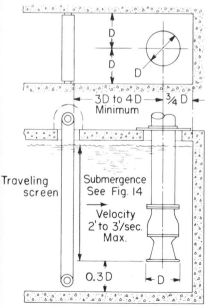

Fig. 10 Standard Vertical Wet Pit Pump

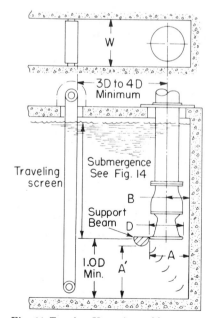

Fig. 11 Turning Vane Assembly

Multiple pump arrangements

The preferred arrangement is to have the pump suction bells located in individual pump bays by means of separator walls or partitions so one pump will not interfere hydraulically with the operation of another. However, if this is not practical, as may be the case with small pumps, a number of units can be installed in a single large sump provided that:

1. They are located in a line running perpendicular to the approaching flow.
2. Minimum spacing of 2D is provided between pump centerlines.
3. Back wall clearance, bottom clearance and submergence same as for single pumps.
4. All pumps are running.
5. The up-stream conditions should provide uniform flow to the suction bells (avoid turns).
6. Each pump capacity is less than 15,000 gpm.

When individual pump bays are provided use dimensions for a single pump in accordance with Fig. 10, page 1-23.

Turning vane intake assemblies

Structural costs can sometimes be reduced by employing a turning vane assembly below the suction bell entrance to achieve a suitable flow pattern as illustrated in Fig. 11. This arrangement normally requires a deeper sump but the width (W) may be reduced to 1.50D or less resulting in reduced screen and construction costs.

The following guidelines are offered with a turning vane assembly:

1. Dimensions A and A' should be equal.
2. Pump bell should be as close as possible to the level of the support beam bottom.
3. Dimension B should be as short as clearance permits.
4. Dimension W should be equal to the bell diameter plus the necessary clearance to allow for variations in structural and casting dimensions.
5. In order to prevent excessive velocity at pump entrance, the suction bell should be 1D or greater above the sump bottom depending on pump size.
6. The turning vanes should slightly accelerate the flow to the pump (i.e. the inlet area of each passage should be greater than the corresponding exit).
7. Intake tunnel velocity should be limited to 1 to 2 ft/sec maximum.

8. Submergence "S" should be per submergence vs capacity chart **Fig. 14,** page 1-26.

Side intake—dry pit pumps

The following guidelines are offered for typical dry pit type pump arrangements as illustrated in Fig. 12 for a horizontal pump and Fig. 13 for a vertical centrifugal or scroll case type of pump. In these illustrations dimension "D" is the diameter, or effective diameter, of the suction intake fitting.

1. Submergence "S" should be approximately one foot for each foot per second at "D." Velocity at "D" should be less than 6 ft/sec.
2. Radius "R" should be as large as possible within structure limitations.
3. Submergence can be reduced to half the values indicated in (1) with either a roof or vertical baffle. A vertical baffle should have ample depth to be effective and centrally located. At location D alternate shapes can be used to further reduce depth; i.e. rectangular or

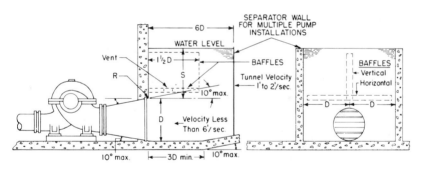

Fig. 12

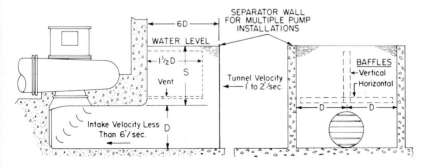

Fig. 13

elliptical areas. Effective "D" then becomes the average diameter of the two axes. Always check NPSHR.

4. Suction bays should be symmetrical with no turn in the approach. With two or more pumps, separator walls extending for a length of 6D and a height "S" should be provided between the intakes of each pump.

5. Minimum water level must always be above the impeller eye. When the level is below the top of the volute priming is preferable.

6. Stop logs in the bay are preferred to a suction valve. If a butterfly valve is used, stem should be horizontal for horizontal double suction pumps and fully open when running.

7. Intake screens should be placed a minimum of 6D from the pump inlet (D = diameter of suction intake fitting).

The above suggestions for alternative pump arrangements are offered as general guidelines and should not be considered as optimum. Analysis and design of intake structures and arrangement of pumps should only be made on the basis of experience together with model and field testing. If new or questionable arrangements are being proposed, model tests should be conducted. In most cases it is desirable to have the Manufacturer's comments before finalizing a design.

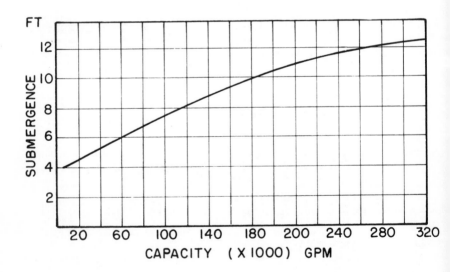

Fig. 14 Capacity Vs Submergence over suction bell for Vertical Wet Pit Pumps.

Work performed in pumping—horsepower

The work performed in pumping or moving a liquid depends on the weight of the liquid being handled in a given time against the total head (in feet of liquid) or differential pressure (in psi) being developed.

Since one horsepower equals 33000 ft lb per minute the useful or theoretical horsepower (usually called the hydraulic horsepower—hyd hp) will equal:

$$\text{Hyd hp} = \frac{\text{lb of liquid per minute} \times \text{H (in feet)}}{33,000}$$

The actual or brake horsepower (bhp) of a pump will be greater than the hyd hp by the amount of losses incurred within the pump through friction, leakage, etc. The pump efficiency will therefore be equal to:

$$\text{Pump efficiency} = \frac{\text{hyd hp}}{\text{bhp}}$$

or

$$\text{Brake hp} = \frac{\text{hyd hp}}{\text{pump efficiency}}$$

Since the above expressions apply to both centrifugal and reciprocating types of pumps, horsepower calculations can be simplified if the weight of liquid being handled (capacity) is expressed in terms of gpm and/or bph—and the differential pressure (H) in terms of head in feet of liquid for centrifugal pumps, and psi (pounds per sq in.) for reciprocating pumps as follows:

$$\text{Brake hp} = \frac{\text{gpm} \times \text{H (in feet)} \times \text{sp gr}}{3960 \times \text{efficiency}} \quad \text{(common centrifugal terms)}$$

$$= \frac{\text{bph} \times \text{H (in feet)} \times \text{sp gr}}{5657 \times \text{efficiency}} \quad \text{(common centrifugal terms)}$$

$$= \frac{\text{gpm} \times \text{psi}}{1714 \times \text{eff}} \quad \text{(common reciprocating terms)}$$

$$= \frac{\text{bph} \times \text{psi}}{2450 \times \text{eff}} \quad \text{(common reciprocating terms)}$$

Note: to obtain the hyd hp from the above expressions use a pump efficiency of 100%.

In the above expressions:

gpm = U S gallons per minute delivered (one gallon = 8.33 lb at 68 Deg F.

bph = barrels (42 gallons) per hour—delivered

H = total head in feet of liquid—differential

psi = lbs per sq in—differential

$$\text{Electrical hp input to motor} = \frac{\text{pump bhp}}{\text{motor efficiency}}$$

$$\text{KW input to motor} = \frac{\text{pump bhp} \times 0.7457}{\text{motor efficiency}}$$

If a variable speed device is used between pump and driver then overall efficiency will equal Pump eff × Motor eff × eff of variable speed drive.

From the above formulas it should be noted that it is important to correct the (gpm) and (H) for the temperature being pumped; it should also be noted that more power is required to pump a given weight of liquid hot against a given pressure than will be required to pump the same weight of liquid cold.

When handling some liquids and for water at very high pressures, the compressibility of the liquid may need to be considered as its density may change within the pump.

Temperature rise—Minimum Flow:

Except for a small amount of power lost in the pump bearings and stuffing boxes the difference between the brake horsepower and hydraulic horsepower developed represents the power losses within the pump itself, most of which are transferred to the liquid passing through the pump causing a temperature rise in the liquid.

It is sometimes desirable to have a curve showing temperature rise versus pump capacity—which can be calculated from this formula:

The allowable minimum flow through a Centrifugal Pump may depend to some extent on the allowable temperature rise permitted. Since items other than thermal (such as hydraulic radial thrust) may have to be considered, the manufacturer should be consulted on the safe minimum flow permitted.

where

$$TR = \frac{H(1.0 - E)}{778\,E}$$

TR = Temperature rise in Deg F

H = Total head in feet

E = Efficiency expressed as a decimal

HYDRAULICS

Characteristic curves

Since the head (in feet of liquid) developed by a centrifugal pump is independent of the specific gravity, water at normal temperatures with a specific gravity of 1.000 is the liquid almost universally used in establishing centrifugal pump performance characteristics. If the head for a specific application is determined in feet, then the desired head and capacity can be read without correction as long as the viscosity of the liquid is similar to that of water. The horsepower curve, which is basis specific gravity of 1.0, can be used for liquids of other gravity (if viscosity is similar to water) by multiplying the horsepower for water by the specific gravity of the liquid being handled.

The hydraulic characteristics of centrifugal pumps usually permit considerable latitude in the range of operating conditions. Ideally, the design point and operating point should be maintained close to the best efficiency point (BEP); however, substantial variations in flow either to the right (increasing) or to the left (decreasing) of the BEP are usually permissible. However, operating back on the curve at reduced flow, or at excessive run out may result in radial thrust, or cavitation causing damage and therefore the manufacturer should be consulted when such conditions may exist.

Since a centrifugal pump is a machine which imparts velocity and converts velocity to pressure, the flow and head developed may be changed by varying the pump speed or changing the impeller diameter. These modifications will change the tip speed or velocity of the impeller vanes and therefore the velocity at which the liquid leaves the impeller. Note that changing impeller diameters may result in a loss in efficiency as the diameter is reduced. For reasonable speed variations the efficiency should not change appreciably.

For pumps in the *centrifugal range of specific speeds* (radial flow impellers) the relationships between capacity, head and horsepower with changes in impeller diameter and speed are approximately as follows:

For small variations in impeller diameter (constant speed)

$$\frac{D_1}{D_2} = \frac{Q_1}{Q_2} = \frac{\sqrt{H_1}}{\sqrt{H_2}}$$

$$\frac{BHP_1}{BHP_2} = \frac{D_1^3}{D_2^3}$$

For variations in speed: (constant impeller diameter)

$$\frac{S_1}{S_2} = \frac{Q_1}{Q_2} = \frac{\sqrt{H_1}}{\sqrt{H_2}}$$

$$\frac{BHP_1}{BHP_2} = \frac{S_1^3}{S_2^3}$$

where

D = Impeller diameters in inches
H = Heads in feet
Q = Capacities in gpm
S = Speeds in rpm
BHP = Brake horsepowers

Note: Subscript 1 is for original design conditions.

The above relationships are known as the *Affinity Laws* and are offered in this text with the understanding their application will be limited to centrifugal (radial flow) type pumps only. When other types such as axial, mixed flow or propeller type are involved consult the manufacturer for instructions.

These laws can be summarized as follows:

With variable speeds the capacity varies directly and the head varies as the square of the speed; efficiencies will not change for reasonable variations in speed. The break horsepower (BHP) varies as the cube of the speeds.

With variable impeller diameters the capacity varies directly and the head varies as the square of the impeller diameter–efficiency will be reduced as the diameter is reduced–check manufacturer for limitations. The brake horsepower (BHP) varies as the cube of impeller diameters. Note: These relations hold only for small changes in impeller diameter.

Stepping curves—Using the above relationships the head—capacity (H_1–Q_1) curves can be stepped up or down within reasonable limits making the necessary efficiency corrections for changes in impeller diameter. Solving for S_2 and D_2 to meet a specified H_2–Q_2 is a cut and try operation if exact values are desired; in all cases the manufacturer should be consulted before making final modifications to the original design conditions.

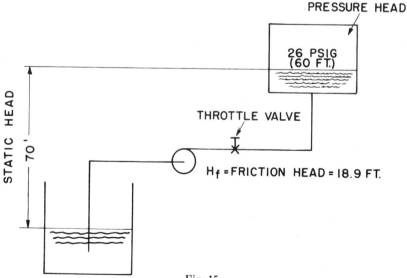

System curves

A centrifugal pump always operates at the intersection of its head-capacity curve and the system curve which shows the head required to make the liquid flow through the system of piping, valves, etc. The head in a typical system is made up of three components:

1. Static head
2. Pressure head
3. All losses; i.e. friction, entrance and exit losses

To illustrate, take a typical system shown in Fig. 15 where the total static head is 70 ft, the pressure head is 60 ft (2.31 × 26) and the friction head through all pipe, valves, fittings, entrance and exit losses is 18.9 ft at the design flow of 1500 gpm, total system head at design flow is 70 + 60 + 18.9 = 148.9 ft.

In drawing the system curve (see Fig. 16, page 1-32) the static head will not change with flow so it is represented by the line AB, the pressure head will not change with flow so it is added to the static head and shown by the horizontal line CD. The friction head through a piping system, however, varies approximately as the

square of the flow so the friction at 500 gpm will be   × 18.9

= 2.1 ft (Point E); likewise the friction at 1000 gpm will be 8.4 ft (Point F), these determine

PRESSURE HEAD

26 PSIG
(60 FT.)

STATIC HEAD

70'

THROTTLE VALVE

H_f = FRICTION HEAD = 18.9 FT.

Fig. 15

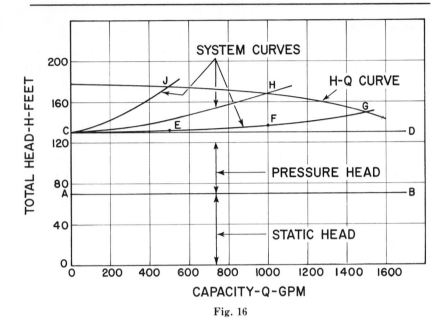

Fig. 16

the final curve CEFG. In Fig 16 the pump head capacity curve has been superimposed on the system curve. Unless something is done to change either the head capacity curve—or the system curve—the pump will operate at 1500 gpm (Point G) indefinitely.

If the throttle valve in the pump discharge line is closed partially it will add friction to the system and the pump can be regulated to operate at Point H (1000 gpm) or at Point J (500 gpm) or at any other point on its curve; this is changing the system curve by throttling and in this case is known as "throttling control."

Parallel and series operation

With properly selected Head-capacity (H-Q) curves (preferably curves with continuously rising characteristics) and subject to certain hydraulic and mechanical considerations parallel and/or series operation of centrifugal pumps can be employed to meet a wide range of service requirements.

In considering multiple pump operation a system head curve for the entire capacity and head requirements must be made available. The individual pump H-Q curves must be super-imposed on the system curve.

For parallel operation of two or more pumps the combined performance curve is obtained by adding horizontally the capacities of the same heads.

For series operation the combined performance curve is obtained by adding vertically the heads at the same capacities.

Since a centrifugal pump always operates at the intersection of its H-Q curve with the system curve, super-imposing the system curve on the pump performance curve clearly indicates what flow can be expected and at what heads each pump or its combination will operate.

Fig. 17 illustrates a two (2) pump series-parallel operation; this could be expanded to a three or more pump combination if desired. In this illustration a typical H-Q curve for a single pump designed for 1000 gpm at 60 ft head is shown; two pumps in series will deliver 1000 gpm at 120 ft; or two pumps in parallel will deliver 2000 gpm at 60 ft; system curves have assumed as shown. If the pumps have "run-out capabilities" — (dotted portion)—they will operate at the intersection of the H-Q curves with the system curves. Note that in this illustration the system curve is based on the assumption that there is 20 ft static head.

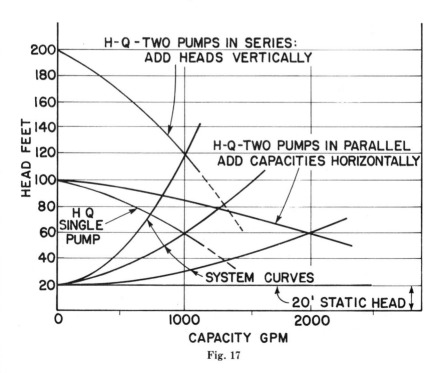

Fig. 17

Water hammer

In fluid flow, water hammer can cause rupture and serious damage to the entire piping system unless essential precautions are taken; in the case of condenser circulating water systems it can cause rupture and serious damage to the tube sheets and water boxes.

It is the result of a rapid increase in pressure which occurs in a closed piping system when the liquid velocity is suddenly changed by sudden starting, stopping or change in speed of a pump; or suddenly opening or closing of a valve which may change the liquid velocity in the system.

This increase, or dynamic change in pressure, is the result of the kinetic energy of the moving mass of liquid being transformed into pressure energy, resulting in an excessive pressure rise which can cause damage on either the suction or discharge side of the pump.

Water hammer may be controlled by regulating valve closure time, surge chambers, relief valves or other means.

Water hammer calculations are quite involved, and it is recommended that specialized engineering services be employed in cases where it may be a problem. For information on this subject the following further references are suggested:

Symposium on Water Hammer
American Society of Mechanical Engineers
1933 (Reprinted 1949)

Symposium on Water Hammer—Transactions
A.S.M.E. 59:651 (1937)

Water Hammer Control—S. L. Kerr
Journal of American Water Works Assoc.
43:985 (December 1951)

Practical Aspects of Water Hammer—S. L. Kerr
Journal of American Water Works Assoc.
40:599 (June 1948)

Elements of Graphical Solution of Water Hammer
Problems in Centrifugal Pump Systems—A. J. Stepanoff
Transactions of A.S.M.E. 71:515 (1949)

Water Hammer Analysis—J. Parmakian
Prentice Hall Publication, New York (1955)

Pump Drivers—speed torque curves

The driver must be capable of supplying more torque at each successive speed from zero to full load than required by the pump in order to reach rated speed. This condition seldom presents any problem with the average centrifugal pump driven by standard induction or synchronous motors, but with certain applications such as with high specific speed pumps having high shut-off horsepower, or with reduced voltage starting, motors with high pull-in torque may be required.

Where centrifugal pumps in the low to medium specific speed range (under 3500) are started with the discharge valve closed the minimum torque requirements at various speeds for this condition is calculated as follows:

Determine the maximum horsepower required at rated speed under shut off conditions. Convert this horsepower to torque in (lb. ft.) by using the formula:

$$T \text{ in (lb. ft.)} = \frac{5250 \times hp}{rpm}$$

Torque varies as the square of the speed; therefore, to obtain torque at:

¾ speed—multiply full speed torque by 0.563
½ speed—multiply full speed torque by 0.250
¼ speed—multiply full speed torque by 0.063
⅛ speed—multiply full speed torque by 0.016

At zero speed the torque would theoretically be zero, but the driver must overcome stuffing box friction, rotating element inertia and bearing friction in order to start the shaft turning. This requires a torque at zero speed of from 2½ percent to 15 percent of the maximum.

Speed torque requirements for starting conditions other than with closed discharge will vary depending on the horsepower requirements at each successive speed. This can be determined by superimposing the pump H-Q curve on the system curve; selecting several speeds and calculating the horsepower at each of the speeds selected; then calculating the torque for each speed selected.

On vertical axial flow and propeller pumps with high specific speeds (and high shut off horsepower) it is standard practice to start the pumps with discharge valves partially open to reduce starting horsepower and thrust. In the case of the second of two pumps starting with the first already pumping, it is possible that the water may be flowing back through the discharge of the idle pump turning it backwards. This complicates the speed torque calculation which should be referred to the pump manufacturer. See motor torque page 6-4.

Engine drivers

If reciprocating engine drivers are being considered the speed-torque requirements of the pump must be checked against the speed torque capabilities of the engine to assure their compatability.

Caution must be used in the selection of reciprocating engine drivers because excessive cyclic stresses may be superimposed on the pump shaft due to the periodic power impulses produced by each engine cylinder. These cyclic pulses produce a torsional vibration whose magnitude depends on the state of resonance of the entire system; this results in an increase in the cyclic tensile loading of the pump shaft. For these reasons the allowable pump shaft horsepower per 100 rpm (hp/100 rpm) limits must be reduced substantially.

Due to the torsional vibration problems that may develop, the pump manufacturers should be checked to determine the suitability of the engine drive being considered.

Impeller Profiles

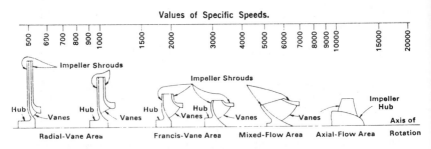

Fig. 18 showing profiles of impeller designs ranging from the low specific speed radial flow design on the left to a high specific axial flow design on the right. (Courtesy of Hydraulic Institute.)

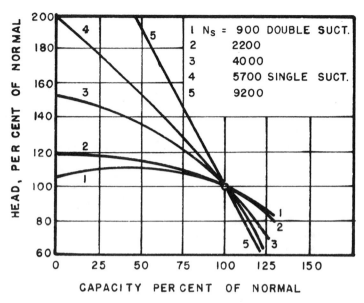

Fig. 19 showing shape of typical head-capacity curves for various specific speeds.

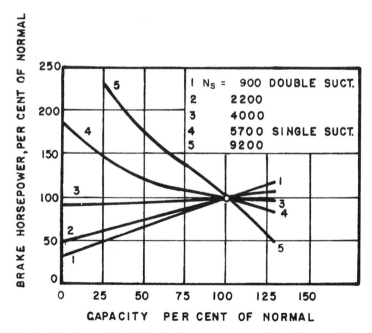

Fig. 20 showing shape of typical brake horsepower curves for various specific speeds.

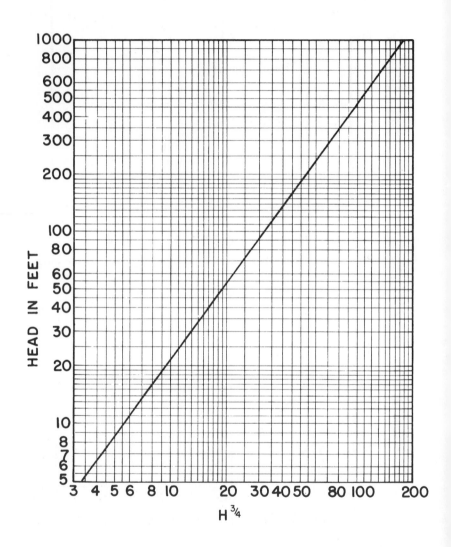

Fig. 21 Values of H$^{3/4}$

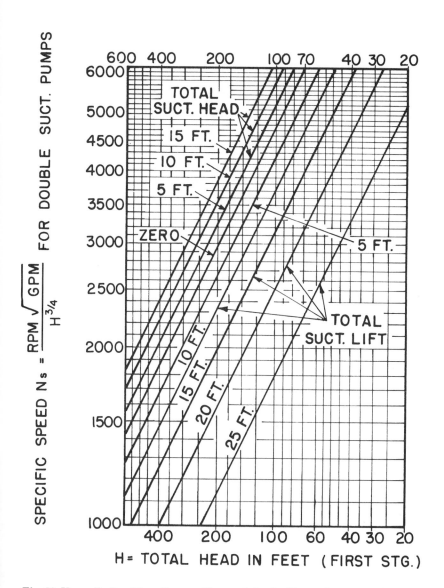

Fig. 22 Upper limits of impeller specific speed for double suction pumps handling clear water at 85° F at sea level. (Courtesy of Hydraulic Institute.)

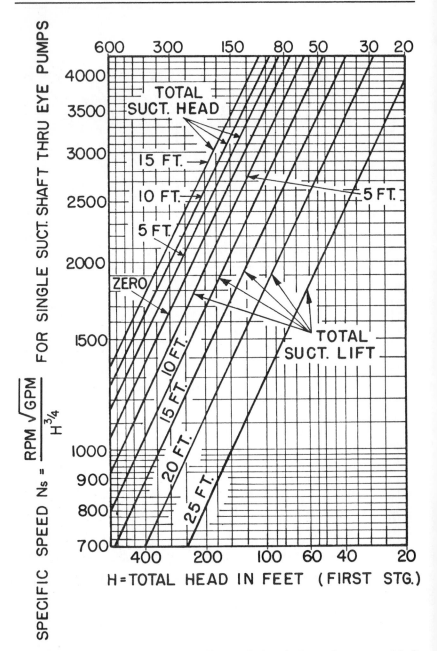

Fig. 23 Upper limits of impeller specific speeds for single suction pumps (shaft through eye of impeller) handling clear water at 85° F sea level. (Courtesy of Hydraulic Institute.)

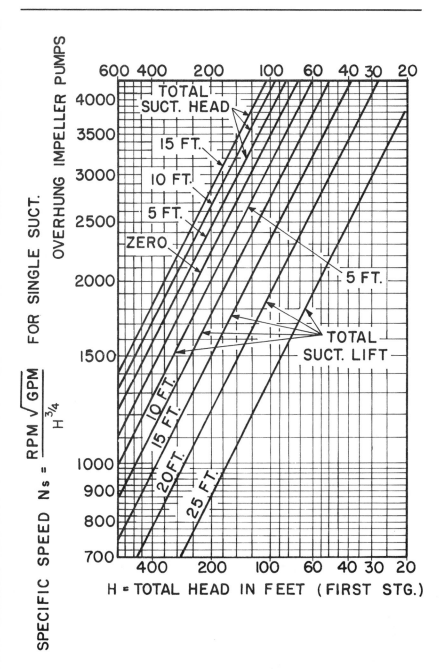

Fig. 24 Upper limits of impeller specific speeds for single suction overhung impeller pumps handling clear water at 85° F sea level. (Courtesy of Hydraulic Institute.)

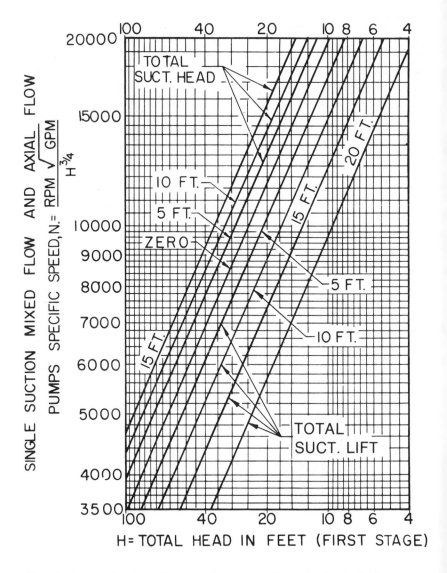

Fig. 25 Upper limits of specific speeds for single suction, mixed and axial flow pumps handling clear water at 85° F sea level. (Courtesy of Hydraulic Institute.)

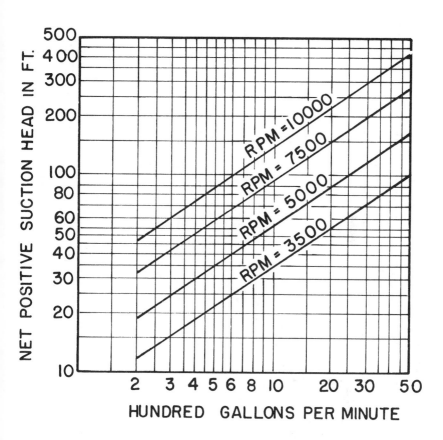

Fig. 26 Recommended minimum net positive suction head for centrifugal pumps handling hot water at temperatures of 212° F and above—single suction (over hung —end suction type). (Courtesy of Hydraulic Institute.)

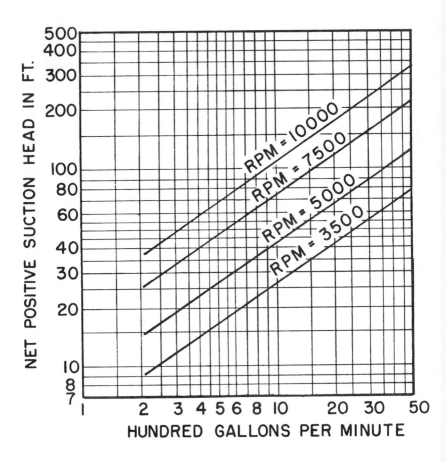

Fig. 27 Recommended minimum net positive suction head for centrifugal pumps handling hot water at temperatures of 212° F and above—double suction first stage—shaft through eye of impeller. (Courtesy of Hydraulic Institute.)

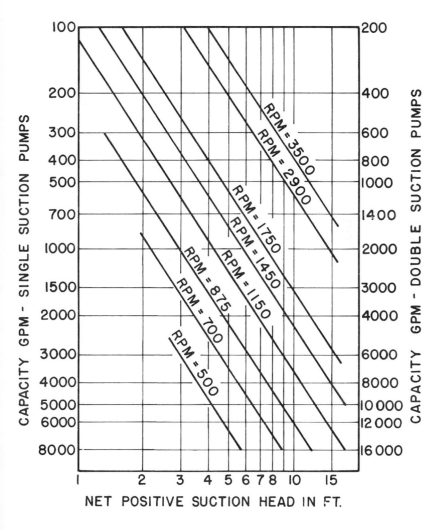

Fig. 28 Capacity and speed limitations for condensate pumps with shaft through eye of impeller (for pumps with maximum of three stages). For single suction over hung impeller divide the specified capacity, if 400 gpm or less by 1.2; and if greater than 400 gpm by 1.15 (Courtesy of Hydraulic Institute.)

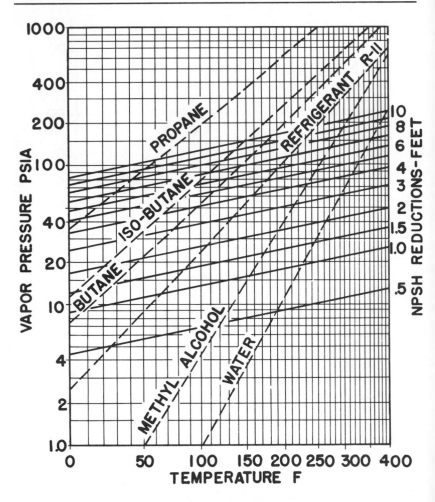

Fig. 29 NPSH reductions for pumps handling hydrocarbon liquids. (Courtesy of Hydraulic Institute.) See discussion, pages 1-15 and 1-16.

HYDRAULICS

BIBLIOGRAPHY

The following references are among those available if it is desired to investigate the subjects discussed herein in further detail:

Crane Technical Paper No 410—Flow of Fluids through Valves, Fittings and Pipe. Crane Company, Advertising Division, 300 Park Avenue, New York, N.Y. 10022 Crane Technical Paper No. 410M—Metric Edition—SI Units is now available; order from above address. (orders for Crane Papers must be prepaid).

Hydraulic Institute Standards and Engineering Data Book—Address: Hydraulic Institute, 712 Lakewood Center North, Cleveland, Ohio 44107.

The following are published by McGraw-Hill Inc.:

Baumeister and Marks—Standard Handbook for Mechanical Engineers.

Chow—Handbook of Applied Hydrology.

Hicks—Standard Handbook of Engineering Calculations.

Kallen—Handbook of Instrumentation and Controls.

King and Brater—Handbook of Hydraulics.

Merritt—Standard Handbook for Civil Engineers.

Perry—Engineering Manual.

Streeter—Handbook of Fluid Dynamics.

Streeter and Wylie—Fluid Mechanics.

Urguhart—Civil Engineering Handbook.

Karassik, Krutzsch, Fraser and Messina—Pump Handbook.

Shames—Mechanics of Fluids.

The following are published by the Macmillan Publishing Company:

Sabersky, Acosta and Hauptmann—Fluid Flow.

The following are published by John Wiley & Sons:

Stepanoff—Centrifugal and Axial Flow Pumps.

Rouse—Engineering Hydraulics.

Vennard & Street—Elementary Fluid Dynamics.

The following are published by Prentice Hall:

Binder—Fluid Mechanics.

Albertson, Barton and Simons—Fluid Mechanics for Engineers.

Butterworth Publishers, 10 Tower Office Park
Woburn, Ma. 01801
Telephone 1-617-933-8260

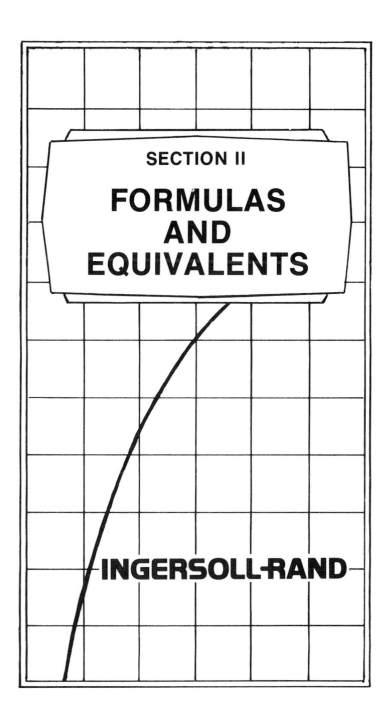

SECTION II

FORMULAS
AND
EQUIVALENTS

2

INGERSOLL-RAND

CONTENTS OF SECTION 2

Selected Formulas and Equivalents

(For metric formulas see page 8-28)

FORMULAS AND EQUIVALENTS

General—Information on Liquids

In this section the more commonly used Formulas and Equivalents are included for the convenience of the user.

With references to Volume and Weight Equivalents, the following comments on temperature, specific gravity, and specific weight should be of interest.

Temperature affects the characteristics of a liquid. For most liquids an increase in temperature decreases viscosity, decreases specific gravity and increases volume (see page 1-6).

The Specific Gravity of a solid or liquid is the ratio of the mass of the body to the mass of an equal volume of water at some selected base or standard temperature. **Specific Gravity of Water** is usually given as 1.000 at 60°F (15.6°C). However, in some cases, for convenience, it may be given as 1.000 at 68°F (20°C); and in other cases as 1.000 at 39.2°F (4°C) which is its point of maximum density. Based on using water having a specific gravity of 1.000 at 39.2°F (4°C) as a reference point, water at 60°F (15.6°C) will have a specific gravity of 0.9991, and 0.9983 at 68°F (20°C)—therefore, for practical applications which temperature (39.2°F—60°F or 68°F) is selected as a base for reference makes little difference. At the present time the base of 39.2°F (4°C) is commonly used by physicists, but the engineer usually uses 60°F (15.6°C) or 68°F (20°C) as a base. For actual specific gravities and specific weights of water for other temperatures to 705.47°F (374.15°C) see page 4-4.

Specific Gravities of Other Liquids is given relative to water—usually at 60°F (15.6°C). Numerically, specific gravity is about the same as the density in grams per cubic centimeter in the cgs system. Other systems of measuring specific gravity or density are related; conversion tables are shown on pages 4-6 to 4-19.

Specific Weight as used in this discussion, is the weight in lb per cu ft. The specific weight of water at 39.2°F is 62.4258 lb per cu ft., at 60°F is 62.3714 lb per cu ft; at 68°F is 62.3208 lb per cu ft. For other temperatures proper specific weight values should be used (see page 4-4).

Density is the mass per unit volume. It is usually stated in lb/ft³, or g/cm³ or kg/m³. For a detailed discussion see page 4-3.

Volume and Weight Equivalents

Volume & Weight Equivalents
Example: 20 U S gallons × 3.7854 = 75.708 liters

Convert from \ Convert to	Volume and weight equivalents						*Weight equivalent basis water at 60°F (15.6°C)		
	US gallons	Imperial gallons	Cubic inches	Cubic feet	Liters	Cubic meters	Pounds	US tons	Kilograms
U S gallons	1	0.8327	231	0.13368	3.7854	0.0037854	8.338	0.00417	3.782
Imperial gallons	1.20094	1	277.39	0.16054	4.546	0.004546	10.0134	0.005	4.542
Cubic inches	0.004329	0.003605	1	0.0005787	0.016387	0.000016387	0.036095		0.016372
Cubic feet	7.48052	6.229	1728	1	28.317	0.02832	62.3714	0.03119	28.291
Liters	0.2642	0.2200	61.024	0.035315	1	0.001	2.2029	0.0011	0.1000
Cubic meters	264.2	220.0	61024	35.315	1000	1	2202.65	1.10133	1000.0
Pounds*	0.1199	0.09987	27.71	0.016033	0.4539	.000454	1	0.0005	0.45359
U S tons*	239.87	199.7	55409	32.066	907.9	0.908	2000	1	907.2
Kilograms*	0.2644	0.2202	61.08	0.03534	1.000	0.001	2.205	0.0011	1

The capacity of a barrel varies in different industries. For instance
1 bbl of beer = 31 U S gallons
1 bbl of wine = 31.5 U S gallons
1 bbl of oil = 42 U S gallons
1 bbl of whiskey = 45 U S gallons

DRUMS:
The drum is not considered to be a unit of measure as is the barrel. Drums are usually built to specifications and are available in sizes from 2½ gallons to 55 gallons; the most popular sizes are the 5 gallon, 30 gallon and 55 gallon drums.

2

Head and Pressure Equivalents

Equivalents of Head and Pressure
Example: 15 lb/ft² × 4.88241 = 73.236 kg/m²

Convert from \ Convert to	lb/in²	lb/ft²	Atmospheres	kg/cm²	kg/m²	in. water (68F)*	ft. water (68F)*	in. mercury (32F)†	mm mercury (32F)†	Bars ‡	Mega-Pascals (MPa)‡
lb/in²	1	144.	0.068046	0.070307	703.070	27.7276	2.3106	2.03602	51.7150	0.06895	0.006895
lb/ft²	0.0069444	1	0.000473	0.000488	4.88241	0.1926	0.01605	0.014139	0.35913	0.000479	0.0000479
Atmospheres	14.696	2116.22	1	1.0332	10332.27	407.484	33.9570	29.921	760.	1.01325	0.101325
kg/cm²	14.2233	2048.155	0.96784	1	10000.	394.38	32.8650	28.959	735.559	0.98067	0.098067
kg/m²	0.001422	0.204768	0.0000968	0.0001	1	0.03944	0.003287	0.0002896	0.073556	0.000098	0.0000098
in. water*	0.036092	5.1972	0.002454	0.00253	25.375	1	0.08333	0.073430	1.8651	0.00249	0.000249
ft. water*	0.432781	62.3205	0.029449	0.03043	304.275	12.	1	0.88115	22.3813	0.029839	0.0029839
in. mercury†	0.491154	70.7262	0.033421	0.03453	345.316	13.6185	1.1349	1	25.40005	0.033864	0.0033864
mm mercury†	0.0193368	2.78450	0.0013158	0.0013595	13.59509	0.53616	0.044680	0.03937	1	0.001333	0.0001333
Bars‡	14.5038	2088.55	0.98692	1.01972	10197.2	402.156	33.5130	29.5300	750.062	1	0.10
MPa‡	145.038	20885.5	9.8692	10.1972	101972.0	4021.56	335.130	295.300	7500.62	10.0	1

* Water at 68 F (20 C) † mercury at 32 F (0 C) ‡ 1 MPa (MegaPascal) = 10 Bars = 1,000,000 N/m² (Newtons/meter²)
Courtesy of Crane Co., Technical Paper 410.

Flow Equivalents

Flow Equivalents—For any Liquid
Example; 100 U S gal/min × 0.0631 = 6.31 liters/sec

Convert from \ Convert to	U S gal/min	Imp gal/min	U S million gal/day	Cu ft per sec (sec-ft)	Cu meters per hour	Liters per sec	Barrels (42 gal) per min	Barrels (42 gal) per day
U S gal/min	1	0.8327	0.00144	0.00223	0.2271	0.0631	0.0238	34.286
Imp gal/min	1.201	1	0.00173	0.002676	0.2727	0.0758	0.02859	41.176
U S million gal/day	694.4	578.25	1	1.547	157.7	43.8	16.53	23810
Cu ft/sec	448.83	373.7	0.646	1	101.9	28.32	10.686	15388
Cu m/sec	15852	13200	22.83	35.35	3600	1000	377.4	......
Cu m/min	264.2	220	0.3804	0.5886	60.0	16.667	6.290	9058
Cu m/hr	4.403	3.67	0.00634	0.00982	1	0.2778	0.1048	151
Liters/sec	15.85	13.20	0.0228	0.0353	3.60	1	0.3773	543.3
Liters/min	0.2642	0.220	0.000380	0.000589	0.060	0.0167	0.00629	9.058
Barrels (42 gal)/min	42	34.97	0.0605	0.0937	9.538	2.65	1	1440
Barrels (42 gal)/day	0.0292	0.0243	0.000042	0.000065	0.00662	0.00184	0.00069	1

1 miners inch of water {
= 8.977 gpm (in Idaho, Kansas, Nebraska, New Mexico, N. Dakota, S. Dakota, and Utah)
= 11.22 gpm (in Arizona, California, Montana, Nevada and Oregon)
= 11.69 gpm (in Colorado)

Barrel per day {
31 gal × 0.02153 = gpm (beer)
31½ gal × 0.02188 = gpm (wine)
42 gal × 0.02917 = gpm (oil)
45 gal × 0.03125 = gpm (whiskey)

FORMULAS AND EQUIVALENTS

Flow Equivalents

Cu Ft per Sec				Gallons per 24 hours			
Cu ft per sec	Gallons per minute	Gallons per 24 hrs	m²/hr	Gallons per 24 hrs	Gallons per minute	Cu ft per sec	m³/hr
0.2	90	129,263	20.39	100,000	69	0.15	15.77
0.4	180	258,526	40.78	125,000	87	0.19	19.71
0.6	269	387,789	61.17	200,000	139	0.31	31.54
0.8	359	517,052	81.56	400,000	278	0.62	63.08
1.0	449	646,315	102.0	500,000	347	0.77	78.85
1.2	539	775,578	122.3	600,000	417	0.93	94.62
1.4	628	904,841	142.7	700,000	486	1.08	110.4
1.6	718	1,034,104	163.1	800,000	556	1.24	126.2
1.8	808	1,163,367	183.5	900,000	625	1.39	141.9
2.0	898	1,292,630	203.9	1,000,000	694	1.55	157.7
2.2	987	1,421,893	224.3	2,000,000	1,389	3.09	315.4
2.4	1,077	1,551,156	244.7	3,000,000	2,083	4.64	473.1
2.6	1,167	1,680,420	265.1	4,000,000	2,778	6.19	630.8
2.8	1,257	1,809,683	285.5	5,000,000	3,472	7.74	788.5
3.0	1,346	1,938,946	305.9	6,000,000	4,167	9.28	946.2
3.2	1,436	2,068,209	326.2	7,000,000	4,861	10.83	1,104
3.4	1,526	2,197,472	346.6	8,000,000	5,556	12.38	1,262
3.6	1,616	2,326,735	367.0	9,000,000	6,250	13.92	1,419
3.8	1,705	2,455,998	387.4	10,000,000	6,944	15.47	1,577
4.0	1,795	2,585,261	407.8	12,000,000	8,333	18.56	1,892
4.2	1,885	2,714,524	428.2	12,500,000	8,680	19.34	1,971
4.4	1,975	2,843,787	448.6	14,000,000	9,722	21.65	2,208
4.6	2,068	2,973,050	469.0	15,000,000	10,417	23.20	2,366
4.8	2,154	3,102,313	489.4	16,000,000	11,111	24.75	2,523
5.0	2,244	3,231,576	509.8	18,000,000	12,500	26.85	2,839
10.0	4,488	6,463,152	1,020	20,000,000	13,889	30.94	3,154
20.0	8,987	12,926,304	2,039	25,000,000	17,361	38.68	3,943
30.0	13,464	19,389,456	3,059	30,000,000	20,833	46.41	4,731
40.0	17,952	25,852,261	4,078	40,000,000	27,778	61.88	6,308
50.0	22,440	32,315,760	5,098	50,000,000	34,722	77.35	7,885
60.0	26,928	38,778,912	6,117	60,000,000	41,667	92.82	9,462
70.0	31,416	45,242,064	7,137	70,000,000	48,611	108.29	11,039
75.0	33,660	48,473,640	7,646	75,000,000	52,083	116.04	11,828
80.0	35,904	51,705,216	8,156	80,000,000	55,556	123.76	12,616
90.0	40,392	58,168,368	9,176	90,000,000	62,500	139.23	14,193
100.0	44,880	64,631,520	10,195	100,000,000	69,444	154.72	15,770
101.0	45,329	65,277,835	10,297	125,000,000	86,805	193.40	19,713
102.0	45,778	65,924,150	10,399	150,000,000	104,167	232.08	23,665
103.0	46,226	66,570,466	10,501	175,000,000	121,528	270.76	27,598
104.0	46,675	67,216,781	10,603	200,000,000	138,889	309.44	31,540
105.0	47,124	67,863,096	10,705	225,000,000	156,250	348.12	35,483
106.0	47,572	68,509,411	10,807	250,000,000	173,611	386.80	39,425
107.0	48,022	69,155,726	10,909	300,000,000	208,333	464.16	47,310
108.0	48,470	69,802,042	11,011	400,000,000	277,778	618.88	63,080
109.0	48,919	70,448,357	11,113	500,000,000	347,220	773.60	78,850
110.0	49,368	71,094,672	11,215	600,000,000	416,664	928.32	94,620
120.0	53,856	77,557,824	12,234	700,000,000	486,108	1,083.04	110,390
125.0	56,100	80,798,400	12,744	750,090,000	520,328	1,160.40	118,275
130.0	58,344	84,020,976	13,254	800,000,000	555,552	1,237.76	126,160
140.0	62,832	90,484,128	14,273	900,000,000	624,996	1,392.48	141,930
150.0	67,320	96,947,230	15,293	1,000,000,000	694,440	1,547.20	157,700

Note—gpm and gal per 24 hr given to the nearest whole number.
The value 7.48 gallons equals 1 cu ft is used in calculating above table.

FLOW THROUGH ORIFICES AND NOZZLES

Approximate discharge through orifice or nozzle.

$$Q = 19.636 \ C d_1{}^2 \sqrt{h} \ \sqrt{\dfrac{1}{1 - \left(\dfrac{d_1}{d_2}\right)^4}} \text{ where } \dfrac{d_1}{d_2} \text{ is greater than } 0.3$$

$$Q = 19.636 \ C d_1{}^2 \sqrt{h} \text{ where } \dfrac{d_1}{d_2} \text{ is less than } 0.3$$

Q = flow, in gpm
d_1 = dia of orifice or nozzle opening, inches
h = differential head at orifice, in feet of liquid.
d_2 = dia of pipe in which orifice is placed, inches
C = discharge coefficient (typical values below for water)

RE-ENTRANT TUBE	SHARP-EDGED	SQUARE EDGED	RE-ENTRANT TUBE	SQUARE EDGED	WELL ROUNDED
LENGTH ·1/2 to 1 DIA.		STREAM CLEARS SIDES	LENGTH = 2-1/2 DIA.	TUBE FLOWS FULL	
C = .52	C = .61	C = .61	C = .73	C = .82	C = .98

Table on next page shows flow using a value of C = 1.00. These flows values may be multiplied by the C value for a particular discharge to obtain actual flow.

Approximate flow through Venturi tube.

$$Q = 19.05 \ d_1{}^2 \sqrt{H} \ \sqrt{\dfrac{1}{1 - \left(\dfrac{d_1}{d_2}\right)^4}} \text{ for any Venturi tube}$$

$$Q = 19.17 \ d_1{}^2 \sqrt{H} \text{ for a Venturi tube in which } d_1 = 1/3 \ d_2$$

Q = flow, in gpm
d_1 = dia. of venturi throat, inches
d_2 = dia. of main pipe, inches
H = diff. in head between upstream end and throat (ft.)

These formulas are suitable for any liquid with viscosities similar to water. The values given here are for water. A value of 32.174 ft. per sec² was used for the acceleration of gravity and a value of 7.48 gal. per cu ft in computing the constants.

Flow Data — Nozzles

Theoretical Discharge of Nozzles in U S Gallons Per Minute

Head* psi	feet**	Velocity of disch ft/sec	1/16	1/8	3/16	1/4	3/8	1/2	5/8	3/4	7/8	1	1 1/8	1 1/4	1 3/8
10	23.1	38.6	0.37	1.48	3.32	5.91	13.3	23.6	36.9	53.1	72.4	94.5	120	148	179
15	34.6	47.25	0.45	1.81	4.06	7.24	16.3	28.9	45.2	65.0	88.5	116.	147	181	219
20	46.2	54.55	0.52	2.09	4.69	8.35	18.8	33.4	52.2	75.1	102.	134.	169	209	253
25	57.7	61.0	0.58	2.34	5.25	9.34	21.0	37.3	58.3	84.0	114.	149.	189	234	283
30	69.3	66.85	0.64	2.56	5.75	10.2	23.0	40.9	63.9	92.0	125.	164.	207	256	309
35	80.8	72.2	0.69	2.77	6.21	11.1	24.8	44.2	69.0	99.5	135.	177.	224	277	334
40	92.4	77.2	0.74	2.96	6.64	11.8	26.6	47.3	73.8	106.	145.	188.	239	296	357
45	103.9	81.8	0.78	3.13	7.03	12.5	28.2	50.1	78.2	113.	153.	200.	253	313	379
50	115.5	86.25	0.83	3.30	7.41	13.2	29.7	52.8	82.5	119.	162.	211.	267	330	399
55	127.0	90.5	0.87	3.46	7.77	13.8	31.1	55.3	86.4	125.	169.	221.	280	346	418
60	138.6	94.5	0.90	3.62	8.12	14.5	32.5	57.8	90.4	130.	177.	231.	293	362	438
65	150.1	98.3	0.94	3.77	8.45	15.1	33.8	60.2	94.0	136.	184.	241.	305	376	455
70	161.7	102.1	0.98	3.91	8.78	15.7	35.2	62.5	97.7	141.	191.	250.	317	391	473
75	173.2	105.7	1.01	4.05	9.08	16.2	36.4	64.7	101.	146.	198.	259.	327	404	489
80	184.8	109.1	1.05	4.18	9.39	16.7	37.6	66.8	104.	150.	205.	267.	338	418	505
85	196.3	112.5	1.08	4.31	9.67	17.3	38.8	68.9	108.	155.	211.	276.	349	431	521
90	207.9	115.8	1.11	4.43	9.95	17.7	39.9	70.8	111.	160.	217.	284.	359	443	536
95	219.4	119.0	1.14	4.56	10.2	18.2	41.0	72.8	114.	164.	223.	292.	369	456	551
100	230.9	122.0	1.17	4.67	10.5	18.2	42.1	74.7	117.	168.	229.	299.	378	467	565
105	242.4	125.0	1.20	4.79	10.8	19.2	43.1	76.5	120.	172.	234.	306.	388	479	579
110	254.0	128.0	1.23	4.90	11.0	19.6	44.1	78.4	122.	176.	240.	314.	397	490	593
115	265.5	130.9	1.25	5.01	11.2	20.0	45.1	80.1	125.	180.	245.	320.	406	501	606
120	277.1	133.7	1.28	5.12	11.5	20.5	46.0	81.8	128.	184.	251.	327.	414	512	619
130	300.2	139.1	1.33	5.33	12.0	21.3	48.0	85.2	133.	192.	261.	341.	432	533	645
140	323.3	144.3	1.38	5.53	12.4	22.1	49.8	88.4	138.	199.	271.	354.	448	553	668
150	346.4	149.5	1.43	5.72	12.9	22.9	51.6	91.5	143.	206.	280.	366.	463	572	692
175	404.1	161.4	1.55	6.18	13.9	24.7	55.6	98.8	154.	222.	302.	395.	500	618	747
200	461.9	172.6	1.65	6.61	14.8	26.4	59.5	106.	165.	238.	323.	423.	535	660	799
250	577.4	193.0	1.85	7.39	16.6	29.6	66.5	118.	185.	266.	362.	473.	598	739	894
300	692.8	211.2	2.02	8.08	18.2	32.4	72.8	129.	202.	291.	396.	517.	655	808	977

Head* psi	feet**	Velocity of disch ft/sec	1 1/2	1 3/4	2	2 1/4	2 1/2	2 3/4	3	3 1/2	4	4 1/2	5	5 1/2	6
10	23.1	38.6	213	289	378	479	591	714	851	1158	1510	1915	2365	2855	3405
15	34.6	47.25	260	354	463	585	723	874	1041	1418	1850	2345	2890	3490	4165
20	46.2	54.55	301	409	535	676	835	1009	1203	1638	2135	2710	3340	4040	4810
25	57.7	61.0	336	458	598	756	934	1128	1345	1830	2385	3025	3730	4510	5380
30	69.3	66.85	368	501	655	828	1023	1236	1473	2005	2615	3315	4090	4940	5895
35	80.8	72.2	398	541	708	895	1106	1335	1591	2168	2825	3580	4415	5340	6370
40	92.4	77.2	425	578	756	957	1182	1428	1701	2315	3020	3830	4725	5610	6810
45	103.9	81.8	451	613	801	1015	1252	1512	1802	2455	3200	4055	5000	6050	7120
50	115.5	86.25	475	647	845	1070	1320	1595	1900	2590	3375	4275	5280	6380	7600
55	127.0	90.4	498	678	886	1121	1385	1671	1991	2710	3540	4480	5530	6690	7970
60	138.6	94.5	521	708	926	1172	1447	1748	2085	2835	3700	4685	5790	6980	8330
65	150.1	98.3	542	737	964	1220	1506	1819	2165	2950	3850	4875	6020	7270	8670
70	161.7	102.1	563	765	1001	1267	1565	1888	2250	3065	4000	5060	6250	7560	9000
75	173.2	105.7	582	792	1037	1310	1619	1955	2330	3170	4135	5240	6475	7820	9320
80	184.8	109.1	602	818	1070	1354	1672	2020	2405	3280	4270	5410	6690	8080	9630
85	196.3	112.5	620	844	1103	1395	1723	2080	2480	3375	4400	5575	6890	8320	9920
90	207.9	115.8	638	868	1136	1436	1773	2140	2550	3475	4530	5740	7090	8560	10210
95	219.4	119.0	656	892	1168	1476	1824	2200	2625	3570	4655	5900	7290	8800	10500
100	230.9	122.0	672	915	1196	1512	1870	2255	2690	3660	4775	6050	7470	9030	10770
105	242.4	125.0	689	937	1226	1550	1916	2312	2755	3750	4890	6200	7650	9260	11020
110	254.0	128.0	705	960	1255	1588	1961	2366	2820	3840	5010	6340	7840	9470	11300
115	265.5	130.9	720	980	1282	1621	2005	2420	2885	3930	5120	6490	8010	9680	11550
120	277.1	133.7	736	1002	1310	1659	2050	2470	2945	4015	5225	6630	8180	9900	11800
130	300.2	139.1	767	1043	1365	1726	2132	2575	3070	4175	5450	6900	8530	10300	12290
140	323.3	144.3	795	1082	1415	1790	2212	2650	3180	4330	5650	7160	8850	10690	12730
150	346.4	149.5	824	1120	1466	1853	2290	2760	3295	4485	5850	7410	9150	11070	13200
175	404.1	161.4	890	1210	1582	2000	2473	2985	3560	4840	6310	8000	9890	11940	14250
200	461.9	172.6	950	1292	1691	2140	2645	3190	3800	5175	6760	8550	10580	12770	15220
250	577.4	193.0	1063	1447	1891	2392	2955	3570	4250	5795	7550	9570	11820	14290	17020
300	692.8	211.2	1163	1582	2070	2615	3235	3900	4650	6330	8260	10480	12940	15620	18610

The actual quantity discharged by a nozzle will be less than above table. A well tapered smooth nozzle may be assumed to give 97 to 99% of the values in the tables.
* Where there is both an upstream and downstream pressure, the head is a differential head.
** Head in feet basis water at approx. 60°F.

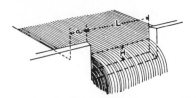

Discharge From Rectangular Weir with End Contractions

Figures in Table are in Gallons Per Minute

Head (H) in inches	Length (L) of weir in feet				Head (H) in inches	Length (L) of weir in feet		
	1	3	5	Additional gpm for each ft over 5 ft		3	5	Additional gpm for each ft over 5 ft
1	35.4	107.5	179.8	36.05	8	2338	3956	814
1¼	49.5	150.4	250.4	50.4	8¼	2442	4140	850
1½	64.9	197	329.5	66.2	8½	2540	4312	890
1¾	81	248	415	83.5	8¾	2656	4511	929
2	98.5	302	506	102	9	2765	4699	970
2¼	117	361	605	122	9¼	2876	4899	1011
2½	136.2	422	706	143	9½	2985	5098	1051
2¾	157	485	815	165	9¾	3101	5288	1091
3	177.8	552	926	187	10	3216	5490	1136
3¼	199.8	624	1047	211	10½	3480	5940	1230
3½	222	695	1167	236	11	3716	6355	1320
3¾	245	769	1292	261	11½	3960	6780	1410
4	269	846	1424	288	12	4185	7165	1495
4¼	293.6	925	1559	316	12½	4430	7595	1575
4½	318	1006	1696	345	13	4660	8010	1660
4¾	344	1091	1835	374	13½	4950	8510	1780
5	370	1175	1985	405	14	5215	8980	1885
5¼	395.5	1262	2130	434	14½	5475	9440	1985
5½	421.6	1352	2282	465	15	5740	9920	2090
5¾	449	1442	2440	495	15½	6015	10400	2165
6	476.5	1535	2600	528	16	6290	10900	2300
6¼		1632	2760	560	16½	6565	11380	2410
6½		1742	2920	596	17	6925	11970	2520
6¾		1826	3094	630	17½	7140	12410	2640
7		1928	3260	668	18	7410	12900	2745
7¼		2029	3436	701.5	18½	7695	13410	2855
7½		2130	3609	736	19	7980	13940	2970
7¾		2238	3785	774	19½	8280	14460	3090

This table is based on Francis formula:

$$Q = 3.33 (L - 0.2H)H^{1.5}$$

in which

Q = ft³ of water flowing per second.
L = length of weir opening in feet (should be 4 to 8 times H).
H = head on weir in feet (to be measured at least 6 ft back of weir opening).
a = should be at least 3 H.

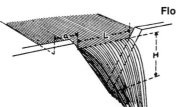

Flow Data Weirs

Discharge from Triangular Notch Weirs with End Contractions

Head (H) in inches	Flow in gallons per min		Head (H) in inches	Flow in gallons per min		Head (H) in inches	Flow in gallons per min	
	90° notch	60° notch		90° notch	60° notch		90° notch	60° notch
1	2.19	1.27	6¾	260	150	15	1912	1104
1¼	3.83	2.21	7	284	164	15½	2073	1197
1½	6.05	3.49	7¼	310	179	16	2246	1297
1¾	8.89	5.13	7½	338	195	16½	2426	1401
2	12.4	7.16	7¾	367	212	17	2614	1509
2¼	16.7	9.62	8	397	229	17½	2810	1623
2½	21.7	12.5	8¼	429	248	18	3016	1741
2¾	27.5	15.9	8½	462	267	18½	3229	1864
3	34.2	19.7	8¾	498	287	19	3452	1993
3¼	41.8	24.1	9	533	308	19½	3684	2127
3½	50.3	29.0	9¼	571	330	20	3924	2266
3¾	59.7	34.5	9½	610	352	20½	4174	2410
4	70.2	40.5	9¾	651	376	21	4433	2560
4¼	81.7	47.2	10	694	401	21½	4702	2715
4½	94.2	54.4	10½	784	452	22	4980	2875
4¾	108	62.3	11	880	508	23½	5268	3041
5	123	70.8	11½	984	568	23	4565	3213
5¼	139	80.0	12	1094	632	23½	5873	3391
5½	156	89.9	12½	1212	700	24	6190	3574
5¾	174	100	13	1337	772	24½	6518	3763
6	193	112	13½	1469	848	25	6855	3958
6¼	214	124	14	1609	929			
6½	236	136	14½	1756	1014			

Based on Thompson formula:

$$Q = (C)(4/15)(L)(H)\sqrt{2gH}$$

in which

Q = flow of water in ft³/sec
L = width of notch in ft at H distance above apex
H = head of water above apex of notch in ft
C = constant varying with conditions, .57 being used for this table
a = should not be less than ¾L.

For 90° notch the formula becomes

$$Q = 2.4381\ H^{5/2}$$

For 60° notch the formula becomes

$$Q = 1.4076\ H^{5/2}$$

Irrigation Table

Flow gpm	ft³ sec	ft³ min	1 in deep	2 in deep	3 in deep	4 in deep	6 in deep	8 in deep	10 in deep	12 in deep
						Number of acres covered in twelve hours pumping				
20	.0446	2.675	.529	.2645	.1765	.1324	.08825	.06625	.0529	.04415
50	.1112	6.68	1.328	.664	.4425	.332	.2213	.166	.1328	.1105
100	.2225	13.37	2.96	1.325	.883	.6625	.442	.3313	.265	.221
150	.3345	20.05	3.98	1.991	1.328	.995	.664	.4975	.398	.332
225	.502	30.05	5.97	2.985	1.990	1.492	.994	.747	.597	.4975
300	.668	40.01	7.96	3.980	2.655	1.99	1.327	.995	.796	.663
400	.891	53.40	10.61	5.305	3.535	2.652	1.770	1.328	1.061	.884
700	1.560	93.50	18.58	9.28	6.18	4.64	3.095	2.32	1.858	1.548
900	2.008	120.40	23.85	11.95	7.96	5.97	3.98	2.975	2.385	1.99
1200	2.675	160.50	31.82	15.92	10.61	7.95	5.305	3.975	3.182	2.65
1600	3.565	213.50	42.35	21.20	14.15	10.61	7.075	5.305	4.235	2.535
3000	6.68	400.50	79.50	39.75	26.50	19.88	13.25	9.94	7.95	6.625
4500	10.03	602.00	119.30	59.70	39.75	29.85	19.90	14.93	11.93	9.95
6000	13.36	802.00	159.10	79.60	53.00	39.75	26.52	18.89	15.91	13.26
7000	15.61	936.00	185.70	92.80	61.90	46.45	30.95	23.20	18.57	15.47
8500	18.95	1137.00	225.50	112.80	75.20	56.35	37.60	28.19	22.55	18.79
10000	22.25	1337.00	265.00	132.50	88.30	66.25	44.20	33.15	26.50	22.10
14000	31.15	1871.00	371.00	185.50	123.70	92.75	61.80	46.35	37.10	30.95

1 Acrefoot = 1 acre covered to a depth of 1 ft = 43,560 ft³.

FORMULAS AND EQUIVALENTS

Frequently Used Formulas and Equivalents

Velocity:

$$Q = AV \text{ or } V = Q/A$$

$$V = \frac{0.4085 \text{ gpm}}{d^2} = \frac{0.2859 \text{ bph}}{d^2} = \frac{0.0028368 \text{ gpm}}{D^2} = \frac{0.001985 \text{ bph}}{D^2}$$

where:

V = velocity of flow—ft/sec
Q = capacity—ft³/sec
A = area of pipe or conduit—ft²
d = diameter of circular pipe or conduit—inches
D = diameter of circular pipe or conduit—ft
gpm = U S gallons per minute
bph = barrels per hour (42 gals—oil)

Velocity equivalents:

ft/sec × 0.3048 = m/sec
m/sec × 3.2808 = ft/sec

Fluid flow—any liquid:

U S gpm × 0.002228 = ft³/sec
U S gpm × 0.2271 = m³/hr
U S gpm × 0.227 = metric tons per hour (water at
approximately 60°F)
mgd (U S) × 694.5 = U S gpm
ft³/sec × 448.83 = U S gpm
m³/hr × 4.403 = U S gpm
U S gallon × 0.8327 = Imperial gallons
Imperial gallons × 1.201 = U S gallons

$$\text{gpm} = \frac{\text{lb per hr}}{500 \times \text{sp gr}} \text{ (water at 60°F)}$$

gpm = boiler hp × 0.069

Fluid flow—oil:

barrels × 42 = U S gallons
barrels per hour × 0.7 = U S gpm
barrels per day × 0.02917 = U S gpm
U S gpm × 1.4286 = barrels per hour
U. S gpm × 34.286 = barrels per day

Head and pressure: (For water at normal temperatures (60°F))

$$\text{Head in feet} = \frac{\text{Head in psi} \times 2.31}{\text{sp gr}}$$

$$\text{Head in psi} = \frac{\text{Head in feet} \times \text{sp gr}}{2.31}$$

Pumping power—See page 1-27

$$
\begin{aligned}
\text{horsepower} \times 550 &= \text{ft-lb/sec}\\
\times 33000 &= \text{ft-lb/min}\\
\times 2546 &= \text{BTU/hr}\\
\times 745.7 &= \text{watts}\\
\times 0.7457 &= \text{kilowatts}\\
\times 1.014 &= \text{metric horsepower}
\end{aligned}
$$

$$\text{Brake hp} = \frac{\text{gpm} \times \text{H (in feet)} \times \text{sp gr}}{3960 \times \text{efficiency}} \quad \text{(centrifugal terminology)}$$

$$= \frac{\text{bph} \times \text{H (in feet)} \times \text{sp gr}}{5657 \times \text{efficiency}} \quad \text{(centrifugal terminology)}$$

$$= \frac{\text{gpm} \times \text{psi}}{1714 \times \text{eff}} \quad \text{(reciprocating terminology)}$$

$$= \frac{\text{bph} \times \text{psi}}{2449 \times \text{eff}} \quad \text{(reciprocating terminology)}$$

Note: To obtain the hydraulic horsepower from the above expressions assume a pump efficiency of 100%.

In the above expressions:

gpm = U S gallons per minute delivered (one gallon = 8.338 lbs at 60 Deg F.

bph = barrels (42 gallons) per hour—delivered = 0.7 gpm

H = total head in feet of liquid—differential

psi = lb per sq in—differential

sp gr = specific gravity

eff = efficiency expressed as a decimal

$$\text{Electrical hp input to motor} = \frac{\text{pump bhp}}{\text{motor efficiency}}$$

$$\text{KW input to motor} = \frac{\text{pump bhp} \times 0.7457}{\text{motor efficiency}}$$

FORMULAS AND EQUIVALENTS

Torque—See page 1-35

$$\text{Torque in lb-ft} = \frac{\text{bhp} \times 5250}{\text{rpm}}$$

bhp = brake horsepower

rpm = revolutions per minute

Specific speed—See page 1-19

$$\text{Impeller specific speed} = N_s = \frac{\text{rpm}\sqrt{\text{gpm}}}{H^{3/4}} \quad \text{(See page 1-20)}$$

where

gpm = design capacity at best efficiency point

H = head per stage at best efficiency point

rpm = speed

$$\text{Suction specific speed} = S = \frac{\text{rpm}\sqrt{\text{gpm}}}{(\text{NPSHR})^{3/4}} \quad \text{(See page 1-21)}$$

where

gpm = design capacity at best efficiency point for single suction first stage impellers, or one half design capacity for double suction impellers.

Affinity laws (See page 1-30)

At constant impeller diameter:—(Variable speed)

$$\frac{\text{RPM}_1}{\text{RPM}_2} = \frac{\text{gpm}_1}{\text{gpm}_2} = \frac{\sqrt{H_1}}{\sqrt{H_2}}$$

At constant speed:—Variable impeller diameter)

$$\frac{D_1}{D_2} = \frac{\text{gpm}_1}{\text{gpm}_2} = \frac{\sqrt{H_1}}{\sqrt{H_2}}$$

2

Miscellaneous

Temperature equivalents:

	Kelvin	Degrees Rankine	Degrees Celsius	Degrees Fahrenheit
Absolute zero	0	0	−273.15	−459.67
Water freezing point: (14.696 psia 101.325 KPa)	273.15	491.67	0	32
Water boiling point: (14.696 psia 101.325 KPa)	373.15	671.67	100	212

Celsius/Fahrenheit conversions:

$$\text{Deg C} = 5/9\,(°F - 32)$$
$$\text{Deg F} = 9/5\,°C + 32$$

Reynolds Number (R): (see page 1-4)

$$R = \frac{VD}{v}$$

V = Average velocity—ft/sec
D = Average internal diameter—ft
v = Kinematic viscosity of the fluid—ft²/sec (For pure fresh water at 60°F. v = 0.000 0 012 16 ft²/sec.)

Darcy-Weisbach (see page 3-3)

$$h_f = f\,\frac{L}{D}\,\frac{V^2}{2g}$$

Hazen and Williams (see page 3-7)

$$h_f = 0.002083\,L\left(\frac{100}{C}\right)^{1.85} \times \frac{gpm^{1.85}}{d^{4.8655}}$$

NOTE: For selected arithmetical and geometrical formulas refer to page 7-3

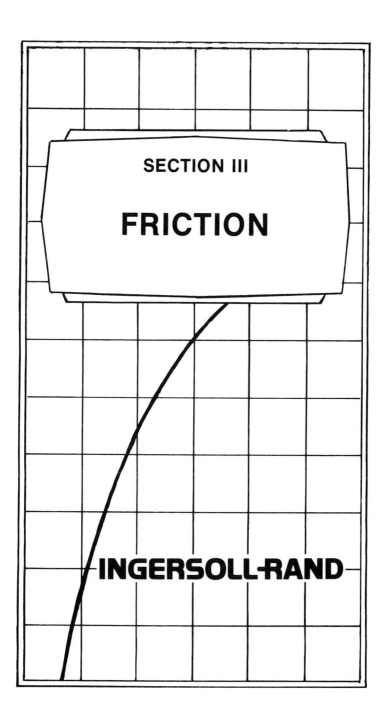

SECTION III

FRICTION

INGERSOLL-RAND

3

CONTENTS OF SECTION 3

Friction Data:

* *NOTE:* Pages 3-103 through 3-109 are located in this section (fol-
        lowing Paper Stock Friction Data) for convenience and
        ready reference.

Friction Losses in Pipe

The resistance to flow as a liquid is moved through a pipe results in a loss of head or pressure and is called friction (measured in feet of liquid). This resistance to flow is due to viscous shear stresses within the liquid and turbulence that occurs along the pipe walls due to roughness.

The amount of head loss for a given system depends on the characteristics of the liquid being handled; i.e. viscosity, size of pipe, condition (roughness) of pipe's interior surface and length of travel; also loss through various valves, fittings, etc. (see page 3-110).

A vast amount of research has been conducted to determine the amount of friction loss for different conditions, and various expressions based on experimental data have been developed for calculating friction loss. The expression most commonly used in present day practice and the one on which the tables in this book are based is the *Darcy-Weisbach equation. This formula recognizes that pipe friction is dependent on condition (roughness of pipe's interior surface), internal diameter of pipe, velocity of liquid and its viscosity. It is expressed as:

$$h_f = f \frac{L}{D} \frac{V^2}{2g}$$

where

h_f = friction loss—ft of liquid
L = pipe length—feet
D = average inside diameter of pipe—feet
V = average pipe velocity in ft/sec
g = gravitational constant (32.174 ft/sec^2)
f = friction factor—a dimensionless number which has been determined experimentally and for turbulent flow depends on the roughness of the pipe's interior surface and the Reynolds number (see page 3-5).

For laminar (viscous) flow (Reynolds number below 2000) the roughness or condition of the pipe's interior surface has no effect (except as it affects the cross sectional area) and the friction factor (f) becomes:

$$f = \frac{64}{R}$$

For turbulent flow (Reynolds number above 4000) the friction factor is affected by both the roughness of the pipe's interior surface

* Also known as the Fanning Formula.

and the Reynolds Number and can be determined from an equation developed by C. F. Colebrook (1939); i.e.

$$\frac{1}{\sqrt{f}} = -2 \log_{10}\left(\frac{\epsilon}{3.7D} + \frac{2.51}{R\sqrt{f}}\right)$$

where

R = Reynold's Number = $\dfrac{VD}{v}$

f = Friction Factor

ϵ = Absolute Roughness—in feet—(See following table)

D = Inside diameter of pipe—ft

V = Average pipe velocity—ft/sec

v = Kinematic Viscosity—ft²/sec

Since the Colebrook equation is non-factorable in f, awkward and difficult to solve, the value of f may be obtained from a graph or chart developed by L. F. Moody (ASME 1944) and included herein on page 3-11. This graph shows the relation between the friction factor f, the Reynolds Number R, and the *relative roughness* ϵ/D, where ϵ is the absolute roughness in feet and D is the pipe diameter in feet; Note that for convenience the relative roughness is used in developing the graph on page 3-11.

However, to avoid possible errors in reading the friction factor f from the Moody graph the friction loss data presented in the tables on pages 3-12 to 3-88 were calculated mathematically (programmed on a digital computer) basis the following assumptions:

(a) *Turbulent Flow*—Reynolds Numbers above 2000 except as noted (see pages 1-4 and 1-5).

(b) *Absolute Roughness Parameters* (ϵ)—of 0.00015 for new clean steel pipe (schedules as listed) and 0.0004 for new asphalt dipped cast iron pipe; and 0.000005 for smooth copper tubing and brass pipe.

(c) *Water Friction*—Pages 3-12 to 3-48 based on pure fresh water at a temperature of 60°F (15.6 °C); Kinematic viscosity (v) = 0.000 012 16 ft²/sec (1.130 Centistokes.) It should be noted that since the viscosity of water can vary appreciably from 32°F to 212°F the friction can increase or decrease as much as 40% between the two temperature extremes.

(d) *Viscous Liquids-Friction*—Pages 3-48 to 3-88, absolute roughness parameter of 0.00015 for new clean steel pipe—schedules as listed (see viscosity discussion page 4-23).

For pipes with other absolute roughness parameters see the following table.

Type of pipe (new, clean, condition)	Absolute roughness* ϵ (in feet)
Drawn tubing—glass, brass, plastic	0.000005
Commercial steel or wrought iron	0.00015
Cast iron—asphalt dipped	0.0004
Galvanized iron	0.0005
Cast iron—uncoated	0.00085
Wood stave	0.0006–0.0003
Concrete	0.001–0.01
Riveted steel	0.003–0.03

* Basis data from Hydraulic Institute Engineering Data Book.

3

To obtain friction loss in pipes having other roughness parameters, the applicable friction factor can be obtained from the Moody chart on page 3-11 and then, if desired, checked for accuracy with the Colebrook formula. In using the Moody chart on page 3-11 the relative roughness (ϵ/D) is used where "ϵ" is the absolute roughness in feet and "D" is the pipe diameter in feet.

Friction losses for pipe sizes between those listed in the tables may be found with reasonable accuracy using a ratio of the fifth power of the diameters; thus

Desired friction loss in pipe B

$$= \text{Known friction loss in pipe A} \left(\frac{\text{dia A}}{\text{dia B}} \right)^5$$

Use of a general multiplier to correct the head loss shown in these tables to head loss for pipes of other roughness characteristics is not recommended, or safe; multipliers can be developed, but they would apply accurately to only one flow or capacity. Instead the best procedures to follow is to: Calculate the applicable Reynolds Number, select the applicable friction factor from the Moody Chart and use it in the Darcy formula to determine the head loss desired.

The effect of aging and the allowances that should be made in estimating friction loss is beyond the scope of this discussion. It will depend on the particular properties of the fluid being handled and its effect on the interior pipe surface; any safety factors to allow for this effect must be estimated for local conditions and the requirements of each particular installation.

CAUTION—Since the friction loss data in the tables in this book are calculated on the basis of the roughness parameters for clean new pipe with no allowances for aging, manufacturing tolerances and other conditions which may cause variations of the interior pipe surfaces, it is suggested that for most commercial design purposes a safety factor of 15 to 20% be added to the values in the tables.

For a more detailed discussion of friction loss calculations and the various items that should be considered, reference is suggested to the Engineering Data Book of the Hydraulic Institute; also to Crane Technical Paper No. 410. See page 1-47 for bibliography.

For convenient reference formulas used in connection with the Darcy-Weisbach/Colebrook method are:

Head Loss

$$h_f = f \frac{L}{D} \frac{V^2}{2g} = f \frac{0.03112 \, L(gpm)^2}{d^5} = f \frac{0.0153 \, L(bph)^2}{d^5} = f \frac{LV^2}{4m2g}$$

Friction Factor (f): (also see graph page 3-11.)

$$\frac{1}{\sqrt{f}} = -2 \log_{10} \left[\frac{\epsilon}{3.7D} + \frac{2.51}{R\sqrt{f}} \right]$$

For R less than 2000 (laminar flow): $f = \dfrac{64}{R}$

Reynolds Number:

$$R = \frac{VD}{v} = \frac{VD\rho}{\mu \, 32.174} = \frac{3162(gpm)}{dk} = \frac{2214(bph)}{dk}$$

$$R \text{ (water at } 60°F) = \frac{2799.5(gpm)}{d}$$

Velocity:

$$V = \frac{0.4085(gpm)}{d^2} = \frac{0.2859(bph)}{d^2}$$

Velocity Head:

$$h_v = \frac{V^2}{2g} = 0.0155V^2 = \frac{0.00259(gpm)^2}{d^4} = \frac{0.00127(bph)^2}{d^4}$$

SYMBOLS USED IN FORMULAS, PAGES 3-6 and 3-7

bph = flow of liquid, barrels (42 gal) per hour.
  d = inside diameter of circular pipe—inches
  C = Friction Factor for Hazen & Williams
  D = inside diameter of circular pipe—feet
  f = Darcy-Weisbach friction factor, dimensionless.

g = acceleration of gravity, ft/sec² (taken as 32.174 ft/sec² in making conversions).

h_f = head loss due to friction, ft of liquid

ϵ = absolute roughness in feet — see **page 3-5**

h_v = Velocity head — ft of liquid

k = kinematic viscosity, centistokes = $\dfrac{z}{s}$

v = kinematic viscosity, —ft²/sec

L = length of pipe including equivalent length for loss through fittings — ft

m = hydraulic radius = $\dfrac{\text{flow area}}{\text{wetted perimeter}}$ = ft

(use in calculating flow in open channels or unfilled pipes)

ρ = density at temp. and press. at which liquid is flowing, lb/ft³

gpm = flow of liquid, gallons per minute.

μ = absolute or dynamic viscosity, lb-sec/ft²

V = velocity of flow, ft/sec

s = density, g/cm³ (water at 4°C or 39.2°F = 1.000)

z = absolute or dynamic viscosity — centipoises

HAZEN AND WILLIAMS

Although the Darcy-Weisbach/Colebrook method (on which the tables in this book are based) offers a rational mathematical solution to friction loss calculations (since it can be applied to any liquid except plastics and those carrying suspended solids) some engineers prefer to use one of the many empirical formulas that have been developed for water flowing under turbulent conditions.

Of these, the most widely used and accepted is the *Hazen and Williams* empirical formula since it is convenient to use and experience has shown that it produces reliable results. In a convenient form it reads:

$$h_f = 0.002083\ L \left(\frac{100}{C} \right)^{1.85} \times \frac{\text{gpm}^{1.85}}{d^{4.8655}}$$

This formula is basis a fluid having a kinematic viscosity, v = 0.000 012 16 ft²/sec (1.130 centistokes) or 31.5 SSU which is the case for water at 60°F. But since the viscosity of water can vary appreciably from 32°F to 212°F the friction can decrease or increase as much as 40% between the two temperature extremes. However, this formula can be used for any liquid having a viscosity in the range of 1.130 centistokes.

Values of C for various types of pipe with suggested design values are given in the following table with corresponding multipliers that can be applied, when appropriate, to obtain approximate results.

Hazen and Williams—Friction Factor C**

Type of pipe	Values of C		
	Range— High = best, smooth, well laid— Low = poor or corroded	Average value for clean, new pipe	Commonly used value for design purposes
Cement—Asbestos	160–140	150	140
Fibre	—	150	140
Bitumastic-enamel-lined iron or steel centrifugally applied	160–130	148	140
Cement-lined iron or steel centrifugally applied	—	150	140
Copper, brass, lead, tin or glass pipe and tubing	150–120	140	130
Wood-stave	145–110	120	110
Welded and seamless steel	150–80	130	100
Interior riveted steel (no projecting rivets).................................	—	139	100
Wrought-iron, Cast-iron	150–80	130	100
Tar-coated cast-iron	145–50	130	100
Girth-riveted steel (projecting rivets in girth seams only)	—	130	100
Concrete..................................	152–85	120	100
Full-riveted steel (projecting rivets in girth and horizontal seams)	—	115	100
Vitrified, Spiral-riveted steel (flow with lap)	—	110	100
Spiral-riveted steel (flow against lap)	—	100	90
Corrugated steel	—	60	60

Values of C	150	140	130	120	110	100	90	80	70	60
*Multiplier (Basis C = 100)	.47	.54	.62	.71	.84	1.0	1.22	1.50	1.93	2.57

* Multiplier to correct friction loss tables (in previous editions—14th Edition and earlier); cannot be used with tables in this book which are based on the Darcy-Weisbach-Colebrook formula.

** **Note:** the Hazen Williams friction factor "C" must not be confused with the Darcy-Weisbach-Colebrook friction factor "f"; these two friction factors are not in any way related to each other.

Friction—head loss—sample calculation:

To illustrate the application of the friction and head loss data in calculating the total system head for a specific system the following example is offered:

Problem—referring to the accompanying figure, page 3-10, a pump takes water (68°F) from a sump and delivers it through 1250 feet of 4″ diameter schedule 40 steel pipe. The suction pipe is 4″ vertical 5 feet long and includes a foot valve and a long-radius elbow. The discharge line includes two standard 90 degree flanged elbows, a swing check valve and an open wedge—disc gate valve. It is required to find the suction lift (h_s) and the discharge head (h_d) when the rate of flow is 200 gpm.

Solution

(a) SUCTION LIFT—Data from table on page 3-20.

$$\text{Velocity head} = \frac{V^2}{2g} = 0.395 \text{ ft}$$

Pipe friction loss $h_f = 2.25$ ft per 100 ft of pipe.
The resistance coefficient for the foot valve (page 3-115) is $K = 1.3$ and for the long-radius elbow (page 3-112) is $K = 0.27$.

The head loss due to pipe friction will be:

$$h_f = 2.25 \times \frac{5}{100} = 0.11 \text{ ft}$$

The head loss in the foot valve and long-radius elbow will be:

$$h_f = K \frac{V^2}{2g} = (1.3 + 0.27) \times 0.395 = 0.62 \text{ ft}$$

Total suction lift (h_s) $= (28.62 - 24.00) + 0.62 + 0.11 = 5.35$ ft

(b) DISCHARGE HEAD—The head loss due to pipe friction in the 4″ discharge line will be:

$$h_f = 2.25 \times \frac{1250}{100} = 28.13 \text{ ft}$$

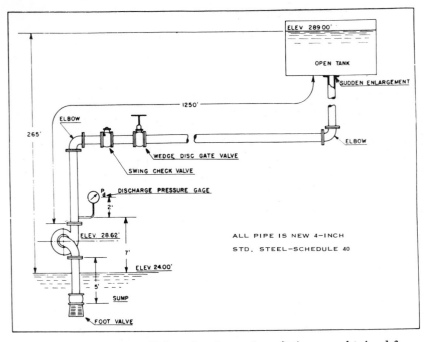

The resistance coefficient for the various fittings as obtained from the tables will be:

Standard 90 degree flanged elbow (pg. 3-112)	$K = 0.51$
Swing check valve (pg. 3-115)	$K = 1.70$
Wedge-disc gate valve (pg. 3-111)	$K = 0.14$
Sudden enlargement (pg. 3-116 to 3-118)	$K = 1.00$

The total resistance coefficient for the fittings on the discharge side and sudden enlargement at exit will be:

$$K = 2 \times 0.51 + 1.70 + 0.14 + 1.0 = 3.86$$

Therefore the head loss due to the fittings on the discharge side and sudden enlargement will be:

$$h_f = K \frac{V^2}{2g} = 3.86 \times 0.395 = 1.52 \text{ ft}$$

The total discharge head (h_d) will be:

$$h_d = (289.00 - 28.62) + 1.52 + 28.13 = 290 \text{ ft}$$

Total system head (H) = $h_d + h_s = 290 + 5.35 = 295$ ft

Add a reasonable safety factor to allow for any abnormal condition of pipe's interior or surface (see page 3-5).

Friction Factors for Commercial Pipe
(for Darcy-Weisbach formula, page 3-3)

Relative Roughness $= \dfrac{\epsilon}{D}$

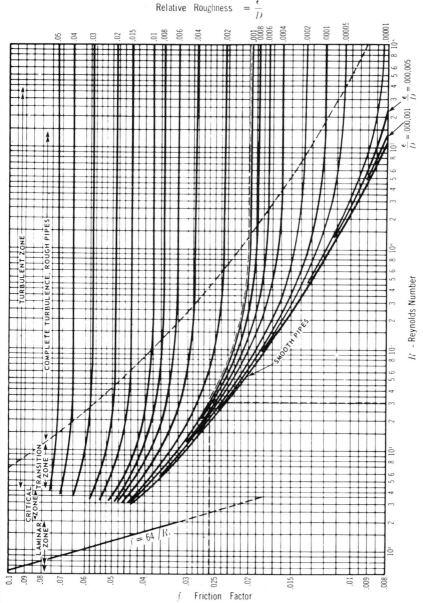

Moody diagram. (V. L. Streeter, "Fluid Mechanics," 5th ed. Copyright 1971 by McGraw-Hill Book Company, New York)

Note: Chart shows relation of relative roughnesss — ϵ/D where ϵ is absolute roughness in feet and D is diameter in feet.

Friction of Water   New Steel Pipe
(Based on Darcy's Formula)

¼ Inch

| Flow U S gal per min | Standard wt steel—sch 40 | | | Extra strong steel—sch 80 | | |
| | 0.364" inside dia | | | 0.302" inside dia | | |
	Velocity ft per sec	Velocity head-ft	**Head loss ft per 100 ft**	Velocity ft per sec	Velocity head-ft	**Head loss ft per 100 ft**
0.4	1.23	0.024	**3.7**	1.79	0.05	**9.18**
0.6	1.85	0.053	**7.6**	2.69	0.11	**19.0**
0.8	2.47	0.095	**12.7**	3.59	0.20	**32.3**
1.0	3.08	0.148	**19.1**	4.48	0.31	**48.8**
1.2	3.70	0.213	**26.7**	5.38	0.45	**68.6**
1.4	4.32	0.290	**35.6**	6.27	0.61	**91.7**
1.6	4.93	0.378	**45.6**	7.17	0.80	**118.1**
1.8	5.55	0.479	**56.9**	8.07	1.01	**147.7**
2.0	6.17	0.591	**69.4**	8.96	1.25	**180.7**
2.4	7.40	0.850	**98.1**	10.75	1.79	**256**
2.8	8.63	1.157	**132**	12.54	2.44	**345**

⅜ Inch

| Flow U S gal per min | Standard wt steel—sch 40 | | | Extra strong steel—sch 80 | | |
| | 0.493" inside dia | | | 0.423" inside dia | | |
	Velocity ft per sec	Velocity head-ft	**Head loss ft per 100 ft**	Velocity ft per sec	Velocity head-ft	**Head loss ft per 100 ft**
0.5	0.84	0.011	**1.26**	1.14	0.02	**2.63**
1.0	1.68	0.044	**4.26**	2.28	0.08	**9.05**
1.5	2.52	0.099	**8.85**	3.43	0.18	**19.0**
2.0	3.36	0.176	**15.0**	4.57	0.32	**32.4**
2.5	4.20	0.274	**22.7**	5.71	0.51	**49.3**
3.0	5.04	0.395	**32.0**	6.85	0.73	**69.6**
3.5	5.88	0.538	**42.7**	8.00	0.99	**93.3**
4.0	6.72	0.702	**55.0**	9.14	1.30	**120**
5.0	8.40	1.097	**84.2**	11.4	2.0	**185**
6.0	10.08	1.58	**119**	13.7	2.9	**263**

Calculations on pages 3-12 to 3-34 are by Ingersoll-Rand Co.

Note: No allowance has been made for age, difference in diameter, or any abnormal condition of interior surface. Any factor of safety must be estimated from the local conditions and the requirements of each particular installation. It is recommended that for most commercial design purposes a safety factor of 15 to 20% be added to the values in the tables—see page 3-5.

Friction of Water   New Steel Pipe *(Continued)*
(Based on Darcy's Formula)
½ Inch

Flow U S gal per min	Standard wt steel—sch 40 .622" inside dia			Extra strong steel—sch 80 .546" inside dia			Schedule 160 .464" inside dia		
	Velocity ft per sec	Velocity head ft	Head loss ft per 100 ft	Velocity ft per sec	Velocity head ft	Head loss ft per 100 ft	Velocity ft per sec	Velocity head ft	Head loss ft per 100 ft
0.7	0.739	.008	0.74	.96	.01	1.39			
1.0	1.056	.017	1.86	1.37	.03	2.58	1.90	.056	1.68
1.5	1.58	.039	2.82	2.06	.07	5.34	2.85	.126	5.73
2.0	2.11	.069	4.73	2.74	.12	9.02	3.80	.224	12.0
2.5	2.64	.108	7.10	3.43	.18	13.6	4.74	.349	20.3
3.0	3.17	.156	9.94	4.11	.26	19.1	5.69	.503	30.8
3.5	3.70	.212	13.2	4.80	.36	25.5	6.64	.684	43.5
4.0	4.22	.277	17.0	5.48	.47	32.7	7.59	.894	58.2
4.5	4.75	.351	21.1	6.17	.59	40.9	8.54	1.13	75.0
5.0	5.28	.433	25.8	6.86	.73	50.0	9.49	1.40	94.0
5.5	5.81	.524	30.9	7.54	.88	59.9	10.44	1.69	115
6.0	6.34	.624	36.4	8.23	1.05	70.7	11.38	2.01	138
6.5	6.86	.732	42.4	8.91	1.23	82.4	12.33	2.36	163
7.0	7.39	.849	48.8	9.60	1.43	95.0	13.28	2.74	190
7.5	7.92	.975	55.6	10.3	1.6	109	14.23	3.14	220
8.0	8.45	1.109	63.0	11.0	1.9	123			
8.5	8.98	1.25	70.7	11.6	2.1	138			
9.0	9.50	1.40	78.9	12.3	2.4	154			
9.5	10.03	1.56	87.6	13.0	2.6	171			
10	10.56	1.73	96.6	13.7	2.9	189			

¾ Inch

Flow U S gal per min	Standard wt steel—sch 40 .824" inside dia			Extra strong steel—sch 80 .742" inside dia			Steel—schedule 160 .612" inside dia		
	Velocity ft per sec	Velocity head ft	Head loss ft per 100 ft	Velocity ft per sec	Velocity head ft	Head loss ft per 100 ft	Velocity ft per sec	Velocity head ft	Head loss ft per 100 ft
1.5	0.90	.013	0.72	1.11	.02	1.19	1.64	.042	3.05
2.0	1.20	.023	1.19	1.48	.03	1.99	2.18	.074	5.12
2.5	1.50	.035	1.78	1.86	.05	2.97	2.73	.115	7.70
3.0	1.81	.051	2.47	2.23	.08	4.14	3.27	.166	10.8
3.5	2.11	.069	3.26	2.60	.11	5.48	3.82	.226	14.3
4.0	2.41	.090	4.16	2.97	.14	7.01	4.36	.295	18.4
4.5	2.71	.114	5.17	3.34	.17	8.72	4.91	.374	22.9
5.0	3.01	.141	6.28	3.71	.21	10.6	5.45	.462	28.0
6	3.61	.203	8.80	4.45	.31	14.9	6.54	.665	39.5
7	4.21	.276	11.7	5.20	.42	19.9	7.64	.905	53.0
8	4.81	.360	15.1	5.94	.55	25.6	8.73	1.18	68.4
9	5.42	.456	18.8	6.68	.69	32.1	9.82	1.50	85.8
10	6.02	.563	23.0	7.42	.86	39.2	10.91	1.85	105
11	6.62	.681	27.6	8.17	1.04	47.0	12.00	2.23	126
12	7.22	.722	32.5	8.91	1.23	55.5	13.09	2.66	149
13	7.82	.951	37.9	9.63	1.44	64.8	14.18	3.13	175
14	8.42	1.103	43.7	10.4	1.7	74.7	15.27	3.62	202
16	9.63	1.44	56.4	11.9	2.2	96.7	17.45	4.73	261
18	10.8	1.82	70.8	13.4	2.8	121			
20	12.0	2.25	86.8	14.8	3.4	149			

Note: No allowance has been made for age, difference in diameter, or any abnormal condition of interior surface. Any factor of safety must be estimated from the local conditions and the requirements of each particular installation. It is recommended that for most commercial design purposes a safety factor of 15 to 20% be added to the values in the tables—see page 3-5.

Friction of Water   New Steel Pipe (Continued)
(Based on Darcy's Formula)
1 Inch

Flow U S gal per min	Standard wt steel — sch 40			Extra strong steel — sch 80			Schedule 160 steel		
	1.049" inside dia			.957" inside dia			.815" inside dia		
	Velocity ft per sec	Velocity head ft	Head loss ft per 100 ft	Velocity ft per sec	Velocity head ft	Head loss ft per 100 ft	Velocity ft per sec	Velocity head ft	Head loss ft per 100 ft
2	0.74	.009	.385	.89	.01	.599	1.23	.023	1.26
3	1.11	.019	.787	1.34	.03	1.19	1.85	.053	2.60
4	1.48	.034	1.270	1.79	.05	1.99	2.46	.094	4.40
5	1.86	.054	1.90	2.23	.08	2.99	3.08	.147	6.63
6	2.23	.077	2.65	2.68	.11	4.17	3.69	.211	9.30
8	2.97	.137	4.50	3.57	.20	7.11	4.92	.376	15.9
10	3.71	.214	6.81	4.46	.31	10.8	6.15	.587	24.3
12	4.45	.308	9.58	5.36	.45	15.2	7.38	.845	34.4
14	5.20	.420	12.8	6.25	.61	20.4	8.61	1.15	46.2
16	5.94	.548	16.5	7.14	.79	26.3	9.84	1.50	59.7
18	6.68	.694	20.6	8.03	1.00	32.9	11.07	1.90	74.9
20	7.42	.857	25.2	8.92	1.24	40.3	12.30	2.35	91.8
22	8.17	1.036	30.3	9.82	1.50	48.4	13.53	2.84	110
24	8.91	1.23	35.8	10.7	1.8	57.2	14.76	3.38	131
26	9.65	1.45	41.7	11.6	2.1	66.8	15.99	3.97	153
28	10.39	1.68	48.1	12.5	2.4	77.1			
30	11.1	1.93	55.0	13.4	2.8	88.2			
35	13.0	2.62	74.1	15.6	3.8	119			
40	14.8	3.43	96.1	17.9	5.0	154			
45	16.7	4.33	121	20.1	6.3	194			

1¼ Inch

Flow U S gal per min	Standard wt steel — sch 40			Extra strong steel — sch 80			Schedule 160 — steel		
	1.380" inside dia			1.278" inside dia			1.160" inside dia		
	Velocity ft per sec	Velocity head ft	Head loss ft per 100 ft	Velocity ft per sec	Velocity head ft	Head loss ft per 100 ft	Velocity ft per sec	Velocity head ft	Head loss ft per 100 ft
4	.858	.011	.35	1.00	.015	.51	1.21	.023	.806
5	1.073	.018	.52	1.25	.024	.75	1.52	.036	1.20
6	1.29	.026	.72	1.50	.034	1.04	1.82	.051	1.61
7	1.50	.035	.95	1.75	.048	1.33	2.13	.070	2.14
8	1.72	.046	1.20	2.00	.062	1.69	2.43	.092	2.73
10	2.15	.072	1.74	2.50	.097	2.55	3.04	.143	4.12
12	2.57	.103	2.45	3.00	.140	3.57	3.64	.206	5.78
14	3.00	.140	3.24	3.50	.190	4.75	4.25	.280	7.72
16	3.43	.183	4.15	4.00	.249	6.10	4.86	.366	9.92
18	3.86	.232	5.17	4.50	.315	7.61	5.46	.463	12.4
20	4.29	.286	6.31	5.00	.388	9.28	6.07	.572	15.1
25	5.36	.431	9.61	6.25	.607	14.2	7.59	.894	23.2
30	6.44	.644	13.6	7.50	.874	20.1	9.11	1.29	32.9
35	7.51	.876	18.2	8.75	1.19	27.0	10.63	1.75	44.2
40	8.58	1.14	23.5	10.0	1.55	34.9	12.14	2.29	57.3
50	10.7	1.79	36.2	12.5	2.43	53.7	15.18	3.58	88.3
60	12.9	2.57	51.5	15.0	3.50	76.5	18.22	5.15	126
70	15.0	3.50	69.5	17.5	4.76	103	21.25	7.01	170
80	17.2	4.53	90.2	20.0	6.21	134	24.29	9.16	221
90	19.3	5.79	114	22.5	7.86	168	27.32	11.59	279

Note: No allowance has been made for age, difference in diameter, or any abnormal condition of interior surface. Any factor of safety must be estimated from the local conditions and the requirements of each particular installation. It is recommended that for most commercial design purposes a safety factor of 15 to 20% be added to the values in the tables—see page 3-5.

Friction of Water New Steel Pipe *(Continued)*
(Based on Darcy's Formula)
1½ Inch

Flow US gal per min	Standard wt steel—sch 40			Extra strong steel—sch 80			Schedule 160—steel		
	1.610" inside dia			1.500" inside dia			1.338" inside dia		
	Velocity ft per sec	Velocity head ft	Head loss ft per 100 ft	Velocity ft per sec	Velocity head ft	Head loss ft per 100 ft	Velocity ft per sec	Velocity head ft	Head loss ft per 100 ft
4	.63	.006	.166	.73	.01	.233	.913	.013	.404
5	.79	.010	.246	.91	.01	.346	1.14	.020	.601
6	.95	.014	.340	1.09	.02	.478	1.37	.029	.832
7	1.10	.019	.447	1.27	.03	.630	1.60	.040	1.10
8	1.26	.025	.567	1.45	.03	.800	1.83	.052	1.35
9	1.42	.031	.701	1.63	.04	.990	2.05	.065	1.67
10	1.58	.039	.848	1.82	.05	1.20	2.28	.081	2.03
12	1.89	.056	1.18	2.18	.07	1.61	2.74	.116	2.84
14	2.21	.076	1.51	2.54	.10	2.14	3.20	.158	3.78
16	2.52	.099	1.93	2.90	.13	2.74	3.65	.207	4.85
18	2.84	.125	2.40	3.27	.17	3.41	4.11	.262	6.04
20	3.15	.154	2.92	3.63	.20	4.15	4.56	.323	7.36
22	3.47	.187	3.48	3.99	.25	4.96	5.02	.391	8.81
24	3.78	.222	4.10	4.36	.30	5.84	5.48	.465	10.4
26	4.10	.261	4.76	4.72	.35	6.80	5.93	.546	12.1
28	4.41	.303	5.47	5.08	.40	7.82	6.39	.634	13.9
30	4.73	.347	6.23	5.45	.46	8.91	6.85	.727	15.9
32	5.04	.395	7.04	5.81	.52	10.1	7.30	.828	18.0
34	5.36	.446	7.90	6.17	.59	11.3	7.76	.934	20.2
36	5.67	.500	8.80	6.54	.66	12.6	8.22	1.05	22.5
38	5.99	.577	9.76	6.90	.74	14.0	8.67	1.17	25.0
40	6.30	.618	10.8	7.26	.82	15.4	9.13	1.29	27.6
42	6.62	.681	11.8	7.63	.90	16.9	9.58	1.43	30.3
44	6.93	.747	12.9	7.99	.99	18.5	10.04	1.57	33.1
46	7.25	.817	14.0	8.35	1.08	20.1	10.50	1.71	36.1
48	7.56	.889	15.2	8.72	1.18	21.8	10.95	1.86	39.2
50	7.88	.965	16.5	9.08	1.28	23.6	11.41	2.02	42.4
55	8.67	1.17	19.8	9.99	1.55	28.4	12.55	2.45	51.0
60	9.46	1.39	23.4	10.9	1.8	33.6	13.69	2.91	60.4
65	10.24	1.63	27.3	11.8	2.2	39.2	14.83	3.41	70.6
70	11.03	1.89	31.5	12.7	2.5	45.3	15.97	3.96	81.5
75	11.8	2.17	36.0	13.6	2.9	51.8	17.11	4.55	93.2
80	12.6	2.47	40.8	14.5	3.3	58.7	18.25	5.17	106
85	13.4	2.79	45.9	15.4	3.7	66.0	19.40	5.84	119
90	14.2	3.13	51.3	16.3	4.1	73.8	20.54	6.55	133
95	15.0	3.48	57.0	17.2	4.6	82.0	21.68	7.29	148
100	15.8	3.86	63.0	18.2	5.1	90.7	22.82	8.08	164
110	17.3	4.67	75.8	20.0	6.2	109.3	25.10	9.78	197
120	18.9	5.56	89.9	21.8	7.4	129.6	27.38	11.6	234
130	20.5	6.52	105	23.6	8.7	151.6	29.66	13.7	274
140	22.1	7.56	122	25.4	10.0	175			
150	23.6	8.68	139	27.2	11.5	201			
160	25.2	9.88	158	29.0	13.1	228			
170	26.8	11.15	178	30.9	14.8	257			
180	28.4	12.50	199	32.7	16.6	288			

Note: No allowance has been made for age, difference in diameter, or any abnormal condition of interior surface. Any factor of safety must be estimated from the local conditions and the requirements of each particular installation. It is recommended that for most commercial design purposes a safety factor of 15 to 20% be added to the values in the tables—see page 3-5.

Friction of Water   New Steel Pipe *(Continued)*
(Based on Darcy's Formula)
2 Inch

Flow U S gal per min	Standard wt steel—sch 40			Extra strong steel—sch 80			Schedule 160—steel		
	2.067" inside dia			1.939" inside dia			1.687" inside dia		
	Velocity ft per sec	Velocity head ft	Head loss ft per 100 ft	Velocity ft per sec	Velocity head ft	Head loss ft per 100 ft	Velocity ft per sec	Velocity head ft	Head loss ft per 100 ft
5	.478	.004	.074	.54	.00	.101	.718	.008	.197
6	.574	.005	.102	.65	.01	.139	.861	.012	.271
7	.669	.007	.134	.76	.01	.182	1.01	.016	.357
8	.765	.009	.170	.87	.01	.231	1.15	.020	.452
9	.860	.012	.209	.98	.01	.285	1.29	.026	.559
10	.956	.014	.252	1.09	.02	.343	1.44	.032	.675
12	1.15	.021	.349	1.30	.03	.476	1.72	.046	.938
14	1.34	.028	.461	1.52	.04	.629	2.01	.063	1.20
16	1.53	.036	.586	1.74	.05	.800	2.30	.082	1.53
18	1.72	.046	.725	1.96	.06	.991	2.58	.104	1.90
20	1.91	.057	.878	2.17	.07	1.16	2.87	.128	2.31
22	2.10	.069	1.05	2.39	.09	1.38	3.16	.155	2.76
24	2.29	.082	1.18	2.61	.11	1.62	3.45	.184	3.25
26	2.49	.096	1.37	2.83	.12	1.88	3.73	.216	3.77
28	2.68	.111	1.57	3.04	.14	2.16	4.02	.251	4.33
30	2.87	.128	1.82	3.26	.17	2.46	4.31	.288	4.93
35	3.35	.174	2.38	3.80	.22	3.28	5.02	.392	6.59
40	3.82	.227	3.06	4.35	.29	4.21	5.74	.512	8.49
45	4.30	.288	3.82	4.89	.37	5.26	6.46	.648	10.6
50	4.78	.355	4.66	5.43	.46	6.42	7.18	.799	13.0
55	5.26	.430	5.58	5.98	.56	7.70	7.89	.967	15.6
60	5.74	.511	6.58	6.52	.66	9.09	8.61	1.15	18.4
65	6.21	.600	7.66	7.06	.77	10.59	9.33	1.35	21.5
70	6.69	.696	8.82	7.61	.90	12.2	10.05	1.57	24.8
75	7.17	.799	10.1	8.15	1.03	13.9	10.77	1.80	28.3
80	7.65	.909	11.4	8.69	1.17	15.8	11.48	2.05	32.1
85	8.13	1.03	12.8	9.03	1.27	17.7	12.20	2.31	36.1
90	8.60	1.15	14.3	9.78	1.49	19.8	12.92	2.59	40.3
95	9.08	1.28	15.9	10.3	1.6	22.0	13.64	2.89	44.8
100	9.56	1.42	17.5	10.9	1.8	24.3	14.35	3.20	49.5
110	10.52	1.72	21.0	12.0	2.2	29.2	15.79	3.87	59.6
120	11.5	2.05	24.9	13.0	2.6	34.5	17.22	4.61	70.6
130	12.4	2.40	29.1	14.1	3.1	40.3	18.66	5.40	82.6
140	13.4	2.78	33.6	15.2	3.6	46.6	20.10	6.27	95.5
150	14.3	3.20	38.4	16.3	4.1	53.3	21.53	7.20	109
160	15.3	3.64	43.5	17.4	4.7	60.5	22.97	8.19	124
170	16.3	4.11	49.0	18.5	5.3	68.1	24.40	9.24	140
180	17.2	4.60	54.8	19.6	6.0	76.1	25.84	10.36	156
190	18.2	5.13	60.9	20.6	6.6	84.6	27.27	11.54	174
200	19.1	5.68	67.3	21.7	7.3	93.6	28.71	12.79	192
220	21.0	6.88	81.1	23.9	8.9	113			
240	22.9	8.18	96.2	26.9	10.6	134			
260	24.9	9.60	113	28.3	12.4	157			
280	26.8	11.14	130	30.4	14.4	181			
300	28.7	12.8	149	32.6	16.5	208			

Note: No allowance has been made for age, difference in diameter, or any abnormal condition of interior surface. Any factor of safety must be estimated from the local conditions and the requirements of each particular installation. It is recommended that for most commercial design purposes a safety factor of 15 to 20% be added to the values in the tables—see page 3-5.

Friction of Water   New Steel Pipe *(Continued)*
(Based on Darcy's Formula)
2½ Inch

Flow U S gal per min	Standard wt steel—sch 40			Extra strong steel—sch 80			Schedule 160—steel		
	2.469" inside dia			2.323" inside dia			2.125" inside dia		
	Velocity ft per sec	Velocity head ft	Head loss ft per 100 ft	Velocity ft per sec	Velocity head ft	Head loss ft per 100 ft	Velocity ft per sec	Velocity head ft	Head loss ft per 100 ft
8	.536	.005	.072	.61	.01	.097	.724	.008	.149
10	.670	.007	.107	.76	.01	.144	.905	.013	.221
12	.804	.010	.148	.91	.01	.199	1.09	.018	.305
14	.938	.014	.195	1.06	.02	.261	1.27	.025	.403
16	1.07	.018	.247	1.21	.02	.332	1.45	.033	.512
18	1.21	.023	.305	1.36	.03	.411	1.63	.041	.634
20	1.34	.028	.369	1.51	.04	.497	1.81	.051	.767
22	1.47	.034	.438	1.67	.04	.590	1.99	.061	.912
24	1.61	.040	.513	1.82	.05	.691	2.17	.073	1.03
26	1.74	.047	.593	1.97	.06	.800	2.35	.086	1.20
28	1.88	.055	.679	2.12	.07	.915	2.53	.100	1.37
30	2.01	.063	.770	2.27	.08	1.00	2.71	.114	1.56
35	2.35	.086	0.99	2.65	.11	1.33	3.17	.156	2.08
40	2.68	.112	1.26	3.03	.14	1.71	3.62	.203	2.66
45	3.02	.141	1.57	3.41	.18	2.13	4.07	.257	3.32
50	3.35	.174	1.91	3.79	.22	2.59	4.52	.318	4.05
55	3.69	.211	2.28	4.16	.27	3.10	4.98	.384	4.85
60	4.02	.251	2.69	4.54	.32	3.65	5.43	.457	5.72
65	4.36	.295	3.13	4.92	.38	4.25	5.88	.537	6.66
70	4.69	.342	3.60	5.30	.44	4.89	6.33	.622	7.67
75	5.03	.393	4.10	5.68	.50	5.58	6.79	.714	8.75
80	5.36	.447	4.64	6.05	.57	6.31	7.24	.813	9.90
85	5.70	.504	5.20	6.43	.64	7.08	7.69	.918	11.1
90	6.03	.565	5.80	6.81	.72	7.89	8.14	1.03	12.4
95	6.37	.630	6.43	7.19	.80	8.76	8.59	1.15	13.8
100	6.70	.698	7.09	7.57	.89	9.66	9.05	1.27	15.2
110	7.37	.844	8.51	8.33	1.08	11.6	9.95	1.54	18.3
120	8.04	1.00	10.1	9.08	1.28	13.7	10.86	1.83	21.6
130	8.71	1.18	11.7	9.84	1.50	16.0	11.76	2.15	25.2
140	9.38	1.37	13.5	10.6	1.7	18.5	12.67	2.49	29.1
150	10.05	1.57	15.5	11.3	2.0	21.1	13.57	2.86	33.3
160	10.7	1.79	17.5	12.1	2.3	23.9	14.47	3.25	37.8
170	11.4	2.02	19.7	12.9	2.6	26.9	15.38	3.67	42.5
180	12.1	2.26	22.0	13.6	2.9	30.1	16.28	4.12	47.5
190	12.7	2.52	24.4	14.4	3.2	33.4	17.19	4.59	52.8
200	13.4	2.79	27.0	15.1	3.5	36.9	18.09	5.08	58.4
220	14.7	3.38	32.5	16.7	4.3	44.4	19.90	6.15	70.3
240	16.1	4.02	38.5	18.2	5.1	52.7	21.71	7.32	83.4
260	17.4	4.72	45.0	19.7	6.0	61.6	23.52	8.59	97.6
280	18.8	5.47	52.3	21.2	7.0	71.2	25.33	9.96	113
300	20.1	6.28	59.6	22.7	8.0	81.6	27.14	11.43	129
350	23.5	8.55	80.6	26.5	10.9	110	31.66	15.56	175
400	26.8	11.2	105	30.3	14.3	144	36.19	20.32	228.
450	30.2	14.1	132	34.1	18.1	181	40.71	25.72	288
500	33.5	17.4	163	37.9	22.3	223	45.23	31.75	354

Note: No allowance has been made for age, difference in diameter, or any abnormal condition of interior surface. Any factor of safety must be estimated from the local conditions and the requirements of each particular installation. It is recommended that for most commercial design purposes a safety factor of 15 to 20% be added to the values in the tables—see page 3-5.

Friction of Water   Asphalt-dipped Cast Iron and New Steel Pipe
(Based on Darcy's Formula)   *(Continued)*
3 Inch

Flow US gal per min	Asphalt-dipped cast iron 3.0" inside dia			Std wt steel sch 40 3.068" inside dia			Extra strong steel sch 80 2.900" inside dia			Schedule 160—steel 2.624" inside dia		
	Velocity ft per sec	Velocity head ft	Head loss ft per 100 ft	Velocity ft per sec	Velocity head ft	Head loss ft per 100 ft	Velocity ft per sec	Velocity head ft	Head loss ft per 100 ft	Velocity ft per sec	Velocity head ft	Head loss ft per 100 ft
10	.454	.00	.042	.434	.003	.038	.49	.00	.050	.593	.005	.080
15	.681	.01	.088	.651	.007	.077	.73	.01	.101	.890	.012	.164
20	.908	.01	.149	.868	.012	.129	.97	.02	.169	1.19	.022	.275
25	1.13	.02	.225	1.09	.018	.192	1.21	.02	.253	1.48	.034	.411
30	1.36	.03	.316	1.30	.026	.267	1.45	.03	.351	1.78	.049	.572
35	1.59	.04	.421	1.52	.036	.353	1.70	.04	.464	2.08	.067	.757
40	1.82	.05	.541	1.74	.047	.449	1.94	.06	.592	2.37	.087	.933
45	2.04	.06	.676	1.95	.059	.557	2.18	.07	.734	2.67	.111	1.16
50	2.27	.08	.825	2.17	.073	.676	2.43	.09	.860	2.97	.137	1.41
55	2.50	.10	.990	2.39	.089	.776	2.67	.11	1.03	3.26	.165	1.69
60	2.72	.12	1.17	2.60	.105	.912	2.91	.13	1.21	3.56	.197	1.99
65	2.95	.14	1.36	2.82	.124	1.06	3.16	.15	1.40	3.86	.231	2.31
70	3.18	.16	1.57	3.04	.143	1.22	3.40	.18	1.61	4.15	.268	2.65
75	3.40	.18	1.79	3.25	.165	1.38	3.64	.21	1.83	4.45	.307	3.02
80	3.63	.21	2.03	3.47	.187	1.56	3.88	.23	2.07	4.75	.350	3.41
85	3.86	.23	2.28	3.69	.211	1.75	4.12	.26	2.31	5.04	.395	3.83
90	4.08	.26	2.55	3.91	.237	1.95	4.37	.29	2.58	5.34	.443	4.27
95	4.31	.29	2.83	4.12	.264	2.16	4.61	.33	2.86	5.63	.493	4.73
100	4.54	.32	3.12	4.34	.293	2.37	4.85	.36	3.15	5.93	.546	5.21
110	4.99	.39	3.75	4.77	.354	2.84	5.33	.44	3.77	6.53	.661	6.25
120	5.45	.46	4.45	5.21	.421	3.35	5.81	.52	4.45	7.12	.787	7.38
130	5.90	.54	5.19	5.64	.495	3.90	6.30	.62	5.19	7.71	.923	8.61
140	6.35	.63	6.00	6.08	.574	4.50	6.79	.71	5.98	8.31	1.07	9.92
150	6.81	.72	6.87	6.51	.659	5.13	7.28	.82	6.82	8.90	1.23	11.3
160	7.26	.82	7.79	6.94	.749	5.80	7.76	.93	7.72	9.49	1.40	12.8
180	8.17	1.04	9.81	7.81	.948	7.27	8.72	1.01	9.68	10.68	1.77	16.1
200	9.08	1.28	12.1	8.68	1.17	8.90	9.70	1.46	11.86	11.87	2.19	19.8
220	9.98	1.55	14.5	9.55	1.42	10.7	10.7	1.78	14.26	13.05	2.64	23.8
240	10.9	1.84	17.3	10.4	1.69	12.7	11.6	2.07	16.88	14.24	3.15	28.2
260	11.8	2.16	20.2	11.3	1.98	14.8	12.6	2.46	19.71	15.43	3.69	32.9
280	12.7	2.51	23.4	12.2	2.29	17.1	13.6	2.88	22.77	16.61	4.28	38.0
300	13.6	2.88	26.8	13.0	2.63	19.5	14.5	3.26	26.04	17.80	4.92	43.5
320	14.5	3.28	30.4	13.9	3.00	22.1	15.5	3.77	29.53	18.99	5.59	49.4
340	15.4	3.70	34.3	14.8	3.38	24.9	16.5	4.22	33.24	20.17	6.32	55.6
360	16.3	4.15	38.4	15.6	3.79	27.8	17.5	4.73	37.16	21.36	7.08	62.2
380	17.2	4.62	42.7	16.5	4.23	30.9	18.4	5.27	41.31	22.55	7.89	69.2
400	18.2	5.12	47.3	17.4	4.68	34.2	19.4	5.81	45.67	23.73	8.74	76.5
420	19.1	5.65	52.1	18.2	5.16	37.6	20.4	6.43	50.25	24.92	9.64	84.2
440	20.0	6.20	57.1	19.1	5.67	41.2	21.4	7.13	55.05	26.11	10.58	92.2
460	20.9	6.77	62.4	20.0	6.19	44.9	22.3	7.75	60.06	27.29	11.56	101
480	21.8	7.38	67.9	20.8	6.74	48.8	23.3	8.37	65.30	28.48	12.59	109
500	22.7	8.00	73.6	21.7	7.32	52.9	24.2	9.15	70.75	29.66	13.66	119
550	25.0	9.68	88.9	23.9	8.85	63.8	26.7	11.1	85.33	32.63	16.53	143
600	27.2	11.5	106	26.0	10.5	75.7	29.1	13.1	101	35.60	19.67	170
650	29.5	13.5	124	28.2	12.4	88.6	31.6	15.5	119	38.56	23.08	199

Note: No allowance has been made for age, difference in diameter, or any abnormal condition of interior surface. Any factor of safety must be estimated from the local conditions and the requirements of each particular installation. It is recommended that for most commercial design purposes a safety factor of 15 to 20% be added to the values in the tables—see page 3-5.

Friction of Water   Asphalt-dipped Cast Iron and New Steel Pipe
(Based on Darcy's Formula)   *(Continued)*
3½ Inch

Flow U S gal per min	Asphalt-dipped cast iron			Std wt steel sch 40			Extra strong steel sch 80		
	3.5" inside dia			3.548" inside dia			3.364" inside dia		
	Velocity ft per sec	Velocity head ft	Head loss ft per 100 ft	Velocity ft per sec	Velocity head ft	Head loss ft per 100 ft	Velocity ft per sec	Velocity head ft	Head loss ft per 100 ft
15	.500	.004	**.043**	.487	.004	**.038**	.54	.00	**.050**
20	.667	.007	**.070**	.649	.007	**.064**	.72	.01	**.083**
25	.834	.011	**.105**	.811	.010	**.095**	.90	.01	**.123**
30	1.000	.016	**.146**	.974	.015	**.132**	1.08	.02	**.171**
35	1.167	.021	**.195**	1.14	.020	**.174**	1.26	.02	**.225**
40	1.334	.028	**.250**	1.30	.026	**.221**	1.44	.03	**.287**
45	1.501	.035	**.311**	1.46	.033	**.274**	1.63	.04	**.355**
50	1.667	.043	**.379**	1.62	.041	**.332**	1.80	.05	**.430**
60	2.001	.062	**.535**	1.95	.059	**.463**	2.17	.07	**.601**
70	2.334	.085	**.717**	2.27	.080	**.614**	2.53	.10	**.769**
80	2.67	.110	**.924**	2.60	.105	**.757**	2.89	.13	**.986**
90	3.00	.140	**.160**	2.92	.133	**.943**	3.25	.16	**1.23**
100	3.34	.173	**1.42**	3.25	.164	**1.15**	3.61	.20	**1.50**
110	3.67	.209	**1.70**	3.57	.198	**1.37**	3.97	.24	**1.79**
120	4.00	.249	**2.01**	3.89	.236	**1.62**	4.33	.29	**2.11**
130	4.34	.292	**2.35**	4.22	.277	**1.88**	4.69	.34	**2.46**
140	4.67	.338	**2.71**	4.54	.321	**2.16**	5.05	.40	**2.83**
150	5.00	.388	**3.10**	4.87	.368	**2.47**	5.41	.45	**3.22**
160	5.34	.442	**3.52**	5.19	.419	**2.79**	5.78	.52	**3.64**
170	5.67	.499	**3.96**	5.52	.473	**3.13**	6.14	.59	**4.09**
180	6.00	.56	**4.42**	5.84	.530	**3.49**	6.50	.66	**4.56**
190	6.34	.62	**4.92**	6.17	.591	**3.86**	6.85	.73	**5.06**
200	6.67	.69	**5.43**	6.49	.655	**4.26**	7.22	.81	**5.58**
220	7.34	.84	**6.55**	7.14	.792	**5.12**	7.94	.98	**6.70**
240	8.00	.99	**7.76**	7.79	.943	**6.04**	8.66	1.17	**7.92**
260	8.67	1.17	**9.08**	8.44	1.11	**7.05**	9.38	1.37	**9.24**
280	9.34	1.35	**10.5**	9.09	1.28	**8.13**	10.1	1.6	**10.66**
300	10.0	1.55	**12.0**	9.74	1.47	**9.29**	10.8	1.8	**12.2**
320	10.7	1.77	**13.7**	10.4	1.68	**10.5**	11.5	2.1	**13.8**
340	11.3	2.00	**15.4**	11.0	1.89	**11.8**	12.3	2.4	**15.5**
360	12.0	2.24	**17.2**	11.7	2.12	**13.2**	13.0	2.6	**17.4**
380	12.7	2.49	**19.2**	12.3	2.36	**14.7**	13.7	2.9	**19.3**
400	13.3	2.76	**21.2**	13.0	2.62	**16.2**	14.4	3.2	**21.3**
420	14.0	3.05	**23.3**	13.6	2.89	**17.8**	15.2	3.6	**23.4**
440	14.7	3.34	**25.6**	14.3	3.17	**19.5**	15.9	3.9	**25.7**
460	15.3	3.65	**27.9**	14.9	3.46	**21.3**	16.6	4.3	**28.0**
480	16.0	3.98	**30.4**	15.6	3.77	**23.1**	17.3	4.7	**30.4**
500	16.7	4.32	**32.9**	16.2	4.09	**25.1**	18.1	5.1	**32.9**
550	18.3	5.22	**39.8**	17.8	4.95	**30.2**	19.9	6.2	**39.7**
600	20.0	6.21	**47.2**	19.5	5.89	**35.8**	21.7	7.3	**47.1**
650	21.7	7.29	**55.4**	21.1	6.91	**41.9**	23.5	8.6	**55.1**
700	23.3	8.46	**64.1**	22.7	8.02	**48.4**	25.3	9.4	**63.7**
750	25.0	9.71	**73.5**	24.3	9.20	**55.4**	27.1	11.4	**73.0**
800	26.7	11.0	**83.6**	26.0	10.5	**62.9**	28.9	13.0	**82.9**
850	28.3	12.5	**94.2**	27.6	11.8	**70.9**	30.7	14.6	**93.4**

Note: No allowance has been made for age, difference in diameter, or any abnormal condition of interior surface. Any factor of safety must be estimated from the local conditions and the requirements of each particular installation. It is recommended that for most commercial design purposes a safety factor of 15 to 20% be added to the values in the tables—see page 3-5.

Friction of Water — Asphalt-dipped Cast Iron and New Steel Pipe
(Based on Darcy's Formula)
4 Inch   (Continued)

Flow US gal per min	Asphalt-dipped cast iron 4.0" inside dia			Std wt steel sch 40 4.026" inside dia			Extra strong steel sch 80 3.826" inside dia			Schedule 160—steel 3.438" inside dia		
	Velocity ft per sec	Velocity head ft	Head loss ft per 100 ft	Velocity ft per sec	Velocity head ft	Head loss ft per 100 ft	Velocity ft per sec	Velocity head ft	Head loss ft per 100 ft	Velocity ft per sec	Velocity head ft	Head loss ft per 100 ft
20	.511	.004	.038	.504	.004	.035	.56	.00	.045	.691	.007	.074
30	.766	.009	.076	.756	.009	.072	.84	.01	.092	1.04	.017	.154
40	1.02	.016	.128	1.01	.016	.120	1.12	.02	.153	1.38	.030	.258
50	1.28	.025	.194	1.26	.025	.179	1.40	.03	.230	1.73	.046	.387
60	1.53	.037	.273	1.51	.036	.250	1.67	.04	.320	2.07	.067	.540
70	1.79	.050	.365	1.76	.048	.330	1.95	.06	.424	2.42	.091	.691
80	2.04	.065	.470	2.02	.063	.422	2.23	.08	.541	2.77	.119	.885
90	2.30	.082	.588	2.27	.080	.523	2.51	.10	.649	3.11	.150	1.10
100	2.55	.101	.719	2.52	.099	.613	2.79	.12	.789	3.46	.185	1.34
110	2.81	.123	.862	2.77	.119	.732	3.07	.15	.943	3.80	.224	1.61
120	3.06	.146	1.02	3.02	.142	.861	3.35	.17	1.11	4.15	.267	1.89
130	3.32	.171	1.19	3.28	.167	1.00	3.63	.20	1.29	4.49	.313	2.20
140	3.57	.199	1.37	3.53	.193	1.15	3.91	.24	1.48	4.84	.363	2.53
150	3.83	.228	1.57	3.78	.222	1.31	4.19	.27	1.69	5.18	.417	2.89
160	4.08	.259	1.77	4.03	.253	1.48	4.47	.31	1.91	5.53	.475	3.26
170	4.34	.293	1.99	4.28	.285	1.66	4.75	.35	2.14	5.88	.536	3.66
180	4.60	.328	2.23	4.54	.320	1.85	5.02	.39	2.38	6.22	.601	4.09
190	4.85	.368	2.47	4.79	.356	2.05	5.30	.44	2.64	6.57	.669	4.53
200	5.11	.406	2.73	5.04	.395	2.25	5.58	.48	2.91	6.91	.742	5.00
220	5.62	.490	3.29	5.54	.478	2.70	6.14	.59	3.49	7.60	.897	6.00
240	6.13	.583	3.90	6.05	.569	3.19	6.70	.70	4.13	8.30	1.07	7.09
260	6.64	.685	4.55	6.55	.667	3.72	7.26	.82	4.81	8.99	1.25	8.27
280	7.15	.794	5.26	7.06	.774	4.28	7.82	.95	5.54	9.68	1.45	9.55
300	7.66	.912	6.02	7.56	.888	4.89	8.38	1.09	6.33	10.37	1.67	10.9
320	8.17	1.04	6.84	8.06	1.01	5.53	8.94	1.24	7.17	11.06	1.90	12.4
340	8.68	1.17	7.70	8.57	1.14	6.22	9.50	1.40	8.06	11.75	2.14	13.9
360	9.19	1.31	8.61	9.07	1.28	6.94	10.0	1.6	9.00	12.44	2.40	15.5
380	9.70	1.46	9.58	9.58	1.43	7.71	10.6	1.7	9.99	13.13	2.68	17.3
400	10.2	1.62	10.6	10.1	1.58	8.51	11.2	1.9	11.0	13.82	2.97	19.1
420	10.7	1.79	11.6	10.6	1.74	9.35	11.7	2.1	12.1	14.52	3.27	21.0
440	11.2	1.96	12.8	11.1	1.91	10.2	12.3	2.3	13.3	15.21	3.59	22.9
460	11.7	2.14	13.9	11.6	2.09	11.2	12.8	2.5	14.5	15.90	3.92	25.0
480	12.3	2.33	15.2	12.1	2.27	12.1	13.4	2.8	15.7	16.59	4.27	27.2
500	12.8	2.53	16.4	12.6	2.47	13.1	14.0	3.0	17.0	17.28	4.64	29.5
550	14.0	3.06	19.8	13.9	2.99	15.8	15.3	3.6	20.5	19.00	5.61	35.5
600	15.3	3.65	23.6	15.1	3.55	18.7	16.7	4.3	24.3	20.74	6.67	42.1
650	16.6	4.28	27.6	16.4	4.17	21.7	18.1	5.1	28.4	22.46	7.83	49.2
700	17.9	4.96	32.0	17.6	4.84	25.3	19.5	5.9	32.8	24.19	9.08	57.0
750	19.1	5.70	36.6	18.9	5.55	28.9	20.9	6.8	37.6	25.92	10.4	65.2
800	20.4	6.48	41.6	20.2	6.32	32.8	22.3	7.7	42.7	27.65	11.7	74.1
850	21.7	7.32	46.9	21.4	7.13	37.0	23.7	8.7	48.1	29.38	13.4	83.4
900	23.0	8.20	52.6	22.7	8.00	41.4	25.1	9.8	53.8	31.10	15.0	93.4
950	24.3	9.14	58.5	23.9	8.91	46.0	26.5	10.9	59.8	32.83	16.7	104
1000	25.5	10.1	64.8	25.2	9.87	50.9	27.9	12.1	66.2	34.56	18.5	115
1100	28.1	12.3	78.3	27.7	11.9	61.4	30.7	14.6	79.8	38.02	22.4	139

Note: No allowance has been made for age, difference in diameter, or any abnormal condition of interior surface. Any factor of safety must be estimated from the local conditions and the requirements of each particular installation. It is recommended that for most commercial design purposes a safety factor of 15 to 20% be added to the values in the tables—see page 3-5.

Friction of Water *New Steel Pipe *(Continued)*
(Based on Darcy's Formula)
5 Inch

Flow U S gal per min	Standard wt steel—sch 40			Extra strong steel—sch 80			Schedule 160—steel		
	5.047" inside dia			4.813" inside dia			4.313" inside dia		
	Velocity ft per sec	Velocity head ft	Head loss ft per 100 ft	Velocity ft per sec	Velocity head ft	Head loss ft per 100 ft	Velocity ft per sec	Velocity head ft	Head loss ft per 100 ft
30	.481	.004	.024	.53	.00	.030	.659	.007	.051
40	.641	.006	.040	.71	.01	.051	.878	.012	.086
50	.802	.010	.060	.88	.01	.075	1.10	.019	.128
60	.962	.014	.083	1.06	.02	.105	1.32	.027	.178
70	1.12	.020	.110	1.23	.02	.138	1.54	.037	.236
80	1.28	.026	.140	1.41	.03	.176	1.76	.048	.301
90	1.44	.032	.173	1.59	.04	.218	1.98	.061	.373
100	1.60	.040	.210	1.76	.05	.265	2.20	.075	.453
120	1.92	.058	.293	2.11	.07	.370	2.64	.108	.612
140	2.25	.078	.389	2.47	.09	.491	3.07	.147	.816
160	2.57	.102	.480	2.82	.12	.607	3.51	.192	1.05
180	2.89	.129	.598	3.17	.16	.757	3.95	.243	1.31
200	3.21	.160	.728	3.52	.19	.922	4.39	.299	1.60
220	3.53	.193	.870	3.88	.23	1.10	4.83	.362	1.91
240	3.85	.230	1.03	4.23	.28	1.30	5.27	.431	2.25
260	4.17	.270	1.19	4.58	.33	1.51	5.71	.506	2.63
280	4.49	.313	1.37	4.94	.38	1.74	6.15	.587	3.02
300	4.81	.360	1.56	5.29	.43	1.99	6.59	.674	3.45
320	5.13	.409	1.77	5.64	.49	2.25	7.03	.766	3.91
340	5.45	.462	1.98	5.99	.56	2.52	7.47	.865	4.39
360	5.77	.518	2.21	6.35	.63	2.81	7.91	.970	4.90
380	6.09	.577	2.45	6.70	.70	3.12	8.35	1.08	5.43
400	6.41	.639	2.71	7.05	.77	3.44	8.78	1.20	6.00
420	6.74	.705	2.97	7.40	.85	3.78	9.22	1.32	6.59
440	7.06	.774	3.25	7.76	.94	4.13	9.66	1.45	7.21
460	7.38	.846	3.54	8.11	1.02	4.50	10.10	1.58	7.85
480	7.70	.921	3.84	8.46	1.11	4.88	10.54	1.73	8.53
500	8.02	.999	4.15	8.82	1.21	5.28	10.98	1.87	9.23
550	8.82	1.21	4.99	9.70	1.46	6.35	12.08	2.26	11.1
600	9.62	1.44	5.90	10.6	1.7	7.51	13.18	2.70	13.1
650	10.4	1.69	6.89	11.5	2.1	8.77	14.27	3.16	15.4
700	11.2	1.96	7.95	12.3	2.4	10.1	15.37	3.67	17.8
750	12.0	2.25	9.09	13.2	2.7	11.6	16.47	4.21	20.3
800	12.8	2.56	10.3	14.1	3.1	13.1	17.57	4.79	23.0
850	13.6	2.89	11.6	15.0	3.5	14.8	18.67	5.41	25.9
900	14.4	3.24	13.0	15.9	3.9	16.5	19.76	6.06	29.0
950	15.2	3.61	14.4	16.7	4.3	18.4	20.86	6.76	32.3
1000	16.0	4.00	15.9	17.6	4.8	20.3	21.96	7.49	36.7
1100	17.6	4.84	19.2	19.4	5.8	24.5	24.16	9.06	43.0
1200	19.2	5.76	22.7	21.1	6.9	29.0	26.35	10.78	51.0
1300	20.8	6.75	26.6	22.9	8.2	34.0	28.55	12.65	59.8
1400	22.5	7.83	30.7	24.7	9.5	39.3	30.74	14.67	69.2
1500	24.1	8.99	35.2	26.4	10.8	45.0	32.94	16.84	79.2
1600	25.7	10.2	40.0	28.2	12.4	51.1	35.14	19.16	90.0
1700	27.3	11.6	45.1	30.0	14.0	57.6	37.33	21.63	101

* Cast iron not commercially available in this size.

Note: No allowance has been made for age, difference in diameter, or any abnormal condition of interior surface. Any factor of safety must be estimated from the local conditions and the requirements of each particular installation. It is recommended that for most commercial design purposes a safety factor of 15 to 20% be added to the values in the tables—see page 3-5.

Friction of Water   **Asphalt-dipped Cast Iron and New Steel Pipe**
(Based on Darcy's Formula)   **(Continued)**

6 Inch

Flow US gal per min	Asphalt-dipped cast iron			Std wt steel sch 40			Extra strong steel sch 80			Schedule 160—steel		
	6.0" inside dia			6.065" inside dia			5.761" inside dia			5.187" inside dia		
	Velocity ft per sec	Velocity head ft	Head loss ft per 100 ft	Velocity ft per sec	Velocity head ft	Head loss ft per 100 ft	Velocity ft per sec	Velocity head ft	Head loss ft per 100 ft	Velocity ft per sec	Velocity head ft	Head loss ft per 100 ft
50	.57	.005	.027	.56	.005	.025	.62	.01	.032	.759	.009	.053
60	.68	.007	.038	.67	.007	.034	.74	.01	.044	.911	.013	.073
70	.79	.010	.048	.78	.009	.045	.86	.01	.058	1.06	.018	.096
80	.91	.013	.062	.89	.012	.057	.98	.01	.074	1.22	.023	.123
90	1.02	.016	.077	1.00	.016	.071	1.11	.02	.091	1.37	.029	.152
100	1.13	.020	.094	1.11	.019	.086	1.23	.02	.110	1.52	.036	.184
120	1.36	.029	.132	1.33	.028	.120	1.48	.03	.154	1.82	.052	.256
140	1.59	.039	.176	1.55	.038	.158	1.72	.05	.203	2.13	.070	.340
160	1.82	.051	.226	1.78	.049	.202	1.97	.06	.260	2.43	.092	.435
180	2.04	.065	.283	2.00	.062	.251	2.22	.08	.323	2.73	.116	.522
200	2.27	.080	.346	2.22	.077	.304	2.46	.09	.392	3.04	.143	.635
220	2.50	.097	.415	2.44	.093	.363	2.71	.11	.451	3.34	.173	.760
240	2.72	.115	.490	2.66	.110	.411	2.96	.14	.530	3.64	.206	.895
260	2.95	.135	.571	2.89	.130	.477	3.20	.16	.616	3.95	.242	1.04
280	3.18	.157	.658	3.11	.150	.548	3.45	.19	.708	4.25	.281	1.20
300	3.40	.180	.752	3.33	.172	.624	3.69	.21	.807	4.56	.322	1.36
320	3.63	.205	.851	3.55	.196	.705	3.94	.24	.911	4.86	.366	1.54
340	3.86	.231	.957	3.78	.222	.790	4.19	.27	1.02	5.16	.414	1.73
360	4.08	.259	1.07	4.00	.240	.880	4.43	.31	1.14	5.47	.464	1.93
380	4.31	.289	1.19	4.22	.277	.975	4.68	.34	1.26	5.77	.517	2.14
400	4.54	.320	1.31	4.44	.307	1.07	4.93	.38	1.39	6.07	.572	2.36
450	5.10	.403	1.65	5.00	.388	1.34	5.54	.48	1.74	6.82	.725	2.95
500	5.67	.500	2.02	5.55	.479	1.64	6.16	.59	2.13	7.59	.894	3.61
550	6.24	.605	2.44	6.11	.580	1.97	6.77	.71	2.55	8.35	1.08	4.34
600	6.81	.720	2.89	6.66	.690	2.33	7.39	.85	3.02	9.11	1.29	5.13
650	7.37	.845	3.38	7.22	.810	2.71	8.00	.99	3.52	9.87	1.51	5.99
700	7.94	.980	3.90	7.77	.939	3.13	8.63	1.16	4.06	10.63	1.75	6.92
750	8.51	1.12	4.47	8.33	1.08	3.57	9.24	1.33	4.64	11.39	2.01	7.91
800	9.08	1.28	5.07	8.88	1.23	4.04	9.85	1.51	5.25	12.15	2.29	8.96
850	9.64	1.44	5.72	9.44	1.38	4.55	10.5	1.7	5.90	12.91	2.59	10.1
900	10.2	1.62	6.40	9.99	1.55	5.08	11.1	1.9	6.60	13.67	2.90	11.3
950	10.8	1.80	7.11	10.5	1.73	5.64	11.7	2.1	7.33	14.42	3.23	12.5
1000	11.3	2.00	7.87	11.1	1.92	6.23	12.3	2.4	8.09	15.18	3.58	13.8
1100	12.5	2.42	9.50	12.2	2.32	7.49	13.5	2.8	9.74	16.71	4.33	16.7
1200	13.6	2.88	11.3	13.3	2.76	8.87	14.8	3.4	11.5	18.22	5.15	19.8
1300	14.7	3.38	13.2	14.4	3.24	10.4	16.0	4.0	13.5	19.74	6.05	23.1
1400	15.9	3.92	15.3	15.5	3.76	12.0	17.2	4.6	15.6	21.26	7.01	26.7
1500	17.0	4.50	17.5	16.7	4.31	13.7	18.5	5.3	17.8	22.78	8.05	30.6
1600	18.2	5.12	19.9	17.8	4.91	15.6	19.7	6.0	20.3	24.29	9.16	34.7
1700	19.3	5.78	22.4	18.9	5.54	17.5	20.9	6.8	22.8	25.81	10.34	39.1
1800	20.4	6.48	25.1	20.0	6.21	19.6	22.2	7.7	25.5	27.33	11.59	43.8
1900	21.6	7.22	28.0	21.1	6.91	21.8	23.4	8.4	28.4	28.85	12.92	48.7
2000	22.7	8.00	31.0	22.2	7.67	24.1	24.6	9.4	31.4	30.37	14.31	53.9
2200	25.0	9.68	37.4	24.4	9.27	29.1	27.1	11.4	37.9	33.40	17.32	65.0
2400	27.2	11.5	44.5	26.6	11.0	34.5	29.6	13.6	44.9	36.44	20.61	77.2

Note: No allowance has been made for age, difference in diameter, or any abnormal condition of interior surface. Any factor of safety must be estimated from the local conditions and the requirements of each particular installation. It is recommended that for most commercial design purposes a safety factor of 15 to 20% be added to the values in the tables—see page 3-5.

Friction of Water — Asphalt-dipped Cast Iron and New Steel Pipe *(Continued)*
(Based on Darcy's Formula)
8 Inch

Flow U S gal per min	Asphalt-dipped cast iron 8.0" inside dia			Std wt steel sch 40 7.981" inside dia			Extra strong steel sch 80 7.625" inside dia			Schedule 160—steel 6.813" inside dia		
	Velocity ft per sec	Velocity head ft	Head loss ft per 100 ft	Velocity ft per sec	Velocity head ft	Head loss ft per 100 ft	Velocity ft per sec	Velocity head ft	Head loss ft per 100 ft	Velocity ft per sec	Velocity head ft	Head loss ft per 100 ft
130	.83	.011	**.037**	.83	.011	**.036**	.91	.01	**.046**	1.14	.020	**.079**
140	.89	.012	**.042**	.90	.013	**.042**	.98	.01	**.052**	1.23	.024	**.090**
150	.96	.014	**.048**	.96	.014	**.047**	1.05	.02	**.059**	1.32	.027	**.102**
160	1.02	.016	**.054**	1.03	.016	**.053**	1.12	.02	**.066**	1.41	.031	**.115**
170	1.08	.018	**.060**	1.09	.018	**.059**	1.19	.02	**.074**	1.50	.035	**.128**
180	1.15	.021	**.067**	1.15	.021	**.066**	1.26	.02	**.082**	1.58	.039	**.142**
190	1.21	.023	**.074**	1.22	.023	**.073**	1.33	.03	**.091**	1.67	.043	**.157**
200	1.28	.025	**.082**	1.28	.026	**.080**	1.41	.03	**.099**	1.76	.048	**.172**
220	1.40	.031	**.098**	1.41	.031	**.095**	1.55	.04	**.118**	1.94	.058	**.205**
240	1.53	.037	**.115**	1.54	.037	**.111**	1.69	.04	**.139**	2.11	.069	**.241**
260	1.66	.043	**.134**	1.67	.043	**.128**	1.83	.05	**.161**	2.29	.081	**.279**
280	1.79	.050	**.154**	1.80	.050	**.147**	1.97	.06	**.184**	2.46	.094	**.320**
300	1.91	.057	**.175**	1.92	.058	**.167**	2.11	.07	**.209**	2.64	.108	**.350**
350	2.23	.077	**.235**	2.24	.089	**.222**	2.46	.09	**.278**	3.08	.147	**.467**
400	2.55	.101	**.303**	2.57	.102	**.284**	2.81	.12	**.343**	3.52	.192	**.601**
450	2.87	.128	**.380**	2.89	.129	**.341**	3.16	.15	**.428**	3.96	.243	**.750**
500	3.19	.158	**.465**	3.21	.160	**.416**	3.51	.19	**.522**	4.40	.301	**.916**
550	3.51	.191	**.559**	3.53	.193	**.497**	3.86	.23	**.625**	4.84	.364	**1.10**
600	3.83	.228	**.661**	3.85	.230	**.586**	4.22	.28	**.736**	5.28	.433	**1.30**
650	4.15	.267	**.772**	4.17	.271	**.682**	4.57	.32	**.857**	5.72	.508	**1.51**
700	4.47	.310	**.891**	4.49	.313	**.785**	4.92	.38	**.986**	6.16	.589	**1.74**
750	4.79	.356	**1.02**	4.81	.360	**.895**	5.27	.43	**1.13**	6.60	.676	**1.98**
800	5.11	.405	**1.16**	5.13	.409	**1.01**	5.62	.49	**1.27**	7.04	.769	**2.24**
850	5.42	.457	**1.30**	5.45	.462	**1.14**	5.97	.55	**1.43**	7.48	.869	**2.52**
900	5.74	.513	**1.45**	5.77	.518	**1.27**	6.32	.62	**1.59**	7.92	.974	**2.81**
950	6.06	.571	**1.61**	6.09	.577	**1.40**	6.67	.69	**1.77**	8.36	1.09	**3.12**
1000	6.38	.633	**1.78**	6.41	.639	**1.55**	7.03	.77	**1.95**	8.80	1.20	**3.45**
1100	7.02	.766	**2.15**	7.05	.773	**1.86**	7.83	.95	**2.34**	9.68	1.46	**4.14**
1200	7.66	.911	**2.55**	7.70	.920	**2.20**	8.43	1.10	**2.77**	10.56	1.73	**4.91**
1300	8.30	1.07	**2.98**	8.34	1.08	**2.56**	9.13	1.30	**3.23**	11.44	2.03	**5.73**
1400	8.93	1.24	**3.45**	8.98	1.25	**2.96**	9.83	1.5	**3.73**	12.32	2.36	**6.62**
1500	9.57	1.42	**3.95**	9.62	1.44	**3.38**	10.5	1.7	**4.26**	13.20	2.71	**7.57**
1600	10.2	1.62	**4.48**	10.3	1.64	**3.83**	11.2	2.0	**4.83**	14.08	3.08	**8.58**
1800	11.5	2.05	**5.65**	11.5	2.07	**4.81**	12.6	2.5	**6.07**	15.84	3.90	**10.8**
2000	12.8	2.53	**6.96**	12.8	2.56	**5.91**	14.1	3.1	**7.46**	17.60	4.81	**13.3**
2200	14.0	3.06	**8.40**	14.1	3.09	**7.11**	15.5	3.7	**8.98**	19.36	5.82	**16.0**
2400	15.3	3.65	**9.98**	15.4	3.68	**8.43**	16.9	4.4	**10.6**	21.12	6.92	**19.0**
2600	16.6	4.28	**11.7**	16.7	4.32	**9.85**	18.3	5.2	**12.4**	22.88	8.13	**22.2**
2800	17.9	4.96	**13.5**	18.0	5.01	**11.4**	19.7	6.0	**14.4**	24.64	9.43	**25.7**
3000	19.1	5.70	**15.5**	19.2	5.75	**13.0**	21.1	6.9	**16.5**	26.40	10.82	**29.4**
3500	22.3	7.70	**21.1**	22.4	8.9	**17.6**	24.6	9.4	**22.3**	30.80	14.73	**39.8**
4000	25.5	10.1	**27.4**	25.7	10.2	**22:9**	28.1	12.3	**29.0**	35.20	19.23	**51.8**
4500	28.7	12.8	**34.7**	28.9	12.9	**28.9**	31.6	15.5	**36.6**	39.60	24.34	**65.4**
5000	31.9	15.8	**42.7**	32.1	16.0	**35.6**	35.1	19.1	**45.0**	44.00	30.05	**80.6**
5500	35.1	19.1	**51.7**	35.3	19.3	**43.0**	38.6	23.2	**54.4**	48.40	36.36	**97.3**

Note: No allowance has been made for age, difference in diameter, or any abnormal condition of interior surface. Any factor of safety must be estimated from the local conditions and the requirements of each particular installation. It is recommended that for most commercial design purposes a safety factor of 15 to 20% be added to the values in the tables—see page 3-5.

Friction of Water — Asphalt-dipped Cast Iron and New Steel Pipe
(Based on Darcy's Formula) *(Continued)*
10 Inch

Flow US gal per min	Asphalt-dipped cast iron 10.0" inside dia			Std wt steel sch 40 10.020" inside dia			Schedule 80 steel 9.562" inside dia			Schedule 160—steel 8.500" inside dia		
	Velocity ft per sec	Velocity head ft	Head loss ft per 100 ft	Velocity ft per sec	Velocity head ft	Head loss ft per 100 ft	Velocity ft per sec	Velocity head ft	Head loss ft per 100 ft	Velocity ft per sec	Velocity head ft	Head loss ft per 100 ft
180	.74	.008	.023	.73	.008	.022	.804	.010	.027	1.02	.016	.048
200	.82	.010	.028	.81	.010	.026	.894	.012	.033	1.13	.020	.059
220	.90	.013	.032	.90	.013	.031	.983	.015	.039	1.24	.024	.070
240	.98	.015	.038	.98	.015	.037	1.07	.018	.046	1.36	.029	.082
260	1.06	.018	.044	1.06	.017	.042	1.16	.021	.053	1.47	.034	.094
280	1.14	.020	.051	1.14	.020	.049	1.25	.024	.061	1.58	.039	.108
300	1.23	.023	.057	1.22	.023	.055	1.34	.028	.069	1.70	.045	.123
350	1.43	.032	.077	1.42	.032	.073	1.56	.038	.092	1.98	.061	.163
400	1.63	.042	.099	1.63	.041	.093	1.79	.050	.117	2.26	.079	.208
450	1.84	.053	.123	1.83	.052	.116	2.01	.063	.145	2.54	.100	.259
500	2.04	.065	.150	2.03	.064	.140	2.34	.077	.177	2.83	.124	.304
550	2.25	.079	.180	2.24	.078	.167	2.46	.094	.211	3.11	.150	.364
600	2.45	.093	.213	2.44	.093	.197	2.68	.112	.239	3.39	.179	.428
650	2.66	.110	.248	2.64	.109	.228	2.90	.131	.277	3.68	.210	.498
700	2.86	.127	.286	2.85	.126	.253	3.13	.152	.319	3.96	.243	.573
800	3.27	.166	.370	3.25	.165	.325	3.57	.198	.410	4.52	.318	7.38
900	3.68	.210	.464	3.66	.208	.405	4.02	.251	.512	5.09	.402	9.23
1000	4.09	.259	.569	4.07	.257	.494	4.47	.310	.625	5.65	.496	1.13
1100	4.49	.314	.685	4.48	.311	.592	4.92	.375	.749	6.22	.600	1.35
1200	4.90	.373	.811	4.88	.370	.699	5.36	.446	.884	6.79	.714	1.60
1300	5.31	.438	.947	5.29	.435	.814	5.81	.524	1.03	7.35	.839	1.86
1400	5.72	.508	1.09	5.70	.504	.938	6.26	.607	1.19	7.92	.972	2.15
1500	6.13	.584	1.25	6.10	.579	1.07	6.70	.697	1.35	8.48	1.12	2.46
1600	6.54	.664	1.42	6.51	.659	1.21	7.15	.793	1.53	9.05	1.27	2.78
1700	6.94	.749	1.60	6.92	.743	1.36	7.60	.895	1.72	9.61	1.43	3.13
1800	7.35	.840	1.79	7.32	.834	1.52	8.04	1.00	1.92	10.18	1.61	3.49
1900	7.76	.936	1.99	7.73	.929	1.68	8.49	1.12	2.13	10.74	1.79	3.88
2000	8.17	1.04	2.20	8.14	1.03	1.86	8.94	1.24	2.36	11.31	1.99	4.29
2200	8.99	1.26	2.65	8.95	1.25	2.24	9.83	1.50	2.83	12.44	2.40	5.16
2400	9.80	1.49	3.15	9.76	1.48	2.64	10.72	1.79	3.35	13.57	2.86	6.11
2600	10.6	1.75	3.68	10.6	1.74	3.09	11.62	2.09	3.92	14.70	3.35	7.14
2800	11.4	2.03	4.26	11.4	2.02	3.57	12.51	2.43	4.52	15.83	3.89	8.25
3000	12.3	2.33	4.88	12.2	2.32	4.08	13.40	2.79	5.17	16.96	4.47	9.44
3200	13.1	2.66	5.54	13.0	2.63	4.62	14.30	3.17	5.87	18.09	5.08	10.7
3400	13.9	3.00	6.25	13.8	2.97	5.20	15.19	3.58	6.60	19.22	5.74	12.1
3600	14.7	3.36	6.99	14.6	3.33	5.81	16.08	4.02	7.38	20.35	6.43	13.5
3800	15.5	3.74	7.79	15.5	3.71	6.46	16.98	4.47	8.21	21.49	7.17	15.0
4000	16.3	4.15	8.62	16.3	4.12	7.14	17.87	4.96	9.07	22.62	7.94	16.6
4500	18.4	5.25	10.9	18.3	5.21	8.99	20.11	6.27	11.4	25.44	10.05	20.9
5000	20.4	6.48	13.4	20.3	6.43	11.1	22.34	7.75	14.1	28.27	12.40	25.7
5500	22.5	7.85	16.2	22.4	7.78	13.3	24.57	9.37	17.0	31.10	15.01	31.1
6000	24.5	9.34	19.2	24.4	9.26	15.8	26.81	11.15	20.1	33.92	17.86	36.9
6500	26.6	11.0	22.6	26.4	10.9	18.5	29.04	13.09	23.6	36.75	20.96	43.2
7000	28.6	12.7	26.1	28.5	12.6	21.4	31.28	15.18	27.3	39.58	24.31	50.0
7500	30.6	14.6	30.0	30.5	14.5	24.5	33.51	17.43	31.2	42.41	27.91	57.3

Note: No allowance has been made for age, difference in diameter, or any abnormal condition of interior surface. Any factor of safety must be estimated from the local conditions and the requirements of each particular installation. It is recommended that for most commercial design purposes a safety factor of 15 to 20% be added to the values in the tables—see page 3-5.

Friction of Water   Asphalt-dipped Cast Iron and New Steel Pipe
(Based on Darcy's Formula)

12 Inch   *(Continued)*

Flow US gal per min	Asphalt-dipped cast iron 12.0" inside dia			Std wt steel sch 40 11.938" inside dia			Schedule 80 steel 11.374" inside dia			Schedule 160 steel 10.126" inside dia		
	Velocity ft per sec	Velocity head ft	Head loss ft per 100 ft	Velocity ft per sec	Velocity head ft	Head loss ft per 100 ft	Velocity ft per sec	Velocity head ft	Head loss ft per 100 ft	Velocity ft per sec	Velocity head ft	Head loss ft per 100 ft
200	.57	.005	.011	.57	.005	.011	.632	.006	.014	.797	.010	.025
250	.71	.008	.017	.72	.008	.017	.789	.010	.021	.996	.015	.038
300	.85	.011	.024	.86	.012	.024	.947	.014	.030	1.20	.022	.052
350	.99	.015	.031	1.00	.016	.031	1.11	.019	.039	1.39	.030	.069
400	1.13	.020	.040	1.15	.020	.040	1.26	.025	.050	1.59	.039	.088
450	1.28	.025	.049	1.29	.026	.049	1.42	.031	.062	1.79	.050	.110
500	1.42	.031	.060	1.43	.032	.060	1.58	.039	.076	1.99	.062	.133
550	1.56	.038	.072	1.58	.039	.071	1.74	.047	.090	2.19	.075	.159
600	1.70	.045	.085	1.72	.046	.083	1.90	.056	.106	2.39	.089	.187
700	1.99	.061	.114	2.01	.063	.111	2.21	.076	.140	2.79	.121	.240
800	2.27	.080	.147	2.29	.082	.142	2.53	.099	.180	3.19	.158	.308
900	2.55	.101	.184	2.58	.103	.176	2.84	.125	.216	3.59	.200	.384
1000	2.84	.125	.225	2.87	.128	.207	3.16	.155	.263	3.98	.246	.469
1100	3.12	.151	.271	3.15	.154	.247	3.47	.187	.315	4.38	.298	.562
1200	3.40	.180	.320	3.44	.184	.291	3.79	.223	.371	4.78	.355	.663
1300	3.69	.211	.374	3.73	.216	.339	4.11	.262	.432	5.18	.416	.772
1400	3.97	.245	.431	4.01	.250	.390	4.42	.303	.497	5.58	.483	.889
1500	4.26	.281	.493	4.30	.287	.444	4.73	.348	.566	5.98	.554	1.02
1600	4.54	.320	.558	4.59	.327	.502	5.05	.396	.640	6.37	.631	1.15
1800	5.11	.405	.702	5.16	.414	.629	5.68	.501	.802	7.17	.798	1.44
2000	5.67	.500	.862	5.73	.511	.769	6.32	.619	.981	7.97	.985	1.76
2200	6.24	.605	1.04	6.31	.618	.923	6.95	.749	1.18	8.77	1.19	2.12
2400	6.81	.720	1.23	6.88	.735	1.09	7.58	.891	1.39	9.56	1.42	2.51
2600	7.38	.845	1.44	7.45	.863	1.27	8.21	1.05	1.62	10.36	1.67	2.93
2800	7.94	.980	1.67	8.03	1.00	1.47	8.84	1.21	1.87	11.16	1.93	3.38
3000	8.51	1.13	1.91	8.60	1.15	1.68	9.47	1.39	2.14	11.95	2.22	3.86
3500	9.93	1.53	2.58	10.0	1.55	2.26	11.05	1.90	2.89	13.94	3.02	5.22
4000	11.3	2.00	3.36	11.5	2.04	2.92	12.63	2.48	3.74	15.94	3.94	6.77
4500	12.8	2.53	4.24	12.9	2.59	3.68	14.21	3.13	4.71	17.93	4.99	8.52
5000	14.2	3.13	5.21	14.3	3.19	4.52	15.79	3.87	5.78	19.92	6.16	10.5
5500	15.6	3.78	6.30	15.8	3.86	5.44	17.37	4.68	6.97	21.91	7.45	12.6
6000	17.0	4.50	7.48	17.2	4.60	6.45	18.95	5.57	8.26	23.90	8.87	15.0
6500	18.4	5.28	8.76	18.6	5.39	7.54	20.53	6.54	9.66	25.90	10.41	17.5
7000	19.9	6.13	10.1	20.1	6.26	8.72	22.10	7.58	11.2	27.89	12.07	20.3
7500	21.3	7.03	11.6	21.5	7.18	9.98	23.68	8.71	12.8	29.88	13.86	23.3
8000	22.7	8.00	13.2	22.9	8.17	11.3	25.26	9.90	14.5	31.87	15.77	26.4
8500	24.1	9.04	14.9	24.4	9.22	12.8	26.84	11.18	16.4	33.86	17.80	29.8
9000	25.5	10.1	16.7	25.8	10.3	14.3	28.42	12.54	18.3	35.86	19.95	33.3
9500	26.9	11.3	18.6	27.2	11.5	15.9	30.00	13.97	20.4	37.85	22.23	37.1
10,000	28.4	12.5	20.6	28.7	12.8	17.6	31.58	15.48	22.6	39.84	24.64	41.0
11,000	31.2	15.1	24.9	31.5	15.4	21.2	34.73	18.73	27.2	43.82	29.81	49.6
12,000	34.0	18.0	29.6	34.4	18.3	25.2	37.89	22.29	32.3	47.81	35.47	58.7
13,000	36.9	21.1	34.7	37.3	21.6	29.5	41.05	26.15	37.9	51.79	41.63	69.0
14,000	39.7	24.5	40.2	40.1	25.0	34.2	44.21	30.33	43.8	55.78	48.28	79.9
15,000	42.6	28.1	46.1	43.0	28.7	39.2	47.37	34.82	50.3	59.76	55.43	91.6

Note: No allowance has been made for age, difference in diameter, or any abnormal condition of interior surface. Any factor of safety must be estimated from the local conditions and the requirements of each particular installation. It is recommended that for most commercial design purposes a safety factor of 15 to 20% be added to the values in the tables—see page 3-5.

Friction of Water *(Continued)*
(Based on Darcy's Formula)
Asphalt-dipped cast iron and new steel pipe

14 Inch   16 Inch

Flow U S gal per min	Asphalt-dipped cast iron 14.0" inside dia			New steel schedule 40 13.124" inside dia			Flow U S gal per min	Asphalt-dipped cast iron 16.0" inside dia			New steel schedule 40 15.000" inside dia		
	Velocity ft per sec	Velocity head ft	Head loss ft per 100 ft	Velocity ft per sec	Velocity head ft	Head loss ft per 100 ft		Velocity ft per sec	Velocity head ft	Head loss ft per 100 ft	Velocity ft per sec	Velocity head ft	Head loss ft per 100 ft
300	.625	.006	.011	.712	.008	.015	500	.798	.010	.015	.908	.013	.020
400	.834	.011	.019	.949	.014	.025	600	.957	.014	.020	1.09	.018	.027
500	1.04	.017	.028	1.19	.022	.038	700	1.12	.019	.027	1.27	.025	.036
600	1.25	.024	.039	1.42	.031	.052	800	1.28	.025	.035	1.45	.033	.046
700	1.46	.033	.053	1.66	.043	.070	900	1.44	.032	.043	1.63	.041	.058
800	1.67	.043	.068	1.90	.056	.089	1000	1.60	.040	.053	1.82	.051	.070
900	1.88	.055	.085	2.14	.071	.111	1200	1.92	.057	.075	2.18	.074	.098
1000	2.08	.067	.103	2.37	.087	.134	1400	2.23	.077	.100	2.54	.100	.130
1100	2.29	.082	.124	2.61	.106	.160	1600	2.55	.101	.130	2.91	.131	.161
1200	2.50	.097	.147	2.85	.126	.182	1800	2.87	.128	.162	3.27	.166	.201
1300	2.71	.114	.171	3.08	.148	.212	2000	3.19	.158	.199	3.63	.205	.245
1400	2.92	.132	.197	3.32	.171	.243	2500	3.99	.247	.306	4.54	.320	.374
1500	3.13	.152	.225	3.56	.196	.277	3000	4.79	.356	.436	5.45	.460	.530
1600	3.34	.173	.255	3.80	.223	.313	3500	5.59	.484	.589	6.35	.627	.712
1700	3.54	.195	.286	4.03	.252	.351	4000	6.38	.632	.764	7.26	.819	.920
1800	3.75	.218	.320	4.27	.283	.391	4500	7.18	.800	.962	8.17	1.04	1.15
1900	3.96	.243	.355	4.51	.315	.434	5000	7.98	.988	1.18	9.08	1.28	1.42
2000	4.17	.270	.392	4.74	.349	.478	6000	9.57	1.42	1.69	10.89	1.84	2.01
2500	5.21	.421	.605	5.93	.546	.732	7000	11.17	1.94	2.29	12.71	2.51	2.72
3000	6.25	.607	.864	7.12	.786	1.04	8000	12.77	2.53	2.98	14.52	3.27	3.53
3500	7.30	.826	1.17	8.30	1.07	1.40	9000	14.36	3.20	3.77	16.34	4.14	4.44
4000	8.34	1.08	1.52	9.49	1.40	1.81	10,000	15.96	3.95	4.64	18.16	5.12	5.45
4500	9.38	1.37	1.91	10.67	1.77	2.27	11,000	17.55	4.78	5.60	19.97	6.19	6.58
5000	10.42	1.69	2.35	11.86	2.18	2.79	12,000	19.15	5.69	6.65	21.79	7.37	7.80
6000	12.51	2.43	3.37	14.23	3.14	3.98	13,000	20.74	6.68	7.98	23.60	8.65	9.13
7000	14.6	3.30	4.49	16.60	4.28	5.37	14,000	22.3	7.75	9.03	25.42	10.03	10.6
8000	16.7	4.32	5.86	18.97	5.59	6.98	15,000	23.9	8.89	10.4	27.23	11.51	12.1
9000	18.8	5.47	7.39	21.35	7.07	8.79	16,000	25.5	10.1	11.8	29.05	13.10	13.7
10,000	20.8	6.75	9.11	23.72	8.73	10.8	17,000	27.1	11.4	13.3	30.86	14.79	15.5
11,000	22.9	8.17	11.0	26.09	10.56	13.0	18,000	28.7	12.8	14.9	32.68	16.58	17.3
12,000	25.0	9.71	13.3	28.46	12.57	15.5	20,000	31.9	15.8	18.3	36.31	20.46	21.3
13,000	27.1	11.4	15.3	30.83	14.75	18.1	22,000	35.1	19.1	22.2	38.94	24.76	25.8
14,000	29.2	13.2	17.7	33.20	17.11	21.0	24,000	38.3	22.8	26.4	45.57	29.47	30.6
15,000	31.3	15.2	20.3	35.58	19.64	24.0	26,000	41.5	26.7	30.9	47.20	34.58	35.9
16,000	33.3	17.3	23.1	37.95	22.35	27.3	28,000	44.7	31.0	35.8	50.84	40.11	41.5
17,000	35.4	19.5	26.1	40.32	25.23	30.8	30,000	47.9	35.6	41.1	54.47	46.04	47.6
18,000	37.5	21.8	29.7	42.69	28.27	34.5	32,000	51.1	40.5	46.7	58.10	52.39	54.1
20,000	41.7	27.0	36.0	47.43	34.92	42.9	34,000	54.3	45.7	52.7	61.73	59.14	61.0
22,000	45.9	32.7	43.5	52.18	42.26	51.3	36,000	57.4	51.2	59.1	65.36	66.30	68.4
24,000	50.0	38.8	52.7	56.92	50.29	61.0	38,000	60.6	57.1	65.8	68.99	73.88	76.1

Note: No allowance has been made for age, difference in diameter, or any abnormal condition of interior surface. Any factor of safety must be estimated from the local conditions and the requirements of each particular installation. It is recommended that for most commercial design purposes a safety factor of 15 to 20% be added to the values in the tables—see page 3-5.

Friction of Water *(Continued)*
(Based on Darcy's Formula)

Asphalt-dipped cast iron and new steel pipe

18 Inch

Flow US gal per min	Asphalt-dipped cast iron 18.0″ inside dia			New steel schedule 40 16.876″ inside dia		
	Velocity ft per sec	Velocity head ft	Head loss ft per 100 ft	Velocity ft per sec	Velocity head ft	Head loss ft per 100 ft
500	.630	.006	.008	.717	.008	.011
600	.756	.009	.012	.861	.011	.015
700	.883	.012	.016	1.00	.016	.020
800	1.01	.016	.019	1.15	.020	.026
900	1.14	.020	.024	1.29	.026	.032
1000	1.26	.025	.029	1.43	.032	.039
1200	1.51	.036	.041	1.72	.046	.055
1400	1.77	.048	.056	2.08	.063	.073
1600	2.02	.063	.072	2.96	.082	.093
1800	2.27	.080	.090	2.58	.103	.116
2000	2.52	.099	.110	2.87	.128	.137
2500	3.15	.154	.168	3.59	.200	.208
3000	3.78	.222	.239	4.30	.287	.294
3500	4.41	.302	.323	5.02	.391	.394
4000	5.04	.395	.418	5.74	.511	.508
4500	5.67	.500	.526	6.46	.647	.637
5000	6.30	.617	.647	7.17	.798	.780
6000	7.57	.888	.924	8.61	1.15	1.11
7000	8.83	1.21	1.25	10.0	1.57	1.49
8000	10.1	1.58	1.63	11.5	2.04	1.94
9000	11.3	2.00	2.05	12.9	2.59	2.43
10,000	12.6	2.47	2.52	14.3	3.19	2.99
12,000	15.1	3.55	3.62	17.2	4.60	4.27
14,000	17.7	4.84	4.91	20.1	6.26	5.77
16,000	20.2	6.32	6.40	22.9	8.18	7.51
18,000	22.7	7.99	8.08	25.8	10.3	9.46
20,000	25.2	9.87	9.96	28.7	12.8	11.6
22,000	27.7	11.9	12.0	31.6	15.5	14.1
24,000	30.3	14.2	14.3	34.4	18.4	16.7
26,000	32.8	16.7	16.8	37.3	21.6	19.5
28,000	35.3	19.3	19.4	40.2	25.0	22.6
30,000	37.8	22.2	22.3	43.0	28.7	25.9
32,000	40.3	25.3	25.3	45.9	32.7	29.5
34,000	42.9	28.5	28.6	48.8	36.9	33.2
36,000	45.4	32.0	32.0	51.6	41.4	37.2
38,000	47.9	35.6	35.7	54.5	46.1	41.4
40,000	50.4	39.5	39.5	57.4	51.1	45.9
42,000	53.0	43.5	43.6	60.2	56.3	50.5
44,000	55.5	47.8	47.8	63.1	61.8	55.4
46,000	58.0	52.2	52.2	66.0	67.6	60.5

20 Inch

Flow US gal per min	Asphalt-dipped cast iron 20.0″ inside dia			New steel schedule 40 18.812″ inside dia		
	Velocity ft per sec	Velocity head ft	Head loss ft per 100 ft	Velocity ft per sec	Velocity head ft	Head loss ft per 100 ft
800	.817	.010	.012	.923	.013	.015
1000	1.02	.016	.017	1.15	.021	.023
1200	1.23	.023	.025	1.39	.030	.032
1400	1.43	.032	.033	1.62	.041	.043
1600	1.63	.041	.042	1.85	.053	.055
1800	1.84	.052	.053	2.08	.067	.068
2000	2.04	.065	.065	2.31	.083	.083
2400	2.45	.093	.091	2.77	.119	.112
2800	2.86	.127	.123	3.23	.162	.150
3200	3.27	.166	.159	3.69	.212	.193
3600	3.68	.210	.199	4.16	.268	.241
4000	4.09	.259	.245	4.62	.331	.295
5000	5.10	.405	.377	5.77	.517	.452
6000	6.13	.583	.539	6.93	.744	.641
7000	7.15	.793	.728	8.08	1.01	.862
8000	8.17	1.04	.946	9.23	1.32	1.12
9000	9.19	1.31	1.19	10.4	1.68	1.40
10,000	10.2	1.62	1.47	11.5	2.07	1.72
12,000	12.3	2.33	2.10	13.9	2.98	2.45
14,000	14.3	3.17	2.85	16.2	4.05	3.32
15,000	15.3	3.64	3.27	17.3	4.65	3.79
16,000	16.3	4.14	3.71	18.5	5.29	4.31
18,000	18.4	5.25	4.68	20.8	6.70	5.42
20,000	20.4	6.48	5.77	23.1	8.27	6.67
22,000	22.5	7.84	6.97	25.4	10.0	8.05
24,000	24.5	9.32	8.29	27.7	11.9	9.55
26,000	26.6	10.9	9.71	30.0	14.0	11.2
28,000	28.6	12.7	11.3	32.3	16.2	12.9
30,000	30.6	14.6	12.9	34.6	18.6	14.8
32,000	32.7	16.6	14.7	36.9	21.2	16.9
34,000	34.7	18.7	16.6	39.2	23.9	19.0
36,000	36.8	21.0	18.5	41.6	26.8	21.3
38,000	38.8	23.4	20.7	43.9	29.9	23.7
40,000	40.9	25.9	22.9	46.2	33.1	26.2
45,000	46.0	32.8	28.9	51.9	41.9	33.1
50,000	51.1	40.5	35.7	57.7	51.7	40.8
55,000	56.2	49.0	43.1	63.5	62.6	49.3
60,000	62.3	58.3	51.3	69.3	74.5	58.6
65,000	66.4	68.4	60.2	75.0	87.4	68.6
70,000	71.5	79.3	69.8	80.8	101	79.5

Note: No allowance has been made for age, difference in diameter, or any abnormal condition of interior surface. Any factor of safety must be estimated from the local conditions and the requirements of each particular installation. It is recommended that for most commercial design purposes a safety factor of 15 to 20% be added to the values in the tables—see page 3-5.

Friction of Water *(Continued)*
(Based on Darcy's Formula)
Asphalt-dipped cast iron and new steel pipe

24 Inch   30 Inch

Flow U S gal per min	Asphalt-dipped cast iron 24.0" inside dia			New steel schedule 40 22.624" inside dia			Flow U S gal per min	Asphalt-dipped cast iron 30.0" inside dia			New steel schedule 30 28.750" inside dia		
	Ve-locity ft per sec	Ve-locity head ft	Head loss ft per 100 ft	Ve-locity ft per sec	Ve-locity head ft	Head loss ft per 100 ft		Ve-locity ft per sec	Ve-locity head ft	Head loss ft per 100 ft	Ve-locity ft per sec	Ve-locity head ft	Head loss ft per 100 ft
800	.567	.005	.005	.638	.006	.006	1000	.454	.003	.002	.494	.004	.003
1000	.709	.008	.007	.798	.010	.009	1200	.545	.005	.003	.593	.005	.004
1200	.851	.011	.010	.958	.014	.013	1400	.635	.006	.005	.692	.007	.005
1400	.993	.015	.013	1.12	.019	.017	1600	.726	.008	.006	.791	.010	.007
1600	1.14	.020	.017	1.28	.025	.022	1800	.817	.010	.007	.890	.012	.009
1800	1.28	.025	.021	1.44	.032	.028	2000	.908	.013	.009	.988	.015	.010
2000	1.42	.031	.026	1.60	.040	.034	2400	1.09	.018	.012	1.19	.022	.015
2400	1.70	.045	.037	1.92	.057	.047	2800	1.27	.025	.016	1.38	.030	.019
2800	1.99	.061	.049	2.24	.078	.063	3200	1.45	.033	.021	1.58	.039	.025
3200	2.27	.080	.063	2.55	.101	.080	3600	1.63	.041	.026	1.78	.049	.031
3600	2.55	.101	.079	2.87	.128	.096	4000	1.82	.051	.032	1.98	.061	.037
4000	2.84	.125	.097	3.19	.158	.118	5000	2.27	.080	.048	2.47	.095	.057
5000	3.55	.195	.149	3.99	.247	.179	6000	2.72	.115	.069	2.97	.136	.077
6000	4.26	.281	.212	4.79	.356	.254	7000	3.18	.157	.092	3.46	.186	.103
7000	4.96	.383	.287	5.59	.484	.341	8000	3.63	.205	.119	3.95	.243	.133
8000	5.67	.500	.372	6.39	.633	.440	9000	4.09	.259	.150	4.45	.307	.166
9000	6.38	.632	.468	7.18	.801	.552	10,000	4.54	.320	.184	4.94	.379	.203
10,000	7.09	.781	.575	7.98	.989	.676	12,000	5.45	.460	.263	5.93	.546	.287
12,000	8.51	1.12	.823	9.58	1.42	.962	14,000	6.35	.627	.355	6.92	.743	.386
14,000	9.93	1.53	1.11	11.2	1.94	1.30	16,000	7.26	.819	.461	7.91	.970	.500
16,000	11.3	2.00	1.45	12.8	2.53	1.68	18,000	8.17	1.04	.581	8.90	1.23	.627
18,000	12.8	2.53	1.83	14.4	3.20	2.12	20,000	9.08	1.28	.714	9.88	1.52	.769
20,000	14.2	3.12	2.25	16.0	3.95	2.60	22,000	9.99	1.55	.861	10.9	1.84	.926
22,000	15.6	3.78	2.72	17.6	4.79	3.13	24,000	10.9	1.84	1.02	11.9	2.18	1.10
24,000	17.0	4.50	3.23	19.2	5.69	3.71	26,000	11.8	2.16	1.20	12.9	2.56	1.28
26,000	18.4	5.28	3.78	20.8	6.68	4.34	28,000	12.7	2.51	1.39	13.8	2.97	1.48
28,000	19.9	6.12	4.38	22.3	7.75	5.03	30,000	13.6	2.88	1.59	14.8	3.41	1.69
30,000	21.3	7.03	5.02	23.9	8.90	5.76	35,000	15.9	3.92	2.15	17.3	4.64	2.29
34,000	24.1	9.02	6.44	27.1	11.4	7.36	40,000	18.2	5.12	2.81	19.8	6.07	2.97
38,000	27.0	11.3	8.03	30.3	14.3	9.17	45,000	20.4	6.48	3.54	22.2	7.68	3.75
42,000	29.8	13.8	9.80	33.5	17.4	11.2	50,000	22.7	7.99	4.37	24.7	9.48	4.61
46,000	32.6	16.5	11.7	36.7	20.9	13.4	55,000	25.0	9.67	5.28	27.2	11.5	5.56
50,000	35.5	19.5	13.9	39.9	24.7	15.8	60,000	27.2	11.5	6.27	29.7	13.6	6.60
60,000	42.6	28.1	19.9	47.9	35.6	22.6	65,000	29.5	13.5	7.35	32.1	16.0	7.73
70,000	49.6	38.3	27.1	55.9	48.4	30.7	70,000	31.8	15.7	8.52	34.6	18.6	8.95
80,000	56.7	50.0	35.3	63.8	63.3	40.0	75,000	34.0	18.0	9.77	37.1	21.3	10.3
90,000	63.8	63.2	44.7	71.8	80.1	50.6	80,000	36.3	20.5	11.1	39.5	24.3	11.7
100,000	70.9	78.1	55.1	79.8	98.9	62.3	85,000	38.6	23.1	12.5	42.0	27.4	13.1
110,000	78.0	94.3	65.6	87.8	110	75.3	90,000	40.9	25.9	14.0	44.5	30.7	14.7
120,000	85.1	112	78.5	95.8	142	89.6	100,000	45.4	32.0	17.3	49.4	37.9	18.1

Note: No allowance has been made for age, difference in diameter, or any abnormal condition of interior surface. Any factor of safety must be estimated from the local conditions and the requirements of each particular installation. It is recommended that for most commercial design purposes a safety factor of 15 to 20% be added to the values in the tables—see page 3-5.

Friction of Water *(Continued)*
(Based on Darcy's Formula)
Asphalt-dipped cast iron and new steel pipe

36 Inch

Flow US gal per min	Asphalt-dipped cast iron 36.0" inside dia			New steel schedule 40 34.500" inside dia		
	Velocity ft per sec	Velocity head ft	Head loss ft per 100 ft	Velocity ft per sec	Velocity head ft	Head loss ft per 100 ft
1400	.441	.003	.002	.480	.004	.002
1600	.504	.004	.002	.549	.005	.003
1800	.567	.005	.003	.618	.006	.004
2000	.630	.006	.004	.686	.007	.004
2400	.756	.009	.005	.824	.011	.006
2800	.883	.012	.007	.961	.014	.008
3200	1.01	.016	.008	1.10	.019	.010
3600	1.14	.020	.010	1.24	.024	.013
4000	1.26	.025	.013	1.37	.029	.015
5000	1.58	.039	.019	1.72	.046	.023
6000	1.89	.056	.027	2.06	.066	.033
7000	2.21	.076	.037	2.40	.090	.043
8000	2.52	.099	.048	2.75	.117	.054
9000	2.84	.125	.060	3.09	.148	.067
10,000	3.15	.154	.073	3.43	.183	.082
12,000	3.78	.222	.104	4.12	.263	.115
14,000	4.41	.302	.140	4.81	.358	.155
16,000	5.04	.395	.182	5.49	.468	.200
18,000	5.67	.500	.228	6.18	.592	.250
20,000	6.30	.617	.281	6.86	.731	.307
25,000	7.88	.962	.433	8.58	1.14	.471
30,000	9.46	1.39	.622	10.30	1.65	.671
35,000	11.0	1.89	.843	12.0	2.24	.906
40,000	12.6	2.47	1.10	13.7	2.93	1.18
50,000	15.8	3.86	1.70	17.2	4.57	1.82
60,000	18.9	5.55	2.45	20.6	6.58	2.60
70,000	22.1	7.56	3.32	24.0	8.96	3.52
80,000	25.2	9.87	4.33	27.5	11.7	4.58
90,000	28.4	12.5	5.47	30.9	14.8	5.77
100,000	31.5	15.4	6.74	34.3	18.3	7.11
110,000	34.7	18.7	8.15	37.7	22.1	8.58
120,000	37.8	22.2	9.69	41.2	26.3	10.2
130,000	41.0	26.1	11.4	44.6	30.9	11.9
140,000	44.1	30.2	13.2	48.0	35.8	13.8
150,000	47.3	34.7	15.1	51.5	41.1	15.8
160,000	50.4	39.5	17.2	54.9	46.8	18.0
170,000	53.6	44.6	19.4	58.3	52.8	20.3
180,000	56.7	50.0	21.7	61.8	59.2	22.8
190,000	59.9	55.7	24.2	65.2	66.0	25.3
200,000	63.0	61.7	26.8	68.6	73.1	28.0

42 Inch

Flow US gal per min	42.0" inside dia		Cast iron asphalt dipped	New steel
	Velocity ft per sec	Velocity head ft	Head loss ft/100 ft	Head loss ft/100 ft
2000	.463	.003	.002	.002
3000	.695	.007	.004	.003
4000	.926	.013	.006	.006
5000	1.16	.021	.009	.009
6000	1.39	.030	.013	.012
7000	1.62	.041	.017	.017
8000	1.85	.053	.022	.021
9000	2.08	.067	.027	.026
10,000	2.32	.083	.034	.032
11,000	2.55	.101	.040	.037
12,000	2.78	.120	.048	.043
14,000	3.24	.163	.064	.058
16,000	3.71	.213	.083	.075
18,000	4.17	.270	.104	.094
20,000	4.63	.333	.128	.114
25,000	5.79	.520	.198	.175
30,000	6.95	.749	.282	.249
35,000	8.11	1.02	.382	.335
40,000	9.26	1.33	.497	.434
45,000	10.4	1.69	.626	.545
50,000	11.6	2.08	.771	.669
60,000	13.9	3.00	1.11	.954
70,000	16.2	4.08	1.50	1.29
80,000	18.5	5.33	1.95	1.67
90,000	20.8	6.74	2.47	2.11
100,000	23.2	8.32	3.04	2.60
110,000	25.5	10.1	3.67	3.13
120,000	27.8	12.0	4.37	3.72
130,000	30.1	14.1	5.12	4.35
140,000	32.4	16.3	5.93	5.04
150,000	34.7	18.7	6.80	5.77
160,000	37.1	21.3	7.73	6.56
170,000	39.4	24.1	8.73	7.39
180,000	41.7	27.0	9.78	8.28
190,000	44.0	30.0	10.9	9.21
200,000	46.3	33.3	12.1	10.2
250,000	57.9	52.0	18.8	15.6
300,000	69.5	74.9	27.1	22.4
350,000	81.1	102	36.8	30.4
400,000	92.6	133	48.0	39.6

Note: No allowance has been made for age, difference in diameter, or any abnormal condition of interior surface. Any factor of safety must be estimated from the local conditions and the requirements of each particular installation. It is recommended that for most commercial design purposes a safety factor of 15 to 20% be added to the values in the tables—see page 3-5.

3

Friction of Water (Continued)
(Based on Darcy's Formula)
Asphalt-dipped cast iron and new steel pipe

48 Inch   54 Inch

48.0" inside dia					54.0" inside dia				
Flow U S gal per min	Velocity ft per sec	Velocity head ft	Cast iron asphalt dipped	New steel	Flow U S gal per min	Velocity ft per sec	Velocity head ft	Cast iron asphalt dipped	New steel
			head loss ft/100 ft					head loss ft per 100 ft	
2000	.355	.002	.001	.00:	10,000	1.40	.030	.010	.009
3000	.532	.004	.002	.002	12,000	1.68	.044	.013	.013
4000	.709	.008	.003	.003	14,000	1.96	.060	.018	.017
5000	.887	.012	.005	.005	16,000	2.24	.078	.023	.022
6000	1.06	.018	.007	.006	18,000	2.52	.099	.029	.027
7000	1.24	.024	.009	.009	20,000	2.80	.122	.036	.033
8000	1.42	.031	.011	.010	22,000	3.08	.147	.043	.039
9000	1.60	.040	.014	.014	24,000	3.36	.175	.051	.047
10,000	1.77	.049	.017	.017	26,000	3.64	.206	.059	.054
12,000	2.13	.070	.024	.023	28,000	3.92	.239	.069	.062
14,000	2.48	.096	.033	.031	30,000	4.20	.274	.079	.071
16,000	2.84	.125	.042	.039	35,000	4.90	.373	.106	.096
18,000	3.19	.158	.053	.048	40,000	5.60	.487	.137	.123
20,000	3.55	.195	.065	.059	45,000	6.30	.617	.173	.154
25,000	4.43	.304	.100	.092	50,000	7.00	.761	.213	.189
30,000	5.32	.439	.143	.130	60,000	8.41	1.10	.304	.267
35,000	6.21	.598	.193	.175	70,000	9.81	1.49	.412	.360
40,000	7.09	.779	.251	.225	80,000	11.2	1.95	.536	.465
45,000	7.98	.987	.316	.279	90,000	12.6	2.47	.676	.584
50,000	8.87	1.22	.389	.340	100,000	14.0	3.05	.833	.717
55,000	9.75	1.47	.469	.406	110,000	15.4	3.69	1.01	.862
60,000	10.64	1.76	.556	.485	120,000	16.8	4.39	1.19	1.02
70,000	12.41	2.39	.754	.654	130,000	18.2	5.15	1.40	1.19
80,000	14.18	3.12	.982	.849	140,000	19.6	5.97	1.62	1.38
90,000	15.96	3.95	1.24	1.07	150,000	21.0	6.85	1.86	1.58
100,000	17.73	4.88	1.53	1.31	160,000	22.4	7.80	2.11	1.79
110,000	19.50	5.90	1.84	1.58	170,000	23.8	8.80	2.38	2.02
120,000	21.28	7.03	2.19	1.88	180,000	25.2	9.87	2.67	2.26
130,000	23.05	8.25	2.52	2.20	190,000	26.6	11.0	2.97	2.51
140,000	24.82	9.56	2.98	2.54	200,000	28.0	12.2	3.29	2.77
150,000	26.60	11.0	3.41	2.91	250,000	35.0	19.0	5.13	4.30
200,000	35.5	19.5	6.04	5.14	300,000	42.0	27.4	7.37	6.16
250,000	44.3	30.5	9.42	7.99	350,000	49.0	37.3	10.0	8.36
300,000	53.2	43.9	13.5	11.5	400,000	56.0	48.7	13.1	10.9
350,000	62.1	59.8	18.4	15.6	450,000	63.0	61.7	16.5	13.7
400,000	70.9	78.1	24.0	20.3	500,000	70.0	76.1	20.4	16.9
450,000	79.8	98.8	30.4	25.6	550,000	77.0	92.1	24.7	20.5
500,000	88.7	122	37.5	31.6	600,000	84.0	110	29.3	24.3
550,000	97.5	148	45.4	38.2	650,000	91.1	129	34.4	28.5
600,000	106	176	54.0	45.4	700,000	98.1	149	39.9	33.0

Note: No allowance has been made for age, difference in diameter, or any abnormal condition of interior surface. Any factor of safety must be estimated from the local conditions and the requirements of each particular installation. It is recommended that for most commercial design purposes a safety factor of 15 to 20% be added to the values in the tables—see page 3-5.

FRICTION

Friction of Water   New Steel Pipe *(Continued)*
(Based on Darcy's Formula)

60 Inch **72 Inch** **84 Inch**

Flow US gal per min	Nominal size 60.0" inside dia			Flow US gal per min	Nominal size 72" inside dia			Flow US gal per min	Nominal size 84.0" inside dia		
	Velocity ft per sec	Velocity head ft	Head loss ft per 100 ft		Velocity ft per sec	Velocity head ft	Head loss ft per 100 ft		Velocity ft per sec	Velocity head ft	Head loss ft per 100 ft
14,000	1.59	.039	.010	18,000	1.42	.031	.007	24,000	1.39	.030	.005
16,000	1.82	.051	.013	20,000	1.58	.039	.008	26,000	1.51	.035	.006
18,000	2.04	.065	.017	22,000	1.73	.047	.010	28,000	1.62	.041	.007
20,000	2.27	.080	.020	24,000	1.89	.056	.012	30,000	1.74	.047	.008
22,000	2.50	.097	.023	26,000	2.05	.065	.013	35,000	2.03	.064	.011
24,000	2.72	.115	.027	28,000	2.21	.076	.015	40,000	2.32	.083	.014
26,000	2.95	.135	.032	30,000	2.36	.087	.018	45,000	2.61	.105	.017
28,000	3.18	.157	.037	35,000	2.76	.118	.023	50,000	2.90	.130	.021
30,000	3.40	.180	.042	40,000	3.15	.154	.029	55,000	3.18	.157	.025
35,000	3.97	.245	.056	45,000	3.55	.195	.036	60,000	3.47	.187	.029
40,000	4.54	.320	.072	50,000	3.94	.241	.045	70,000	4.05	.255	.039
45,000	5.11	.405	.091	60,000	4.73	.347	.063	80,000	4.63	.333	.051
50,000	5.67	.500	.111	70,000	5.52	.472	.085	90,000	5.21	.421	.063
60,000	6.81	.719	.157	80,000	6.30	.617	.110	100,000	5.79	.520	.078
70,000	7.94	.979	.212	90,000	7.09	.781	.137	110,000	6.37	.629	.093
80,000	9.08	1.28	.274	100,000	7.88	.964	.168	120,000	6.95	.749	.110
90,000	10.2	1.62	.345	110,000	8.67	1.17	.203	130,000	7.53	.879	.129
100,000	11.3	2.00	.423	120,000	9.46	1.39	.240	140,000	8.11	1.02	.149
110,000	12.5	2.42	.509	130,000	10.2	1.63	.280	150,000	8.64	1.17	.170
120,000	13.6	2.88	.603	140,000	11.0	1.89	.323	160,000	9.26	1.33	.192
130,000	14.8	3.38	.705	150,000	11.8	2.17	.370	170,000	9.84	1.50	.216
140,000	15.9	3.92	.815	160,000	12.6	2.47	.419	180,000	10.4	1.69	.242
150,000	17.0	4.50	.933	170,000	13.4	7.89	.472	190,000	11.0	1.88	.269
160,000	18.2	5.12	1.06	180,000	14.2	3.12	.528	200,000	11.6	2.08	.297
170,000	19.3	5.78	1.19	190,000	15.0	3.48	.587	250,000	14.5	3.25	.459
180,000	20.4	6.48	1.33	200,000	15.8	3.86	.648	300,000	17.4	4.68	.655
190,000	21.6	7.21	1.48	250,000	19.7	6.02	1.00	350,000	20.3	6.37	.886
200,000	22.7	7.99	1.64	300,000	23.6	8.67	1.44	400,000	23.2	8.32	1.15
250,000	28.4	12.5	2.55	350,000	27.6	11.8	1.95	450,000	26.1	10.5	1.45
300,000	34.0	18.0	3.65	400,000	31.5	15.4	2.53	500,000	28.9	13.0	1.79
350,000	39.7	24.5	4.95	450,000	35.5	19.5	3.20	550,000	31.8	15.7	2.16
400,000	45.4	32.0	6.45	500,000	39.4	24.1	3.94	600,000	34.7	18.7	2.56
450,000	51.1	40.5	8.14	550,000	43.3	29.2	4.75	650,000	37.6	22.0	3.00
500,000	56.7	50.0	10.0	600,000	47.3	34.7	5.65	700,000	40.5	25.5	3.48
550,000	62.4	60.5	12.1	650,000	51.2	40.7	6.62	750,000	43.4	29.3	3.99
600,000	68.1	71.9	14.4	700,000	55.2	47.2	7.66	800,000	46.3	33.3	4.53
650,000	73.8	84.4	16.9	750,000	59.1	54.2	8.79	850,000	49.2	37.6	5.11
700,000	79.4	97.9	19.7	800,000	63.0	61.7	9.99	900,000	52.1	42.1	5.72
750,000	85.1	112	22.4	850,000	67.0	69.6	11.3	950,000	55.0	46.9	6.37
800,000	90.8	128	25.5	900,000	70.9	78.1	12.6	1,000,000	57.9	52.0	7.05

Note: No allowance has been made for age, difference in diameter, or any abnormal condition of interior surface. Any factor of safety must be estimated from the local conditions and the requirements of each particular installation. It is recommended that for most commercial design purposes a safety factor of 15 to 20% be added to the values in the tables—see page 3-5.

Friction of Water   New Steel Pipe *(Continued)*
(Based on Darcy's Formula)

96 Inch   **108 Inch**   **120 Inch**

Flow U S gal per min	Nominal size 96.0″ inside dia			Flow U S gal per min	Nominal size 108.0″ inside dia			Flow U S gal per min	Nominal size 120.0″ inside dia		
	Ve-locity ft per sec	Ve-locity head ft	Head loss ft per 100 ft		Ve-locity ft per sec	Ve-locity head ft	Head loss ft per 100 ft		Ve-locity ft per sec	Ve-locity head ft	Head loss ft per 100 ft
12,000	.532	.004	.001	15,000	.525	.004	.001	20,000	.567	.005	.001
14,000	.621	.006	.001	20,000	.700	.008	.001	30,000	.851	.011	.001
16,000	.709	.008	.001	25,000	.876	.012	.002	40,000	1.14	.020	.002
18,000	.798	.010	.002	30,000	1.05	.017	.002	50,000	1.42	.031	.004
20,000	.887	.012	.002	35,000	1.23	.023	.003	60,000	1.70	.045	.005
22,000	.975	.015	.002	40,000	1.40	.030	.004	70,000	1.99	.061	.007
24,000	1.06	.018	.003	45,000	1.58	.039	.005	80,000	2.27	.080	.009
26,000	1.15	.021	.003	50,000	1.75	.048	.006	90,000	2.55	.101	.011
28,000	1.24	.024	.004	60,000	2.10	.069	.009	100,000	2.84	.125	.013
30,000	1.33	.027	.004	70,000	2.45	.093	.011	110,000	3.12	.151	.016
40,000	1.77	.049	.007	80,000	2.80	.122	.015	120,000	3.40	.180	.019
50,000	2.22	.076	.011	90,000	3.15	.154	.018	130,000	3.69	.211	.022
60,000	2.66	.110	.015	100,000	3.50	.190	.022	140,000	3.97	.245	.025
70,000	3.10	.149	.020	110,000	3.85	.230	.027	150,000	4.26	.281	.028
80,000	3.55	.195	.026	120,000	4.20	.274	.031	160,000	4.54	.320	.032
90,000	3.99	.247	.033	130,000	4.55	.322	.037	170,000	4.83	.361	.036
100,000	4.43	.305	.040	140,000	4.90	.373	.042	180,000	5.11	.405	.040
110,000	4.88	.369	.048	150,000	5.25	.428	.048	190,000	5.39	.451	.045
120,000	5.32	.439	.056	160,000	5.60	.487	.054	200,000	5.67	.500	.049
130,000	5.76	.515	.066	170,000	5.95	.550	.061	250,000	7.09	.781	.076
140,000	6.21	.598	.076	180,000	6.30	.617	.068	300,000	8.51	1.12	.108
150,000	6.65	.686	.087	190,000	6.65	.687	.076	350,000	9.93	1.53	.145
160,000	7.09	.781	.098	200,000	7.00	.761	.084	400,000	11.3	2.00	.188
170,000	7.54	.881	.110	250,000	8.76	1.19	.129	450,000	12.8	2.53	.237
180,000	7.98	.988	.123	300,000	10.5	1.71	.183	500,000	14.2	3.12	.291
190,000	8.42	1.10	.137	350,000	12.3	2.33	.247	600,000	17.0	4.50	.416
200,000	8.87	1.22	.151	400,000	14.0	3.05	.321	700,000	19.9	6.12	.562
250,000	11.1	1.91	.233	450,000	15.8	3.86	.404	800,000	22.7	7.99	.731
300,000	13.3	2.74	.333	500,000	17.5	4.76	.497	900,000	25.5	10.1	.922
350,000	15.5	3.74	.449	600,000	21.0	6.85	.710	1,000,000	28.4	12.5	1.14
400,000	17.7	4.88	.584	700,000	24.5	9.33	.962	1,100,000	31.2	15.1	1.37
450,000	19.9	6.18	.735	800,000	28.0	12.2	1.25	1,200,000	34.0	18.0	1.63
500,000	22.2	7.62	.905	900,000	31.5	15.4	1.58	1,300,000	36.9	21.1	1.91
600,000	26.6	11.0	1.30	1,000,000	35.0	19.0	1.94	1,400,000	39.7	24.5	2.21
700,000	31.0	14.9	1.76	1,100,000	38.5	23.0	2.35	1,500,000	42.6	28.1	2.53
800,000	35.5	19.5	2.29	1,200,000	42.0	27.4	2.79	1,600,000	45.4	32.0	2.87
900,000	39.9	24.7	2.88	1,300,000	45.5	32.2	3.27	1,700,000	48.2	36.1	3.24
1,000,000	44.3	30.5	3.55	1,400,000	49.0	37.3	3.78	1,800,000	51.1	40.5	3.63
1,100,000	48.8	36.9	4.29	1,500,000	52.5	42.8	4.34	1,900,000	53.9	45.1	4.04
1,200,000	53.2	43.9	5.10					2,000,000	56.7	50.0	4.47

Note: No allowance has been made for age, difference in diameter, or any abnormal condition of interior surface. Any factor of safety must be estimated from the local conditions and the requirements of each particular installation. It is recommended that for most commercial design purposes a safety factor of 15 to 20% be added to the values in the tables—see page 3-5.

Friction of Water New Steel Pipe *(Continued)*
(Based on Darcy's Formula)

144 Inch **168 Inch** **192 Inch**

Flow U S gal per min	Nominal size 144.0″ inside dia			Flow U S gal per min	Nominal size 168.0″ inside dia			Flow U S gal per min	Nominal size 192.0″ inside dia		
	Ve-locity ft per sec	Ve-locity head ft	Head loss ft per 100 ft		Ve-locity ft per sec	Ve-locity head ft	Head loss ft per 100 ft		Ve-locity ft per sec	Ve-locity head ft	Head loss ft per 100 ft
30,000	.591	.005	.001	50,000	.724	.008	.001	60,000	.665	.007	.001
40,000	.788	.010	.001	60,000	.868	.012	.001	80,000	.887	.012	.001
50,000	.985	.015	.002	70,000	1.01	.016	.001	100,000	1.11	.019	.001
60,000	1.18	.022	.002	80,000	1.16	.021	.002	120,000	1.33	.027	.002
70,000	1.38	.030	.003	90,000	1.30	.026	.002	140,000	1.55	.037	.003
80,000	1.58	.039	.004	100,000	1.45	.033	.003	150,000	1.66	.043	.003
90,000	1.77	.049	.005	120,000	1.74	.047	.004	160,000	1.77	.049	.003
100,000	1.97	.060	.006	140,000	2.03	.064	.005	180,000	2.00	.062	.004
110,000	2.17	.073	.006	150,000	2.17	.073	.005	200,000	2.22	.076	.005
120,000	2.36	.087	.008	160,000	2.32	.083	.006	220,000	2.44	.092	.006
130,000	2.56	.102	.009	180,000	2.61	.105	.008	240,000	2.66	.110	.007
140,000	2.76	.118	.010	200,000	2.90	.130	.009	250,000	2.77	.119	.007
150,000	2.96	.136	.011	220,000	3.18	.157	.011	260,000	2.88	.129	.008
160,000	3.15	.154	.013	240,000	3.47	.187	.013	280,000	3.10	.149	.009
170,000	3.35	.174	.015	250,000	3.62	.203	.014	300,000	3.32	.172	.010
180,000	3.55	.195	.016	260,000	3.76	.220	.015	350,000	3.88	.233	.014
190,000	3.74	.217	.018	280,000	4.05	.255	.018	400,000	4.43	.305	.018
200,000	3.94	.241	.020	300,000	4.34	.293	.020	450,000	5.00	.386	.022
250,000	4.93	.376	.030	350,000	5.07	.398	.027	500,000	5.54	.476	.027
300,000	5.91	.542	.043	400,000	5.79	.520	.035	600,000	6.65	.686	.039
350,000	6.90	.738	.058	450,000	6.51	.658	.043	700,000	7.76	.934	.052
400,000	7.88	.964	.075	500,000	7.24	.813	.053	800,000	8.87	1.22	.068
450,000	8.87	1.22	.094	600,000	8.68	1.17	.076	900,000	9.97	1.54	.085
500,000	9.85	1.51	.116	700,000	10.1	1.59	.102	1,000,000	11.1	1.91	.104
600,000	11.8	2.17	.165	800,000	11.6	2.08	.133	1,200,000	13.3	2.74	.149
700,000	13.8	2.95	.223	900,000	13.0	2.63	.167	1,400,000	15.5	3.74	.201
800,000	15.8	3.86	.289	1,000,000	14.5	3.25	.205	1,600,000	17.7	4.88	.261
900,000	17.7	4.88	.364	1,200,000	17.4	4.68	.293	1,800,000	19.9	6.18	.329
1,000,000	19.7	6.02	.448	1,400,000	20.3	6.37	.396	2,000,000	22.2	7.62	.405
1,200,000	23.6	8.67	.641	1,600,000	23.7	8.73	.547	2,200,000	24.4	9.22	.488
1,400,000	27.6	11.8	.869	1,800,000	26.7	11.1	.690	2,400,000	26.6	11.0	.580
1,500,000	29.6	13.6	.995	2,000,000	29.6	13.6	.850	2,600,000	28.8	12.9	.679
1,600,000	31.5	15.4	1.13	2,200,000	32.6	16.5	1.03	2,800,000	31.0	14.9	.786
1,800,000	35.5	19.5	1.43	2,400,000	35.6	19.6	1.22	3,000,000	33.2	17.2	.900
2,000,000	39.4	24.1	1.76	2,600,000	38.5	23.1	1.43	3,200,000	35.5	19.5	1.02
2,200,000	43.3	29.2	2.12	2,800,000	41.5	26.7	1.65	3,400,000	37.7	22.0	1.15
2,400,000	47.3	34.7	2.52	3,000,000	44.5	30.7	1.89	3,600,000	39.9	24.7	1.29
2,500,000	49.3	37.6	2.73	3,200,000	47.4	34.9	2.15	3,800,000	42.1	27.5	1.44
2,600,000	51.2	40.7	2.95	3,400,000	50.4	39.4	2.43	4,000,000	44.3	30.5	1.59
2,800,000	55.2	47.2	3.42	3,600,000	53.4	44.2	2.72	4,500,000	49.9	38.6	2.01

Note: No allowance has been made for age, difference in diameter, or any abnormal condition of interior surface. Any factor of safety must be estimated from the local conditions and the requirements of each particular installation. It is recommended that for most commercial design purposes a safety factor of 15 to 20% be added to the values in the tables—see page 3-5.

Friction Losses in Smooth Tubing and Pipe

Copper Tubing (Type K, L and M)—S.P.S. Copper and Brass Pipe, Plastic and Glass Pipe.

Smooth copper tubing and pipe, brass pipe, plastic and glass pipe are available in various sizes and types to meet individual requirements as specified—sizes may be different than standard. To avoid the necessity of interpolation and applying correction factors to the values for cast iron and steel pipe, a special set of tables is included herewith on pages 3-34 to 3-48 figured on the basis of commercially available copper tubing, and S.P.S. copper and brass pipe.

These tables are calculated using the Darcy-Weisbach equation (see page 3-3) and basis an absolute roughness parameter of 0.000005 (see page 3-5); since this roughness parameter applies to very smooth pipe or tubing a safety factor should be applied in those cases to compensate for possible questionable conditions; as discussed on page 3-5 it is suggested that for most commercial design purposes a safety factor of 15 to 20% be added to the head loss values in the tables.

It should be noted that the head loss data can apply to any fluid having a kinematic viscosity $v = 0.000\ 012\ 16$ ft²/sec (1.130 centistokes), which is the viscosity for pure fresh water at 60°F. Greater viscosities (colder water) will increase the friction; lower viscosities (warmer water) will decrease the friction.

Friction losses for tubing and pipe sizes between those listed in the tables may be determined with reasonable accuracy using a ratio of the fifth powers of the diameters; for example:

Desired friction loss pipe B = known friction loss pipe A $\left(\dfrac{\text{Dia A}}{\text{Dia B}} \right)^5$

Friction of Water
(Based on Darcy's Formula)

Copper Tubing—*S.P.S. Copper and Brass Pipe
⅜ Inch

Flow — U S gal per min	Type K tubing .402″ inside dia .049″ wall thk		Type L tubing .430″ inside dia .035″ wall thk		Type M tubing .450″ inside dia .025″ wall thk		*Pipe .494″ inside dia .0905″ wall thk		Flow — U S gal per min
	Velocity ft/sec	Head loss ft/100 ft	Velocity ft/sec	Head loss ft/100 ft	Velocity ft/sec	Head loss ft/100 ft	Velocity ft/sec	Head loss ft/100 ft	
0.2	0.51	0.66	0.44	0.48	0.40	0.39	0.34	0.26	0.2
0.4	1.01	2.15	0.88	1.57	0.81	1.27	0.67	0.82	0.4
0.6	1.52	4.29	1.33	3.12	1.21	2.52	1.00	1.63	0.6
0.8	2.02	7.02	1.77	5.11	1.61	4.12	1.34	2.66	0.8
1	2.52	10.32	2.20	7.50	2.01	6.05	1.68	3.89	1
1½	3.78	20.86	3.30	15.15	3.02	12.21	2.51	7.84	1½
2	5.04	34.48	4.40	20.03	4.02	20.16	3.35	12.94	2
2½	6.30	51.03	5.50	37.01	5.03	29.80	4.19	19.11	2½
3	7.55	70.38	6.60	51.02	6.04	41.07	5.02	26.32	3
3½	8.82	92.44	7.70	66.98	7.04	53.90	5.86	34.52	3½
4	10.1	117.1	8.80	84.85	8.05	68.26	6.70	43.70	4
4½	11.4	144.4	9.90	104.6	9.05	84.11	7.53	53.82	4½
5	12.6	174.3	11.0	126.1	10.05	101.4	8.36	64.87	5

Calculations on pages 3-34 to 3-48 are by Ingersoll-Rand Co.

Note: No allowance has been made for age, difference in diameter, or any abnormal condition of interior surface. Any factor of safety must be estimated from the local conditions and the requirements of each particular installation. It is recommended that for most commercial design purposes a safety factor of 15 to 20% be added to the values in the tables—see page 3-5.

Friction of Water (Continued)
(Based on Darcy's Formula)
Copper Tubing—*S.P.S. Copper and Brass Pipe

½ Inch

Flow — U S gal per min	Type K tubing .527" inside dia .049" wall thk		Type L tubing .545" inside dia .040" wall thk		Type M tubing .569" inside dia .028" wall thk		*Pipe .625" inside dia .1075" wall thk		Flow — U S gal per min
	Velocity ft/sec	Head loss ft/100 ft	Velocity ft/sec	Head loss ft/100 ft	Velocity ft/sec	Head loss ft/100 ft	Velocity ft/sec	Head loss ft/100 ft	
½	0.74	0.88	0.69	0.75	0.63	0.62	0.52	0.40	½
1	1.47	2.87	1.38	2.45	1.26	2.00	1.04	1.28	1
1½	2.20	5.77	2.06	4.93	1.90	4.02	1.57	2.58	1½
2	2.94	9.52	2.75	8.11	2.53	6.61	2.09	4.24	2
2½	3.67	14.05	3.44	11.98	3.16	9.76	2.61	6.25	2½
3	4.40	19.34	4.12	16.48	3.79	13.42	3.13	8.59	3
3½	5.14	25.36	4.81	21.61	4.42	17.59	3.66	11.25	3½
4	5.87	32.09	5.50	27.33	5.05	22.25	4.18	14.22	4
4½	6.61	39.51	6.19	33.65	5.68	27.39	4.70	17.50	4½
5	7.35	47.61	6.87	40.52	6.31	32.99	5.22	21.07	5
6	8.81	65.79	8.25	56.02	7.59	45.57	6.26	29.09	6
7	10.3	86.57	9.62	73.69	8.84	59.93	7.31	38.23	7
8	11.8	109.9	11.0	93.50	10.1	76.03	8.35	48.47	8
9	13.2	135.6	12.4	115.4	11.4	93.82	9.40	59.79	9
10	14.7	163.8	13.8	139.4	12.6	113.3	10.4	72.16	10

⅝ Inch

Flow — U S gal per min	Type K tubing .652" inside dia .049" wall thk		Type L tubing .666" inside dia .042" wall thk		Type M tubing .690" inside dia .030" wall thk		*Pipe		Flow — U S gal per min
	Velocity ft/sec	Head loss ft/100 ft	Velocity ft/sec	Head loss ft/100 ft	Velocity ft/sec	Head loss ft/100 ft			
½	0.48	0.31	0.46	0.29	0.43	0.24			½
1	0.96	1.05	0.92	0.95	0.86	0.76			1
1½	1.44	2.11	1.38	1.91	1.29	1.53			1½
2	1.92	3.47	1.84	3.14	1.72	2.51			2
2½	2.40	5.11	2.30	4.62	2.14	3.68			2½
3	2.88	7.02	2.75	6.35	2.57	5.07			3
3½	3.36	9.20	3.21	8.32	3.00	6.64			3½
4	3.84	11.63	3.67	10.51	3.43	8.40			4
4½	4.32	14.30	4.13	12.93	3.86	10.35			4½
5	4.80	17.22	4.59	15.56	4.29	12.49			5
6	5.75	23.76	5.51	21.47	5.15	17.21			6
7	6.71	31.22	6.42	28.21	6.00	22.58			7
8	7.67	39.58	7.35	35.75	6.85	28.54			8
9	8.64	48.81	8.25	44.09	7.71	35.35			9
10	9.60	58.90	9.18	53.19	8.57	42.48			10
11	10.6	69.83	10.1	63.06	9.43	50.47			11
12	11.5	81.59	11.0	73.67	10.3	59.1			12
13	12.5	94.18	11.9	85.03	11.2	68.8			13

Note: No allowance has been made for age, difference in diameter, or any abnormal condition of interior surface. Any factor of safety must be estimated from the local conditions and the requirements of each particular installation. It is recommended that for most commercial design purposes a safety factor of 15 to 20% be added to the values in the tables—see page 3-5.

Friction of Water (Continued)
(Based on Darcy's Formula)
Copper Tubing—*S.P.S. Copper and Brass Pipe
¾ Inch

Flow — U S gal per min	Type K tubing .745" inside dia .065" wall thk Velocity ft/sec	Head loss ft/100 ft	Type L tubing .785" inside dia .045" wall thk Velocity ft/sec	Head loss ft/100 ft	Type M tubing .811" inside dia .032" wall thk Velocity ft/sec	Head loss ft/100 ft	*Pipe .822" inside dia .114" wall thk Velocity ft/sec	Head loss ft/100 ft	Flow — U S gal per min
1	0.74	0.56	0.66	0.44	0.62	0.38	0.60	0.35	1
2	1.47	1.84	1.33	1.44	1.24	1.23	1.21	1.16	2
3	2.21	3.73	1.99	2.91	1.86	2.49	1.81	2.34	3
4	2.94	6.16	2.65	4.81	2.48	4.12	2.42	3.86	4
5	3.67	9.12	3.31	7.11	3.10	6.09	3.02	5.71	5
6	4.41	12.57	3.98	9.80	3.72	8.39	3.62	7.86	6
7	5.14	16.51	4.64	12.86	4.34	11.01	4.23	10.32	7
8	5.88	20.91	5.30	16.28	4.96	13.94	4.83	13.07	8
9	6.61	25.77	5.96	20.06	5.59	17.17	5.44	16.10	9
10	7.35	31.08	6.62	24.19	6.20	20.70	6.04	19.41	10
11	8.09	36.83	7.29	28.66	6.82	24.52	6.64	22.99	11
12	8.83	43.01	7.95	33.47	7.44	28.63	7.25	26.84	12
13	9.56	49.62	8.61	38.61	8.06	33.02	7.85	30.96	13
14	10.3	56.66	9.27	44.07	8.68	37.69	8.45	35.33	14
15	11.0	64.11	9.94	49.86	9.30	42.64	9.05	39.97	15
16	11.8	71.97	10.6	55.97	9.92	47.86	9.65	44.86	16
17	12.5	80.24	11.25	62.39	10.55	53.35	10.25	50.00	17
18	13.2	88.92	11.92	69.13	11.17	59.10	10.85	55.40	18

1 Inch

Flow — U S gal per min	Type K tubing .995" inside dia .065" wall thk Velocity ft/sec	Head loss ft/100 ft	Type L tubing 1.025" inside dia .050" wall thk Velocity ft/sec	Head loss ft/100 ft	Type M tubing 1.055" inside dia .035" wall thk Velocity ft/sec	Head loss ft/100 ft	*Pipe 1.062" inside dia .1265" wall thk Velocity ft/sec	Head loss ft/100 ft	Flow — U S gal per min
2	0.82	0.47	0.78	0.41	0.73	0.36	0.72	0.35	2
3	1.24	0.95	1.17	0.82	1.10	0.72	1.08	0.70	3
4	1.65	1.56	1.56	1.35	1.47	1.18	1.45	1.14	4
5	2.06	2.30	1.95	2.00	1.83	1.74	1.81	1.69	5
6	2.48	3.17	2.34	2.75	2.20	2.40	2.17	2.32	6
7	2.89	4.15	2.72	3.60	2.56	3.14	2.53	3.04	7
8	3.30	5.25	3.11	4.56	2.93	3.97	2.89	3.85	8
9	3.71	6.47	3.50	5.61	3.30	4.89	3.25	4.74	9
10	4.12	7.79	3.89	6.76	3.66	5.89	3.61	5.71	10
12	4.95	10.76	4.67	9.33	4.40	8.13	4.34	7.88	12
14	5.77	14.15	5.45	12.27	5.13	10.69	5.05	10.36	14
16	6.60	17.94	6.22	15.56	5.86	13.55	5.78	13.13	16
18	7.42	22.14	7.00	19.20	6.60	16.72	6.50	16.20	18
20	8.24	26.73	7.78	23.18	7.33	20.18	7.22	19.55	20
25	10.30	39.87	9.74	34.56	9.16	30.09	9.03	29.15	25
30	12.37	55.33	11.68	47.96	11.00	41.74	10.84	40.43	30
35	14.42	73.06	13.61	63.31	12.82	55.09	12.65	53.37	35
40	16.50	93.00	15.55	80.58	14.66	70.11	14.45	67.90	40
45	18.55	115.1	17.50	99.72	16.50	86.75	16.25	84.02	45
50	20.60	139.4	19.45	120.7	18.32	105.0	18.05	101.7	50

Note: No allowance has been made for age, difference in diameter, or any abnormal condition of interior surface. Any factor of safety must be estimated from the local conditions and the requirements of each particular installation. It is recommended that for most commercial design purposes a safety factor of 15 to 20% be added to the values in the tables—see page 3-5.

Friction of Water *(Continued)*
(Based on Darcy's Formula)
Copper Tubing—*S.P.S. Copper and Brass Pipe
1¼ Inch

Flow — U S gal per min	Type K tubing 1.245" inside dia .065" wall thk Velocity ft/sec	Head loss ft/100 ft	Type L tubing 1.265" inside dia .055" wall thk Velocity ft/sec	Head loss ft/100 ft	Type M tubing 1.291" inside dia .042" wall thk Velocity ft/sec	Head loss ft/100 ft	*Pipe 1.368" inside dia .146" wall thk Velocity ft/sec	Head loss ft/100 ft	Flow — U S gal per min
5	1.31	0.79	1.28	0.74	1.22	0.67	1.09	0.51	5
6	1.58	1.09	1.53	1.01	1.47	0.92	1.31	0.70	6
7	1.84	1.43	1.79	1.32	1.71	1.20	1.53	0.91	7
8	2.11	1.81	2.04	1.67	1.96	1.52	1.75	1.15	8
9	2.37	2.22	2.30	2.06	2.20	1.87	1.96	1.42	9
10	2.63	2.67	2.55	2.48	2.45	2.25	2.18	1.71	10
12	3.16	3.69	3.06	3.42	2.93	3.10	2.62	2.35	12
15	3.95	5.47	3.83	5.07	3.66	4.60	3.27	3.49	15
20	5.26	9.13	5.10	8.46	4.89	7.67	4.36	5.81	20
25	6.58	13.59	6.38	12.59	6.11	11.42	5.46	8.65	25
30	7.90	18.83	7.65	17.44	7.33	15.82	6.55	11.98	30
35	9.21	24.83	8.94	23.00	8.55	20.86	7.65	15.79	35
40	10.5	31.57	10.2	29.24	9.77	26.51	8.74	20.06	40
45	11.8	38.03	11.5	36.15	11.0	32.77	9.83	24.80	45
50	13.2	47.20	12.8	43.71	12.2	39.63	10.9	29.98	50
60	15.8	65.65	15.3	60.78	14.7	55.10	13.1	41.66	60
70	18.4	86.82	17.9	80.38	17.1	72.86	15.3	55.07	70
80	21.1	110.7	20.4	102.5	19.6	92.85	17.5	70.16	80
90	23.7	137.2	23.0	127.0	22.0	115.1	19.6	86.91	90
100	26.3	166.3	25.5	153.9	24.4	139.4	21.8	105.3	100

1½ Inch

Flow — U S gal per min	Type K tubing 1.481" inside dia .072" wall thk Velocity ft/sec	Head loss ft/100 ft	Type L tubing 1.505" inside dia .060" wall thk Velocity ft/sec	Head loss ft/100 ft	Type M tubing 1.527" inside dia .049" wall thk Velocity ft/sec	Head loss ft/100 ft	*Pipe 1.600" inside dia .150" wall thk Velocity ft/sec	Head loss ft/100 ft	Flow — U S gal per min
8	1.49	0.79	1.44	0.73	1.40	0.68	1.27	0.55	8
9	1.67	0.97	1.62	0.90	1.57	0.84	1.43	0.67	9
10	1.86	1.17	1.80	1.08	1.75	1.01	1.59	0.81	10
12	2.23	1.61	2.16	1.49	2.10	1.39	1.91	1.12	12
15	2.79	2.39	2.70	2.21	2.63	2.07	2.39	1.65	15
20	3.72	3.98	3.60	3.68	3.50	3.44	3.19	2.75	20
25	4.65	5.91	4.51	5.48	4.38	5.11	3.98	4.09	25
30	5.58	8.19	5.41	7.58	5.25	7.07	4.78	5.65	30
35	6.51	10.79	6.31	9.99	6.13	9.31	5.58	7.45	35
40	7.44	13.70	7.21	12.68	7.00	11.83	6.37	9.45	40
45	8.37	16.93	8.11	15.67	7.88	14.61	7.16	11.68	45
50	9.30	20.46	9.01	18.94	8.76	17.66	7.96	14.11	50
60	11.2	28.42	10.8	26.30	10.5	24.53	9.56	19.59	60
70	13.0	37.55	12.6	34.74	12.3	32.40	11.2	25.87	70
80	14.9	47.82	14.4	44.24	14.0	41.25	12.8	32.93	80
90	16.7	59.21	16.2	54.78	15.8	51.07	14.4	40.76	90
100	18.6	71.70	18.0	66.34	17.5	61.84	15.9	49.34	100
110	20.5	85.29	19.8	78.90	19.3	73.55	17.5	58.67	110
120	22.3	99.95	21.6	92.46	21.0	86.18	19.1	68.74	120
130	24.2	115.7	23.4	107.0	22.8	99.73	20.7	79.53	130

Note: No allowance has been made for age, difference in diameter, or any abnormal condition of interior surface. Any factor of safety must be estimated from the local conditions and the requirements of each particular installation. It is recommended that for most commercial design purposes a safety factor of 15 to 20% be added to the values in the tables—see page 3-5.

Friction of Water (Continued)
(Based on Darcy's Formula)
Copper Tubing—*S.P.S. Copper and Brass Pipe

2 Inch

	Type K tubing		Type L tubing		Type M tubing		*Pipe		
Flow	1.959" inside dia .083" wall thk		1.985" inside dia .070" wall thk		2.009" inside dia .058" wall thk		2.062" inside dia .1565" wall thk		Flow
U S gal per min	Velocity ft/sec	Head loss ft/100 ft	Velocity ft/sec	Head loss ft/100 ft	Velocity ft/sec	Head loss ft/100 ft	Velocity ft/sec	Head loss ft/100 ft	U S gal per min
10	1.07	0.31	1.04	0.29	1.01	0.27	.96	0.24	10
12	1.28	0.43	1.24	0.40	1.21	0.38	1.15	0.33	12
14	1.49	0.56	1.45	0.52	1.42	0.50	1.34	0.44	14
16	1.70	0.71	1.66	0.66	1.62	0.63	1.53	0.55	16
18	1.92	0.87	1.87	0.82	1.82	0.77	1.72	0.68	18
20	2.13	1.05	2.07	0.98	2.02	0.93	1.92	0.82	20
25	2.66	1.55	2.59	1.46	2.53	1.38	2.39	1.22	25
30	3.19	2.15	3.11	2.01	3.03	1.90	2.87	1.68	30
35	3.73	2.82	3.62	2.65	3.54	2.50	3.35	2.21	35
40	4.26	3.58	4.14	3.36	4.05	3.17	3.83	2.80	40
45	4.79	4.42	4.66	4.15	4.55	3.92	4.30	3.46	45
50	5.32	5.34	5.17	5.01	5.05	4.73	4.80	4.17	50
60	6.39	7.40	6.21	6.95	6.06	6.56	5.75	5.79	60
70	7.45	9.76	7.25	9.16	7.07	8.65	6.70	7.63	70
80	8.52	12.42	8.28	11.65	8.09	11.00	7.65	9.70	80
90	9.58	15.36	9.31	14.41	9.10	13.60	8.61	12.00	90
100	10.65	18.58	10.4	17.43	10.1	16.45	9.57	14.51	100
110	11.71	22.07	11.4	20.71	11.1	19.55	10.5	17.24	110
120	12.78	25.84	12.4	24.25	12.1	22.88	11.5	20.18	120
130	13.85	29.88	13.4	28.04	13.1	26.45	12.5	23.33	130
140	14.9	34.18	14.5	32.07	14.2	30.26	13.4	26.69	140
150	16.0	38.75	15.5	36.36	15.2	34.30	14.4	30.25	150
160	17.0	43.58	16.5	40.89	16.2	38.58	15.3	34.01	160
170	18.1	48.67	17.6	45.66	17.2	43.08	16.3	37.98	170
180	19.2	54.01	18.6	50.67	18.2	47.81	17.2	42.15	180
190	20.2	59.61	19.6	55.92	19.2	52.76	18.2	46.51	190
200	21.3	65.46	20.7	61.41	20.2	57.94	19.2	51.07	200
210	22.4	71.57	21.7	67.14	21.2	63.34	20.1	55.83	210
220	23.4	77.93	22.8	73.10	22.2	68.96	21.0	60.78	220
230	24.5	84.53	23.8	79.29	23.2	74.80	22.0	65.93	230
240	25.6	91.38	24.8	85.72	24.3	80.86	23.0	71.26	240
250	26.6	98.43	25.9	92.37	25.3	87.14	23.9	76.79	250
260	27.7	105.8	26.9	99.26	26.3	93.63	24.9	82.51	260
270	28.8	113.4	27.9	106.4	27.3	100.3	25.8	88.42	270
280	29.8	121.3	29.0	113.7	28.3	107.3	26.8	94.52	280
290	30.9	129.3	30.0	121.3	29.4	114.4	27.8	100.8	290
300	32.0	137.6	31.1	129.1	30.4	121.8	28.7	107.3	300

Note: No allowance has been made for age, difference in diameter, or any abnormal condition of interior surface. Any factor of safety must be estimated from the local conditions and the requirements of each particular installation. It is recommended that for most commercial design purposes a safety factor of 15 to 20% be added to the values in the tables—see page 3-5.

Friction of Water *(Continued)*
(Based on Darcy's Formula)
Copper Tubing—*S.P.S. Copper and Brass Pipe

2½ Inch

Flow — U S gal per min	Type K tubing 2.435" inside dia .095" wall thk		Type L tubing 2.465" inside dia .080" wall thk		Type M tubing 2.495" inside dia .065" wall thk		*Pipe 2.500" inside dia .1875" wall thk		Flow — U S gal per min
	Velocity ft/sec	Head loss ft/100 ft	Velocity ft/sec	Head loss ft/100 ft	Velocity ft/sec	Head loss ft/100 ft	Velocity ft/sec	Head loss ft/100 ft	
20	1.38	0.37	1.34	0.35	1.31	0.33	1.31	0.33	20
25	1.72	0.55	1.68	0.52	1.64	0.49	1.63	0.49	25
30	2.07	0.76	2.02	0.72	1.97	0.68	1.96	0.67	30
35	2.41	1.00	2.35	0.94	2.30	0.89	2.29	0.88	35
40	2.76	1.26	2.69	1.19	2.62	1.13	2.61	1.12	40
45	3.10	1.56	3.02	1.47	2.95	1.39	2.94	1.38	45
50	3.45	1.88	3.36	1.77	3.28	1.68	3.26	1.66	50
60	4.14	2.61	4.03	2.46	3.93	2.32	3.92	2.30	60
70	4.82	3.43	4.70	3.24	4.59	3.06	4.57	3.03	70
80	5.51	4.36	5.37	4.12	5.25	3.88	5.22	3.85	80
90	6.20	5.39	6.04	5.08	5.90	4.80	5.88	4.75	90
100	6.89	6.52	6.71	6.15	6.55	5.80	6.53	5.74	100
110	7.58	7.74	7.38	7.30	7.21	6.89	7.19	6.82	110
120	8.27	9.06	8.05	8.54	7.86	8.05	7.84	7.98	120
130	8.96	10.46	8.73	9.87	8.52	9.31	8.49	9.22	130
140	9.65	11.97	9.40	11.28	9.18	10.64	9.14	10.54	140
150	10.35	13.56	10.1	12.78	9.83	12.06	9.79	11.94	150
160	11.0	15.24	10.8	14.36	10.5	13.55	10.45	13.42	160
170	11.7	17.01	11.4	16.03	11.1	15.12	11.1	14.98	170
180	12.4	18.87	12.1	17.79	11.8	16.78	11.8	16.61	180
190	13.1	20.81	12.8	19.62	12.5	18.51	12.4	18.33	190
200	13.8	22.85	13.4	21.54	13.1	20.31	13.1	20.12	200
220	15.2	27.18	14.8	25.61	14.4	24.16	14.4	23.93	220
240	16.5	31.84	16.1	30.01	15.7	28.31	15.7	28.03	240
260	17.9	36.85	17.5	34.73	17.1	32.75	17.0	32.44	260
280	19.3	42.19	18.8	39.76	18.4	37.50	18.3	37.13	280
300	20.7	47.86	20.1	45.10	19.7	42.53	19.6	42.12	300
320	22.1	53.86	21.5	50.75	21.0	47.86	20.9	47.40	320
340	23.4	60.18	22.8	56.71	22.3	53.48	22.2	52.96	340
360	24.8	66.83	24.2	62.97	23.6	59.38	23.5	58.81	300
380	26.2	73.80	25.5	69.54	24.9	65.57	24.8	64.94	380
400	27.6	81.09	26.9	76.41	26.2	72.04	26.1	71.35	400
420	29.0	88.70	28.2	83.57	27.5	78.80	27.4	78.04	420
440	30.3	96.62	29.5	91.04	28.8	85.83	28.7	85.00	440
460	31.7	104.9	30.9	98.80	30.2	93.15	30.0	92.24	460
480	33.1	113.4	32.2	106.8	31.5	100.7	31.4	99.76	480
500	34.5	122.3	33.6	115.2	32.8	108.6	32.6	107.5	500

Note: No allowance has been made for age, difference in diameter, or any abnormal condition of interior surface. Any factor of safety must be estimated from the local conditions and the requirements of each particular installation. It is recommended that for most commercial design purposes a safety factor of 15 to 20% be added to the values in the tables—see page 3-5.

Friction of Water (Continued)
(Based on Darcy's Formula)
Copper Tubing—*S.P.S. Copper and Brass Pipe

3 Inch

Flow — U S gal per min	Type K tubing 2.907" inside dia .109" wall thk		Type L tubing 2.945" inside dia .090" wall thk		Type M tubing 2.981" inside dia .072" wall thk		*Pipe 3.062" inside dia .219" wall thk		Flow — U S gal per min
	Velocity ft/sec	Head loss ft/100 ft	Velocity ft/sec	Head loss ft/100 ft	Velocity ft/sec	Head loss ft/100 ft	Velocity ft/sec	Head loss ft/100 ft	
20	0.96	0.16	0.94	0.15	0.92	0.14	0.87	0.13	20
30	1.45	0.33	1.41	0.31	1.37	0.29	1.30	0.25	30
40	1.93	0.54	1.88	0.51	1.83	0.48	1.74	0.42	40
50	2.41	0.81	2.35	0.76	2.29	0.72	2.17	0.63	50
60	2.89	1.12	2.82	1.05	2.75	0.99	2.61	0.87	60
70	3.38	1.47	3.29	1.38	3.20	1.30	3.04	1.15	70
80	3.86	1.87	3.76	1.75	3.66	1.65	3.48	1.45	80
90	4.34	2.30	4.23	2.16	4.12	2.04	3.91	1.80	90
100	4.82	2.78	4.70	2.61	4.59	2.47	4.35	2.17	100
110	5.30	3.30	5.17	3.10	5.05	2.93	4.79	2.57	110
120	5.79	3.86	5.64	3.63	5.50	3.42	5.21	3.01	120
130	6.27	4.46	6.11	4.19	5.95	3.95	5.65	3.47	130
140	6.75	5.10	6.58	4.79	6.41	4.52	6.09	3.97	140
150	7.24	5.77	7.05	5.42	6.87	5.12	6.52	4.50	150
160	7.72	6.49	7.52	6.09	7.34	5.75	6.95	5.05	160
170	8.20	7.24	7.99	6.80	7.79	6.41	7.39	5.64	170
180	8.69	8.03	8.46	7.54	8.25	7.11	7.82	6.25	180
190	9.16	8.85	8.93	8.32	8.70	7.84	8.25	6.89	190
200	9.64	9.71	9.40	9.13	9.16	8.61	8.70	7.56	200
220	10.6	11.55	10.3	10.85	10.1	10.23	9.56	8.99	220
240	11.6	13.52	11.3	12.70	11.0	11.98	10.4	10.52	240
260	12.6	15.64	12.2	14.69	11.9	13.85	11.3	12.17	260
280	13.5	17.90	13.2	16.81	12.8	15.85	12.2	13.93	280
300	14.5	20.30	14.1	19.06	13.7	17.97	13.0	15.79	300
320	15.4	22.83	15.0	21.44	14.7	20.22	13.9	17.76	320
340	16.4	25.50	16.0	23.95	15.6	22.58	14.8	19.83	340
360	17.4	28.30	16.9	26.58	16.5	25.06	15.7	22.01	360
380	18.3	31.24	17.9	29.34	17.4	27.66	16.5	24.29	380
400	19.3	34.32	18.8	32.22	18.3	30.38	17.4	26.68	400
450	21.7	42.58	21.2	39.98	20.6	37.69	19.6	33.09	450
500	24.1	51.65	23.5	48.50	22.9	45.72	21.7	40.14	500
550	26.6	61.54	25.8	57.77	25.2	54.46	23.9	47.81	550
600	29.0	72.22	28.2	67.80	27.5	63.91	26.1	56.10	600
650	31.4	83.69	30.6	78.56	29.8	74.05	28.2	65.00	650
700	33.8	95.95	32.9	90.06	32.1	84.89	30.4	74.50	700
750	36.2	109.0	35.2	102.3	34.4	96.41	32.6	84.61	750
800	38.6	122.8	37.6	115.3	36.6	108.6	34.8	95.31	800

Note: No allowance has been made for age, difference in diameter, or any abnormal condition of interior surface. Any factor of safety must be estimated from the local conditions and the requirements of each particular installation. It is recommended that for most commercial design purposes a safety factor of 15 to 20% be added to the values in the tables—see page 3-5.

Friction of Water (Continued)
(Based on Darcy's Formula)

Copper Tubing—*S.P.S. Copper and Brass Pipe

3½ Inch

Flow — U S gal per min	Type K tubing 3.385" inside dia .120" wall thk		Type L tubing 3.425" inside dia .100" wall thk		Type M tubing 3.459" inside dia .083" wall thk		*Pipe 3.500" inside dia .250" wall thk		Flow — U S gal per min
	Velocity ft/sec	Head loss ft/100 ft	Velocity ft/sec	Head loss ft/100 ft	Velocity ft/sec	Head loss ft/100 ft	Velocity ft/sec	Head loss ft/100 ft	
60	2.14	0.54	2.09	0.51	2.05	0.49	2.00	0.46	60
70	2.49	0.71	2.44	0.67	2.39	0.64	2.33	0.60	70
80	2.84	0.90	2.78	0.85	2.73	0.81	2.66	0.77	80
90	3.20	1.11	3.13	1.05	3.07	1.00	3.00	0.95	90
100	3.56	1.34	3.48	1.27	3.41	1.21	3.33	1.14	100
110	3.92	1.59	3.82	1.50	3.76	1.43	3.67	1.35	110
120	4.26	1.86	4.18	1.76	4.10	1.68	4.00	1.58	120
130	4.62	2.15	4.52	2.03	4.45	1.93	4.33	1.83	130
140	4.98	2.45	4.87	2.32	4.79	2.21	4.66	2.09	140
150	5.34	2.78	5.21	2.62	5.12	2.50	5.00	2.36	150
160	5.69	3.12	5.56	2.95	5.46	2.81	5.33	2.66	160
170	6.05	3.48	5.91	3.29	5.80	3.14	5.66	2.96	170
180	6.40	3.86	6.26	3.64	6.16	3.48	6.00	3.28	180
190	6.76	4.25	6.60	4.02	6.49	3.83	6.33	3.62	190
200	7.11	4.67	6.95	4.41	6.82	4.20	6.66	3.97	200
220	7.82	5.54	7.65	5.24	7.51	4.99	7.33	4.72	220
240	8.54	6.49	8.35	6.13	8.19	5.85	8.00	5.52	240
260	9.25	7.50	9.05	7.09	8.87	6.76	8.66	6.39	260
280	9.95	8.58	9.74	8.11	9.55	7.73	9.33	7.30	280
300	10.7	9.73	10.4	9.19	10.2	8.76	10.0	8.28	300
350	12.5	12.87	12.2	12.16	11.9	11.60	11.7	10.95	350
400	14.2	16.42	13.9	15.51	13.7	14.79	13.3	13.97	400
450	16.0	20.36	15.6	19.23	15.4	18.33	15.0	17.32	450
500	17.8	24.68	17.4	23.32	17.1	22.23	16.7	20.99	500
550	19.6	29.39	19.1	27.76	18.8	26.46	18.3	24.99	550
600	21.4	34.47	20.9	32.56	20.5	31.04	20.0	29.31	600
650	23.1	39.92	22.6	37.71	22.2	35.94	21.6	33.95	650
700	24.9	45.75	24.4	43.21	23.9	41.18	23.3	38.89	700
750	26.6	51.94	26.1	49.05	25.6	46.75	25.0	44.15	750
800	28.4	58.49	27.8	55.24	27.3	52.65	26.6	49.72	800
850	30.2	65.40	29.6	61.77	29.0	58.87	28.3	55.59	850
900	32.0	72.68	31.3	68.63	30.7	65.41	30.0	61.77	900
950	33.8	80.31	33.0	75.84	32.4	72.27	31.6	68.24	950
1000	35.6	88.29	34.8	83.37	34.1	79.46	33.3	75.02	1000
1100	39.2	105.3	38.2	99.45	37.6	94.77	36.7	89.47	1100
1200	42.6	123.7	41.8	116.8	41.0	111.3	40.0	105.1	1200
1300	46.2	143.5	45.2	135.5	44.5	129.1	43.3	121.9	1300
1400	49.8	164.7	48.7	155.5	47.9	148.2	46.6	139.9	1400

Note: No allowance has been made for age, difference in diameter, or any abnormal condition of interior surface. Any factor of safety must be estimated from the local conditions and the requirements of each particular installation. It is recommended that for most commercial design purposes a safety factor of 15 to 20% be added to the values in the tables—see page 3-5.

Friction of Water (Continued)
(Based on Darcy's Formula)
Copper Tubing—*S.P.S. Copper and Brass Pipe

4 Inch

Flow — U S gal per min	Type K tubing 3.857" inside dia .134" wall thk Velocity ft/sec	Head loss ft/100 ft	Type L tubing 3.905" inside dia .110" wall thk Velocity ft/sec	Head loss ft/100 ft	Type M tubing 3.935" inside dia .095" wall thk Velocity ft/sec	Head loss ft/100 ft	*Pipe 4.000" inside dia .250" wall thk Velocity ft/sec	Head loss ft/100 ft	Flow — U S gal per min
100	2.74	0.72	2.68	0.68	2.64	0.65	2.55	0.60	100
110	3.02	0.85	2.94	0.80	2.90	0.77	2.81	0.71	110
120	3.29	0.99	3.21	0.94	3.16	0.90	3.06	0.83	120
130	3.57	1.15	3.48	1.08	3.42	1.04	3.31	0.96	130
140	3.84	1.31	3.74	1.23	3.69	1.19	3.57	1.10	140
150	4.11	1.48	4.01	1.40	3.95	1.35	3.83	1.25	150
160	4.39	1.67	4.28	1.57	4.21	1.51	4.08	1.39	160
170	4.66	1.86	4.55	1.75	4.48	1.69	4.33	1.56	170
180	4.94	2.06	4.81	1.94	4.74	1.87	4.58	1.73	180
190	5.21	2.27	5.08	2.14	5.00	2.06	4.84	1.91	190
200	5.49	2.49	5.35	2.35	5.27	2.26	5.10	2.09	200
220	6.04	2.96	5.89	2.79	5.80	2.68	5.61	2.48	220
240	6.59	3.46	6.42	3.26	6.32	3.14	6.12	2.90	240
260	7.14	4.00	6.95	3.77	6.85	3.63	6.63	3.36	260
280	7.69	4.57	7.49	4.31	7.38	4.15	7.14	3.84	280
300	8.24	5.18	8.02	4.88	7.90	4.70	7.65	4.35	300
350	9.60	6.85	9.36	6.46	9.22	6.22	8.92	5.75	350
400	11.0	8.74	10.7	8.23	10.5	7.93	10.2	7.33	400
450	12.4	10.83	12.0	10.20	11.9	9.83	11.5	9.08	450
500	13.7	13.12	13.4	12.36	13.2	11.91	12.8	11.00	500
550	15.1	15.61	14.7	14.71	14.5	14.17	14.1	13.09	550
600	16.5	18.31	16.0	17.24	15.8	16.61	15.3	15.35	600
650	17.9	21.19	17.4	19.96	17.1	19.23	16.6	17.77	650·
700	19.2	24.28	18.7	22.86	18.4	22.03	17.9	20.35	700
750	20.6	27.55	20.1	25.95	19.8	25.00	19.1	23.09	750
800	22.0	31.01	21.4	29.21	21.1	28.14	20.4	25.99	800
850	23.3	34.67	22.8	32.65	22.4	31.46	21.7	29.05	850
900	24.7	38.51	24.1	36.27	23.7	34.94	23.0	32.27	900
950	26.1	42.54	25.4	40.06	25.0	38.60	24.2	35.64	950
1000	27.4	46.76	26.8	44.03	26.4	42.42	25.5	39.17	1000
1100	30.2	55.74	29.4	52.48	29.0	50.56	28.1	46.69	1100
1200	32.9	65.45	32.1	61.62	31.6	59.37	30.6	54.82	1200
1300	35.7	75.89	34.8	71.45	34.2	68.83	33.1	63.55	1300
1400	38.4	87.05	37.4	81.95	36.9	78.95	35.7	72.89	1400
1500	41.1	98.23	40.1	93.13	39.5	89.71	38.3	82.82	1500
1600	43.9	111.5	42.8	105.0	42.1	101.1	40.8	93.34	1600
1800	49.4	138.8	48.1	130.6	47.4	125.8	45.8	116.1	1800
2000	54.9	168.9	53.5	158.9	52.7	153.1	51.0	141.3	2000
2200	60.4	201.7	58.9	189.8	58.0	182.8	56.1	168.7	2200

Note: No allowance has been made for age, difference in diameter, or any abnormal condition of interior surface. Any factor of safety must be estimated from the local conditions and the requirements of each particular installation. It is recommended that for most commercial design purposes a safety factor of 15 or 20% be added to the values in the tables—see page 3-5.

Friction of Water (Continued)
(Based on Darcy's Formula)
Copper Tubing—*S.P.S. Copper and Brass Pipe

5 Inch

Flow — U S gal per min	Type K tubing 4.805" inside dia .160" wall thk		Type L tubing 4.875" inside dia .125" wall thk		Type M tubing 4.907" inside dia .109" wall thk		*Pipe 5.063" inside dia .250" wall thk		Flow — U S gal per min
	Velocity ft/sec	Head loss ft/100 ft	Velocity ft/sec	Head loss ft/100 ft	Velocity ft/sec	Head loss ft/100 ft	Velocity ft/sec	Head loss ft/100 ft	
150	2.64	0.52	2.58	0.48	2.53	0.47	2.38	0.40	150
160	2.82	0.58	2.75	0.54	2.70	0.52	2.54	0.45	160
170	3.00	0.65	2.92	0.60	2.87	0.58	2.70	0.50	170
180	3.17	0.72	3.09	0.67	3.04	0.65	2.86	0.56	180
190	3.35	0.79	3.26	0.74	3.21	0.71	3.02	0.61	190
200	3.53	0.87	3.44	0.81	3.38	0.78	3.18	0.67	200
220	3.88	1.03	3.78	0.96	3.72	0.93	3.50	0.80	220
240	4.24	1.20	4.12	1.12	4.05	1.09	3.81	0.94	240
260	4.59	1.39	4.46	1.30	4.39	1.26	4.14	1.08	260
280	4.94	1.59	4.81	1.48	4.73	1.43	4.45	1.23	280
300	5.29	1.80	5.15	1.68	5.07	1.63	4.76	1.40	300
350	6.17	2.38	6.01	2.22	5.91	2.15	5.56	1.85	350
400	7.05	3.03	6.87	2.82	6.75	2.73	6.35	2.35	400
450	7.94	3.75	7.73	3.49	7.60	3.39	7.15	2.91	450
500	8.81	4.54	8.59	4.23	8.45	4.10	7.95	3.53	500
550	9.70	5.40	9.45	5.03	9.29	4.88	8.75	4.19	550
600	10.6	6.32	10.3	5.90	10.1	5.71	9.54	4.91	600
650	11.5	7.32	11.2	6.82	11.0	6.61	10.3	5.68	650
700	12.4	8.37	12.0	7.81	11.8	7.57	11.1	6.50	700
750	13.2	9.50	12.9	8.86	12.7	8.58	11.9	7.38	750
800	14.1	10.69	13.7	9.97	13.5	9.65	12.7	8.30	800
850	15.0	11.94	14.6	11.13	14.4	10.79	13.5	9.27	850
900	15.9	13.26	15.5	12.36	15.2	11.98	14.3	10.29	900
950	16.8	14.64	16.3	13.67	16.1	13.22	15.1	11.36	950
1000	17.6	16.08	17.2	14.99	16.9	14.52	15.9	12.48	1000
1100	19.4	19.16	18.9	17.86	18.6	17.30	17.5	14.86	1100
1200	21.2	22.48	20.6	20.95	20.3	20.30	19.1	17.44	1200
1300	22.9	26.04	22.4	24.27	22.0	23.51	20.6	20.20	1300
1400	24.7	29.85	24.0	27.82	23.7	26.95	22.2	23.15	1400
1500	26.4	33.84	25.8	31.59	25.4	30.60	23.8	26.28	1500
1600	28.2	38.18	27.5	35.59	27.0	34.47	25.4	29.60	1600
1800	31.8	47.46	30.9	44.23	30.4	42.85	28.6	36.79	1800
2000	35.3	57.68	34.4	53.75	33.8	52.06	31.8	44.70	2000
2200	38.8	68.82	37.8	64.13	37.2	62.12	35.0	53.32	2200
2400	42.4	80.89	41.2	75.37	40.5	73.00	38.1	62.65	2400
2600	45.9	93.86	44.6	87.45	44.0	84.70	41.4	72.69	2600
2800	49.4	107.7	48.1	100.4	47.3	97.21	44.5	83.42	2800
3000	52.9	122.5	51.5	114.1	50.7	110.5	47.6	94.84	3000

Note: No allowance has been made for age, difference in diameter, or any abnormal condition of interior surface. Any factor of safety must be estimated from the local conditions and the requirements of each particular installation. It is recommended that for most commercial design purposes a safety factor of 15 to 20% be added to the values in the tables—see page 3-5.

Friction of Water (Continued)
(Based on Darcy's Formula)
Copper Tubing—*S.P.S. Copper and Brass Pipe

6 Inch

Flow — U S gal per min	Type K tubing 5.741" inside dia .192" wall thk		Type L tubing 5.845" inside dia .140" wall thk		Type M tubing 5.881" inside dia .122 wall thk		*Pipe 6.125" inside dia .250" wall thk		Flow — U S gal per min
	Velocity ft/sec	Head loss ft/100 ft	Velocity ft/sec	Head loss ft/100 ft	Velocity ft/sec	Head loss ft/100 ft	Velocity ft/sec	Head loss ft/100 ft	
240	2.98	0.51	2.87	0.47	2.84	0.46	2.61	0.38	240
260	3.22	0.59	3.11	0.54	3.07	0.53	2.83	0.43	260
280	3.48	0.67	3.35	0.62	3.31	0.60	3.05	0.49	280
300	3.72	0.76	3.58	0.70	3.54	0.68	3.26	0.56	300
350	4.35	1.01	4.19	0.93	4.14	0.90	3.81	0.74	350
400	4.97	1.28	4.79	1.18	4.72	1.14	4.35	0.94	400
450	5.59	1.59	5.38	1.46	5.31	1.42	4.90	1.16	450
500	6.20	1.92	5.98	1.76	5.90	1.71	5.44	1.41	500
550	6.82	2.29	6.57	2.10	6.50	2.04	5.98	1.67	550
600	7.45	2.68	7.17	2.46	7.10	2.38	6.53	1.96	600
650	8.07	3.10	7.76	2.84	7.68	2.76	7.07	2.27	650
700	8.69	3.54	8.36	3.25	8.27	3.15	7.61	2.59	700
750	9.31	4.02	8.96	3.68	8.86	3.57	8.15	2.94	750
800	9.93	4.52	9.56	4.14	9.45	4.02	8.70	3.31	800
850	10.6	5.05	10.2	4.63	10.0	4.49	9.25	3.69	850
900	11.2	5.60	10.8	5.14	10.6	4.99	9.79	4.10	900
950	11.8	6.18	11.4	5.67	11.2	5.50	10.3	4.52	950
1000	12.4	6.79	12.0	6.23	11.8	6.04	10.9	4.97	1000
1100	13.7	8.08	13.2	7.41	13.0	7.19	12.0	5.91	1100
1200	14.9	9.48	14.3	8.69	14.2	8.44	13.1	6.93	1200
1300	16.1	10.98	15.5	11.06	15.4	9.77	14.1	8.02	1300
1400	17.4	12.58	16.7	11.53	16.5	11.19	15.2	9.19	1400
1500	18.6	14.28	17.9	13.09	17.7	12.70	16.3	10.43	1500
1600	19.9	16.07	19.1	14.73	18.9	14.30	17.4	11.74	1600
1800	22.4	19.96	21.5	18.30	21.2	17.76	19.6	14.58	1800
2000	24.8	24.24	23.9	22.22	23.6	21.56	21.8	17.70	2000
2200	27.3	24.91	26.3	26.49	26.0	25.71	23.9	21.10	2200
2400	29.8	33.95	28.7	31.11	28.4	30.19	26.1	24.77	2400
2600	32.3	39.37	31.1	36.07	30.7	35.01	28.3	28.72	2600
2800	34.8	45.16	33.5	41.37	33.1	40.15	30.4	32.94	2800
3000	37.2	51.32	35.8	47.02	35.4	46.63	32.6	37.42	3000
3200	39.7	57.85	38.2	53.00	37.8	51.43	34.8	42.18	3200
3400	42.2	64.75	40.6	59.31	40.1	57.56	37.0	47.20	3400
3600	44.7	72.01	43.0	65.96	42.5	64.01	39.2	52.48	3600
3800	47.1	79.63	45.4	72.94	44.9	70.78	41.4	58.03	3800
4000	49.6	87.62	47.8	80.25	47.2	77.87	43.5	63.83	4000
4200	52.1	95.96	50.1	87.89	49.6	85.28	45.7	69.90	4200
4400	54.6	104.7	52.5	95.85	52.0	93.01	47.9	76.23	4400

Note: No allowance has been made for age, difference in diameter, or any abnormal condition of interior surface. Any factor of safety must be estimated from the local conditions and the requirements of each particular installation. It is recommended that for most commercial design purposes a safety factor of 15 to 20% be added to the values in the tables—see page 3-5.

Friction of Water (Continued)
(Based on Darcy's Formula)
Copper Tubing—*S.P.S. Copper and Brass Pipe

8 Inch

Flow — U S gal per min	Type K tubing 7.583" inside dia .271" wall thk		Type L tubing 7.725" inside dia .200" wall thk		Type M tubing 7.785" inside dia .170" wall thk		*Pipe 8.000" inside dia .3125" wall thk		Flow — U S gal per min
	Velocity ft/sec	Head loss ft/100 ft	Velocity ft/sec	Head loss ft/100 ft	Velocity ft/sec	Head loss ft/100 ft	Velocity ft/sec	Head loss ft/100 ft	
500	3.55	0.50	3.42	0.46	3.37	0.44	3.19	0.39	500
550	3.91	0.60	3.76	0.55	3.71	0.53	3.51	0.46	550
600	4.26	0.70	4.10	0.64	4.05	0.62	3.83	0.54	600
650	4.61	0.81	4.44	0.74	4.39	0.71	4.15	0.63	650
700	4.97	0.93	4.78	0.85	4.72	0.82	4.46	0.72	700
750	5.32	1.05	5.12	0.96	5.06	0.92	4.79	0.81	750
800	5.68	1.18	5.46	1.08	5.40	1.04	5.10	0.91	800
850	6.04	1.32	5.80	1.20	5.73	1.16	5.42	1.02	850
900	6.39	1.46	6.15	1.34	6.06	1.29	5.74	1.13	900
950	6.75	1.61	6.49	1.47	6.40	1.42	6.05	1.25	950
1000	7.10	1.77	6.84	1.62	6.74	1.56	6.38	1.37	1000
1100	7.81	2.11	7.52	1.93	7.42	1.85	7.01	1.63	1100
1200	8.52	2.47	8.20	2.26	8.10	2.17	7.65	1.91	1200
1300	9.24	2.86	8.88	2.61	8.76	2.51	8.30	2.20	1300
1400	9.95	3.27	9.56	2.99	9.44	2.88	8.93	2.52	1400
1500	10.7	3.71	10.3	3.39	10.1	3.27	9.56	2.86	1500
1600	11.4	4.17	10.9	3.81	10.8	3.67	10.2	3.22	1600
1800	12.8	5.18	12.3	4.73	12.1	4.56	11.5	4.00	1800
2000	14.2	6.28	13.7	5.74	13.5	5.53	12.8	4.85	2000
2200	15.6	7.48	15.0	6.84	14.9	6.59	14.0	5.77	2200
2400	17.0	8.78	16.4	8.02	16.2	7.73	15.3	6.77	2400
2600	18.5	10.17	17.8	9.29	17.5	8.95	16.6	7.84	2600
2800	19.9	11.66	19.2	10.65	18.9	10.26	17.9	8.99	2800
3000	21.3	13.24	20.5	12.10	20.2	11.65	19.1	10.21	3000
3200	22.7	14.91	21.9	13.62	21.6	13.12	20.4	11.49	3200
3400	24.2	16.68	23.2	15.24	22.9	14.67	21.7	12.85	3400
3600	25.6	18.53	24.6	16.93	24.3	16.31	23.0	14.28	3600
3800	27.0	20.48	26.0	18.71	25.6	18.02	24.2	15.78	3800
4000	28.4	22.52	27.3	20.57	27.0	19.81	25.5	17.35	4000
4200	29.8	24.65	28.7	22.52	28.3	21.68	26.8	18.99	4200
4400	31.2	26.87	30.0	24.54	29.7	23.64	28.0	20.70	4400
4600	32.7	29.17	31.4	26.65	31.0	25.66	29.4	22.47	4600
4800	34.1	31.57	32.8	28.84	32.4	27.77	30.6	24.32	4800
5000	35.5	34.06	34.2	31.11	33.7	29.96	31.9	26.23	5000
5500	39.1	40.65	37.6	37.13	37.1	35.75	35.1	31.30	5500
6000	42.6	47.80	41.0	43.65	40.5	42.03	38.3	36.79	6000
6500	46.1	55.48	44.4	50.67	43.9	48.76	41.5	42.70	6500
7000	49.7	63.70	47.9	58.17	47.2	56.01	44.6	49.02	7000

Note: No allowance has been made for age, difference in diameter, or any abnormal condition of interior surface. Any factor of safety must be estimated from the local conditions and the requirements of each particular installation. It is recommended that for most commercial design purposes a safety factor of 15 to 20% be added to the values in the tables—see page 3-5.

Friction of Water (Continued)
(Based on Darcy's Formula)
Copper Tubing—*S.P.S. Copper and Brass Pipe
10 Inch

Flow — U S gal per min	Type K tubing 9.449" inside dia		Type L tubing 9.625" inside dia		Type M tubing 9.700" inside dia		*Pipe 10.020" inside dia		Flow — U S gal per min
	Velocity ft/sec	Head loss ft/100 ft	Velocity ft/sec	Head loss ft/100 ft	Velocity ft/sec	Head loss ft/100 ft	Velocity ft/sec	Head loss ft/100 ft	
500	2.29	0.18	2.21	0.16	2.17	0.15	2.03	0.13	500
550	2.52	0.21	2.43	0.19	2.39	0.18	2.24	0.16	550
600	2.75	0.24	2.65	0.22	2.61	0.21	2.44	0.18	600
650	2.97	0.28	2.87	0.26	2.82	0.25	2.65	0.21	650
700	3.20	0.32	3.09	0.29	3.04	0.28	2.85	0.24	700
750	3.43	0.36	3.31	0.33	3.26	0.32	3.05	0.27	750
800	3.66	0.41	3.53	0.37	3.47	0.36	3.26	0.31	800
850	3.89	0.46	3.75	0.42	3.69	0.40	3.46	0.34	850
900	4.12	0.51	3.97	0.46	3.91	0.45	3.66	0.38	900
950	4.35	0.56	4.19	0.51	4.13	0.49	3.87	0.42	950
1000	4.56	0.61	4.41	0.56	4.34	0.54	4.07	0.46	1000
1100	5.03	0.73	4.48	0.67	4.78	0.64	4.32	0.50	1100
1200	5.49	0.85	5.29	0.78	5.21	0.75	4.71	0.59	1200
1300	5.95	0.99	5.73	0.90	5.64	0.87	5.10	0.68	1300
1400	6.41	1.13	6.17	1.03	6.08	1.00	5.50	0.78	1400
1500	6.86	1.28	6.61	1.17	6.51	1.13	5.89	0.89	1500
1600	7.32	1.44	7.06	1.32	6.95	1.27	6.28	1.00	1600
1800	8.24	1.79	7.94	1.63	7.82	1.57	7.32	1.35	1800
2000	9.15	2.17	8.82	1.98	8.68	1.91	8.14	1.63	2000
2200	10.1	2.58	9.70	2.36	9.55	2.27	8.95	1.94	2200
2400	11.0	3.02	10.6	2.76	10.4	2.66	9.77	2.28	2400
2600	11.9	3.50	11.5	3.20	11.3	3.08	10.6	2.63	2600
2800	12.8	4.01	12.3	3.67	12.2	3.53	11.4	3.02	2800
3000	13.7	4.55	13.2	4.16	13.0	4.01	12.2	3.42	3000
3500	16.0	6.04	15.4	5.52	15.2	5.32	14.2	4.55	3500
4000	18.3	7.72	17.6	7.06	17.4	6.80	16.3	5.81	4000
4500	20.6	9.60	19.8	8.78	19.5	8.45	18.3	7.22	4500
5000	22.9	11.66	22.0	10.66	21.7	10.26	20.3	8.77	5000
5500	25.2	13.91	24.3	12.71	23.9	12.24	22.4	10.45	5500
6000	27.5	16.34	26.5	14.93	26.1	14.38	24.4	12.28	6000
6500	29.7	18.95	28.7	17.32	28.2	16.68	26.4	14.24	6500
7000	32.0	21.74	30.9	19.87	30.4	19.13	28.5	16.33	7000
7500	34.3	24.71	33.1	22.59	32.6	21.75	30.5	18.56	7500
8000	36.6	27.86	35.3	25.46	34.7	24.52	32.6	20.92	8000
8500	38.9	31.19	37.5	28.50	36.9	27.44	34.6	23.42	8500
9000	41.2	34.69	39.7	31.70	39.1	30.52	36.6	26.05	9000
9500	43.5	38.37	41.9	35.06	41.2	33.75	38.7	28.80	9500
10,000	45.6	42.22	44.1	38.57	43.4	37.14	40.7	31.69	10,000

Note: No allowance has been made for age, difference in diameter, or any abnormal condition of interior surface. Any factor of safety must be estimated from the local conditions and the requirements of each particular installation. It is recommended that for most commercial design purposes a safety factor of 15 to 20% be added to the values in the tables—see page 3-5.

Friction of Water (Continued)
(Based on Darcy's Formula)
Copper Tubing—*S.P.S. Copper and Brass Pipe

12 Inch

Flow — U S gal per min	Type K tubing 11.315" inside dia		Type L tubing 11.565" inside dia		Type M tubing 11.617" inside dia		*Pipe 12.000" inside dia		Flow — U S gal per min
	Velocity ft/sec	Head loss ft/100 ft	Velocity ft/sec	Head loss ft/100 ft	Velocity ft/sec	Head loss ft/100 ft	Velocity ft/sec	Head loss ft/100 ft	
800	2.55	0.17	2.44	0.16	2.42	0.15	2.27	0.13	800
900	2.87	0.21	2.75	0.19	2.72	0.19	2.55	0.16	900
1000	3.19	0.26	3.05	0.23	3.03	0.23	2.84	0.19	1000
1100	3.51	0.31	3.36	0.28	3.33	0.27	3.12	0.23	1100
1200	3.83	0.36	3.67	0.32	3.63	0.32	3.40	0.27	1200
1300	4.15	0.41	3.97	0.37	3.94	0.36	3.69	0.31	1300
1400	4.47	0.47	4.28	0.43	4.24	0.42	3.97	0.36	1400
1500	4.79	0.54	4.58	0.48	4.54	0.47	4.26	0.40	1500
1600	5.11	0.60	4.89	0.54	4.84	0.53	4.54	0.45	1600
1800	5.74	0.75	5.50	0.67	5.45	0.66	5.11	0.56	1800
2000	6.38	0.91	6.11	0.82	6.05	0.80	5.67	0.68	2000
2200	7.02	1.08	6.72	0.97	6.66	0.95	6.24	0.81	2200
2400	7.66	1.26	7.33	1.14	7.27	1.11	6.81	0.95	2400
2600	8.30	1.46	7.94	1.32	7.87	1.29	7.38	1.10	2600
2800	8.93	1.68	8.55	1.51	8.48	1.48	7.94	1.26	2800
3000	9.57	1.90	9.16	1.71	9.08	1.67	8.51	1.43	3000
3500	11.2	2.52	10.7	2.27	10.6	2.22	9.93	1.90	3500
4000	12.8	3.22	12.2	2.90	12.1	2.84	11.3	2.42	4000
4500	14.4	4.00	13.7	3.60	13.6	3.52	12.8	3.01	4500
5000	16.0	4.86	15.3	4.37	15.1	4.27	14.2	3.65	5000
5500	17.5	5.79	16.8	5.21	16.6	5.10	15.6	4.35	5500
6000	19.1	6.80	18.3	6.11	18.2	5.98	17.0	5.11	6000
6500	20.7	7.88	19.9	7.09	19.7	6.93	18.4	5.92	6500
7000	22.3	9.04	21.4	8.13	21.2	7.95	19.6	6.79	7000
7500	23.9	10.27	22.9	9.23	22.7	9.03	21.3	7.71	7500
8000	25.5	11.57	24.4	10.40	24.2	10.18	22.7	8.69	8000
8500	27.1	12.95	26.0	11.64	25.7	11.39	24.1	9.72	8500
9000	28.7	14.39	27.5	12.94	27.2	12.66	25.5	10.81	9000
9500	30.3	15.91	29.0	14.31	28.8	14.00	27.0	11.95	9500
10,000	31.9	17.50	30.5	15.73	30.7	15.39	28.4	13.14	10,000
10,500	33.5	19.17	32.1	17.23	31.8	16.85	29.8	14.39	10,500
11,000	35.1	20.90	33.6	18.78	33.3	18.38	31.2	15.69	11,000
11,500	36.7	22.70	35.1	20.40	34.8	19.96	32.6	17.04	11,500
12,000	38.3	24.57	36.7	22.08	36.3	21.60	34.0	18.44	12,000
12,500	39.9	26.51	38.2	23.83	37.8	23.31	35.5	19.89	12,500
13,000	41.5	28.52	39.7	25.63	39.4	25.08	36.9	21.40	13,000
14,000	44.7	32.75	42.8	29.43	42.4	28.79	39.7	24.57	14,000
15,000	47.9	37.25	45.8	33.47	45.4	32.75	42.6	27.94	15,000

Note: No allowance has been made for age, difference in diameter, or any abnormal condition of interior surface. Any factor of safety must be estimated from the local conditions and the requirements of each particular installation. It is recommended that for most commercial design purposes a safety factor of 15 to 20% be added to the values in the tables—see page 3-5.

Friction Loss for Viscous Liquids
(Based on Darcy's Formula)
Loss in Feet of Liquid per 1000 Feet of Pipe
1 Inch (1.049″ inside dia) Sch 40 New Steel Pipe

Flow		Kinematic viscosity—centistokes									
		0.6	1.1	2.1	2.7	4.3	7.4	10.3	13.1	15.7	20.6
U S gal per min	Bbl per hr (42 gal)	Approx SSU viscosity									
		31.5	33	35	40	50	60	70	80	100	
.5	.71	.29	.28	.55	.70	1.12	1.93	2.68	3.41	4.08	5.35
1	1.4	.96	1.13	1.09	1.41	2.24	3.86	5.36	6.82	8.16	10.7
2	2.9	3.23	3.72	4.41	4.80	4.48	7.72	10.7	13.6	16.3	21.4
3	4.3	6.84	7.63	9.04	9.48	10.8	11.6	16.1	20.5	24.5	32.1
4	5.7	11.4	12.2	14.9	15.9	17.6	15.4	21.5	27.3	32.6	42.8
5	7.1	17.2	19.2	22.1	23.4	26.3	19.3	26.8	34.1	40.8	53.5
6	8.6	24.2	26.8	30.5	32.1	36.8	41.3	32.2	40.9	49.0	64.2
7	10.0	32.3	35.4	40.8	42.6	47.4	53.8	37.5	47.7	57.2	74.9
8	11.4	41.6	45.5	51.1	54.3	59.9	68.2	75.3	54.5	65.2	85.6
9	12.9	51.8	56.2	63.5	66.3	73.4	84.9	91.7	61.4	73.4	96.3
10	14.3	62.7	68.1	76.2	80.1	88.2	101	111	115	81.6	107
12	17.1	89.3	95.3	106	111	122	142	151	162	167	129
14	20.0	120	129	140	147	160	185	198	212	221	150
16	22.8	155	164	181	188	205	234	257	268	279	295
18	25.7	194	202	224	233	254	286	305	326	341	365
20	28.6	237	250	272	281	308	342	372	394	405	437
25	35.7	368	383	410	429	464	501	551	583	599	651
30	42.9	523	545	582	600	640	712	759	803	842	904
35	50.0	708	735	780	795	852	933				

Flow		Kinematic viscosity—centistokes									
		26.4	32.0	43.2	65.0	108.4	162.3	216.5	325	435	650
U S gal per min	Bbl per hr (42 gal)	Approx SSU viscosity									
		125	150	200	300	500	750	1000	1500	2000	3000
.1	.14	1.37	1.66	2.25	3.38	5.65	8.45	11.3	16.9	22.6	33.8
.3	.43	4.12	4.98	6.75	10.2	17.0	25.3	33.8	50.7	67.8	102
.5	.71	6.86	8.32	11.3	16.9	28.3	42.3	56.4	85	113	169
1	1.4	13.7	16.6	22.5	33.8	56.5	84.5	113	169	226	338
2	2.9	27.5	33.2	45.0	67.6	113	169	226	338	452	676
3	4.3	41.2	49.8	67.5	102	170	253	338	507	678	
4	5.7	55.0	66.5	90.0	136	226	338	452	677	904	
5	7.1	68.7	83.2	113	169	283	423	564	846		
6	8.6	82.4	99.7	135	203	339	507	677			
7	10	96.2	117	158	237	395	591	790			
8	11.4	110	133	180	271	452	676	903			
9	12.9	124	150	203	303	508	760				
10	14.3	137	167	225	338	565	845				
12	17.1	165	200	270	406	678					
14	20.0	192	233	315	474	792					
16	22.8	220	266	360	541	904					
18	25.7	248	299	405	609						
20	28.6	470	332	450	677						

For this pipe size: V = 0.371 × gpm; h_v = 0.00214 gpm².
Figures in shaded area are laminar (viscous) flow.
Calculations on pages 3-48 to 3-88 are by Ingersoll-Rand Co.
For velocity data see page 3-14.

Note: No allowance has been made for age, difference in diameter, or any abnormal condition of interior surface. Any factor of safety must be estimated from the local conditions and the requirements of each particular installation. It is recommended that for most commercial design purposes a safety factor of 15 to 20% be added to the values in the tables—see page 3-5.

Friction Loss for Viscous Liquids *(Continued)*
(Based on Darcy's Formula)
Loss in Feet of Liquid per 1000 Feet of Pipe
1½ Inch (1.610″ inside dia) Sch 40 New Steel Pipe

Flow		Kinematic viscosity—centistokes									
		0.6	1.1	2.1	2.7	4.3	7.4	10.3	13.1	15.7	20.6
U S gal per min	Bbl per hr (42 gal)	Approx SSU viscosity									
		31.5	33	35	40	50	60	70	80	100
1	1.4	.13	.10	.20	.25	.41	.69	.97	1.23	1.47	1.93
2	2.9	.42	.49	.39	.51	.83	1.39	1.93	2.46	2.94	3.86
3	4.3	.86	.98	1.17	1.25	1.24	2.08	2.89	3.68	4.41	5.79
4	5.7	1.43	1.63	1.92	2.07	1.65	2.78	3.86	4.91	5.88	7.72
5	7.1	2.11	2.42	2.83	3.05	2.06	3.47	4.82	6.14	7.35	9.65
6	8.6	2.90	3.36	3.89	4.18	4.69	4.17	5.79	7.37	8.82	11.6
8	11.4	4.97	5.60	6.44	6.87	7.77	9.02	7.72	9.83	11.8	15.5
10	14.3	7.51	8.34	9.58	10.1	11.6	13.2	9.65	12.3	14.7	19.3
12	17.1	10.4	11.6	13.4	14.0	15.6	17.9	19.8	14.7	17.6	23.2
15	21.4	16.0	17.4	19.6	20.7	23.2	26.5	29.1	31.1	21.0	29.0
20	28.6	27.2	29.5	32.9	34.6	38.2	43.9	47.6	51.1	53.8	38.6
25	35.7	41.4	44.8	49.5	51.8	57.5	65.7	70.1	75.2	78.9	84.7
30	42.9	58.8	63.0	69.1	72.0	79.0	89.3	97.1	103	109	116.5
40	57.1	102	107	117	122	132	150	160	170	178	191
50	71.4	157	164	178	183	198	222	237	251	263	281
60	85.7	224	233	249	259	279	306	330	347	362	388
70	100	300	312	333	343	369	402	436	457	477	508
80	114	389	403	427	440	470	516	551	580	602	643
90	129	498	508	536	550	585	634	681	715	746	792
100	143	601	624	656	670	714	774	820	863	898	949

Flow		Kinematic viscosity—centistokes									
		26.4	32.0	43.2	65.0	108.4	162.3	216.5	325	435	650
U S gal per min	Bbl per hr (42 gal)	Approx SSU viscosity									
		125	150	200	300	500	750	1000	1500	2000	3000
1	1.4	2.47	3.00	4.14	6.09	10.2	15.2	20.3	30.4	40.8	69.0
2	2.9	4.95	6.00	8.28	12.2	20.3	30.4	40.6	60.8	81.5	122
3	4.3	7.42	9.00	12.4	18.3	30.4	45.6	60.9	91.3	122	183
4	5.7	9.90	12.0	16.6	24.4	40.6	60.8	81.2	122	163	244
5	7.1	12.4	15.0	20.7	30.4	50.7	76.0	102	152	204	304
6	8.6	14.9	18.0	24.8	36.5	60.8	91.2	122	183	244	365
8	11.4	19.8	24.0	33.1	48.7	81.2	122	163	243	326	487
10	14.3	24.7	30.0	41.4	60.9	102	152	203	304	408	609
12	17.1	29.7	36.0	49.7	73.2	122	182	244	365	490	732
15	21.4	37.1	45.0	62.2	91.4	152	228	304	457	612	914
20	28.6	49.5	60.0	82.8	122	203	304	406	608	815	
25	35.7	61.9	75.0	103	152	254	380	507	760		
30	42.9	124	90.0	124	183	304	456	609	913		
40	57.1	204	216	166	244	406	608	812			
50	71.4	302	317	342	304	507	760				

For this pipe size: $V = 0.1576 \times gpm$; $h_v = 0.000385\ gpm^2$.
Figures in shaded area are laminar (viscous) flow.
For velocity data see page 3-15.

Note: No allowance has been made for age, difference in diameter, or any abnormal condition of interior surface. Any factor of safety must be estimated from the local conditions and the requirements of each particular installation. It is recommended that for most commercial design purposes a safety factor of 15 to 20% be added to the values in the tables—see page 3-5.

Friction Loss for Viscous Liquids *(Continued)*
(Based on Darcy's Formula)

Loss in Feet of Liquid per 1000 Feet of Pipe
2 Inch (2.067″ inside dia) Sch 40 New Steel Pipe

Flow		Kinematic viscosity—centistokes									
		.6	1.1	2.1	2.7	4.3	7.4	10.3	13.1	15.7	20.6
U S gal per min	Bbl per hr (42 gal)	Approx SSU viscosity									
		31.5	33	35	40	50	60	70	80	100
1	1.4	.04	.04	.07	.09	.15	.26	.36	.45	.54	.71
2	2.9	.13	.15	.15	.19	.30	.51	.71	.90	1.08	1.42
4	5.7	.43	.50	.58	.63	.59	1.02	1.42	1.81	2.17	2.84
6	8.6	.87	1.00	1.20	1.27	1.46	1.53	2.13	2.71	3.25	4.26
8	11.4	1.47	1.68	1.97	2.13	2.38	2.04	2.84	3.61	4.33	5.68
10	14.3	2.20	2.55	2.90	3.09	3.52	2.56	3.56	4.52	5.42	7.11
12	17.1	3.06	3.46	3.97	4.23	4.78	5.57	4.27	5.43	6.51	8.53
14	20.0	4.07	4.51	5.22	5.51	6.26	7.28	4.98	6.33	7.59	9.96
16	22.8	5.17	5.79	6.65	7.01	7.92	9.16	9.95	7.23	8.67	11.4
18	25.7	6.44	7.16	8.18	8.63	9.67	11.2	12.6	13.1	9.76	12.8
20	28.6	7.82	8.64	9.77	10.4	11.6	13.5	14.8	15.5	10.8	14.2
25	35.7	11.9	13.0	14.7	15.4	17.2	19.9	21.6	22.8	24.1	17.8
30	42.9	17.0	18.2	20.4	21.5	23.8	27.2	29.9	31.2	33.0	35.6
35	50.0	22.3	24.1	27.0	28.2	31.2	35.6	38.6	40.4	43.4	47.3
40	57.1	28.8	31.0	34.2	36.0	39.6	44.6	48.8	52.9	54.1	60.7
50	71.4	44.1	47.2	52.0	54.0	59.2	66.4	72.0	76.9	78.4	86.2
60	85.7	62.7	66.5	72.2	74.2	82.3	91.8	98.6	105	111	119
70	100	84.1	83.5	95.8	99.4	108	120	130	137	145	156
80	114	109	114	123	127	138	154	166	174	182	195
90	129	137	143	154	158	171	192	204	215	225	239
100	143	167	176	188	193	208	230	244	260	269	289
110	157	202	211	225	231	246	275	290	307	319	335
120	171	238	249	265	273	290	321	341	358	375	396
130	186	277	290	307	316	335	372	392	411	432	459
140	200	320	347	352	364	383	424	449	472	491	521
150	214	366	382	403	415	437	479	510	529	553	586
160	228	414	431	457	469	494	536	572	595	621	659
170	243	467	485	513	522	553	601	639	665	694	729
180	257	524	543	572	583	619	665	714	743	767	804
190	271	584	602	634	649	688	733	792	825	846	884
200	286	643	666	699	716	756	808	851	901	927	977
210	300	709	731	768	786	826	880	935	975		
220	314	778	798	838	858	902	958				
230	328	851	873	912	934	982					
240	343	922	945	988							

For this pipe size: V = 0.0956 × gpm; h_v = 0.000142 gpm^2.
Figures in shaded area are laminar (viscous) flow.
For velocity data see page 3-16.

Note: No allowance has been made for age, difference in diameter, or any abnormal condition of interior surface. Any factor of safety must be estimated from the local conditions and the requirements of each particular installation. It is recommended that for most commercial design purposes a safety factor of 15 to 20% be added to the values in the tables—see page 3-5.

Friction Loss for Viscous Liquids (Continued)
(Based on Darcy's Formula)

Loss in Feet of Liquid per 1000 Feet of Pipe
2 Inch (2.067″ inside dia) Sch 40 New Steel Pipe

Flow		Kinematic viscosity—centistokes									
		26.4	32.0	43.2	65.0	108.4	162.3	216.5	325	435	650
U S gal per min	Bbl per hr (42 gal)	Approx SSU viscosity									
		125	150	200	300	500	750	1000	1500	2000	3000
1	1.4	.91	1.10	1.49	2.24	3.74	5.60	7.48	11.2	15.0	22.4
2	2.9	1.82	2.21	2.98	4.48	7.49	11.2	15.0	22.4	30.0	44.9
3	4.3	2.73	3.31	4.47	6.73	11.2	16.8	22.4	33.6	45.0	67.4
4	5.7	3.64	4.42	5.96	8.98	15.4	22.4	29.9	44.8	60.0	89.9
5	7.1	4.56	5.52	7.45	11.2	18.7	28.0	37.4	56.0	75.0	112
6	8.6	5.47	6.63	8.95	13.5	22.5	33.6	44.8	67.2	90.0	135
7	10.0	6.38	7.73	10.4	15.7	26.2	39.2	52.3	78.4	105	157
8	11.4	7.29	8.84	11.9	18.0	30.0	44.8	59.8	89.6	120	180
9	12.9	8.20	9.94	13.4	20.2	33.7	50.4	67.3	101	135	202
10	14.3	9.11	11.0	14.9	22.4	37.4	56.0	74.8	112	150	224
12	17.1	10.9	13.3	18.9	26.9	44.9	67.3	89.7	135	180	269
14	20.0	12.7	15.5	20.9	31.4	52.4	78.4	105	157	210	314
16	22.8	14.6	17.7	23.9	35.9	59.9	89.6	120	179	240	359
18	25.7	16.4	19.9	26.8	40.3	67.4	101	135	202	270	404
20	28.6	18.2	22.1	29.8	44.9	74.9	112	150	224	300	449
25	35.7	22.8	27.6	37.3	56.1	93.6	140	187	280	375	562
30	42.9	27.3	33.1	44.7	67.3	112	168	224	336	450	674
35	50.0	31.9	38.7	52.2	78.5	131	196	262	392	525	786
40	57.1	63.0	44.2	59.6	89.8	150	224	299	448	600	899
45	64.3	70.8	80.2	67.1	101	168	252	336	503	675	
50	71.4	92.8	97.1	74.5	112	187	280	374	560	750	
60	85.7	127	134	146	135	225	336	448	672	900	
70	100	162	176	189	157	262	392	523	784		
80	114	208	219	238	180	300	448	598	896		
90	129	257	270	293	327	337	504	673			
100	143	309	322	352	388	374	560	748			
110	157	364	379	412	465	412	617	823			
120	171	423	445	463	537	449	673	898			
130	186	487	510	549	618	487	728				
140	200	548	580	627	703	524	784				
150	214	622	655	705	792	909	840				
160	228	697	737	792	887	896					
170	243	775	808	882	952						
180	257	858	871	962							
190	271	947	986								

Loss in lb per sq in = .433 (sp gr) (figures from table).
Figures in shaded area are laminar (viscous) flow.
For velocity data see page 3-16.

Note: No allowance has been made for age, difference in diameter, or any abnormal condition of interior surface. Any factor of safety must be estimated from the local conditions and the requirements of each particular installation. It is recommended that for most commercial design purposes a safety factor of 15 to 20% be added to the values in the tables—see page 3-5.

Friction Loss for Viscous Liquids (Continued)
(Based on Darcy's Formula)

Loss in Feet of Liquid per 1000 Feet of Pipe
2½ Inch (2.469″ inside dia) Sch 40 New Steel Pipe

Flow		Kinematic viscosity—centistokes									
		.6	1.1	2.1	2.7	4.3	7.4	10.3	13.1	15.7	20.6
U S gal per min	Bbl per hr (42 gal)	Approx SSU viscosity									
		31.5	33	35	40	50	60	70	80	100
10	14.3	.92	1.05	1.23	1.31	1.48	1.26	1.75	2.22	2.66	3.50
12	17.1	1.28	1.47	1.70	1.80	2.04	1.51	2.10	2.67	3.19	4.19
14	20.0	1.68	1.92	2.23	2.37	2.65	3.09	2.45	3.11	3.73	4.89
16	22.8	2.15	2.43	2.81	2.99	3.34	3.86	2.80	3.56	4.26	5.59
18	25.7	2.68	2.99	3.46	3.68	4.21	4.77	5.26	4.00	4.80	6.28
20	28.6	3.23	3.61	4.27	4.42	4.94	5.73	6.26	4.44	5.33	6.98
25	35.7	4.88	5.39	6.17	6.55	7.31	8.42	9.20	9.79	6.66	8.73
30	42.9	6.87	7.57	8.55	9.07	10.1	11.5	12.6	13.5	14.1	10.5
35	50.0	9.18	9.97	11.3	11.8	13.3	15.1	16.4	17.7	18.5	20.0
40	57.1	11.8	12.8	14.3	15.0	16.8	19.0	20.7	22.1	23.2	25.0
45	64.3	14.8	15.9	17.7	18.7	20.8	23.5	25.6	27.1	28.4	30.6
50	71.4	18.1	19.3	21.4	22.4	24.9	28.3	30.6	32.5	34.1	36.8
60	85.7	25.6	27.2	29.9	31.1	34.2	39.1	42.1	44.7	46.7	50.4
70	100	34.2	36.2	39.6	41.4	45.2	51.4	55.4	58.5	61.5	66.0
80	114	44.1	46.7	50.6	53.0	57.3	64.5	69.7	74.2	77.5	82.7
90	129	55.2	58.8	63.2	65.4	70.9	80.0	86.6	91.2	95.3	103
100	143	67.2	72.3	76.7	79.4	85.8	96.3	104	109	115	123
110	157	80.9	86.2	92.4	94.8	103	113	121	130	135	146
120	171	95.7	102	108	112	121	133	143	151	158	169
130	186	112	118	125	130	139	155	166	176	181	194
140	200	129	136	144	150	160	176	188	198	209	221
150	214	147	155	165	170	181	198	212	223	234	250
160	228	167	175	187	191	203	224	238	253	262	281
170	243	188	196	210	214	226	248	267	283	290	312
180	257	210	219	234	239	253	277	297	311	322	345
190	271	233	243	260	265	280	306	328	339	356	378
200	286	258	269	286	292	308	334	357	373	391	417
220	314	310	322	343	351	369	400	427	448	461	486
240	343	367	381	404	416	436	469	494	522	539	573
260	371	429	445	470	482	505	543	575	599	621	660
280	400	497	513	540	556	580	630	657	686	710	758
300	429	568	586	617	632	659	705	748	775	803	849
320	457	643	663	695	716	747	799	837	875	903	952
340	486	725	745	776	800	839	894	933	980		
360	514	809	835	866	892	936	994				

For this pipe size: V = 0.0670 × gpm; $h_v = 6.97 \times 10^{-5} \times gpm^2$.
Figures in shaded area are laminar (viscous) flow.
For velocity data see page 3-17.

Note: No allowance has been made for age, difference in diameter, or any abnormal condition of interior surface. Any factor of safety must be estimated from the local conditions and the requirements of each particular installation. It is recommended that for most commercial design purposes a safety factor of 15 to 20% be added to the values in the tables—see page 3-5.

Friction Loss for Viscous Liquids (Continued)
(Based on Darcy's Formula)

Loss in Feet of Liquid per 1000 Feet of Pipe
2½ Inch (2.469″ inside dia) Sch 40 New Steel Pipe

Flow		Kinematic viscosity—centistokes									
		26.4	32.0	43.2	65.0	108.4	162.3	216.5	325	435	650
U S gal per min	Bbl per hr (42 gal)	Approx SSU viscosity									
		125	150	200	300	500	750	1000	1500	2000	3000
1	1.4	.45	.54	.73	1.10	1.84	2.75	3.67	5.52	7.38	11.0
2	2.9	.90	1.09	1.47	2.20	3.68	5.50	7.35	11.0	14.8	22.0
4	5.7	1.79	2.17	2.93	4.41	7.36	11.0	14.7	22.1	29.5	44.1
6	8.6	2.69	3.26	4.40	6.62	11.0	16.5	22.0	33.1	44.3	66.2
8	11.4	3.58	4.34	5.87	8.82	14.7	22.0	29.4	44.1	59.1	88.2
10	14.3	4.48	5.43	7.33	11.0	18.4	27.5	36.7	55.2	73.8	110
12	17.1	5.38	6.51	8.80	13.2	22.1	33.0	44.1	66.2	88.6	132
14	20.0	6.27	7.60	10.3	15.4	25.7	38.5	51.4	77.2	103	154
16	22.8	7.16	8.68	11.7	17.6	29.4	44.0	58.8	88.2	118	176
18	25.7	8.06	9.77	13.2	19.8	33.1	49.5	66.1	99.3	133	198
20	28.6	8.96	10.9	14.7	22.0	36.8	55.0	73.4	110	148	220
25	35.7	11.2	13.6	18.3	27.6	46.0	68.8	91.8	138	185	276
30	42.9	13.4	16.3	22.0	33.1	55.2	82.5	110	165	222	331
35	50.0	15.7	19.0	25.6	38.6	64.4	96.3	129	193	258	386
40	57.1	17.9	21.7	29.3	44.2	73.6	110	147	221	295	441
45	64.3	33.0	24.4	33.0	49.6	82.8	124	165	248	332	496
50	71.4	39.2	27.2	36.6	55.2	92.0	138	184	276	369	551
60	85.7	54.0	56.5	44.0	66.2	110	165	220	331	443	662
70	100	70.0	73.5	51.3	77.2	129	193	257	386	517	772
80	114	87.7	93.4	101	88.3	147	220	294	441	591	882
90	129	110	115	125	99.3	166	248	330	497	665	993
100	143	130	137	148	110	184	275	367	552	738	
110	157	154	164	176	197	202	303	403	607	812	
120	171	180	188	205	226	221	330	441	662	886	
130	186	206	216	232	263	239	358	477	717	960	
140	200	234	247	267	299	257	385	514	772		
150	214	265	279	305	333	276	413	551	827		
160	228	296	312	338	374	294	440	588	882		
170	243	328	345	373	415	312	468	624	937		
180	257	364	384	412	461	530	495	661	993		
190	271	403	420	454	514	587	523	698			
200	286	438	457	493	550	628	550	734			
220	314	522	540	586	658	752	605	808			
240	343	612	633	682	760	866	660	881			
260	371	711	732	782	867		715	955			

Loss in lb per sq in = .433 (sp gr) (figures in table).
Figures in shaded area are laminar (viscous) flow.
For velocity data see page 3-17.

Note: No allowance has been made for age, difference in diameter, or any abnormal condition of interior surface. Any factor of safety must be estimated from the local conditions and the requirements of each particular installation. It is recommended that for most commercial design purposes a safety factor of 15 to 20% be added to the values in the tables—see page 3-5.

Friction Loss for Viscous Liquids (Continued)
(Based on Darcy's Formula)

Loss in Feet of Liquid per 1000 Feet of Pipe
3 Inch (3.068" inside dia) Sch 40 New Steel Pipe

Flow		Kinematic viscosity—centistokes									
		.6	1.1	2.1	2.7	4.3	7.4	10.3	13.1	15.7	20.6
US gal per min	Bbl per hr (42 gal)	Approx SSU viscosity									
			31.5	33	35	40	50	60	70	80	100
8	11.4	.22	.25	.29	.32	.24	.42	.59	.74	.89	1.18
10	14.3	.32	.37	.43	.47	.54	.53	.73	.93	1.11	1.47
15	21.4	.70	.76	.89	.94	1.07	.79	1.10	1.40	1.67	2.20
20	28.6	1.12	1.27	1.47	1.57	1.78	2.07	1.46	1.86	2.23	2.93
25	35.7	1.69	1.93	2.23	2.31	2.61	3.01	3.29	2.33	2.79	3.66
30	42.9	2.36	2.64	2.99	3.22	3.60	4.12	4.50	4.83	3.35	4.40
35	50.0	3.13	3.48	3.97	4.21	4.66	5.41	5.89	6.35	6.61	5.13
40	57.1	4.03	4.42	5.02	5.29	5.90	6.80	7.46	7.93	8.37	5.87
50	71.4	6.10	6.70	7.50	7.93	8.76	10.1	10.9	11.7	12.3	13.2
60	85.7	8.57	9.32	10.4	11.0	12.0	13.7	15.0	16.0	16.8	18.0
70	100	11.5	12.4	13.8	14.5	15.9	18.0	19.6	20.9	21.9	23.6
80	114	14.7	15.9	17.5	18.4	20.3	22.9	24.6	26.4	27.7	29.8
90	129	18.4	19.9	21.8	22.8	25.0	28.0	30.4	32.4	33.8	36.3
100	143	22.4	24.2	26.3	27.5	30.2	33.7	36.4	39.0	40.8	43.6
120	171	31.8	34.1	36.9	38.6	41.9	46.8	50.5	53.4	56.4	60.0
140	200	42.4	45.6	49.4	50.9	55.4	65.5	66.0	70.0	73.2	78.6
160	228	54.8	58.0	63.3	65.4	70.4	79.1	83.8	87.9	92.3	98.2
180	257	69.0	72.7	78.7	81.6	87.2	97.2	104	109	114	122
200	286	84.7	88.9	95.7	99.4	106	117	125	131	137	146
225	322	107	112	120	124	132	145	155	164	169	180
250	357	131	137	147	151	160	175	188	195	204	218
275	393	158	164	175	180	191	208	226	233	243	258
300	429	187	193	204	212	225	244	260	273	281	298
325	464	218	225	238	247	261	283	300	316	325	345
350	500	253	260	275	283	300	324	344	361	373	396
375	536	288	298	314	322	341	367	388	407	424	448
400	571	328	339	354	363	385	414	436	458	476	498
425	607	368	381	397	407	432	463	488	511	529	550
450	643	410	427	443	455	480	515	543	568	587	619
475	679	457	473	493	504	532	571	599	625	646	681
500	714	504	524	544	555	587	627	658	684	707	750
525	750	555	574	597	609	644	688	720	748	770	821
550	786	606	627	651	665	703	748	783	814	838	890
575	822	663	685	708	723	761	814	852	886	912	962
600	857	721	742	767	783	820	882	919	960	989	

For this pipe size: V = 0.0434 × gpm; $h_v = 2.923^{-5} \times gpm^2$.
Figures in shaded area are laminar (viscous) flow.
For velocity data see page 3-18.

Note: No allowance has been made for age, difference in diameter, or any abnormal condition of interior surface. Any factor of safety must be estimated from the local conditions and the requirements of each particular installation. It is recommended that for most commercial design purposes a safety factor of 15 to 20% be added to the values in the tables—see page 3-5.

Friction Loss for Viscous Liquids (Continued)
(Based on Darcy's Formula)

Loss in Feet of Liquid per 1000 Feet of Pipe
3 Inch (3.068″ inside dia) Sch 40 New Steel Pipe

Flow		Kinematic viscosity—centistokes									
U S gal per min	Bbl per hr (42 gal)	26.4	32.0	43.2	65.0	108.4	162.3	216.5	325	435	650
		Approx SSU viscosity									
		125	150	200	300	500	750	1000	1500	2000	3000
4	5.7	.75	.91	1.23	1.85	3.08	4.62	6.16	9.25	12.4	18.5
6	8.6	1.13	1.37	1.84	2.77	4.62	6.92	9.24	13.9	18.5	27.7
8	11.4	1.50	1.82	2.45	3.70	6.16	9.23	12.3	18.5	24.7	36.9
10	14.3	1.88	2.28	3.06	4.62	7.70	11.5	15.4	23.1	30.9	46.2
12	17.1	2.25	2.73	3.68	5.55	9.24	13.8	18.5	27.7	37.1	55.5
14	20.0	2.63	3.18	4.29	6.47	10.8	16.2	21.5	32.3	43.3	64.7
16	22.8	3.00	3.64	4.90	7.39	12.3	18.5	24.6	37.0	49.5	73.9
18	25.7	3.38	4.09	5.52	8.31	13.9	20.8	27.7	41.6	55.6	83.2
20	28.6	3.76	4.55	6.13	9.24	15.4	23.1	30.8	46.2	61.8	92.4
25	35.7	4.69	5.69	7.67	11.5	19.3	28.8	38.5	57.7	77.3	115
30	42.9	5.63	6.83	9.20	13.9	23.1	34.6	46.2	69.3	92.7	139
35	50.0	6.57	7.97	10.7	16.2	27.0	40.3	53.8	80.9	108	162
40	51.1	7.51	9.10	12.3	18.5	30.8	46.2	61.6	92.5	124	185
50	71.4	9.39	11.4	15.3	23.1	38.5	57.7	77.0	115	154	231
60	85.7	19.2	13.7	18.4	27.7	46.2	69.2	92.4	139	185	277
70	100	25.3	26.8	21.5	32.3	53.9	80.8	108	162	216	323
80	114	31.6	33.6	24.7	37.0	61.6	92.3	123	185	247	369
90	129	38.9	40.9	44.6	41.6	69.3	104	139	208	278	416
100	143	46.1	49.5	53.0	46.2	77.0	115	154	231	309	462
120	171	64.0	67.6	72.9	55.5	92.4	138	185	277	371	555
140	200	83.9	89.1	94.9	108	108	162	215	323	433	647
160	228	106	111	120	135	123	185	246	370	495	739
180	257	131	137	148	164	139	208	277	416	556	832
200	286	157	163	179	198	154	231	308	462	618	924
225	322	191	204	223	242	279	260	346	520	696	
250	357	229	242	261	291	332	288	385	577	773	
275	393	271	285	311	343	396	317	423	635	850	
300	429	316	331	361	398	456	346	462	693	927	
325	464	364	381	416	458	527	375	500	751		
350	500	415	436	467	523	593	672	538	809		
375	536	469	493	528	586	672	746	577	867		
400	571	526	550	592	656	751	843	616	925		
425	607	587	612	656	728	834	937	654	982		
450	643	652	675	728	802	928					
475	679	718	744	801	889						

Loss in lb per sq in = .433 (sp gr) (figures in table).
Figures in shaded area are laminar (viscous) flow.
For velocity data see page 3-18.

Note: No allowance has been made for age, difference in diameter, or any abnormal condition of interior surface. Any factor of safety must be estimated from the local conditions and the requirements of each particular installation. It is recommended that for most commercial design purposes a safety factor of 15 to 20% be added to the values in the tables—see page 3-5.

Friction Loss for Viscous Liquids (Continued)
(Based on Darcy's Formula)
Loss in Feet of Liquid per 1000 Feet of Pipe
3½ Inch (3.548″ inside dia) Sch 40 New Steel Pipe

Flow		Kinematic viscosity—centistokes									
		.6	1.1	2.1	2.7	4.3	7.4	10.3	13.1	15.7	20.6
U S gal per min	Bbl per hr (42 gal)				Approx SSU viscosity						
			31.5	33	35	40	50	60	70	80	100
20	28.6	.56	.63	.72	.78	.88	1.03	.82	1.04	1.25	1.64
25	35.7	.82	.93	1.08	1.14	1.29	1.52	1.67	1.30	1.56	2.05
30	42.9	1.15	1.29	1.50	1.57	1.78	2.09	2.30	1.56	1.87	2.46
35	50.0	1.53	1.70	1.94	2.08	2.31	2.68	2.97	3.18	2.18	2.87
40	57.1	1.95	2.17	2.49	2.68	2.91	3.35	3.70	4.00	4.21	3.28
45	64.3	2.46	2.68	3.03	3.22	3.59	4.11	4.57	4.91	5.19	3.69
50	71.4	2.95	3.25	3.68	3.90	4.32	4.98	5.42	5.87	6.20	6.64
60	85.7	4.17	4.54	5.12	5.38	6.00	6.82	7.41	7.97	8.41	9.21
70	100	6.78	6.02	6.78	7.11	7.84	8.87	9.76	10.4	10.9	11.9
80	114	7.19	7.72	8.57	8.79	9.81	11.2	12.3	13.0	13.7	14.9
90	129	8.92	9.59	10.6	11.2	12.5	13.9	15.0	16.1	16.8	18.3
100	143	10.8	11.7	12.9	13.6	14.8	16.8	18.0	19.3	20.2	21.7
120	171	15.4	16.4	18.1	18.7	20.5	22.9	25.0	26.3	27.7	29.7
140	200	20.5	22.0	23.9	24.9	27.3	30.5	33.1	34.6	36.0	39.1
160	228	26.4	28.3	30.9	31.9	35.0	38.4	41.8	43.9	45.6	49.0
180	257	33.0	35.0	38.0	39.6	42.5	47.7	50.8	54.0	56.3	60.1
200	286	40.3	43.0	46.3	48.0	51.4	57.1	61.8	65.5	68.0	72.2
225	322	50.7	53.2	57.7	59.7	64.7	71.2	75.9	80.1	84.3	88.8
250	357	62.6	65.0	70.9	72.7	78.9	86.5	92.7	96.9	101	107
275	393	75.4	77.9	84.6	87.1	93.3	102	110	115	120	127
300	429	89.2	92.2	99.6	103	109	119	128	135	140	148
325	464	104	108	116	120	127	138	147	154	161	171
350	500	121	124	133	138	146	159	169	178	183	194
375	536	138	142	152	157	167	181	191	200	207	220
400	571	156	161	171	178	188	203	213	225	233	248
425	607	176	181	192	200	211	225	238	252	259	279
450	643	196	203	213	221	234	250	265	280	287	309
475	679	219	225	235	244	257	276	292	310	319	336
500	714	241	249	259	268	282	304	321	340	350	368
550	786	290	300	311	323	340	365	385	407	415	440
600	857	343	355	367	377	399	426	452	466	480	510
650	929	400	414	428	440	461	498	522	540	557	587
700	1000	464	480	494	505	532	572	597	621	637	675
750	1070	532	548	567	576	604	651	682	704	725	769
800	1140	606	624	641	652	684	730	765	794	815	861

For this pipe size: $V = 0.03245 \times$ gpm; $h_v = 1.634 \times 10^{-5}$ gpm^2.
Figures in shaded area are laminar (viscous) flow.
For velocity data see page 3-19.

Note: No allowance has been made for age, difference in diameter, or any abnormal condition of interior surface. Any factor of safety must be estimated from the local conditions and the requirements of each particular installation. It is recommended that for most commercial design purposes a safety factor of 15 to 20% be added to the values in the tables—see page 3-5.

Friction Loss for Viscous Liquids *(Continued)*
(Based on Darcy's Formula)
Loss in Feet of Liquid per 1000 Feet of Pipe
3½ Inch (3.548″ inside dia) Sch 40 New Steel Pipe

Flow		Kinematic viscosity—centistokes									
US gal per min	Bbl per hr (42 gal)	26.4	32.0	43.2	65.0	108.4	162.3	216.5	325	435	650
		Approx SSU viscosity									
		125	150	200	300	500	750	1000	1500	2000	3000
10	14.3	1.05	1.27	1.72	2.58	4.32	6.46	8.62	12.9	16.9	25.8
15	21.4	1.57	1.91	2.58	3.88	6.47	9.68	12.9	19.4	25.4	38.8
20	28.6	2.10	2.54	3.44	5.17	8.63	12.9	17.3	25.8	33.8	51.7
25	35.7	2.62	3.18	4.29	6.47	10.8	16.1	21.6	32.3	42.3	64.7
30	42.9	3.15	3.82	5.15	7.76	13.0	19.4	25.9	38.8	50.7	77.6
35	50.0	3.67	4.45	6.01	9.05	15.1	22.6	30.2	45.3	59.2	90.6
40	57.1	4.20	5.09	6.87	10.3	17.3	25.8	34.5	51.7	67.6	103
45	64.3	4.72	5.73	7.73	11.6	19.4	29.0	38.8	58.2	76.1	116
50	71.4	5.25	6.36	8.59	12.9	21.6	32.3	43.1	64.7	84.5	129
60	85.7	6.30	7.64	10.3	15.5	25.9	38.8	51.8	77.6	101	155
70	100	12.8	8.91	12.0	18.1	30.2	45.2	60.4	90.6	118	181
80	114	16.1	16.9	13.7	20.7	34.5	51.6	69.0	103	135	207
90	129	19.6	20.8	15.5	23.3	38.8	58.1	77.6	116	152	233
100	143	23.6	24.8	17.2	25.9	43.2	64.6	86.2	129	169	258
120	171	31.9	34.0	37.1	31.0	51.8	77.5	104	155	203	310
140	200	41.5	43.8	48.2	36.2	60.4	90.4	121	181	236	362
160	228	52.3	55.3	60.5	67.7	69.1	103	138	207	270	413
180	257	64.6	67.3	73.9	83.4	77.7	116	155	233	304	466
200	286	77.3	81.5	87.9	99.9	86.3	129	173	258	338	517
225	322	94.4	99.8	108	122	97.1	145	194	291	380	528
250	357	114	120	129	146	108	161	216	323	422	647
275	393	134	141	153	172	199	177	237	356	465	711
300	429	157	164	178	198	233	194	259	388	507	776
325	464	181	188	205	227	266	210	280	420	549	840
350	500	206	215	233	258	301	226	302	452	592	906
375	536	234	245	262	291	339	242	323	485	634	970
400	571	261	274	291	326	379	423	345	517	676	
425	607	291	303	325	363	419	473	367	550	718	
450	643	322	337	359	402	462	525	388	582	761	
475	679	353	368	395	440	505	572	410	614	803	
500	714	389	403	433	482	551	626	431	647	845	
550	786	459	481	514	566	648	733	795	712	930	
600	857	538	566	600	658	749	851	923	776		
650	929	620	648	690	755	865	978		841		
700	1000	708	735	789	863	987			906		

Loss in lb per sq in = .433 (sp gr) (figures in table).
Figures in shaded area are laminar (viscous) flow.
For velocity data see page 3-19.

Note: No allowance has been made for age, difference in diameter, or any abnormal condition of interior surface. Any factor of safety must be estimated from the local conditions and the requirements of each particular installation. It is recommended that for most commercial design purposes a safety factor of 15 to 20% be added to the values in the tables—see page 3-5.

Friction Loss for Viscous Liquids (Continued)
(Based on Darcy's Formula)
Loss in Feet of Liquid per 1000 Feet of Pipe
4 Inch (4.026″ inside dia) Sch 40 New Steel Pipe

Flow US gal per min	Bbl per hr (42 gal)	Kinematic viscosity—centistokes .6	1.1	2.1	2.7	4.3	7.4	10.3	13.1	15.7	20.6
		Approx SSU viscosity	31.5	33	35	40	50	60	70	80	100
20	28.6	.30	.34	.40	.43	.49	.57	.50	.63	.75	.99
30	42.9	.62	.70	.82	.87	.98	1.14	1.25	.95	1.13	1.48
40	57.1	1.05	1.18	1.35	1.44	1.62	1.86	2.04	2.20	1.51	1.96
50	71.4	1.58	1.76	2.02	2.13	2.37	2.75	3.00	3.21	3.40	2.47
60	85.7	2.22	2.44	2.80	2.93	3.27	3.77	4.12	4.29	4.62	5.01
70	100	2.96	3.24	3.69	3.88	4.31	4.93	5.39	5.72	6.03	6.53
80	114	3.79	4.16	4.67	4.93	5.44	6.20	6.78	7.23	7.55	8.17
90	129	4.72	5.15	5.77	6.08	6.72	7.63	8.32	8.87	9.29	10.0
100	143	5.77	6.27	6.91	7.33	8.12	9.15	9.97	10.6	11.2	12.0
120	171	8.09	8.81	9.66	10.2	11.2	12.7	13.6	14.6	15.3	16.5
140	200	10.8	11.7	12.9	13.4	14.8	16.6	17.9	19.0	20.0	21.6
160	228	13.9	15.0	16.4	17.1	18.8	21.1	22.7	24.0	25.2	27.2
180	257	17.4	18.7	20.4	21.5	23.2	26.0	28.1	29.6	30.8	33.3
200	286	21.4	22.7	24.9	25.9	28.0	31.4	33.7	35.7	36.9	40.0
220	314	25.6	27.2	29.8	30.8	33.2	37.3	40.2	42.3	44.0	47.0
240	343	30.3	32.0	34.9	36.1	38.8	43.4	46.8	49.1	51.4	54.6
260	371	35.4	37.2	40.4	42.0	45.0	50.1	53.9	56.7	59.3	62.7
280	400	40.8	42.7	46.4	48.2	51.7	57.4	61.6	65.0	67.4	71.3
300	429	46.6	48.7	53.0	54.8	58.8	64.9	69.6	73.3	76.0	81.0
350	500	62.7	65.6	70.6	72.8	77.9	85.4	91.2	96.2	101	107
400	571	81.4	84.7	90.4	93.7	99.8	109	116	122	127	135
450	643	102	106	113	117	124	135	144	151	157	167
500	714	125	130	137	142	151	164	174	182	189	201
550	786	151	157	165	170	180	195	206	216	224	239
600	857	179	185	195	200	212	229	242	253	263	278
650	929	209	216	228	231	246	266	280	291	303	319
700	1000	242	249	260	267	283	306	322	333	346	365
750	1070	276	285	298	305	321	348	366	377	391	414
800	1140	314	324	337	345	362	392	411	426	439	465
850	1215	355	364	378	387	406	438	459	476	489	519
900	1285	396	408	424	434	453	486	510	531	543	574
950	1360	441	451	470	481	502	536	563	584	600	632
1000	1430	488	500	521	527	550	591	621	641	662	694
1100	1570	587	602	627	634	659	708	740	765	790	822
1200	1715	699	712	741	754	780	835	869	898	924	966

For this pipe size: $V = 0.0252 \times gpm$; $h_v = 9.858 \times 10^{-6} \, gpm^2$.
Figures in shaded area are laminar (viscous) flow.
For velocity data see page 3-20.

Note: No allowance has been made for age, difference in diameter, or any abnormal condition of interior surface. Any factor of safety must be estimated from the local conditions and the requirements of each particular installation. It is recommended that for most commercial design purposes a safety factor of 15 to 20% be added to the values in the tables—see page 3-5.

Friction Loss for Viscous Liquids *(Continued)*
(Based on Darcy's Formula)
Loss in Feet of Liquid per 1000 Feet of Pipe
4 Inch (4.026″ inside dia) Sch 40 New Steel Pipe

Flow		Kinematic viscosity—centistokes									
		26.4	32.0	43.2	65.0	108.4	162.3	216.5	325	435	650
U S gal per min	Bbl per hr (42 gal)	Approx SSU viscosity									
		125	150	200	300	500	750	1000	1500	2000	3000
15	21.4	.95	1.15	1.55	2.34	3.91	5.85	7.80	11.7	15.7	23.4
20	28.6	1.27	1.54	2.07	3.12	5.21	7.80	10.4	15.6	20.9	31.2
30	42.9	1.90	2.30	3.11	4.68	7.82	11.7	15.6	23.4	31.3	46.8
40	57.1	2.54	3.08	4.15	6.25	10.4	15.6	20.8	31.2	41.8	62.5
50	71.4	3.17	3.84	5.18	7.81	13.0	19.5	26.0	39.0	52.2	78.1
60	85.7	3.80	4.61	6.22	9.37	15.6	23.4	31.2	46.8	62.7	93.7
70	100	4.44	5.38	7.25	10.9	18.2	27.3	36.4	54.6	73.2	109
80	114	8.81	6.15	8.29	12.5	20.8	31.2	41.6	62.4	83.6	125
90	129	10.8	11.3	9.33	14.1	23.4	35.1	46.8	70.2	94.1	141
100	143	12.9	13.7	10.4	15.6	26.0	39.0	52.0	78.0	105	156
120	171	17.6	18.6	20.3	18.8	31.2	46.8	62.4	93.7	125	187
140	200	22.9	24.3	26.5	21.9	36.4	54.6	72.8	109	146	218
160	228	29.0	30.3	33.2	25.0	41.7	62.4	83.2	125	167	250
180	257	35.5	37.4	40.7	45.7	46.9	70.2	93.6	140	188	281
200	286	42.6	45.0	48.7	54.8	52.1	78.0	104	156	209	312
220	314	50.3	53.0	57.1	64.7	57.3	85.8	114	172	230	343
240	343	58.5	61.5	65.1	74.7	62.5	93.6	125	187	251	375
260	371	67.2	70.8	76.8	85.7	67.7	101	135	203	272	406
280	400	76.4	80.5	87.2	97.3	73.0	109	146	218	292	437
300	429	85.8	90.8	98.5	110	127	117	156	234	313	468
325	464	98.5	104	113	125	146	127	169	254	340	508
350	500	112	118	128	143	166	136	182	273	366	547
375	536	127	133	145	161	187	146	195	293	932	585
400	571	143	149	162	180	208	156	208	312	418	625
450	643	178	184	198	222	254	285	234	351	470	703
500	714	213	221	237	265	305	343	260	390	523	781
550	786	252	263	280	313	360	404	286	429	575	860
600	857	296	305	328	364	417	467	507	468	627	937
650	929	338	353	378	419	480	528	583	507	680	
700	1000	386	402	433	474	546	608	663	546	732	
750	1070	437	455	488	533	616	685	745	585	784	
800	1140	490	510	546	570	687	764	830	624	836	
850	1215	544	570	608	663	763	848	920	663	889	
900	1285	603	629	674	739	844	939			941	
950	1360	666	696	743	813	927				993	

Loss in lb per sq in = .433 (sp gg) (figures from table).
Figures in shaded area are laminar (viscous) flow.
For velocity data see page 3-20.

Note: No allowance has been made for age, difference in diameter, or any abnormal condition of interior surface. Any factor of safety must be estimated from the local conditions and the requirements of each particular installation. It is recommended that for most commercial design purposes a safety factor of 15 to 20% be added to the values in the tables—see page 3-5.

Friction Loss for Viscous Liquids (Continued)
(Based on Darcy's Formula)
Loss in Feet of Liquid per 1000 Feet of Pipe
6 Inch (6.065″ inside dia) Sch 40 New Steel Pipe

Flow		Kinematic viscosity—centistokes									
		.6	1.1	2.1	2.7	4.3	7.4	10.3	13.1	15.7	20.6
US gal per min	Bbl per hr (42 gal)	Approx SSU viscosity									
		31.5	33	35	40	50	60	70	80	100
75	107	.45	.49	.58	.61	.68	.80	.86	.93	.98	.72
100	143	.77	.85	.96	1.01	1.14	1.30	1.42	1.52	1.62	1.74
125	178	1.14	1.27	1.43	1.51	1.68	1.95	2.10	2.23	2.35	2.57
150	214	1.61	1.78	2.01	2.09	2.32	2.66	2.86	3.08	3.20	3.46
175	250	2.13	2.37	2.63	2.79	3.04	3.52	3.74	3.97	4.24	4.51
200	286	2.75	3.00	3.34	3.55	3.85	4.41	4.76	5.02	5.31	5.69
225	322	3.42	3.74	4.17	4.38	4.78	5.39	5.89	6.16	6.45	7.05
250	357	4.15	4.55	5.07	5.21	5.76	6.94	7.11	7.47	7.77	8.41
275	393	4.99	5.42	6.02	6.28	6.88	7.60	8.35	8.86	9.18	9.81
300	429	5.87	6.38	7.06	7.37	8.09	8.94	9.69	10.3	10.8	11.4
350	500	7.90	8.45	9.38	9.80	10.5	11.8	12.6	13.5	14.2	15.0
400	571	10.2	10.9	11.8	12.5	13.4	15.0	16.0	17.0	18.0	19.1
450	643	12.8	13.6	14.8	15.5	16.7	18.5	19.7	20.1	21.8	23.7
500	714	15.6	16.6	18.0	18.7	20.4	22.6	24.0	25.1	26.4	28.5
550	786	18.8	19.8	21.5	22.3	24.3	26.8	28.5	29.6	29.9	33.4
600	857	22.1	23.3	25.1	26.2	28.4	31.1	33.2	35.0	36.2	38.8
650	929	25.8	27.2	29.2	30.4	32.8	36.1	38.5	40.4	41.8	44.7
700	1000	29.7	31.2	33.5	34.9	37.5	41.1	44.2	46.3	47.9	51.3
750	1070	33.9	35.6	38.2	39.7	42.5	46.7	49.9	51.8	54.0	57.2
800	1140	38.3	40.5	43.2	44.4	47.8	52.7	56.1	58.5	60.9	64.3
900	1285	48.5	50.7	54.4	55.6	59.3	65.4	69.1	72.8	74.6	79.9
1000	1430	59.5	62.2	66.4	67.5	72.4	79.3	83.4	87.6	91.0	95.9
1100	1570	71.6	74.8	79.4	80.8	86.7	94.5	99.6	104	109	114
1200	1715	84.6	87.9	93.4	95.6	102	111	117	121	126	133
1400	2000	115	118	126	128	135	146	155	161	167	177
1600	2285	150	153	162	164	173	187	199	207	213	224
1800	2570	188	193	203	206	216	232	246	256	264	278
2000	2860	231	237	247	253	264	284	296	311	320	334
2200	3140	277	286	297	303	316	338	354	371	382	398
2400	3430	330	341	352	356	374	395	417	430	448	470
2600	3710	387	395	408	418	433	461	485	500	520	543
2800	4000	449	458	470	482	497	526	553	574	595	621
3000	4285	515	526	536	550	567	597	628	655	666	706
3250	4640	605	613	629	641	665	701	729	757	777	817
3500	5000	697	711	729	739	771	808	841	869	897	938

For this pipe size: V = 0.0111 × gpm; $h_v = 1.914 \times 10^{-6}$ gpm².
Figures in shaded area are laminar (viscous) flow.
For velocity data see page 3-22.

Note: No allowance has been made for age, difference in diameter, or any abnormal condition of interior surface. Any factor of safety must be estimated from the local conditions and the requirements of each particular installation. It is recommended that for most commercial design purposes a safety factor of 15 to 20% be added to the values in the tables—see page 3-5.

Friction Loss for Viscous Liquids (Continued)
(Based on Darcy's Formula)
Loss in Feet of Liquid per 1000 Feet of Pipe
6 Inch (6.065″ inside dia) Sch 40 New Steel Pipe

Flow		Kinematic viscosity—centistokes									
		26.4	32.0	43.2	65.0	108.4	162.3	216.5	325	435	650
U S gal per min	Bbl per hr (42 gal)	Approx SSU viscosity									
		125	150	200	300	500	750	1000	1500	2000	3000
50	71.4	.62	.74	1.00	1.51	2.52	3.78	5.04	7.57	10.1	15.1
75	107	.92	1.12	1.51	2.27	3.78	5.66	7.56	11.4	15.2	22.7
100	143	1.23	1.49	2.01	3.03	5.05	7.55	10.1	15.1	20.3	30.2
125	178	2.75	1.86	2.51	3.79	6.31	9.45	12.6	18.9	25.3	37.8
150	214	3.75	3.96	3.01	4.54	7.58	11.3	15.1	22.7	30.4	45.4
175	250	4.90	5.17	5.62	5.30	8.84	13.2	17.6	26.5	35.5	53.0
200	286	6.10	6.51	7.07	6.06	10.1	15.1	20.2	30.3	40.5	60.6
225	322	7.43	7.93	8.66	6.82	11.4	17.0	22.7	34.1	45.6	68.1
250	357	8.91	9.43	10.4	7.57	12.6	18.9	25.2	37.8	50.7	75.7
275	393	10.6	11.1	12.2	13.7	13.9	20.8	27.7	41.7	55.8	83.2
300	429	12.3	12.9	14.2	15.9	15.1	22.6	30.2	45.4	60.9	90.8
350	500	15.9	17.1	18.3	20.8	17.7	26.4	35.3	53.0	71.0	106
400	571	20.1	21.3	23.1	26.2	20.2	30.2	40.3	60.6	81.1	121
450	643	24.7	26.0	28.6	31.9	36.9	34.0	45.3	68.2	91.3	136
500	714	30.0	31.3	34.1	28.0	44.2	37.8	50.4	75.7	101	151
550	786	35.6	36.9	40.2	44.6	52.1	41.6	55.4	83.3	112	166
600	857	41.5	43.1	46.4	51.7	59.1	45.3	60.5	90.9	122	182
650	929	47.7	50.0	53.4	59.6	69.4	49.1	65.5	98.5	132	197
700	1000	54.1	57.0	60.8	68.6	78.8	88.3	70.6	106	142	212
750	1070	60.8	64.4	68.5	76.8	88.5	99.4	75.6	114	152	227
800	1140	68.0	72.1	76.9	85.7	97.8	111	80.6	121	162	242
900	1285	83.9	88.5	95.2	105	120	136	148	136	183	272
1000	1430	101	106	115	126	144	163	177	151	203	302
1100	1570	120	125	136	148	171	192	208	167	223	333
1200	1715	140	146	158	173	200	220	242	182	243	363
1400	2000	184	193	206	230	258	287	316	353	284	424
1600	2285	234	244	260	288	323	363	393	445	324	484
1800	2570	292	299	322	350	399	452	480	543	591	545
2000	2860	350	364	387	425	481	535	576	652	707	605
2200	3140	417	435	459	510	573	628	683	771	833	666
2400	3403	487	507	535	585	668	730	799	885	968	726
2600	3710	564	587	620	677	769	841	913			787
2800	4000	645	669	714	773	874	954				
3000	4285	734	751	805	867	993					
3200	4570	827	850	909	982						

Loss in lb per sq in = .433 (sp gg) (figures in table).
Figures in shaded area are laminar (viscous) flow.
For velocity data see page 3-22.

Note: No allowance has been made for age, difference in diameter, or any abnormal condition of interior surface. Any factor of safety must be estimated from the local conditions and the requirements of each particular installation. It is recommended that for most commercial design purposes a safety factor of 15 to 20% be added to the values in the tables—see page 3-5.

Friction Loss for Viscous Liquids (Continued)
(Based on Darcy's Formula)
Loss in Feet of Liquid per 1000 Feet of Pipe
8 Inch (7.981″ inside dia) Sch 40 New Steel Pipe

Flow		Kinematic viscosity—centistokes									
		.6	1.1	2.1	2.7	4.3	7.4	10.3	13.1	15.7	20.6
U S gal per min	Bbl per hr (42 gal)	Approx SSU viscosity									
			31.5	33	35	40	50	60	70	80	100
150	214	.42	.47	.53	.56	.63	.72	.79	.84	.88	.96
200	286	.71	.78	.89	.94	1.05	1.15	1.30	1.38	1.45	1.57
250	357	1.07	1.18	1.33	1.40	1.56	1.77	1.92	2.04	2.14	2.30
300	429	1.50	1.65	1.85	1.94	2.15	2.43	2.65	2.80	2.93	3.15
350	500	2.01	2.19	2.45	2.57	2.81	3.20	3.46	3.69	3.85	4.13
400	571	2.58	2.78	3.12	3.26	3.58	4.04	4.37	4.64	4.83	5.21
450	643	3.21	3.48	3.85	4.05	4.42	5.08	5.39	5.70	5.96	6.38
500	714	3.94	4.23	4.69	4.90	5.33	5.98	6.49	6.82	7.18	7.91
600	857	5.54	5.95	6.61	6.82	7.44	8.27	8.89	9.48	9.83	10.6
700	1000	7.44	7.96	8.71	9.04	9.84	10.9	11.9	12.4	13.0	13.9
800	1140	9.66	10.2	11.1	11.7	12.6	13.9	14.8	15.8	16.4	17.4
900	1285	12.1	12.8	13.8	14.4	15.5	17.1	18.4	19.4	20.2	21.5
1000	1430	14.8	15.6	16.8	17.4	18.7	20.8	22.2	23.3	24.4	26.0
1200	1715	21.0	22.0	23.7	24.5	26.4	28.9	30.7	32.4	33.5	35.9
1400	2000	28.3	29.6	31.8	32.6	35.6	38.2	40.7	42.6	44.3	47.5
1600	2285	36.7	38.4	40.6	42.1	44.5	48.7	51.9	54.1	56.1	59.3
1800	2570	46.1	48.0	50.8	52.3	55.4	60.4	64.5	67.0	69.4	73.5
2000	2860	56.5	58.8	61.9	63.8	67.3	73.4	77.7	81.1	83.8	88.8
2200	3140	67.9	70.2	74.4	76.3	80.5	87.5	92.1	96.8	99.6	105
2400	3430	80.8	83.0	88.0	90.2	94.7	103	108	114	117	123
2600	3710	94.2	97.5	103	105	110	119	125	131	135	142
2800	4000	109	112	118	121	127	136	144	149	155	163
3000	4285	125	129	135	138	145	155	164	170	176	184
3200	4570	142	146	153	156	162	174	184	191	197	208
3400	4860	160	164	172	174	182	196	206	213	220	232
3600	5140	178	183	192	196	204	217	228	237	244	258
3800	5425	199	204	212	217	226	240	251	262	269	285
4000	5715	220	225	234	238	249	265	277	289	295	311
4500	6425	276	284	294	300	311	331	345	358	368	385
5000	7145	341	348	360	365	380	404	418	433	447	466
5500	7855	410	419	433	439	457	480	500	518	532	555
6000	8570	488	498	512	519	540	567	592	609	623	654
6500	9280	573	581	601	609	630	662	686	707	723	755
7000	10000	664	673	692	702	725	763	791	810	829	867
7500	10700	760	773	789	806	827	865	897	925	946	984

For this pipe size: V = 0.00641 × gpm; h, = 6.383 × 10 ^{7} × gpm².
For velocity data see page 3-23.

Note: No allowance has been made for age, difference in diameter, or any abnormal condition of interior surface. Any factor of safety must be estimated from the local conditions and the requirements of each particular installation. It is recommended that for most commercial design purposes a safety factor of 15 to 20% be added to the values in the tables—see page 3-5.

Friction Loss for Viscous Liquids *(Continued)*
(Based on Darcy's Formula)
Loss in Feet of Liquid per 1000 Feet of Pipe
8 Inch (7.981″ inside dia) Sch 40 New Steel Pipe

Flow		Kinematic viscosity — centistokes									
		26.4	32.0	43.2	65.0	108.4	162.3	216.5	325	435	650
U S gal per min	Bbl per hr (42 gal)	Approx SSU viscosity									
		125	150	200	300	500	750	1000	1500	2000	3000
50	71.4	.21	.25	.34	.50	.84	1.26	1.68	2.52	3.38	5.05
100	143	.41	.50	.67	1.01	1.68	2.52	3.36	5.04	6.76	10.1
150	214	1.03	.75	1.01	1.51	2.52	3.78	5.04	7.56	10.1	15.1
200	286	1.67	1.78	1.34	2.02	3.37	5.04	6.72	10.1	13.5	20.2
250	357	2.46	2.60	2.85	2.52	4.21	6.30	8.40	12.6	16.9	25.3
300	429	3.37	3.56	3.89	3.03	5.05	7.56	10.1	15.1	20.3	30.3
350	500	4.39	4.63	5.04	5.69	5.89	8.82	11.8	17.7	23.6	35.3
400	571	5.54	5.83	6.35	7.18	6.73	10.1	13.5	20.2	27.0	40.4
450	643	6.79	7.16	7.75	8.76	7.58	11.3	15.1	22.7	30.4	45.4
500	714	8.17	8.58	9.32	10.4	8.42	12.6	16.8	25.2	33.8	50.5
550	786	9.65	10.1	11.0	12.3	9.26	13.9	18.5	27.8	37.2	55.5
600	857	11.2	11.8	12.8	14.3	16.6	15.1	20.2	30.3	40.5	60.6
700	1000	14.7	15.5	16.7	18.6	21.7	17.6	23.5	35.3	47.3	70.6
800	1140	18.6	19.4	21.0	23.4	27.1	20.1	26.9	40.3	54.0	80.7
900	1285	22.9	24.0	25.9	28.7	33.1	37.4	30.2	45.4	60.8	90.8
1000	1430	27.4	28.8	31.0	34.4	39.7	44.9	33.6	50.4	67.6	101
1200	1715	37.8	39.4	42.8	47.3	54.3	60.9	66.4	60.5	81.0	121
1400	2000	49.7	52.0	56.1	62.0	70.8	79.3	86.7	70.6	94.5	141
1600	2285	63.2	65.7	70.6	78.0	89.3	99.4	108	80.7	108	161
1800	2570	77.9	81.3	86.9	96.2	110	122	132	150	122	182
2000	2860	93.4	98.0	105	116	132	147	159	180	135	202
2200	3140	111	116	124	137	155	173	186	211	149	222
2400	3430	130	135	145	159	181	201	217	244	266	242
2600	3710	149	155	168	183	208	231	250	279	306	262
2800	4000	170	178	191	210	236	262	283	317	347	282
3000	4285	193	201	215	236	267	296	319	357	389	303
3200	4570	217	225	240	265	299	332	357	398	433	323
3400	4860	242	251	268	294	333	369	397	441	480	343
3600	5140	268	284	296	326	369	407	438	488	529	598
3800	5425	296	307	328	359	404	447	482	536	582	656
4000	5715	325	337	358	394	441	488	526	586	635	718
4500	6425	405	417	442	485	543	601	646	718	777	876
5000	7145	488	505	536	582	656	726	776	860	932	
5500	7855	579	605	634	689	773	855	913			
6000	8570	678	706	744	810	910	993				

Loss in lb per sq in = .433 (sp gr) (figures in table).
Figures in shaded area are laminar (viscous) flow.
For velocity data see page 3-23.

Note: No allowance has been made for age, difference in diameter, or any abnormal condition of interior surface. Any factor of safety must be estimated from the local conditions and the requirements of each particular installation. It is recommended that for most commercial design purposes a safety factor of 15 to 20% be added to the values in the tables—see page 3-5.

Friction Loss for Viscous Liquids *(Continued)*
(Based on Darcy's Formula)
Loss in Feet of Liquid per 1000 Feet of Pipe
10 Inch (10.02″ inside dia) Sch 40 New Steel Pipe

Flow		Kinematic viscosity—centistokes									
		.6	1.1	2.1	2.7	4.3	7.4	10.3	13.1	15.7	20.6
U S gal per min	Bbl per hr (42 gal)	Approx SSU viscosity									
			31.5	33	35	40	50	60	70	80	100
400	571	.83	.92	1.03	1.09	1.19	1.35	1.46	1.55	1.63	1.75
500	714	1.27	1.38	1.53	1.60	1.78	2.00	2.16	2.30	2.40	2.59
600	857	1.78	1.91	2.14	2.24	2.47	2.77	2.98	3.15	3.31	3.54
700	1000	2.39	2.55	2.84	2.97	3.26	3.62	3.93	4.14	4.32	4.67
800	1140	3.06	3.29	3.63	3.79	4.12	4.63	4.99	5.25	5.46	5.86
900	1285	3.84	4.12	4.49	4.72	5.09	5.72	6.14	6.46	6.74	7.19
1000	1430	4.68	4.99	5.42	5.70	6.13	6.90	7.36	7.83	8.10	8.63
1100	1570	5.63	5.97	6.49	6.82	7.34	8.20	8.76	9.25	9.62	10.3
1200	1715	6.61	7.05	7.63	7.85	8.65	9.58	10.3	10.8	11.3	11.9
1300	1855	7.71	8.18	8.85	9.16	9.95	11.0	11.8	12.4	13.0	13.7
1400	2000	8.88	9.42	10.2	10.6	11.4	12.6	13.5	14.2	14.7	15.7
1500	2140	10.1	10.8	11.7	12.0	12.9	14.3	15.3	16.1	16.6	17.8
1600	2285	11.5	12.2	13.2	13.6	14.6	16.0	17.2	18.1	18.7	20.0
1800	2570	14.3	15.1	16.2	16.7	17.9	19.7	20.9	22.1	22.9	24.3
2000	2860	17.8	18.6	19.8	20.6	21.8	24.0	25.5	27.0	28.0	29.5
2200	3140	21.3	22.2	23.7	24.6	26.1	28.6	30.3	32.1	31.8	35.0
2400	3430	25.2	26.3	28.0	28.9	30.7	33.4	35.5	37.3	38.9	41.0
2600	3710	29.6	30.6	32.5	33.5	35.6	38.7	41.0	42.9	44.8	47.3
2800	4000	34.1	35.3	37.4	38.4	40.8	44.5	47.1	49.0	51.0	54.1
3000	4285	39.1	40.2	42.7	43.5	46.6	50.7	53.2	55.7	57.7	61.3
3500	5000	52.5	54.4	57.4	58.9	62.3	66.4	70.6	73.6	76.2	80.8
4000	5715	68.0	70.5	73.9	75.9	79.9	85.8	90.2	94.2	97.1	102
4500	6430	86.1	88.6	92.3	94.8	99.2	107	112	117	120	127
5000	7145	106	109	113	116	122	130	136	142	146	153
5500	7855	128	131	136	139	145	156	162	169	173	182
6000	8570	152	154	161	164	172	183	191	197	204	213
6500	9280	177	180	187	191	201	212	221	228	236	246
7000	10000	205	208	217	220	231	243	255	263	369	282
7500	10700	236	239	248	251	262	277	291	298	303	321
8000	11400	266	272	282	286	296	314	329	337	345	360
8500	12100	301	307	318	321	334	352	367	378	387	403
9000	12900	337	341	354	359	372	392	407	422	429	447
10000	14300	416	422	434	441	453	478	492	511	524	542
11000	15700	503	511	522	533	544	574	593	611	626	649
12000	17150	599	603	617	630	643	679	701	719	737	763

For this pipe size: $V = 0.00407 \times gpm$; $h_1 = 2.569 \times 10^{-7} \times gpm^2$.
For velocity data see page 3-24.

Note: No allowance has been made for age, difference in diameter, or any abnormal condition of interior surface. Any factor of safety must be estimated from the local conditions and the requirements of each particular installation. It is recommended that for most commercial design purposes a safety factor of 15 to 20% be added to the values in the tables—see page 3-5.

Friction Loss for Viscous Liquids *(Continued)*
(Based on Darcy's Formula)
Loss in Feet of Liquid per 1000 Feet of Pipe
10 Inch (10.02″ inside dia) Sch 40 New Steel Pipe

Flow US gal per min	Flow Bbl per hr (42 gal)	Kinematic viscosity—centistokes 26.4	32.0	43.2	65.0	108.4	162.3	216.5	325	435	650
		Approx SSU viscosity 125	150	200	300	500	750	1000	1500	2000	3000
150	214	.25	.30	.40	.61	1.02	1.52	2.03	3.04	4.08	6.09
200	286	.58	.40	.54	.81	1.35	2.03	2.71	4.06	5.43	8.12
300	429	1.15	1.22	1.33	1.22	2.03	3.04	4.06	6.09	8.15	12.2
400	571	1.83	1.98	2.17	1.62	2.71	4.06	5.41	8.12	10.9	16.2
500	714	2.75	2.91	3.18	3.60	3.39	5.07	6.77	10.1	13.6	20.3
600	857	3.78	3.97	4.34	4.89	4.06	6.08	8.12	12.2	16.3	24.4
700	1000	4.94	5.19	5.66	6.37	4.74	7.10	9.47	14.2	19.0	28.4
800	1140	6.21	6.55	7.10	7.97	9.31	8.12	10.8	16.2	21.7	32.5
900	1285	7.66	8.04	8.71	9.76	11.4	9.13	12.2	18.3	24.5	36.5
1000	1430	9.21	9.61	10.5	11.7	13.6	10.1	13.5	20.3	27.2	40.6
1100	1570	10.9	11.4	12.3	13.8	16.0	18.0	14.9	22.3	29.9	44.6
1200	1715	12.6	13.4	14.4	16.0	18.6	21.0	16.2	24.4	32.6	48.7
1300	1855	14.5	15.4	16.4	18.4	21.2	24.0	17.6	26.4	35.3	52.8
1400	2000	16.6	17.5	18.7	20.9	24.1	27.2	18.9	28.4	38.0	56.8
1500	2140	18.7	19.6	21.2	23.6	27.2	30.6	33.3	30.4	40.8	60.9
1600	2285	21.0	21.9	23.7	26.3	30.4	34.1	37.2	32.4	43.5	64.9
1800	2570	26.0	27.3	29.2	32.2	37.1	41.7	45.5	36.5	48.9	73.1
2000	2860	31.3	32.7	35.0	38.6	44.4	49.8	54.4	40.6	54.3	81.2
2200	3140	37.0	38.6	41.3	45.8	52.3	58.8	64.0	71.9	59.8	89.3
2400	3430	43.1	45.1	48.3	53.4	60.9	68.3	74.2	83.8	65.2	97.4
2600	3710	49.8	52.1	55.4	61.4	70.0	78.3	85.0	96.2	70.7	105
2800	4000	56.8	59.2	63.5	70.1	79.7	88.9	96.1	109	76.1	114
3000	4285	64.3	66.8	71.8	78.8	89.8	99.8	108	122	133	122
3500	5000	84.9	88.3	94.4	103	117	131	142	159	180	142
4000	5715	108	112	119	131	149	165	178	199	217	162
4500	6430	133	139	147	162	182	202	218	244	266	300
5000	7145	160	168	179	195	218	241	262	293	318	360
5500	7855	191	199	212	231	258	286	309	345	373	423
6000	8570	223	232	247	268	302	334	359	399	435	489
6500	9280	258	267	286	310	348	384	411	460	499	560
7000	10000	296	305	326	355	396	436	468	522	566	637
7500	10700	335	347	369	402	447	492	529	589	638	766
8000	11400	377	389	414	452	505	550	594	659	710	797
9000	12900	469	482	512	557	624	679	729	809	869	976
10000	14300	567	582	619	666	743	817	872	964		

Loss in lb per sq in = .433 (sp gr) (figures in table).
Figures in shaded area are laminar (viscous) flow.
For velocity data see page 3-24.

Note: No allowance has been made for age, difference in diameter, or any abnormal condition of interior surface. Any factor of safety must be estimated from the local conditions and the requirements of each particular installation. It is recommended that for most commercial design purposes a safety factor of 15 to 20% be added to the values in the tables—see page 3-5.

Friction Loss for Viscous Liquids *(Continued)*
(Based on Darcy's Formula)
Loss in Feet of Liquid per 1000 Feet of Pipe
12 Inch (11.938″ inside dia) Sch 40 New Steel Pipe

Flow		Kinematic viscosity—centistokes									
		0.6	1.13	2.1	2.7	4.3	7.4	10.3	13.1	15.7	20.6
U S gal per min	Bbl per hr (42 gal)	Approx SSU viscosity									
			31.5	33	35	40	50	60	70	80	100
300	429	.21	.24	.27	.28	.31	.36	.38	.41	.43	.47
400	571	.36	.40	.45	.47	.51	.59	.64	.67	.70	.77
500	714	.54	.60	.67	.70	.75	.87	.95	.99	1.03	1.12
600	857	.76	.83	.93	.98	1.04	1.19	1.30	1.39	1.41	1.53
700	1000	.98	1.11	1.23	1.29	1.37	1.56	1.70	1.82	1.84	2.00
800	1140	1.26	1.42	1.57	1.64	1.74	1.98	2.15	2.30	2.36	2.51
900	1285	1.57	1.76	1.94	1.96	2.15	2.44	2.65	2.82	2.94	3.08
1000	1430	1.92	2.07	2.36	2.38	2.61	2.94	3.19	3.40	3.57	3.70
1200	1715	2.73	2.91	3.18	3.32	3.62	4.07	4.41	4.68	4.91	5.08
1400	2000	3.67	3.90	4.24	4.41	4.80	5.37	5.79	6.14	6.43	6.65
1600	2285	4.75	5.02	5.43	5.64	6.12	6.83	7.35	7.78	8.14	8.51
1800	2570	5.96	6.29	6.77	7.02	7.59	8.44	9.07	9.59	10.0	10.6
2000	2860	7.32	7.69	8.25	8.54	9.21	10.2	11.0	11.6	12.1	12.9
2500	3570	11.3	11.8	12.6	13.0	13.9	15.3	16.4	17.3	18.0	19.2
3000	4285	16.1	16.8	17.7	18.3	19.5	21.4	22.8	23.9	24.9	26.5
3500	5000	21.8	22.6	23.8	24.4	26.0	28.3	30.1	31.6	32.9	34.9
4000	5715	28.3	29.2	30.7	31.5	33.3	36.2	38.4	40.3	41.8	44.3
4500	6430	35.7	36.8	38.5	39.4	41.6	45.0	47.7	49.9	51.7	54.8
5000	7145	44.0	45.2	47.1	48.2	50.7	54.7	57.8	60.4	62.6	66.2
5500	7855	53.1	54.4	56.6	57.8	60.7	65.3	68.9	71.9	74.4	78.7
6000	8570	63.0	64.5	66.9	68.3	71.6	76.8	80.9	84.3	87.2	92.1
6500	9280	73.8	75.4	78.1	79.6	83.3	89.2	93.8	97.7	101	106
7000	10000	85.4	87.2	90.1	91.8	95.9	102	108	112	116	122
7500	10700	97.9	99.8	103	105	109	117	122	127	131	138
8000	11400	111	113	117	119	124	132	138	143	148	155
9000	12850	141	143	147	149	155	164	172	178	183	192
10000	14300	173	176	180	183	190	200	209	217	223	233
11000	15700	209	212	217	220	228	240	250	269	266	278
12000	17150	249	252	258	261	269	283	294	304	312	326
13000	18550	291	295	301	305	314	330	342	353	363	373
14000	20000	338	342	348	353	363	380	394	406	416	434
15000	21400	387	392	399	403	414	433	449	462	473	493
16000	22850	440	445	453	457	469	490	507	522	534	556
18000	25700	557	561	571	577	590	614	634	651	666	692
20000	28600	687	692	703	709	725	752	775	795	812	842

For this pipe size: $v = 0.00287 \times gpm$; $h_v = 1.275 \times 10^{-7} \times gpm^2$.
For velocity data see page 3-25.

Note: No allowance has been made for age, difference in diameter, or any abnormal condition of interior surface. Any factor of safety must be estimated from the local conditions and the requirements of each particular installation. It is recommended that for most commercial design purposes a safety factor of 15 to 20% be added to the values in the tables—see page 3-5.

Friction Loss for Viscous Liquids *(Continued)*
(Based on Darcy's Formula)
Loss in Feet of Liquid per 1000 Feet of Pipe
12 Inch (11.938″ inside dia) Sch 40 New Steel Pipe

Flow		Kinematic viscosity—centistokes									
		26.4	32.0	43.2	65.0	108.4	162.3	216.5	325	435	650
U S gal per min	Bbl per hr (42 gal)	Approx SSU viscosity									
		125	150	200	300	500	750	1000	1500	2000	3000
100	143	.08	.10	.13	.20	.34	.51	.68	1.00	1.35	2.00
200	286	.16	.19	.27	.40	.67	1.00	1.37	2.05	2.74	4.01
300	429	.49	.53	.41	.62	1.01	1.51	2.00	3.08	4.11	6.16
400	571	.81	.86	.94	.82	1.34	2.02	2.68	3.98	5.46	8.21
500	714	1.22	1.25	1.37	1.02	1.71	2.50	3.37	5.01	6.84	10.3
600	857	1.66	1.71	1.87	2.12	1.97	3.02	4.05	6.03	7.99	12.3
700	1000	2.15	2.30	2.43	2.75	2.37	3.66	4.68	7.05	9.36	13.9
800	1140	2.70	2.88	3.05	3.45	2.63	4.04	5.36	8.09	10.7	15.9
900	1285	3.31	3.52	3.74	4.21	4.93	4.44	6.05	9.30	12.1	18.0
1000	1430	3.97	4.22	4.48	5.04	5.89	5.13	6.84	10.0	13.5	20.0
1200	1715	5.43	5.77	6.33	6.88	8.01	5.91	7.89	12.1	16.2	24.1
1400	2000	7.10	7.53	8.24	8.96	10.4	11.8	9.47	14.6	18.9	28.2
1600	2285	8.96	9.48	10.4	11.3	13.1	14.8	10.5	16.2	21.7	32.4
1800	2570	11.0	11.6	12.7	13.8	16.0	18.0	19.7	17.7	24.2	36.5
2000	2860	13.2	14.0	15.2	16.6	19.1	21.5	23.6	20.5	27.4	40.1
2500	3570	19.6	20.6	22.4	25.3	28.0	31.5	34.3	25.7	34.2	51.3
3000	4285	27.2	28.4	30.8	34.6	38.4	43.0	46.8	53.1	41.1	61.6
3500	5000	36.2	37.3	40.3	45.2	50.2	56.0	60.9	68.8	47.9	71.9
4000	5715	43.4	47.3	51.0	57.0	63.2	70.5	76.5	86.3	94.5	82.1
4500	6430	57.6	58.3	62.8	69.9	77.6	86.4	93.6	105	115	92.4
5000	7145	69.8	70.3	75.6	84.1	93.3	104	112	126	138	103
5500	7855	82.8	83.6	89.5	99.4	110	122	132	148	162	183
6000	8570	96.8	98.2	104	116	128	142	154	172	188	212
6500	9280	112	114	120	133	148	164	176	197	215	243
7000	10000	128	131	137	152	174	186	201	224	244	275
7500	10700	145	148	155	172	196	210	226	253	274	310
8000	11400	163	167	174	192	220	235	253	282	306	345
9000	12850	202	208	215	237	270	289	311	346	375	422
10000	14300	204	253	260	286	325	347	373	415	450	505
11000	15700	290	301	309	338	384	411	441	490	530	594
12000	17150	341	354	361	395	448	479	514	569	616	689
13000	18550	394	409	417	456	516	551	591	655	707	790
14000	20000	452	469	477	521	588	628	673	745	804	898
15000	21400	513	532	541	589	664	710	760	840	906	
16000	22850	578	598	608	662	745	796	851	940		

Figures in shaded area are laminar (viscous) flow.
For velocity data see page 3-25.

Note: No allowance has been made for age, difference in diameter, or any abnormal condition of interior surface. Any factor of safety must be estimated from the local conditions and the requirements of each particular installation. It is recommended that for most commercial design purposes a safety factor of 15 to 20% be added to the values in the tables—see page 3-5.

3

Friction Loss for Viscous Liquids *(Continued)*
(Based on Darcy's Formula)
Loss in Feet of Liquid per 1000 feet of Pipe
14 Inch (13.124″ inside dia) Sch 40 New Steel Pipe

Flow		Kinematic viscosity—centistokes									
		0.6	1.13	2.1	2.7	4.3	7.4	10.3	13.1	15.7	20.6
U S gal per min	Bbl per hr (42 gal)	Approx SSU viscosity									
		31.5	33	35	40	50	60	70	80	100
400	571	.22	.25	.28	.30	.32	.37	.41	.43	.45	.49
500	714	.34	.38	.42	.45	.48	.55	.61	.62	.66	.72
600	857	.48	.52	.59	.62	.66	.76	.83	.87	.90	.98
700	1000	.63	.70	.78	.81	.87	.99	1.09	1.16	1.18	1.28
800	1140	.81	.89	.99	1.04	1.10	1.26	1.37	1.47	1.49	1.61
900	1285	.98	1.11	1.23	1.28	1.36	1.55	1.69	1.80	1.85	1.97
1000	1430	1.20	1.34	1.49	1.55	1.65	1.87	2.03	2.16	2.25	2.36
1200	1715	1.69	1.82	2.07	2.09	2.29	2.58	2.80	2.98	3.13	3.24
1400	2000	2.27	2.43	2.66	2.77	3.03	3.40	3.68	3.91	4.09	4.23
1600	2285	2.94	3.13	3.40	3.55	3.86	4.32	4.66	4.94	5.18	5.37
1800	2570	3.69	3.91	4.24	4.41	4.78	5.34	5.75	6.09	6.37	6.67
2000	2860	4.52	4.78	5.16	5.36	5.80	6.46	6.94	7.35	7.68	8.11
2500	3570	6.97	7.32	7.84	8.11	8.73	9.67	10.4	10.9	11.4	12.2
3000	4285	9.94	10.4	11.1	11.4	12.2	13.5	14.4	15.2	15.8	16.8
3500	5000	13.4	14.0	14.8	15.3	16.3	17.8	19.0	20.0	20.8	22.2
4000	5715	17.5	18.1	19.1	19.6	20.9	22.8	24.2	25.5	26.5	28.1
4500	6430	22.0	22.7	23.9	24.5	26.0	28.3	30.0	31.5	32.7	34.7
5000	7145	27.0	27.9	29.2	30.0	31.7	34.4	36.4	38.1	39.6	41.9
5500	7855	32.6	33.6	35.1	35.9	37.9	41.0	43.4	45.4	47.0	49.8
6000	8570	38.7	40.0	41.5	42.4	44.6	48.2	50.9	53.2	55.0	58.2
6500	9280	45.3	46.5	48.4	49.4	51.9	55.9	58.9	61.5	63.7	67.3
7000	10000	52.5	53.7	55.8	57.0	59.7	64.1	67.6	70.5	72.9	76.9
7500	10700	60.1	61.5	63.7	65.0	68.1	72.9	76.8	80.0	82.7	87.1
8000	11400	68.3	69.8	72.2	73.6	76.9	82.3	86.5	90.0	93.0	98.0
9000	12850	86.2	87.9	90.7	92.4	96.3	103	108	112	115	121
10000	14300	106	108	111	113	118	125	131	136	140	147
11000	15700	128	130	134	136	141	150	156	162	167	175
12000	17150	152	155	159	161	167	176	184	191	196	205
13000	18550	179	181	186	188	195	205	214	221	227	238
14000	20000	207	210	215	217	224	236	246	254	261	273
15000	21400	237	240	246	249	256	269	280	289	297	310
16000	22850	270	273	279	282	290	304	316	326	334	349
18000	25700	341	345	351	355	365	381	395	407	417	434
20000	28600	420	425	432	436	447	466	482	496	508	528
25000	35700	655	661	671	676	691	716	737	756	772	800

For this pipe size: $v = 0.00237 \times gpm$; $h_v = 8.73 \times 10^{-8} \times gpm^2$.
For velocity data see page 3-26.

Note: No allowance has been made for age, difference in diameter, or any abnormal condition of interior surface. Any factor of safety must be estimated from the local conditions and the requirements of each particular installation. It is recommended that for most commercial design purposes a safety factor of 15 to 20% be added to the values in the tables—see page 3-5.

Friction Loss for Viscous Liquids *(Continued)*
(Based on Darcy's Formula)
Loss in Feet of Liquid per 1000 Feet of Pipe
14 Inch (13.124″ inside dia) Sch 40 New Steel Pipe

Flow		Kinematic viscosity—centistokes									
U S gal per min	Bbl per hr (42 gal)	26.4	32.0	43.2	65.0	108.4	162.3	216.5	325	435	650
		Approx SSU viscosity									
		125	150	200	300	500	750	1000	1500	2000	3000
200	286	.11	.14	.19	.28	.47	.68	.93	1.36	1.86	2.77
300	429	.32	.34	.27	.42	.69	1.02	1.40	2.09	2.71	4.19
400	571	.52	.55	.60	.55	.92	1.39	1.82	2.73	3.72	5.46
500	714	.78	.80	.88	.67	1.16	1.73	2.28	3.46	4.57	6.73
600	857	1.06	1.09	1.20	1.36	1.42	2.07	2.75	4.19	5.58	8.37
700	1000	1.38	1.47	1.56	1.76	1.57	2.51	3.21	4.82	6.43	9.64
800	1140	1.73	1.85	1.95	2.21	1.82	2.73	3.68	5.55	7.44	10.9
900	1285	2.12	2.26	2.39	2.70	2.07	3.19	4.14	6.18	8.29	12.6
1000	1430	2.54	2.70	2.86	3.22	3.78	3.41	4.65	6.91	9.30	13.8
1200	1715	3.47	3.69	3.92	4.40	5.14	4.09	5.67	8.28	11.2	16.7
1400	2000	4.53	4.81	5.27	5.73	6.67	7.57	6.27	10.0	12.9	19.3
1600	2285	5.71	6.05	6.63	7.21	8.36	9.48	7.28	10.9	14.7	22.2
1800	2570	7.01	7.42	8.11	8.83	10.2	11.6	8.29	12.7	16.6	24.7
2000	2860	8.43	8.91	9.72	10.6	12.2	13.8	15.1	13.6	18.6	27.7
2500	3570	12.5	13.2	14.3	15.6	17.9	20.2	22.0	16.8	22.8	34.4
3000	4285	17.2	18.1	19.6	22.1	24.5	27.5	30.0	34.1	27.1	41.9
3500	5000	22.8	23.7	25.7	28.8	32.0	35.8	39.0	44.1	33.0	48.2
4000	5715	29.2	30.0	32.5	36.3	40.4	45.1	48.9	55.3	60.6	54.6
4500	6430	36.4	37.0	39.9	44.6	49.5	55.2	59.9	67.5	73.9	60.9
5000	7145	44.2	44.6	48.1	53.6	59.5	66.2	71.7	80.7	88.3	67.3
5500	7855	52.5	52.8	56.9	63.3	70.2	78.1	84.5	95.0	104	77.4
6000	8570	61.3	61.9	66.3	73.3	81.8	90.8	98.1	110	120	136
6500	9280	70.8	71.8	76.4	84.8	94.1	104	113	126	138	156
7000	10000	80.9	82.3	87.2	96.6	107	119	128	143	156	177
8000	11400	103	105	111	122	140	150	161	180	196	221
9000	12850	127	131	136	150	172	184	198	221	240	270
10000	14300	154	159	165	181	207	221	238	265	287	323
11000	15700	183	190	195	215	264	261	281	312	339	380
12000	17150	215	223	228	251	285	305	327	363	393	441
13000	18550	248	258	264	289	328	351	376	418	451	506
14000	20000	284	295	302	330	374	400	428	475	513	574
15000	21400	323	335	342	373	422	451	484	536	578	646
16000	22850	363	377	384	419	473	506	542	599	647	722
18000	25700	451	468	476	518	583	623	667	736	793	884
20000	28600	548	567	576	626	703	777	803	885	953	

Figures in shaded area are laminar (viscous) flow.
For velocity data see page 3-26.

Note: No allowance has been made for age, difference in diameter, or any abnormal condition of interior surface. Any factor of safety must be estimated from the local conditions and the requirements of each particular installation. It is recommended that for most commercial design purposes a safety factor of 15 to 20% be added to the values in the tables—see page 3-5.

Friction Loss for Viscous Liquids *(Continued)*
(Based on Darcy's Formula)
Loss in Feet of Liquid per 1000 Feet of Pipe
16 Inch (15.000″ inside dia) Sch 40 New Steel Pipe

Flow		Kinematic viscosity—centistokes									
		0.6	1.13	2.1	2.7	4.3	7.4	10.3	13.1	15.7	20.6
U S gal per min	Bbl per hr (42 gal)	Approx SSU viscosity									
		31.5	33	35	40	50	60	70	80	100	
600	857	.25	.27	.31	.32	.35	.40	.44	.46	.48	.52
700	1000	.33	.36	.41	.43	.46	.53	.58	.61	.63	.68
800	1140	.42	.46	.52	.54	.58	.66	.73	.78	.79	.86
900	1285	.52	.58	.64	.67	.72	.82	.89	.95	.97	1.05
1000	1430	.64	.70	.78	.81	.87	.99	1.07	1.15	1.17	1.25
1200	1715	.87	.98	1.08	1.13	1.20	1.36	1.48	1.58	1.65	1.72
1400	2000	1.16	1.30	1.43	1.50	1.59	1.79	1.94	2.06	2.17	2.25
1600	2285	1.50	1.61	1.79	1.84	2.02	2.27	2.46	2.61	2.74	2.83
1800	2570	1.88	2.01	2.20	2.29	2.50	2.80	3.03	3.21	3.37	3.48
2000	2860	2.30	2.45	2.67	2.78	3.03	3.39	3.65	3.87	4.05	4.23
2200	3140	2.77	2.94	3.19	3.32	3.60	4.02	4.33	4.59	4.80	5.05
2400	3430	3.27	3.46	3.75	3.89	4.22	4.70	5.06	5.35	5.59	5.93
2600	3710	3.82	4.03	4.35	4.52	4.89	5.43	5.84	6.17	6.45	6.88
2800	4000	4.41	4.65	5.00	5.18	5.60	6.21	6.67	7.04	7.35	7.87
3000	4285	5.04	5.30	5.69	5.90	6.35	7.04	7.55	7.97	8.31	8.88
3500	5000	6.80	7.12	7.61	7.86	8.44	9.31	9.96	10.5	10.9	11.7
4000	5715	8.82	9.20	9.79	10.1	10.8	11.9	12.7	13.3	13.9	14.8
4500	6430	11.1	11.5	12.2	12.6	13.5	14.7	15.7	16.5	17.2	18.3
5000	7145	13.6	14.2	14.9	15.4	16.4	17.9	19.0	20.0	20.7	22.0
6000	8570	19.5	20.1	21.2	21.7	23.0	25.0	26.5	27.8	28.8	30.5
7000	10000	26.4	27.2	28.4	29.1	30.7	33.2	35.2	36.8	38.1	40.3
8000	11400	34.4	35.3	36.7	37.6	39.5	42.6	44.9	46.9	48.5	51.3
9000	12850	43.3	44.4	46.1	47.1	49.4	53.0	55.8	58.2	60.2	63.5
10000	14300	53.4	54.5	56.5	57.6	60.3	64.5	67.8	70.6	72.9	76.8
12000	17150	76.5	78.0	80.5	81.9	85.3	90.8	95.1	98.8	102	107
14000	20000	104	106	109	110	114	121	127	131	135	142
16000	22850	135	137	141	143	148	156	163	168	173	181
18000	25700	171	173	177	180	185	195	203	210	216	225
20000	28600	211	213	218	221	227	239	248	256	262	274
22000	31400	255	258	263	266	273	286	297	306	313	326
24000	34300	303	306	312	315	323	338	350	360	369	384
26000	37100	355	359	365	369	378	394	407	418	428	445
28000	40000	411	415	422	426	436	454	468	481	492	511
30000	42850	472	476	484	488	499	518	534	548	560	581
32000	45700	537	541	549	554	566	587	604	620	633	656

For this pipe size: v = 0.00182 × gpm; h_v = 5.116 × 10⁻ˣ × gpm².
For velocity data see page 3-26.

Note: No allowance has been made for age, difference in diameter, or any abnormal condition of interior surface. Any factor of safety must be estimated from the local conditions and the requirements of each particular installation. It is recommended that for most commercial design purposes a safety factor of 15 to 20% be added to the values in the tables—see page 3-5.

Friction Loss for Viscous Liquids *(Continued)*
(Based on Darcy's Formula)
Loss in Feet of Liquid per 1000 Feet of Pipe
16 Inch (15.000″ inside dia) Sch 40 New Steel Pipe

Flow		Kinematic viscosity—centistokes									
		26.4	32.0	43.2	65.0	108.4	162.3	216.5	325	435	650
U S gal per min	Bbl per hr (42 gal)	Approx SSU viscosity									
		125	150	200	300	500	750	1000	1500	2000	3000
400	571	.28	.29	.21	.32	.54	.81	1.08	1.61	2.21	3.23
500	714	.40	.43	.47	.41	.68	1.01	1.34	2.05	2.73	4.10
600	857	.57	.58	.64	.50	.79	1.21	1.63	2.42	3.26	4.97
700	1000	.74	.76	.83	.94	.92	1.41	1.89	2.86	3.78	5.59
800	1140	.92	.99	1.04	1.18	1.05	1.68	2.15	3.23	4.30	6.46
900	1285	1.13	1.20	1.27	1.44	1.18	1.77	2.41	3.66	4.83	7.33
1000	1430	1.35	1.44	1.52	1.72	1.38	2.02	2.70	4.04	5.46	8.20
1200	1715	1.85	1.96	2.08	2.35	2.75	2.36	3.15	4.84	6.51	9.68
1400	2000	2.41	2.56	2.81	3.05	3.56	2.86	3.67	5.65	7.56	11.4
1600	2285	3.03	3.22	3.53	3.84	4.46	5.07	4.20	6.71	8.61	12.9
1800	2570	3.72	3.94	4.32	4.70	5.45	6.18	4.72	7.08	9.77	14.7
2000	2860	4.47	4.73	5.17	5.63	6.52	7.38	5.52	8.07	10.8	16.1
2200	3140	5.27	5.58	6.09	6.63	7.67	8.67	9.50	9.06	11.5	17.9
2400	3430	6.14	6.49	7.08	7.71	8.90	10.0	11.0	9.44	12.6	19.4
2600	3710	7.06	7.46	8.13	8.86	10.2	11.5	12.6	10.4	13.6	21.1
2800	4000	8.04	8.49	9.24	10.1	11.6	13.0	14.3	11.4	14.7	22.6
3000	4285	9.08	9.58	10.4	11.4	13.1	14.7	16.0	12.4	15.7	24.3
3500	5000	11.9	12.6	13.6	15.3	17.0	19.1	20.8	23.6	18.9	29.2
4000	5715	15.3	15.9	17.2	19.3	21.4	24.0	26.1	29.5	22.1	32.2
4500	6430	19.0	19.5	21.1	23.7	26.3	29.4	31.9	36.0	39.5	35.4
5000	7145	23.1	23.5	25.4	28.4	31.6	35.2	38.2	43.1	47.2	41.0
6000	8570	32.2	32.5	35.0	39.0	43.3	48.2	52.2	58.7	64.2	49.7
7000	10000	42.5	43.0	46.0	51.1	56.7	63.0	68.1	76.4	83.3	94.5
8000	11400	54.0	55.0	58.3	64.6	71.7	79.4	85.7	96.0	105	118
9000	12850	66.7	68.4	71.8	79.5	91.2	97.5	105	118	128	144
10000	14300	80.7	83.2	86.6	95.7	110	117	126	141	153	172
12000	17150	112	117	120	132	151	161	173	193	209	235
14000	20000	148	155	158	174	197	211	227	252	273	306
16000	22850	189	197	201	220	250	267	287	318	343	384
18000	25700	235	244	249	272	308	329	352	390	421	470
20000	28600	285	296	301	329	371	396	424	469	506	564
22000	31400	340	352	358	390	439	486	502	554	597	664
24000	34300	399	413	420	456	512	566	585	645	694	772
26000	37100	462	478	487	527	591	652	674	742	798	886
28000	40000	530	548	559	602	674	743	768	846	909	

Figures in shaded area are laminar (viscous) flow.

For velocity data see page 3-26.

Note: No allowance has been made for age, difference in diameter, or any abnormal condition of interior surface. Any factor of safety must be estimated from the local conditions and the requirements of each particular installation. It is recommended that for most commercial design purposes a safety factor of 15 to 20% be added to the values in the tables—see page 3-5.

Friction Loss for Viscous Liquids (Continued)
(Based on Darcy's Formula)
Loss in Feet of Liquid per 1000 Feet of Pipe
18 Inch (16.876″ inside dia) Sch 40 New Steel Pipe

Flow		Kinematic viscosity—centistokes									
		0.6	1.13	2.1	2.7	4.3	7.4	10.3	13.1	15.7	20.6
U S gal per min	Bbl per hr (42 gal)	Approx SSU viscosity									
			31.5	33	35	40	50	60	70	80	100
800	1140	.24	.26	.29	.31	.33	.38	.42	.44	.45	.49
1000	1430	.36	.39	.44	.46	.49	.56	.61	.65	.66	.72
1200	1715	.50	.55	.61	.64	.68	.77	.84	.90	.93	.98
1400	2000	.64	.73	.81	.85	.90	1.02	1.11	1.18	1.23	1.28
1600	2285	.83	.93	1.03	1.08	1.14	1.29	1.40	1.49	1.56	1.62
1800	2570	1.04	1.16	1.28	1.34	1.41	1.59	1.72	1.83	1.92	1.99
2000	2860	1.27	1.37	1.55	1.56	1.71	1.92	2.08	2.20	2.31	2.39
2200	3140	1.53	1.63	1.79	1.86	2.03	2.28	2.46	2.61	2.73	2.85
2400	3430	1.80	1.93	2.10	2.19	2.38	2.66	2.87	3.04	3.18	3.34
2600	3710	2.10	2.24	2.43	2.53	2.75	3.08	3.31	3.51	3.67	3.88
2800	4000	2.43	2.58	2.79	2.91	3.15	3.51	3.78	4.00	4.18	4.45
3000	4285	2.77	2.94	3.18	3.30	3.58	3.98	4.28	4.52	4.73	5.05
3500	5000	3.74	3.94	4.24	4.39	4.74	5.26	5.64	5.96	6.21	6.64
4000	5715	4.84	5.08	5.45	5.64	6.06	6.70	7.17	7.56	7.88	8.41
4500	6430	6.09	6.37	6.80	7.03	7.54	8.30	8.87	9.34	9.73	10.4
5000	7145	7.48	7.80	8.30	8.56	9.16	10.1	10.7	11.3	11.8	12.5
5500	7855	9.01	9.37	9.94	10.2	10.9	12.0	12.8	13.4	13.9	14.8
6000	8570	10.7	11.1	11.7	12.1	12.9	14.1	15.0	15.7	16.3	17.3
6500	9280	12.5	12.9	13.7	14.0	14.9	16.3	17.3	18.1	18.8	20.0
7000	10000	14.4	14.9	15.7	16.2	17.1	18.7	19.8	20.7	21.5	22.8
8000	11400	18.8	19.4	20.3	20.8	22.0	23.9	25.3	26.4	27.4	29.0
9000	12850	23.7	24.3	25.4	26.0	27.5	29.7	31.4	32.8	33.9	35.9
10000	14300	29.1	29.9	31.2	31.9	33.5	36.1	38.1	39.7	41.1	43.4
12000	17150	41.7	42.7	44.3	45.2	47.3	50.7	53.3	55.5	57.3	60.4
14000	20000	56.6	57.7	59.7	60.8	63.3	67.6	70.9	73.7	76.1	80.0
16000	22850	73.7	75.1	77.3	78.6	81.8	86.9	90.9	94.4	97.2	102
18000	25700	93.1	94.6	97.3	98.8	102	108	113	117	121	127
20000	28600	115	116	119	121	125	132	138	143	147	154
22000	31400	139	141	144	146	151	159	165	171	175	183
24000	34300	165	167	171	173	178	187	194	201	206	215
26000	37100	193	195	200	202	208	218	226	233	239	249
28000	40000	224	226	231	233	240	251	260	268	275	286
30000	42850	257	259	264	267	274	286	296	305	312	325
34000	48600	329	332	338	341	350	364	376	386	395	410
38000	54300	441	414	421	424	434	451	465	477	487	505

For this pipe size: $v = 0.001434 \times$ gpm; $h_t = 3.193 \times 10^{-8} \times$ gpm^2.
For velocity data see page 3-27.

Note: No allowance has been made for age, difference in diameter, or any abnormal condition of interior surface. Any factor of safety must be estimated from the local conditions and the requirements of each particular installation. It is recommended that for most commercial design purposes a safety factor of 15 to 20% be added to the values in the tables—see page 3-5.

Friction Loss for Viscous Liquids *(Continued)*
(Based on Darcy's Formula)

Loss in Feet of Liquid per 1000 Feet of Pipe
18 Inch (16.876" inside dia) Sch 40 New Steel Pipe

Flow		Kinematic viscosity—centistokes									
US gal per min	Bbl per hr (42 gal)	26.4	32.0	43.2	65.0	108.4	162.3	216.5	325	435	650
		Approx SSU viscosity									
		125	150	200	300	500	750	1000	1500	2000	3000
800	1140	.53	.55	.60	.68	.67	1.01	1.35	2.02	2.74	4.05
1000	1430	.78	.83	.87	.99	.86	1.21	1.67	2.51	3.38	5.02
1200	1715	1.06	1.13	1.20	1.35	1.58	1.50	2.09	3.04	4.03	5.99
1400	2000	1.38	1.47	1.56	1.75	2.05	1.78	2.38	3.52	4.75	7.13
1600	2285	1.74	1.84	2.03	2.20	2.57	2.07	2.66	4.05	5.40	8.10
1800	2570	2.13	2.26	2.48	2.69	3.13	3.56	2.95	4.71	6.04	9.07
2000	2860	2.55	2.71	2.97	3.23	3.75	4.25	3.42	4.85	6.77	10.0
2200	3140	3.01	3.19	3.49	3.80	4.40	4.99	3.71	5.42	7.41	11.2
2400	3430	3.51	3.71	4.06	4.42	5.11	5.77	6.33	6.00	8.38	12.1
2600	3710	4.03	4.26	4.65	5.07	5.86	6.61	7.24	6.56	8.94	13.1
2800	4000	4.59	4.85	5.29	5.76	6.65	7.50	8.20	7.13	9.51	14.1
3000	4285	5.18	5.47	5.96	6.49	7.48	8.43	9.21	7.70	10.1	15.2
3500	5000	6.79	7.16	7.78	8.49	9.75	11.0	12.0	8.91	11.9	17.8
4000	5715	8.60	9.05	9.82	11.1	12.3	13.8	15.0	17.0	13.7	19.4
4500	6430	10.7	11.1	12.1	13.5	15.0	16.8	18.3	20.7	15.5	22.7
5000	7145	13.0	13.4	14.5	16.3	18.1	20.2	21.9	24.8	27.2	26.0
5500	7855	15.5	15.9	17.1	19.2	21.3	23.8	25.8	29.1	31.9	27.5
6000	8570	18.2	18.5	20.0	22.3	24.8	27.6	29.9	33.7	36.9	30.8
6500	9280	21.1	21.3	23.0	25.6	28.5	31.7	34.3	38.7	42.3	32.4
7000	10000	24.1	24.3	26.2	29.2	32.4	36.0	39.0	43.9	47.9	35.6
8000	11400	30.6	31.0	33.1	36.9	40.9	45.4	49.1	55.1	60.1	68.1
9000	12850	37.8	38.6	40.8	45.3	50.3	55.7	60.2	67.4	73.4	83.0
10000	14300	45.7	46.9	49.2	54.5	60.5	66.9	72.2	80.7	87.8	99.2
12000	17150	63.4	65.7	68.1	75.2	86.0	92.0	99.1	110	120	135
14000	20000	83.8	87.3	89.7	98.8	113	121	130	144	156	176
16000	22850	107	111	114	125	142	152	164	182	197	220
18000	25700	132	138	141	154	175	187	201	223	241	270
20000	28600	160	167	170	186	211	226	242	268	289	323
22000	31400	191	198	202	221	250	267	286	316	341	381
24000	34300	224	232	237	258	291	312	333	368	397	442
26000	37100	259	269	274	298	336	372	384	424	456	508
28000	40000	297	308	315	341	383	423	438	482	519	577
30000	42850	338	350	358	386	433	478	494	544	585	650
34000	48600	426	440	451	484	541	596	617	678	729	808
38000	54300	523	540	554	592	660	726	752	825	886	980

Figures in shaded area are laminar (viscous) flow.
For velocity data see page 3-27.

Note: No allowance has been made for age, difference in diameter, or any abnormal condition of interior surface. Any factor of safety must be estimated from the local conditions and the requirements of each particular installation. It is recommended that for most commercial design purposes a safety factor of 15 to 20% be added to the values in the tables—see page 3-5.

Friction Loss for Viscous Liquids (Continued)
(Based on Darcy's Formula)
Loss in Feet of Liquid per 1000 Feet of Pipe
20 Inch (18.812″ inside dia) Sch 40 New Steel Pipe

Flow		Kinematic viscosity—centistokes									
		0.6	1.13	2.1	2.7	4.3	7.4	10.3	13.1	15.7	20.6
U S gal per min	Bbl per hr (42 gal)	Approx SSU viscosity									
		31.5	33	35	40	50	60	70	80	100
2000	2860	.74	.83	.91	.96	1.01	1.14	1.24	1.31	1.38	1.43
3000	4285	1.60	1.71	1.86	1.94	2.11	2.36	2.54	2.69	2.81	2.98
4000	5715	2.79	2.95	3.18	3.30	3.57	3.96	4.25	4.49	4.68	5.00
5000	7145	4.30	4.52	4.84	5.00	5.38	5.94	6.35	6.69	6.97	7.43
6000	8670	6.14	6.41	6.82	7.04	7.53	8.28	8.83	9.28	9.66	10.3
7000	10000	8.29	8.62	9.13	9.41	10.0	11.0	11.7	12.3	12.7	13.5
8000	11400	10.8	11.2	11.8	12.1	12.9	14.0	14.9	15.6	16.2	17.2
9000	12850	13.6	14.0	14.7	15.1	16.0	17.4	18.5	19.3	20.0	21.2
10000	14300	16.7	17.2	18.0	18.5	19.5	21.2	22.4	23.4	24.3	25.7
11000	15700	20.1	20.7	21.7	22.2	23.4	25.3	26.7	27.9	28.9	30.5
12000	17150	23.9	24.5	25.6	26.2	27.5	29.7	31.3	32.7	33.8	35.7
13000	18600	28.0	26.7	29.9	30.5	32.0	34.4	36.3	37.8	39.1	41.3
14000	20000	32.4	33.2	34.4	35.2	36.9	39.5	41.6	43.4	44.8	47.2
15000	21400	37.1	37.9	39.3	40.1	42.0	45.0	47.3	49.2	50.8	53.5
16000	22850	42.1	43.1	44.6	45.4	47.5	50.7	53.3	55.4	57.2	60.2
18000	25700	53.2	54.2	56.0	57.0	59.4	63.3	66.3	68.9	71.0	74.6
20000	28600	65.5	66.7	68.7	69.9	72.6	77.2	80.7	83.7	86.2	90.4
22000	31400	79.1	80.5	82.7	84.0	87.2	92.3	96.4	99.9	103	108
24000	34300	94.0	95.5	98.0	99.5	103	109	113	117	121	126
26000	37100	110	112	115	116	120	127	132	136	140	146
28000	40000	128	129	132	134	139	146	152	157	161	168
30000	42850	146	148	152	154	158	166	173	178	183	191
32000	45700	166	169	172	174	179	188	195	201	206	215
34000	48600	188	190	194	196	202	211	219	225	231	240
36000	51400	210	213	217	219	225	235	244	251	257	267
38000	54300	234	237	241	244	250	261	270	278	284	296
40000	57150	259	262	267	269	276	288	298	306	313	325
42000	60000	286	289	294	296	304	316	326	335	343	356
44000	62900	313	316	322	325	332	346	357	366	374	389
46000	65700	342	346	351	354	362	376	388	398	407	422
48000	68600	373	376	382	385	394	409	421	432	441	457
50000	71450	404	408	414	417	426	442	455	467	477	493
55000	78600	489	493	499	503	513	531	546	559	571	590
60000	86700	581	586	593	597	609	628	645	660	673	695
65000	92850	682	686	695	699	712	734	752	769	783	808

For this pipe size: $v = 0.001154 \times gpm$; $h_\iota = 2.068 \times 10^{-x} \times gpm^2$.
For velocity data see page 3-27.

Note: No allowance has been made for age, difference in diameter, or any abnormal condition of interior surface. Any factor of safety must be estimated from the local conditions and the requirements of each particular installation. It is recommended that for most commercial design purposes a safety factor of 15 to 20% be added to the values in the tables—see page 3-5.

Friction Loss for Viscous Liquids *(Continued)*
(Based on Darcy's Formula)

Loss in Feet of Liquid per 1000 Feet of Pipe
20 Inch (18.812″ inside dia) Sch 40 New Steel Pipe

Flow		Kinematic viscosity—centistokes									
		26.4	32.0	43.2	65.0	108.4	162.3	216.5	325	435	650
U S gal per min	Bbl per hr (42 gal)	Approx SSU viscosity									
		125	150	200	300	500	750	1000	1500	2000	3000
1000	1430	.47	.48	.52	.59	.53	.85	1.08	1.62	2.16	3.25
2000	2860	1.53	1.62	1.78	1.93	2.25	2.56	2.11	3.38	4.39	6.50
3000	4285	3.09	3.27	3.57	3.88	4.48	5.06	5.54		6.34	9.75
4000	5715	5.11	5.40	5.86	6.39	7.34	8.25	9.00	10.2	9.02	13.5
5000	7145	7.66	7.98	8.65	9.72	10.8	12.1	13.1	14.9	11.1	16.3
6000	8670	10.7	11.0	11.9	13.3	14.8	16.5	17.9	20.3	22.2	19.0
7000	10000	14.3	14.4	15.6	17.4	19.3	21.6	23.4	26.3	28.8	23.0
8000	11400	18.2	18.3	19.7	22.0	24.4	27.1	29.4	33.0	36.1	41.0
9000	12850	22.4	22.7	24.3	27.0	30.0	33.3	36.0	40.4	44.0	49.9
10000	14300	27.1	27.6	29.3	32.5	36.1	40.0	43.2	48.4	52.7	59.6
11000	15700	32.1	33.0	34.7	38.4	42.6	47.2	50.9	56.9	62.0	70.0
12000	17150	37.5	38.7	40.5	44.8	51.4	54.9	59.2	66.1	71.9	81.1
13000	18600	43.4	44.9	46.6	51.6	59.1	63.2	68.0	75.9	82.4	92.9
14000	20000	49.6	51.5	53.2	58.8	67.2	71.9	77.4	86.3	93.6	105
15000	21400	56.2	58.5	60.2	66.4	75.8	81.1	87.3	97.2	105	118
16000	22850	63.1	65.8	67.6	74.4	64.9	90.8	97.6	109	118	132
18000	25700	78.1	81.4	83.5	91.7	104	112	120	133	144	162
20000	28600	94.6	98.5	101	111	126	134	144	160	173	194
22000	31400	113	117	120	131	149	159	170	189	204	228
24000	34300	132	137	140	153	173	185	199	220	237	265
26000	37100	153	159	162	177	200	214	229	253	273	304
28000	40000	175	182	186	202	228	252	261	288	310	345
30000	42850	199	206	211	229	257	285	294	325	350	389
32000	45700	224	232	238	257	288	319	330	364	391	435
34000	48600	250	259	266	286	321	355	367	404	435	483
36000	51400	278	288	295	317	356	393	406	447	480	533
38000	54300	307	318	327	350	392	432	447	492	528	586
40000	57150	338	349	359	384	429	473	489	538	578	640
42000	60000	369	382	393	419	469	516	534	586	629	697
44000	62900	403	416	428	456	509	560	580	636	683	756
46000	65700	437	452	465	494	551	606	627	688	738	817
48000	68600	473	489	503	534	595	654	677	742	796	879
50000	71450	511	527	543	575	640	703	728	798	855	944
55000	78600	610	629	647	684	760	833	893	944		
60000	86700	718	739	760	802	889	973				

Figures in shaded area are laminar (viscous) flow.
For velocity data see page 3-27.

Note: No allowance has been made for age, difference in diameter, or any abnormal condition of interior surface. Any factor of safety must be estimated from the local conditions and the requirements of each particular installation. It is recommended that for most commercial design purposes a safety factor of 15 to 20% be added to the values in the tables—see page 3-5.

Friction Loss for Viscous Liquids (Continued)
(Based on Darcy's Formula)

Loss in Feet of Liquid per 1000 Feet of Pipe
24 Inch (22.624″ inside dia) Sch 40 New Steel Pipe

Flow		Kinematic viscosity—centistokes									
		0.6	1.13	2.1	2.7	4.3	7.4	10.3	13.1	15.7	20.6
U S gal per min	Bbl per hr (42 gal)	Approx SSU viscosity									
			31.5	33	35	40	50	60	70	80	100
2000	2860	.31	.34	.37	.39	.41	.47	.51	.55	.57	.59
3000	4285	.63	.71	.78	.82	.86	.97	1.05	1.11	1.17	1.21
4000	5715	1.10	1.18	1.28	1.34	1.45	1.62	1.75	1.85	1.94	2.07
5000	7145	1.70	1.79	1.94	2.02	2.18	2.43	2.61	2.76	2.88	3.07
6000	8670	2.41	2.54	2.73	2.83	3.05	3.38	3.62	3.82	3.98	4.25
7000	10000	3.24	3.41	3.65	3.77	4.06	4.47	4.78	5.03	5.24	5.58
8000	11400	4.21	4.40	4.69	4.85	5.19	5.71	6.09	6.40	6.66	7.08
9000	12850	5.29	5.52	5.86	6.04	6.46	7.08	7.54	7.92	8.23	8.74
10000	14300	6.50	6.76	7.16	7.37	7.85	8.59	9.13	9.58	9.95	10.6
12000	17150	9.29	9.62	10.1	10.4	11.0	12.0	12.7	13.3	13.8	14.6
14000	20000	12.6	13.0	13.6	13.9	14.7	16.0	26.9	17.7	18.3	19.3
16000	22850	16.3	16.8	17.6	18.0	18.9	20.4	21.6	22.5	23.3	24.6
18000	25700	20.6	21.2	22.0	22.5	23.7	25.5	26.8	28.0	28.9	30.5
20000	28600	25.4	26.0	27.0	27.6	28.9	31.0	32.6	33.9	35.0	36.9
22000	31400	30.6	31.3	32.5	33.1	34.6	37.0	38.9	40.4	41.7	43.9
24000	34300	36.4	37.1	38.4	39.1	40.8	43.6	45.7	47.5	49.0	51.4
26000	37100	42.6	43.5	44.9	45.7	47.6	50.6	53.0	55.0	56.7	59.5
28000	40000	49.3	50.3	51.8	52.7	54.8	58.2	60.9	63.1	65.0	68.2
30000	42850	56.6	57.6	59.2	60.2	62.5	66.3	69.2	71.8	73.9	77.4
32000	45700	64.3	65.4	67.2	68.2	70.7	74.9	78.1	80.9	83.2	87.1
34000	48600	72.5	73.6	75.6	76.7	79.5	84.0	87.5	90.6	93.1	97.4
36000	51400	81.2	82.4	84.5	85.7	88.7	93.6	97.4	101	104	108
38000	54300	90.4	91.7	93.9	95.2	98.4	104	108	111	114	120
40000	57150	100	101	104	105	109	114	119	123	126	131
42000	60000	110	112	114	116	119	125	130	134	138	144
44000	62900	121	122	125	127	131	137	142	147	150	157
46000	65700	132	134	137	138	142	149	155	159	163	170
48000	68600	144	145	148	150	154	162	168	173	177	184
50000	71450	156	158	161	163	167	175	181	186	191	199
55000	78600	188	190	194	196	201	210	217	223	228	237
60000	85710	224	226	230	232	238	248	256	263	269	279
65000	92860	263	265	269	272	289	289	298	306	313	324
70000	100000	304	307	312	314	321	333	343	352	359	372
80000	114290	397	400	406	409	417	431	443	454	403	478
90000	128570	502	506	512	515	525	541	555	568	579	597

For this pipe size: $v = 7.98 \times 10^{-4} \times$ gpm; $h_v = 9.886 \times 10^{-9} \times$ gpm^2.
For velocity data see page 3-28.

Note: No allowance has been made for age, difference in diameter, or any abnormal condition of interio surface. Any factor of safety must be estimated from the local conditions and the requirements of eack particular installation. It is recommended that for most commercial design purposes a safety factor of 15 te 20% be added to the values in the tables—see page 3-5.

Friction Loss for Viscous Liquids (Continued)
(Based on Darcy's Formula)
Loss in Feet of Liquid per 1000 Feet of Pipe
24 Inch (22.624" inside dia) Sch 40 New Steel Pipe

Flow		Kinematic viscosity—centistokes									
		26.4	32.0	43.2	65.0	108.4	162.3	216.5	325	435	650
U S gal per min	Bbl per hr (42 gal)	Approx SSU viscosity									
		125	150	200	300	500	750	1000	1500	2000	3000
2000	2860	.64	.68	.72	.81	.95	.79	1.03	1.56	2.10	3.13
3000	4285	1.29	1.36	1.49	1.62	1.88	2.13	1.59	2.33	3.15	4.65
4000	5715	2.12	2.25	2.45	2.67	3.07	3.46	3.79	3.16	4.14	6.25
5000	7145	3.14	3.31	3.60	4.06	4.51	5.06	5.52	6.28	5.25	7.64
6000	8670	4.38	4.56	4.95	5.56	6.18	6.91	7.52	8.52	6.37	9.31
7000	10000	5.82	5.98	6.48	7.26	8.07	9.01	9.79	11.1	12.1	11.0
8000	11400	7.45	7.57	8.18	9.15	10.1	11.3	12.3	13.9	15.2	12.7
9000	12850	9.24	9.33	10.1	11.2	12.5	13.9	15.1	16.9	18.5	14.3
10000	14300	11.2	11.3	12.1	13.5	15.0	16.7	18.0	20.3	22.1	25.1
12000	17150	15.5	15.8	16.7	18.6	20.6	22.9	24.7	27.7	30.2	34.1
14000	20000	20.4	21.0	22.0	24.4	27.0	29.9	32.3	36.1	39.2	44.3
16000	22850	25.9	26.9	27.9	30.8	35.3	37.8	40.7	45.4	49.3	55.5
18000	25700	32.0	33.4	34.4	37.9	43.4	46.4	49.9	55.6	60.3	67.8
20000	28600	38.7	40.4	41.5	45.7	52.2	55.8	60.0	66.7	72.3	81.1
22000	31400	46.0	48.0	49.2	54.2	61.6	66.0	70.9	78.7	85.2	95.5
24000	34300	53.9	56.1	57.5	63.2	71.8	76.9	82.5	91.6	99.0	111
26000	37100	62.3	64.9	66.4	72.9	82.7	88.5	94.9	105	114	127
28000	40000	71.3	74.2	75.9	83.2	94.2	101	108	120	129	144
30000	42850	80.9	84.1	85.9	94.1	106	114	122	135	146	163
32000	45700	91.0	94.5	96.8	106	119	128	137	151	163	182
34000	48600	102	106	108	118	133	147	152	168	181	202
36000	51400	113	117	120	130	147	163	168	186	200	223
38000	54300	125	129	133	144	162	179	185	204	220	244
40000	57150	137	142	146	158	177	196	203	223	240	267
42000	60000	150	155	160	172	193	214	221	243	262	291
44000	62900	163	169	175	187	210	232	240	264	284	315
46000	65700	177	183	189	203	227	251	259	286	307	340
48000	68600	191	198	205	219	245	270	280	308	331	363
50000	71450	206	214	221	236	264	291	301	331	355	393
55000	78600	246	255	264	280	313	344	356	391	420	464
60000	85710	289	299	310	328	365	401	416	456	489	540
65000	92860	336	347	359	379	422	463	480	525	563	621
70000	100000	385	397	412	433	482	528	566	599	641	707
80000	114290	494	509	527	553	613	670	717	759	812	894
90000	128570	616	634	656	685	758	827	885	936	999	

Figures in shaded area are laminar (viscous) flow.
For velocity data see page 3-28.

Note: No allowance has been made for age, difference in diameter, or any abnormal condition of interior surface. Any factor of safety must be estimated from the local conditions and the requirements of each particular installation. It is recommended that for most commercial design purposes a safety factor of 15 to 20% be added to the values in the tables—see page 3-5.

Friction Loss for Viscous Liquids *(Continued)*
(Based on Darcy's Formula)

Loss in Feet of Liquid per 1000 Feet of Pipe
30 Inch (28.750″ inside dia) Sch 30 New Steel Pipe

Flow		Kinematic viscosity—centistokes									
		0.6	1.13	2.1	2.7	4.3	7.4	10.3	13.1	15.7	20.6
U S gal per min	Bbl per hr (42 gal)		Approx SSU viscosity								
			31.5	33	35	40	50	60	70	80	100
3200	4570	.23	.25	.27	.29	.30	.34	.37	.40	.42	.43
3400	4860	.25	.28	.31	.32	.34	.38	.42	.44	.46	.48
3600	5140	.28	.31	.34	.36	.38	.43	.46	.49	.51	.53
3800	5425	.31	.34	.38	.39	.42	.47	.51	.54	.56	.59
4000	5715	.33	.37	.41	.43	.56	.51	.55	.59	.62	.64
5000	7145	.51	.57	.62	.65	.68	.77	.83	.87	.91	.97
6000	8570	.72	.77	.86	.88	.95	1.06	1.14	1.21	1.26	1.35
7000	10000	.97	1.03	1.12	1.16	1.26	1.40	1.51	1.59	1.66	1.77
8000	11400	1.25	1.33	1.49	1.49	1.61	1.79	1.91	2.02	2.11	2.25
9000	12850	1.57	1.66	1.79	1.85	2.00	2.21	2.37	2.49	2.60	2.77
10000	14300	1.92	2.03	2.18	2.25	2.43	2.68	2.86	3.01	3.14	3.34
12000	17150	2.74	2.87	3.07	3.17	3.40	3.73	3.98	4.19	4.35	4.63
14000	20000	3.70	3.86	4.11	4.23	4.52	4.95	5.27	5.53	5.74	6.10
16000	22850	4.80	5.00	5.29	5.44	5.80	6.33	6.72	7.04	7.31	7.75
18000	25700	6.05	6.27	6.62	6.80	7.22	7.86	8.33	8.72	9.05	9.57
20000	28600	7.44	7.69	8.09	8.31	8.80	9.55	10.1	10.6	11.0	11.6
22000	31400	8.97	9.26	9.71	9.95	10.5	11.4	12.0	12.6	13.0	13.8
24000	34300	10.6	11.0	11.5	11.8	12.4	13.4	14.1	14.8	15.3	16.1
26000	37100	12.5	12.8	13.4	13.7	14.4	15.5	16.4	17.1	17.7	18.6
28000	40000	14.4	14.8	15.4	15.8	16.6	17.8	18.8	19.6	20.2	21.3
30000	42850	16.5	16.9	17.6	18.0	18.9	20.3	21.3	22.2	22.9	24.1
35000	50000	22.4	22.9	23.7	24.2	25.3	27.0	28.4	29.5	30.4	32.0
40000	57150	29.1	29.7	30.7	31.3	32.6	34.7	36.4	37.8	38.9	40.8
45000	62290	36.8	37.5	38.6	39.3	40.8	43.3	45.3	47.0	48.3	50.7
50000	71450	45.3	46.1	47.4	48.2	50.0	52.9	55.2	57.1	58.8	61.5
55000	78570	54.8	55.6	57.1	57.9	60.0	63.3	66.0	68.2	70.1	73.3
60000	85710	65.1	66.0	67.7	68.6	70.9	74.7	77.7	80.3	82.4	86.0
65000	92860	76.3	77.3	79.1	80.2	82.7	87.0	90.3	93.2	95.7	99.8
70000	100000	88.4	89.5	91.5	92.6	95.4	100	104	107	110	114
75000	107140	101	103	105	106	109	114	118	122	125	130
80000	114290	115	117	119	120	124	129	134	138	141	147
85000	121430	130	131	134	135	139	145	150	154	158	164
90000	128570	146	147	150	151	155	162	167	172	176	183
95000	135710	162	164	167	168	172	180	185	190	195	202
100000	142860	180	181	184	186	190	198	204	210	214	222

For this pipe size: $v = 4.942 \times 10^{-4} \times gpm$; $h_v = 3.791 \times 10^{-9} \times gpm^2$.
For velocity data see page 3-28.

Note: No allowance has been made for age, difference in diameter, or any abnormal condition of interior surface. Any factor of safety must be estimated from the local conditions and the requirements of each particular installation. It is recommended that for most commercial design purposes a safety factor of 15 to 20% be added to the values in the tables—see page 3-5.

Friction Loss for Viscous Liquids (Continued)
(Based on Darcy's Formula)
Loss in Feet of Liquid per 1000 Feet of Pipe
30 Inch (28.750″ inside dia) Sch 30 New Steel Pipe

Flow		Kinematic viscosity—centistokes									
		26.4	32.0	43.2	65.0	108.4	162.3	216.5	325	435	650
U S gal per min	Bbl per hr (42 gal)	Approx SSU viscosity									
		125	150	200	300	500	750	1000	1500	2000	3000
3200	4570	.46	.49	.54	.58	.68	.77	.65	.94	1.28	1.79
3400	4860	.51	.54	.60	.65	.75	.86	.69	.98	1.36	2.02
3600	5140	.57	.60	.66	.72	.83	.94	.73	1.10	1.44	2.15
3800	5425	.62	.66	.72	.79	.91	1.03	.77	1.13	1.53	2.29
4000	5715	.68	.72	.79	.86	.99	1.12	.81	1.16	1.62	2.39
5000	7145	1.00	1.06	1.16	1.26	1.46	1.64	1.79	1.49	1.95	2.98
6000	8570	1.38	1.46	1.59	1.73	1.99	2.24	2.44	1.83	2.43	3.65
7000	10000	1.81	1.91	2.08	2.34	2.60	2.91	3.17	3.60	2.76	4.14
8000	11400	2.32	2.42	2.62	2.94	3.27	3.66	3.98	4.50	3.24	4.64
9000	12850	2.89	2.97	3.22	3.61	4.01	4.48	4.86	5.49	6.02	5.48
10000	14300	3.51	3.58	3.87	4.33	4.81	5.37	5.82	6.57	7.19	5.96
12000	17150	4.89	4.94	5.33	5.95	6.61	7.35	7.96	8.95	9.78	7.30
14000	20000	6.44	6.54	6.99	7.79	8.65	9.60	10.4	11.7	12.7	14.4
16000	22850	8.17	8.37	8.85	9.84	10.9	12.1	13.1	14.6	15.9	18.0
18000	25700	10.1	10.4	10.9	12.1	13.4	14.9	16.0	17.9	19.5	22.0
20000	28600	12.2	12.7	13.2	14.6	16.7	17.9	19.2	21.5	23.3	26.3
22000	31400	14.5	15.1	15.6	17.2	19.7	21.1	22.7	25.3	27.5	30.9
24000	34300	16.9	17.7	18.2	20.1	23.0	24.6	26.4	29.4	31.9	35.8
26000	37100	19.6	20.4	21.0	23.1	26.4	28.3	30.4	33.8	36.6	41.1
28000	40000	22.4	23.3	24.0	26.4	30.1	32.2	34.6	38.4	41.6	46.6
30000	42850	25.3	26.4	27.1	29.8	34.0	36.4	39.0	43.3	46.9	52.5
35000	50000	33.5	34.9	35.7	39.2	44.5	47.7	51.1	56.6	61.2	68.3
40000	57150	42.7	44.4	45.6	49.8	56.4	60.4	64.6	71.5	77.1	86.0
45000	62290	52.9	55.0	56.7	61.5	69.4	77.0	79.5	87.8	94.6	105
50000	71450	64.2	66.6	68.9	74.2	83.7	92.6	95.8	106	114	126
55000	78570	76.4	79.3	82.2	88.1	99.1	110	113	125	134	149
60000	85710	89.6	92.9	96.5	103	116	128	132	145	156	173
65000	92860	104	108	112	119	133	147	152	167	180	199
70000	100000	119	123	128	136	152	168	174	191	205	227
75000	107140	135	140	146	154	172	190	196	216	231	256
80000	114290	152	158	164	173	193	213	220	242	259	286
85000	121430	170	176	184	193	216	237	245	269	288	318
90000	128570	189	196	204	214	239	262	281	297	319	351
95000	135710	209	216	226	236	263	289	309	327	350	386
100000	142860	230	238	248	259	289	316	339	359	384	423

Figures in shaded area are laminar (viscous) flow.
For velocity data see page 3-28.

Note: No allowance has been made for age, difference in diameter, or any abnormal condition of interior surface. Any factor of safety must be estimated from the local conditions and the requirements of each particular installation. It is recommended that for most commercial design purposes a safety factor of 15 to 20% be added to the values in the tables—see page 3-5.

Friction Loss for Viscous Liquids (Continued)
(Based on Darcy's Formula)
Loss in Feet of Liquid per 1000 Feet of Pipe
36 Inch (34.500″ inside dia) Sch 30 New Steel Pipe

Flow		Kinematic viscosity—centistokes									
		0.6	1.13	2.1	2.7	4.3	7.4	10.3	13.1	15.7	20.6
U S gal per min	Bbl per hr (42 gal)	Approx SSU viscosity									
		31.5	33	35	40	50	60	70	80	100
6000	8670	.29	.33	.36	.37	.39	.44	.48	.51	.53	.56
7000	10000	.39	.43	.47	.50	.52	.58	.63	.66	.69	.74
8000	11400	.50	.54	.60	.62	.66	.74	.80	.84	.88	.94
9000	12850	.63	.67	.73	.76	.82	.92	.98	1.04	1.08	1.16
10000	14300	.77	.82	.89	.92	1.00	1.11	1.19	1.25	1.31	1.40
12000	17150	1.09	1.15	1.25	1.29	1.39	1.54	1.65	1.74	1.81	1.93
14000	20000	1.47	1.55	1.66	1.72	1.85	2.04	2.18	2.29	2.39	2.54
16000	22850	1.90	2.00	2.14	2.21	2.37	2.61	2.78	2.92	3.03	3.22
18000	25700	2.39	2.50	2.67	2.75	2.95	3.23	3.44	3.61	3.75	3.98
20000	28600	2.94	3.07	3.26	3.36	3.58	3.92	4.17	4.37	4.54	4.81
22000	31400	3.54	3.68	3.90	4.02	4.28	4.67	4.96	5.20	5.39	5.71
24000	34300	4.20	4.36	4.60	4.74	5.03	5.48	5.81	6.09	6.31	6.68
26000	37100	4.91	5.09	5.36	5.51	5.85	6.35	6.73	7.04	7.30	7.71
28000	40000	5.67	5.87	6.18	6.34	6.72	7.29	7.71	8.06	8.35	8.82
30000	42850	6.50	6.71	7.05	7.23	7.65	8.28	8.75	9.14	9.46	9.99
35000	50000	8.80	9.06	9.47	9.70	10.2	11.0	11.6	12.1	12.5	13.2
40000	57150	11.4	11.8	12.2	12.5	13.2	14.1	14.9	15.5	16.0	16.8
45000	62290	14.4	14.8	15.4	15.7	16.4	17.6	18.5	19.2	19.9	20.9
50000	71450	17.8	18.2	18.8	19.2	20.1	21.4	22.5	23.4	24.1	25.3
55000	78570	21.5	21.9	22.7	23.1	24.1	25.6	26.9	27.9	28.7	30.1
60000	85710	25.5	26.0	26.8	27.3	28.4	30.2	31.6	32.8	33.7	35.3
65000	92860	29.9	30.4	31.3	31.8	33.1	35.1	36.7	38.0	39.1	40.9
70000	100000	34.6	35.2	36.2	36.8	38.1	40.4	42.1	43.6	44.9	46.9
80000	114290	45.0	45.8	46.9	47.6	49.3	52.0	54.1	55.9	57.5	60.0
90000	128570	56.9	57.7	59.1	59.9	61.8	65.0	67.6	69.7	71.5	74.6
100000	142860	70.1	71.1	72.6	73.5	75.7	79.5	82.4	85.0	87.1	90.7
110000	157140	84.8	85.8	87.5	88.6	91.1	95.3	98.7	102	104	108
120000	171430	101	102	104	105	108	113	116	120	123	127
130000	185710	118	119	122	123	126	131	136	139	142	148
140000	200000	137	138	141	142	145	151	156	160	164	170
150000	214290	157	158	161	163	166	173	178	183	186	193
160000	228570	179	180	183	184	189	196	201	206	211	218
170000	242860	201	203	206	208	212	220	226	232	236	244
180000	257140	226	228	231	233	237	245	252	258	263	272
200000	285710	278	280	284	286	291	301	309	316	322	332

For this pipe size: $v = 3.432 \times 10^{-4} \times gpm$; $h_v = 1.828 \times 10^{-9} \times gpm^2$.
For velocity data see page 3-29.

Note: No allowance has been made for age, difference in diameter, or any abnormal condition of interior surface. Any factor of safety must be estimated from the local conditions and the requirements of each particular installation. It is recommended that for most commercial design purposes a safety factor of 15 or 20% be added to the values in the tables—see page 3-5.

Friction Loss for Viscous Liquids (Continued)
(Based on Darcy's Formula)
Loss in Feet of Liquid per 1000 Feet of Pipe
36 Inch (34.500″ inside dia) Sch 30 New Steel Pipe

Flow		Kinematic viscosity—centistokes									
		26.4	32.0	43.2	65.0	108.4	162.3	216.5	325	435	650
U S gal per min	Bbl per hr (42 gal)	Approx SSU viscosity									
		125	150	200	300	500	750	1000	1500	2000	3000
6000	8670	.58	.61	.67	.73	.84	.95	1.04	.86	1.13	1.73
7000	10000	.76	.80	.88	.95	1.10	1.23	1.35	1.00	1.33	2.02
8000	11400	.96	1.01	1.10	1.24	1.38	1.55	1.69	1.92	1.53	2.37
9000	12850	1.19	1.25	1.35	1.52	1.69	1.89	2.06	2.34	1.74	2.54
10000	14300	1.44	1.50	1.63	1.83	2.03	2.27	2.47	2.79	3.06	2.91
12000	17150	2.02	2.07	2.24	2.51	2.78	3.10	3.37	3.80	4.16	3.45
14000	20000	2.69	2.72	2.93	3.28	3.64	4.05	4.39	4.94	5.40	4.00
16000	22850	3.41	3.45	3.71	4.13	4.59	5.10	5.52	6.20	6.77	7.68
18000	25700	4.21	4.29	4.57	5.08	5.64	6.26	6.76	7.58	8.26	9.36
20000	28600	5.08	5.21	5.50	6.11	6.78	7.52	8.12	9.08	9.89	11.2
22000	31400	6.02	6.21	6.51	7.22	8.02	8.88	9.57	10.7	11.6	13.1
24000	34300	7.04	7.30	7.60	8.42	9.66	10.3	11.1	12.4	13.5	15.2
26000	37100	8.12	8.46	8.76	9.69	11.1	11.9	12.8	14.3	15.5	17.4
28000	40000	9.28	9.70	9.99	11.1	12.6	13.5	14.6	16.2	17.6	19.8
30000	42850	10.5	11.0	11.3	12.5	14.3	15.3	16.4	18.3	19.8	22.2
35000	50000	13.9	14.5	14.9	16.4	18.7	20.0	21.5	23.9	25.8	28.9
40000	57150	17.7	18.4	18.9	20.8	23.6	25.3	27.1	30.1	32.5	36.4
45000	62290	21.9	22.8	23.4	25.6	29.1	31.1	33.4	36.9	39.9	44.5
50000	71450	26.5	27.6	28.4	30.9	35.0	37.5	40.2	44.4	47.9	53.4
55000	78570	31.5	32.8	33.9	36.7	41.4	46.0	47.5	52.5	56.5	62.9
60000	85710	36.9	38.4	39.8	42.9	48.3	53.5	55.3	61.1	65.8	73.1
65000	92860	42.7	44.4	46.1	49.5	55.7	61.6	63.8	70.3	75.6	84.0
70000	100000	48.9	50.8	52.9	56.5	63.6	70.2	72.7	80.1	86.1	95.5
80000	114290	62.5	64.8	67.7	71.8	80.6	88.9	92.1	101	109	120
90000	128570	77.6	80.4	84.2	88.8	99.5	110	113	125	134	148
100000	142860	94.3	97.6	102	107	120	132	137	150	161	178
110000	157140	112	116	122	128	142	156	168	178	190	210
120000	171430	132	136	143	150	167	183	196	207	222	244
130000	185710	153	158	166	173	192	211	226	239	255	281
140000	200000	176	181	191	198	220	240	257	272	291	320
150000	214290	200	206	217	224	249	272	291	308	329	362
160000	228570	225	232	244	252	280	305	326	345	369	405
170000	242860	252	260	273	282	312	340	364	385	411	451
180000	257140	281	289	303	313	346	377	403	426	454	499
200000	285710	342	352	369	380	419	456	486	514	548	600

Figures in shaded area are laminar (viscous) flow.
For velocity data see page 3-29.

Note: No allowance has been made for age, difference in diameter, or any abnormal condition of interior surface. Any factor of safety must be estimated from the local conditions and the requirements of each particular installation. It is recommended that for most commercial design purposes a safety factor of 15 to 20% be added to the values in the tables—see page 3-5.

Friction Loss for Viscous Liquids *(Continued)*
(Based on Darcy's Formula)
Loss in Feet of Liquid per 1000 Feet of Pipe
42 Inch (42.0″ inside dia) New Steel Pipe

Flow		Kinematic viscosity—centistokes									
		0.6	1.13	2.1	2.7	4.3	7.4	10.3	13.1	15.7	20.6
U S gal per min	Bbl per hr (42 gal)					Approx SSU viscosity					
			31.5	33	35	40	50	60	70	80	100
10000	14300	.29	.32	.35	.37	.38	.43	.46	.49	.51	.55
11000	15700	.34	.37	.42	.44	.46	.51	.55	.58	.60	.65
12000	17150	.41	.43	.48	.50	.54	.60	.64	.68	.71	.75
13000	18600	.47	.50	.55	.57	.62	.69	.74	.78	.81	.87
14000	20000	.54	.58	.63	.66	.71	.79	.85	.89	.93	.99
15000	21400	.62	.66	.72	.75	.81	.89	.96	1.01	1.05	1.12
16000	22850	.70	.75	.81	.84	.91	1.00	1.07	1.13	1.18	1.26
17000	24290	.79	.84	.91	.94	1.01	1.12	1.20	1.26	1.31	1.40
18000	25700	.88	.94	1.01	1.05	1.13	1.24	1.33	1.40	1.46	1.55
19000	27140	.98	1.04	1.12	1.16	1.24	1.37	1.47	1.54	1.60	1.71
20000	28600	1.08	1.14	1.23	1.27	1.37	1.51	1.61	1.69	1.76	1.87
25000	35700	1.67	1.75	1.87	1.93	2.07	2.27	2.41	2.53	2.63	2.79
30000	42850	2.39	2.49	2.64	2.72	2.90	3.17	3.36	3.52	3.66	3.87
35000	50000	3.22	3.35	3.54	3.64	3.87	4.21	4.46	4.66	4.83	5.11
40000	57150	4.19	4.34	4.56	4.69	4.96	5.38	5.70	5.95	6.16	6.51
45000	62290	5.28	5.45	5.72	5.86	6.19	6.70	7.07	7.38	7.64	8.05
50000	71450	6.49	6.69	7.00	7.16	7.55	8.14	8.59	8.95	9.25	9.75
60000	85710	9.29	9.54	9.93	10.2	10.7	11.4	12.0	12.5	12.9	13.6
70000	100000	12.6	12.9	13.4	13.6	14.3	15.3	16.0	16.6	17.2	18.0
80000	114290	16.4	16.7	17.3	17.6	18.4	19.6	20.5	21.3	21.9	23.0
90000	128570	20.7	21.1	21.8	22.1	23.0	24.5	25.6	26.5	27.3	28.6
100000	142860	25.5	26.0	26.7	27.1	28.2	29.8	31.1	32.2	33.1	34.7
110000	157140	30.8	31.3	32.2	32.7	33.8	35.7	37.2	38.5	39.6	41.3
120000	171430	36.6	37.2	38.1	38.7	40.0	42.1	43.9	45.3	46.5	48.5
130000	185710	42.9	43.5	44.6	45.2	46.6	49.1	51.0	52.6	54.0	56.3
140000	200000	49.7	50.4	51.5	52.2	53.8	56.5	58.6	60.5	62.0	64.6
150000	214290	57.0	57.7	59.0	59.7	61.5	64.4	66.8	68.8	70.5	73.4
160000	228570	64.8	65.6	66.9	67.7	69.6	72.9	75.5	77.7	79.6	82.7
170000	242860	73.1	73.9	75.4	76.2	78.3	81.8	84.7	87.1	89.2	92.6
180000	257140	81.9	82.8	84.3	85.2	87.5	91.3	94.4	97.0	99.3	103
200000	285710	101	102	104	105	107	112	115	118	121	125
250000	357140	157	159	161	162	166	171	177	181	184	191
300000	428570	226	228	231	232	237	244	250	256	261	269
350000	500000	308	310	313	315	320	329	337	344	350	360
400000	571430	401	404	408	410	416	427	436	444	451	464

For this pipe size: $v = 2.316 \times 10^{-4} \times gpm$; $h_v = 8.322 \times 10^{-10} \times gpm^2$.
For velocity data see page 3-29.

Note: No allowance has been made for age, difference in diameter, or any abnormal condition of interior surface. Any factor of safety must be estimated from the local conditions and the requirements of each particular installation. It is recommended that for most commercial design purposes a safety factor of 15 to 20% be added to the values in the tables—see page 3-5.

Friction Loss for Viscous Liquids *(Continued)*
(Based on Darcy's Formula)
Loss in Feet of Liquid per 1000 Feet of Pipe
42 Inch (42.0″ inside dia) New Steel Pipe

Flow		Kinematic viscosity—centistokes									
		26.4	32.0	43.2	65.0	108.4	162.3	216.5	325	435	650
US gal per min	Bbl per hr (42 gal)	Approx SSU viscosity									
		125	150	200	300	500	750	1000	1500	2000	3000
10000	14300	.56	.59	.64	.72	.80	.90	.98	1.11	.90	1.27
11000	15700	.66	.70	.76	.85	.94	1.06	1.15	1.30	.93	1.42
12000	17150	.78	.81	.88	.99	1.10	1.23	1.33	1.51	1.66	1.57
13000	18600	.90	.93	1.01	1.13	1.26	1.41	1.53	1.73	1.90	1.72
14000	20000	1.03	1.06	1.15	1.29	1.43	1.60	1.74	1.96	2.15	1.87
15000	21400	1.17	1.20	1.30	1.45	1.61	1.80	1.95	2.20	2.41	2.02
16000	22850	1.32	1.34	1.45	1.63	1.81	2.01	2.18	2.46	2.69	2.05
17000	24290	1.48	1.50	1.62	1.81	2.01	2.23	2.42	2.72	2.98	3.39
18000	25700	1.64	1.66	1.79	2.00	2.22	2.47	2.67	3.00	3.28	3.73
19000	27140	1.81	1.82	1.97	2.19	2.44	2.71	2.93	3.29	3.59	4.08
20000	28600	1.98	2.00	2.15	2.40	2.66	2.96	3.20	3.59	3.92	4.45
25000	35700	2.94	3.02	3.19	3.54	3.94	4.36	4.71	5.27	5.73	6.47
30000	42850	4.08	4.24	4.41	4.88	5.60	5.99	6.46	7.21	7.83	8.82
35000	50000	5.38	5.63	5.80	6.41	7.33	7.85	8.44	9.40	10.2	11.5
40000	57150	6.84	7.15	7.35	8.12	9.26	9.91	10.7	11.9	12.8	14.4
45000	62290	8.46	8.83	9.08	10.0	11.4	12.2	13.1	14.5	15.7	17.6
50000	71450	10.2	10.7	11.0	12.1	13.7	14.7	15.7	17.5	18.9	21.1
60000	85710	14.2	14.8	15.3	16.7	18.9	20.2	21.7	24.0	25.9	28.8
70000	100000	18.8	19.6	20.3	22.0	24.8	27.5	28.4	31.4	33.8	37.6
80000	114290	24.0	25.0	26.0	27.9	31.4	34.8	36.0	39.7	42.7	47.4
90000	128570	29.8	31.0	32.3	34.5	38.8	42.8	44.3	48.8	52.4	58.2
100000	142860	36.1	37.5	39.3	41.6	46.8	51.6	53.4	58.7	63.1	69.9
110000	157140	43.1	44.7	46.9	49.4	55.4	61.1	63.3	69.5	74.5	82.5
120000	171430	50.5	52.4	55.0	57.8	64.7	71.2	73.8	81.0	86.8	96.0
130000	185710	58.5	60.6	63.8	66.8	74.7	82.1	85.1	93.3	100	110
140000	200000	67.1	69.5	73.2	76.4	85.3	93.7	101	106	114	126
150000	214290	76.2	78.9	83.2	86.6	96.5	106	114	120	129	142
160000	228570	85.9	88.8	93.7	97.3	108	119	127	135	144	159
170000	242860	96.1	99.3	105	109	121	132	142	150	160	177
180000	257140	107	110	116	121	134	147	157	166	178	195
190000	271430	118	122	128	133	148	161	173	183	195	215
200000	285710	130	134	141	146	162	177	189	200	214	235
250000	357140	197	203	213	220	242	264	282	298	318	348
300000	428570	277	285	298	307	337	367	390	413	440	481
350000	500000	370	380	397	407	447	484	515	565	579	632

Figures in shaded area are laminar (viscous) flow.
For velocity data see page 3-29.

Note: No allowance has been made for age, difference in diameter, or any abnormal condition of interior surface. Any factor of safety must be estimated from the local conditions and the requirements of each particular installation. It is recommended that for most commercial design purposes a safety factor of 15 to 20% be added to the values in the tables—see page 3-5.

3

Friction Loss for Viscous Liquids (Continued)
(Based on Darcy's Formula)
Loss in Feet of Liquid per 1000 Feet of Pipe
48 Inch (48.0″ inside dia) New Steel Pipe

Flow		Kinematic viscosity—centistokes									
		0.6	1.13	2.1	2.7	4.3	7.4	10.3	13.1	15.7	20.6
US gal per min	Bbl per hr (42 gal)	Approx SSU viscosity									
		31.5	33	35	40	50	60	70	80	100
14000	20000	.28	.31	.34	.35	.37	.41	.44	.47	.49	.52
16000	22850	.36	.39	.42	.44	.47	.53	.57	.60	.62	.66
18000	25700	.45	.48	.52	.54	.59	.65	.70	.74	.77	.82
20000	28600	.55	.59	.64	.66	.71	.79	.84	.89	.93	.99
25000	35700	.85	.90	.97	1.00	1.08	1.19	1.27	1.33	1.38	1.47
30000	42850	1.21	1.27	1.36	1.41	1.51	1.65	1.76	1.85	1.92	2.04
35000	50000	1.64	1.71	1.82	1.88	2.01	2.19	2.33	2.44	2.54	2.69
40000	57150	2.12	2.21	2.35	2.42	2.57	2.81	2.98	3.12	3.23	3.42
45000	64290	2.67	2.78	2.93	3.02	3.21	3.49	3.69	3.86	4.00	4.23
50000	71430	3.28	3.40	3.59	3.68	3.90	4.23	4.48	4.68	4.84	5.11
55000	78570	3.96	4.09	4.30	4.41	4.67	5.05	5.34	5.57	5.76	6.08
60000	85710	4.70	4.85	5.08	5.21	5.50	5.94	6.26	6.53	6.75	7.12
65000	92860	5.50	5.66	5.92	6.07	6.39	6.89	7.26	7.57	7.82	8.23
70000	100000	6.36	6.54	6.83	6.99	7.35	7.91	8.33	8.67	8.96	9.42
75000	107140	7.28	7.48	7.80	7.97	8.37	8.99	9.46	9.85	10.2	10.7
80000	114290	8.27	8.49	8.83	9.02	9.46	10.2	10.7	11.1	11.4	12.0
85000	121430	9.32	9.55	9.93	10.1	10.6	11.4	11.9	12.4	12.8	13.4
90000	128570	10.4	10.7	11.1	11.3	11.8	12.7	13.3	13.8	14.2	14.9
95000	135710	11.6	11.9	12.3	12.6	13.1	14.0	14.7	15.2	15.7	16.5
100000	142860	12.9	13.1	13.6	13.9	14.5	15.4	16.1	16.8	17.3	18.1
110000	157140	15.5	15.8	16.4	16.6	17.3	18.4	19.3	20.0	20.6	21.5
120000	171430	18.4	18.8	19.4	19.7	20.5	21.7	22.7	23.5	24.2	25.3
130000	185710	21.6	22.0	22.6	23.0	23.9	25.3	26.3	27.3	28.0	29.3
140000	200000	25.0	25.4	26.1	26.5	27.5	29.1	30.3	31.3	32.2	33.6
160000	228570	32.6	33.1	33.9	34.4	35.5	37.3	38.9	40.2	41.2	43.0
180000	257140	41.2	41.7	42.7	43.3	44.6	46.6	48.6	50.1	51.4	53.5
200000	285710	50.7	51.4	52.5	53.1	54.7	56.7	59.3	61.1	62.6	65.1
250000	357140	79.1	79.9	81.3	82.2	84.2	87.7	90.6	93.1	95.1	98.7
300000	428570	114	115	116	117	120	125	128	131	134	139
350000	500000	154	156	158	159	162	168	172	176	180	186
400000	571430	202	203	205	207	211	217	223	227	232	239
450000	642860	255	256	259	261	265	273	279	285	290	298
500000	714290	314	316	319	321	326	335	342	349	354	364
550000	785710	380	382	386	388	393	403	411	419	426	437
600000	857140	452	454	458	461	467	478	487	496	503	516

For this pipe size: $v = 1.773 \times 10^{-4} \times gpm$; $h_v = 4.877 \times 10^{-10} \times gpm^2$.
For velocity data see page 3-30.

Note: No allowance has been made for age, difference in diameter, or any abnormal condition of interior surface. Any factor of safety must be estimated from the local conditions and the requirements of each particular installation. It is recommended that for most commercial design purposes a safety factor of 15 to 20% be added to the values in the tables—see page 3-5.

Friction Loss for Viscous Liquids *(Continued)*
(Based on Darcy's Formula)
Loss in Feet of Liquid per 1000 Feet of Pipe
48 Inch (48.0″ inside dia) New Steel Pipe

Flow		Kinematic viscosity—centistokes									
		26.4	32.0	43.2	65.0	108.4	162.3	216.5	325	435	650
U S gal per min	Bbl per hr (42 gal)	Approx SSU viscosity									
		125	150	200	300	500	750	1000	1500	2000	3000
14000	20000	.54	.56	.61	.69	.76	.85	.93	1.05	1.15	1.09
16000	22850	.69	.71	.77	.86	.96	1.07	1.16	1.31	1.44	1.25
18000	25700	.86	.88	.95	1.06	1.18	1.31	1.42	1.60	1.75	1.41
20000	28600	1.04	1.05	1.14	1.27	1.41	1.57	1.70	1.92	2.09	1.56
25000	35700	1.55	1.58	1.69	1.88	2.09	2.32	2.50	2.81	3.06	3.46
30000	42850	2.15	2.21	2.33	2.59	2.87	3.18	3.43	3.84	4.17	4.71
35000	50000	2.83	2.94	3.06	3.39	3.89	4.16	4.48	5.00	5.43	6.12
40000	57150	3.60	3.76	3.88	4.29	4.91	5.25	5.65	6.30	6.83	7.67
45000	64290	4.45	4.65	4.79	5.28	6.03	6.46	6.94	7.72	8.36	9.38
50000	71430	5.38	5.62	5.77	6.37	7.26	7.77	8.34	9.27	10.0	11.2
55000	78570	6.38	6.67	6.85	7.54	8.58	9.19	9.86	10.9	11.8	13.2
60000	85710	7.47	7.80	8.00	8.80	10.0	10.7	11.5	12.7	13.7	15.4
65000	92860	8.64	9.01	9.25	10.2	11.5	12.3	13.2	14.6	15.8	17.6
70000	100000	9.88	10.3	10.6	11.6	13.1	14.1	15.1	16.7	18.0	20.0
75000	107140	11.2	11.7	12.1	13.1	14.8	15.9	17.0	18.8	20.2	22.6
80000	114290	12.6	13.1	13.6	14.7	16.6	18.4	19.0	21.0	22.7	25.2
85000	121430	14.1	14.6	15.2	16.4	18.5	20.5	21.2	23.4	25.2	28.0
90000	128570	15.6	16.2	16.7	18.1	20.5	22.7	23.4	25.9	27.8	30.9
95000	135710	17.2	17.9	18.7	20.0	22.5	24.9	25.8	28.4	30.6	33.9
100000	142860	18.9	19.7	20.5	21.9	24.7	27.3	28.2	31.1	33.4	37.1
110000	157140	22.5	23.4	24.5	26.0	29.2	32.3	33.4	36.8	39.5	43.8
120000	171430	26.4	27.4	28.7	30.4	34.1	37.7	39.0	42.9	46.0	50.9
130000	185710	30.5	31.7	33.3	35.1	39.4	43.4	44.9	49.4	52.9	58.5
140000	200000	35.0	36.3	38.2	40.1	44.9	49.5	51.3	56.3	60.3	66.6
150000	214290	39.7	41.2	43.4	45.5	50.8	55.9	58.0	63.5	68.1	75.2
160000	228570	44.7	46.3	48.9	51.1	57.1	62.7	67.3	71.3	76.3	84.1
180000	257140	55.6	57.5	60.8	63.2	70.5	77.3	82.9	87.8	98.9	103
200000	285710	67.6	69.8	73.7	76.5	85.2	93.3	99.9	106	113	124
250000	357140	102	105	111	115	127	139	149	157	168	184
300000	428570	144	148	155	160	177	193	206	218	232	254
350000	500000	191	197	206	212	234	254	271	287	305	334
400000	571430	246	253	264	272	298	324	344	365	388	423
450000	642860	307	315	329	337	370	401	426	466	478	522
500000	714290	374	384	400	410	448	485	515	563	578	629
550000	785710	448	459	478	489	534	576	611	668	685	746

Figures in shaded area are laminar (viscous) flow.
For velocity data see page 3-30.

Note: No allowance has been made for age, difference in diameter, or any abnormal condition of interior surface. Any factor of safety must be estimated from the local conditions and the requirements of each particular installation. It is recommended that for most commercial design purposes a safety factor of 15 to 20% be added to the values in the tables—see page 3-5.

Friction Loss for Viscous Liquids—4000 SSU to 20000 SSU
(Based on Darcy's Formula)
Loss in Feet of Liquid per 1000 Feet of Pipe
1¼" to 6" pipe sizes—Schedule 40
Laminar flow—Figures suitable for any interior roughness

			Kinematic viscosity—centistokes								
			863	1079	1295	1726	2158	2589	3021	3452	4315
Flow US gpm	Nom pipe size in	Velocity of flow ft/sec	Approx SSU viscosity								
			4000	5000	6000	8000	10000	12000	14000	16000	20000
5	1¼	1.07	749	937	1125	1499	1874	2248	2623	2998	3747
	1½	0.79	405	506	607	809	1011	1214	1416	1618	2022
	2	0.48	149	186	223	298	372	447	521	596	744
10	1¼	2.15	1499	1874	2249	2998	3748	4496	5247	5995	7494
	1½	1.58	809	1011	1214	1618	2023	2427	2832	3236	4045
	2	0.95	298	372	447	595	745	893	1042	1191	1489
15	1½	2.36	1213	1517	1821	2427	3035	3641	4248	4854	6068
	2	1.43	447	558	670	893	1117	1340	1564	1787	2233
	2½	1.01	219	274	329	439	549	658	768	877	1097
20	1½	3.15	1618	2023	2428	3236	4046	4854	5664	6472	8090
	2	1.91	596	745	894	1191	1489	1787	2085	2382	2978
	2½	1.34	292	366	440	585	731	878	1024	1170	1463
25	2	2.39	744	931	1117	1489	1862	2233	2606	2978	3722
	2½	1.68	367	458	549	731	914	1098	1280	1463	1828
	3	1.08	153	192	230	307	383	460	537	613	767
30	2	2.87	893	1117	1341	1787	2234	2680	3127	3573	4467
	2½	2.01	440	549	659	879	1095	1315	1536	1755	2194
	3	1.30	184	230	276	368	461	552	643	737	920
40	2	3.82	1191	1489	1787	2382	2979	3573	4170	4764	5956
	2½	2.68	585	732	878	1170	1463	1755	2048	2340	2926
	3	1.74	245	307	368	491	613	736	859	981	1227
50	2	4.78	1489	1862	2234	2978	3723	4467	5212	5956	7445
	2½	3.35	731	914	1098	1463	1829	2194	2560	2926	3657
	3	2.17	307	384	460	614	767	920	1073	1227	1534
60	2	5.73	1786	2234	2681	3573	4468	5360	6255	7147	8934
	2½	4.02	878	1097	1317	1755	2195	2633	3072	3511	4388
	3	2.60	368	460	552	736	921	1104	1289	1473	1840
70	2½	4.69	1024	1280	1537	2048	2560	3072	3584	4096	5120
	3	3.04	429	537	644	859	1074	1288	1503	1718	2147
	4	1.76	144	181	217	290	362	435	507	579	724
80	2½	5.36	1170	1463	1756	2340	2926	3511	4097	4681	5851
	3	3.47	491	614	737	982	1227	1473	1718	1963	2454
	4	2.02	166	207	248	331	414	497	579	662	828
90	2½	6.03	1317	1646	1976	2633	3292	3950	4609	5266	6583
	3	3.90	552	690	829	1104	1381	1657	1933	2209	2761
	4	2.27	186	233	279	372	466	559	652	745	931
100	2½	6.70	1462	1829	2195	2926	3658	4388	5121	5851	7314
	3	4.34	614	767	921	1227	1534	1841	2148	2454	3068
	4	2.52	207	259	310	414	517	621	724	828	1035
125	3	5.42	766	959	1151	1534	1918	2301	2685	3068	3835
	4	3.15	259	323	388	517	647	776	905	1035	1293
	6	1.39	50	63	75	100	126	151	176	201	251
150	3	6.51	920	1151	1381	1841	2301	2761	3222	3681	4602
	4	3.78	310	388	466	621	776	931	1086	1241	1552
	6	1.67	60	75	90	121	151	181	211	241	301

Note: No allowance has been made for age, difference in diameter, or any abnormal condition of interior surface. Any factor of safety must be estimated from the local conditions and the requirements of each particular installation. It is recommended that for most commercial design purposes a safety factor of 15 to 20% be added to the values in the tables—see page 3-5.

Friction Loss for Viscous Liquids—4000 SSU to 20000 SSU (cont.)
(Based on Darcy's Formula)
Loss in Feet of Liquid per 1000 Feet of Pipe
3″ to 18″ pipe sizes—Schedule 40
Laminar flow—Figures suitable for any interior roughness

Flow U S gpm	Nom pipe size in	Velocity of flow ft/sec	Kinematic viscosity—centistokes								
			863	1079	1295	1726	2158	2589	3021	3452	4315
			Approx SSU viscosity								
			4000	5000	6000	8000	10000	12000	14000	16000	20000
175	3	7.59	1074	1342	1611	2147	2684	3221	3758	4295	5369
	4	4.41	362	453	543	724	905	1086	1268	1448	1810
	6	1.94	70	88	105	141	176	211	246	281	352
200	4	5.04	414	517	621	828	1035	1241	1449	1655	2069
	6	2.22	80	100	121	161	201	241	281	321	402
	8	1.28	27	34	40	54	67	80	94	107	134
250	4	6.30	517	647	776	1035	1293	1552	1811	2069	2586
	6	2.78	100	126	151	201	251	301	352	402	502
	8	1.60	33	42	50	67	84	100	117	134	167
300	4	7.56	621	776	931	1241	1552	1862	2173	2483	3104
	6	3.33	121	151	181	241	301	362	422	482	603
	8	1.92	40	50	60	80	101	121	141	161	201
400	6	4.44	161	201	241	321	402	482	563	643	803
	8	2.57	54	67	80	107	134	161	188	214	268
	10	1.63	22	27	32	43	54	65	76	86	108
500	6	5.55	201	251	301	402	502	603	703	803	1004
	8	3.21	67	84	101	134	168	201	235	268	335
	10	2.03	27	34	40	54	67	81	94	108	135
600	6	6.66	241	301	362	482	603	723	844	964	1205
	8	3.85	80	101	121	161	201	241	281	322	402
	10	2.44	32	40	49	65	81	97	113	129	162
700	6	7.77	281	352	422	562	703	844	984	1125	1406
	8	4.49	94	117	141	188	235	281	328	375	469
	10	2.85	38	47	57	74	94	113	132	151	189
800	8	5.13	107	134	161	214	268	322	375	429	536
	10	3.25	43	54	65	86	108	129	151	173	216
	12	2.29	21	27	32	43	54	64	75	86	107
900	8	5.77	121	151	181	241	302	362	422	482	603
	10	3.66	49	61	73	97	121	146	170	194	243
	12	2.58	24	30	36	48	60	72	84	96	120
1000	8	6.41	134	168	201	268	335	402	469	536	670
	10	4.06	54	67	81	108	135	162	189	216	270
	12	2.87	27	33	40	54	67	80	94	107	134
1500	10	6.10	81	101	121	162	202	243	283	324	404
	12	4.30	40	50	60	80	100	120	141	161	201
	14	3.56	27	34	41	55	69	82	96	110	137
2000	12	5.73	54	67	80	107	134	161	187	214	268
	14	4.74	37	46	55	73	92	110	128	147	183
	16	3.63	21	27	32	43	54	64	75	86	107
2500	12	7.16	67	84	100	134	167	201	234	268	335
	14	5.93	46	57	69	92	15	137	160	183	229
	16	4.54	27	37	40	54	67	80	94	107	134
3000	14	7.12	55	69	82	110	137	165	192	220	275
	16	5.45	32	40	48	64	81	97	113	129	161
	18	4.30	20	25	30	40	50	60	70	80	101

Darcy formula for laminar (viscous) flow—$h_f = \dfrac{L(gpm)k}{1587.6\ d^4}$

in which—h_f = friction loss—ft of liquid; L = length of pipe—ft: gpm = flow—gal per min; k = kinematic viscosity—centistokes: d = internal pipe dia—in. Warning: This formula for laminar flow only, i.e. for Reynolds number less than 2000.

Note: No allowance has been made for age, difference in diameter, or any abnormal condition of interior surface. Any factor of safety must be estimated from the local conditions and the requirements of each particular installation. It is recommended that for most commercial design purposes a safety factor of 15 to 20% be added to the values in the tables—see page 3-5.

Friction losses—paper stock flow

Curves relating friction loss to stock flow in pipes are shown on pages 3-91 to 3-101. These curves are based on the University of Maine's correlation of the Brecht and Heller data*. That data correlation produced a relationship between a pseudo-Reynolds Number "Ré" and a friction factor "f" as shown on the chart on page 3-90.

The following equations are applicable here:

$$(1) \qquad \text{pseudo-Reynolds Number "Ré"} = \frac{D^{0.205} \times V \times p}{C^{1.157}}$$

$$(2) \qquad \text{**friction factor "f"} = \frac{3.97}{Ré^{1.636}}$$

$$(3) \qquad \text{average stock velocity "V"} = \frac{Q \times 0.321}{A}$$

$$(4) \qquad \text{friction loss "}h_f\text{"} = \frac{f \times V^2 \times L \times K}{D}$$

where:

A = Pipe flow cross-sectional area—square inches
C = % stock consistency—oven dry
D = Inside diameter of pipe—feet
f = Friction factor**—see page 3-90
h_f = Friction loss—feet of water
K = Friction factor multiplier (see page 3-89)
L = Length of pipe—feet
p = Stock density—lbs./ft³ (assumed to be 62.4)
Q = Volumetric flow rate—U.S. gallons/minute
Ré = Pseudo-Reynold's number
V = Average stock velocity in pipe—feet/second

* Acknowledgements, with the permission of TAPPI
  Brecht and Heller—TAPPI Vol. 33, No. 9
  Durst, Chase and Jenness—TAPPI Vol. 35, No. 12
  Durst and Jenness—TAPPI Vol. 37, No. 10
  P. S. Riegel—TAPPI Vol. 49, No. 3
** Note: This friction factor "f" is not related in any way to the Darcy-Weisbach-Colebrook friction factor previously discussed—(page 3-3).

Note: For pump performance corrections when handling stock see discussion on page 4-49.

Given the pipe size, stock flow, and stock consistency, the stock velocity and Ré number can be calculated using equations (3) and (1). The friction factor "f" corresponding to the calculated Ré number can be taken from the chart on page 3-90 or calculated using equation (2). By using the appropriate given and derived values in equation (4), the stock line friction loss can be calculated. Friction loss values shown on the accompanying curves were derived in the foregoing manner for various diameters of schedule 40 steel pipe.

For pipe diameters other than those shown, it is necessary to calculate friction loss values as described above.

Although the Ré number was originally derived on an OD stock consistency basis, the friction loss curves shown here were calculated on the AD consistency basis, resulting in somewhat larger loss values and, therefore, more conservative results.

Stock temperatures between 18°C and 35°C (65°F and 95°F) will not appreciably affect friction loss; higher temperatures should give somewhat lower friction losses.

For stock consistencies below 2.0%, use water friction values. Stock velocity should not exceed 10 feet/sec. for stock consistencies of 3.0% or lower; for consistencies higher than 3.0%, maximum stock velocity should be 8 feet/sec.

The friction loss curves are based on unbleached, unrefined softwood sulfite pulp; for other types of pulp, the following multiplier values (K) may be applied:

Type of Pulp	*CSF—ml	Friction Factor Multiplier (K)
Unbl. Sulfite—SW	640	1.00
Bl. sulfite—SW	560	0.90
Unbl. kraft—SW	730	0.90
Soda—HW	—	0.90**
Reclaimed fiber	—	0.90**
Pre-steamed groundwood—SW	200	1.00
Stone groundwood—SW	70	1.42

* Canadian Standard Freeness
** Courtesy of Goulds Pumps, Inc.

Note: This friction factor multiplier (K) is not related in any way to the resistance coefficient K in the tables on pages 3-110 to 3-121.

Friction Factors for Stock Flow in Pipes

Friction Factor—"f"

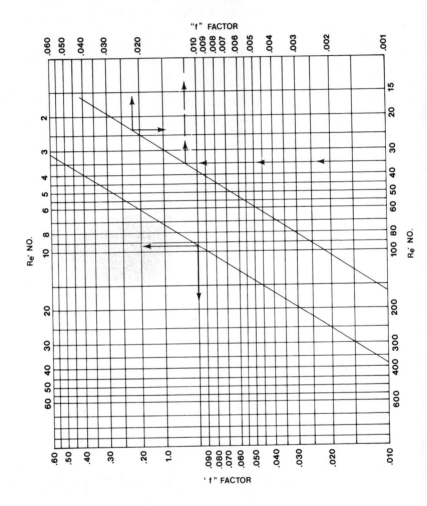

Friction of Paper Stock *(Continued)*

Loss in feet of water per 100 ft of pipe
Basis unbleached sulphite pulp—air dry
3 Inch

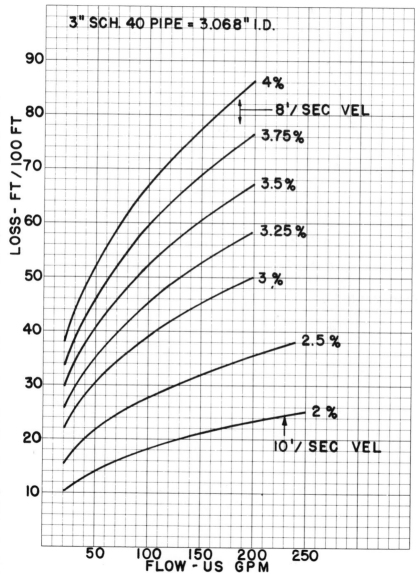

Friction of Paper Stock (Continued)

Loss in feet of water per 100 ft of pipe
Basis unbleached sulphite pulp—air dry

4 Inch

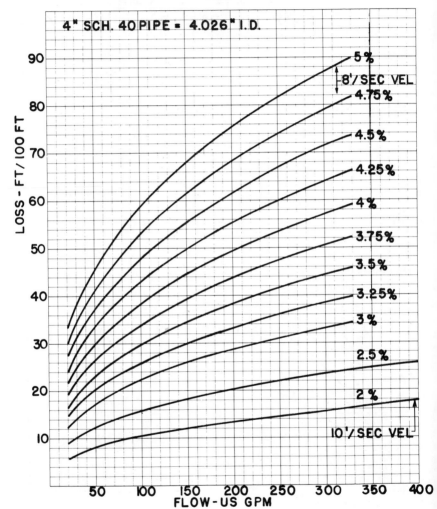

Friction of Paper Stock *(Continued)*

**Loss in feet of water per 100 ft of pipe
Basis unbleached sulphite pulp—air dry**

6 Inch

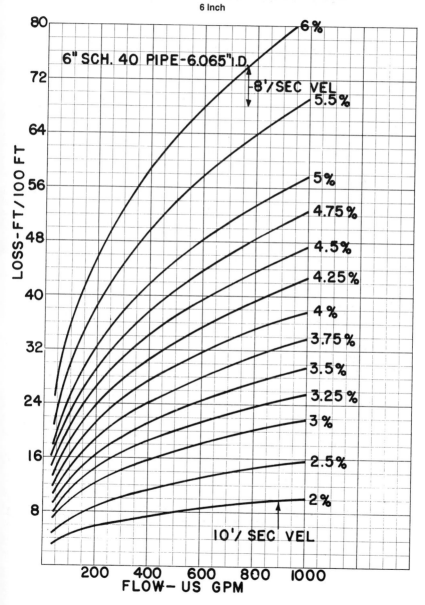

Friction of Paper Stock

Loss in feet of water per 100 ft of pipe
Basis unbleached sulphite pulp—air dry

8 Inch

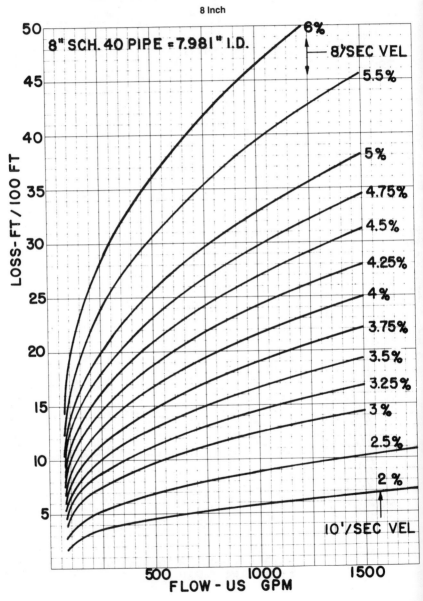

Friction of Paper Stock (Continued)

Loss in feet of water per 100 ft of pipe
Basis unbleached sulphite pulp—air dry

10 Inch

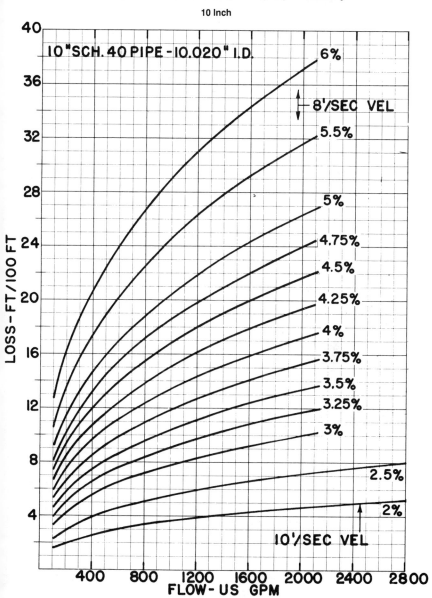

Friction of Paper Stock (Continued)

Loss in feet of water per 100 ft of pipe
Basis unbleached sulphite pulp—air dry

12 Inch

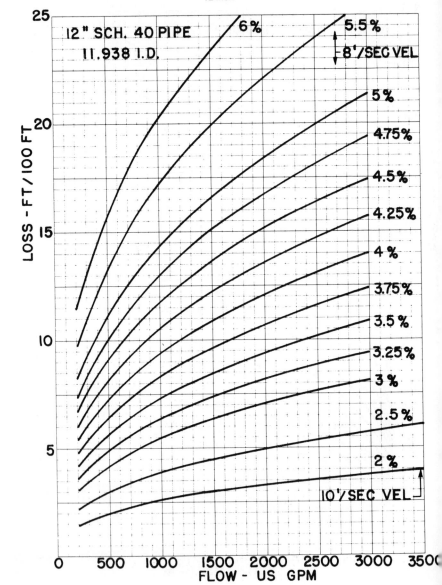

Friction of Paper Stock (Continued)

Loss in feet of water per 100 ft of pipe
Basis unbleached sulphite pulp—air dry

14 Inch

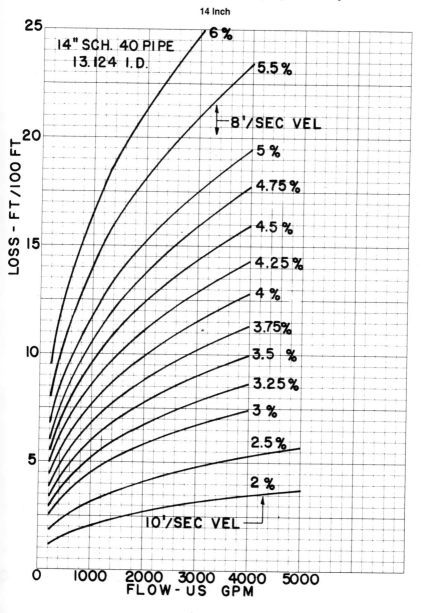

Friction of Paper Stock *(Continued)*

Loss in feet of water per 100 ft of pipe
Basis unbleached sulphite pulp—air dry

16 Inch

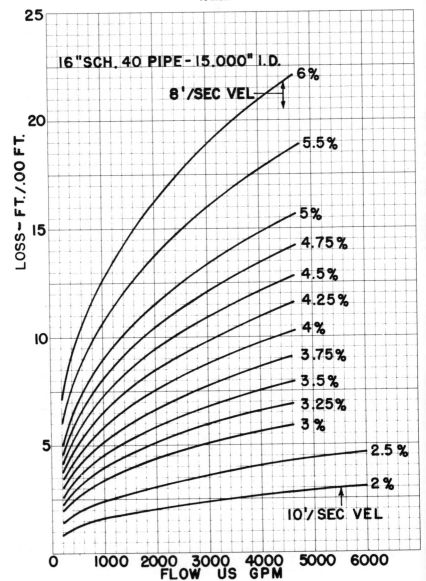

Friction of Paper Stock *(Continued)*

Loss in feet of water per 100 ft of pipe
Basis unbleached sulphite pulp—air dry

18 Inch

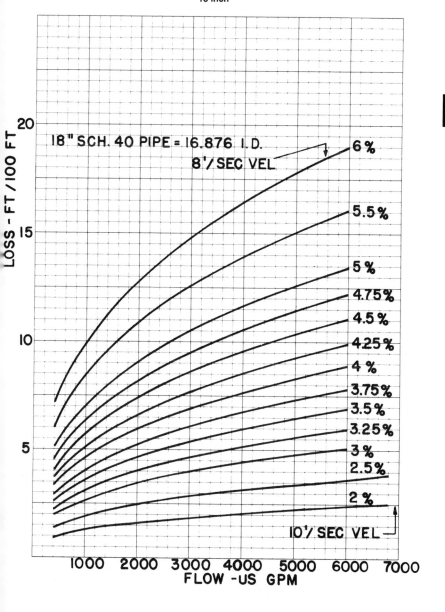

Friction of Paper Stock (Continued)

Loss in feet of water per 100 ft of pipe
Basis unbleached sulphite pulp—air dry

20 Inch

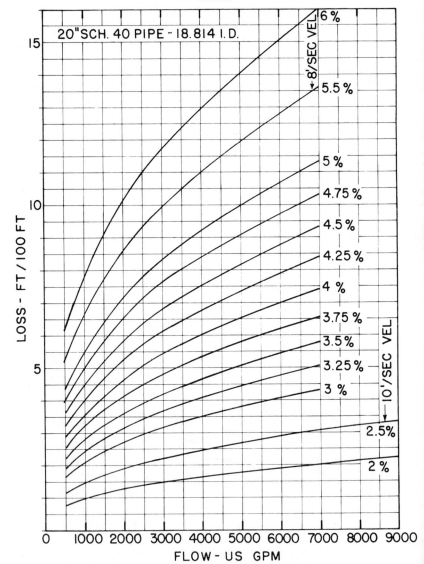

20" SCH. 40 PIPE - 18.814 I.D.

LOSS - FT / 100 FT

FLOW - US GPM

Friction loss in fittings—(paper stock)

To determine frictional resistance of paper stock flowing in elbows and tees use the chart on page 3-102; these curves are drawn for 90° short radius elbows. To determine the frictional resistance for either 90° long radius elbows or 45° elbows, multiply the results obtained from the chart by a 0.8 factor. To determine the frictional resistance of a standard tee, multiply the results obtained from the chart by a 1.7 factor. The following example demonstrates how to use the chart.

Find the frictional resistance in an 8 in. schedule 40, short radius 90° steel elbow for 900 gallons per minute of 3% air dry consistency unbleached sulphite paper stock. Entering the chart with 900 gallons per minute, move horizontally to the intersection of the 8 in. curve. Proceeding vertically to the intersection of the 3% air dry consistency curve results in a frictional resistance value of 1 foot.

For fittings with internal diameters different from schedule 40 steel fittings, it is necessary to determine the flow velocity. The chart can then be entered on the velocity scale and projected upward to the intersection with the consistency curves. The frictional resistance can now be read as before. For the various types of paper stock, the K values from the table on page 3-89 should be used as multipliers of the frictional resistance.

See Page 3-103 for general information on Pulp & Paper Industry.

Friction of Paper Stock (Continued)
Through 90° Elbows

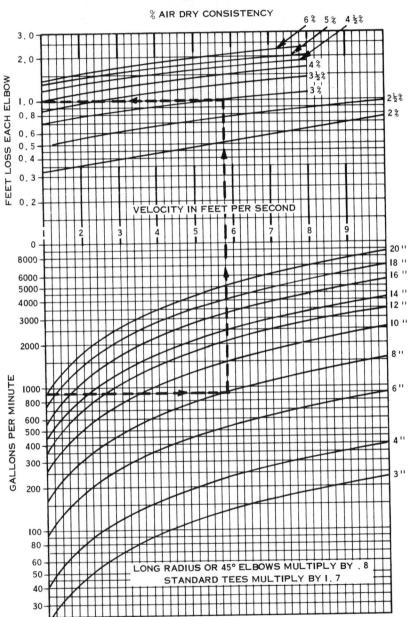

LONG RADIUS OR 45° ELBOWS MULTIPLY BY .8
STANDARD TEES MULTIPLY BY 1.7

Courtesy Goulds Pumps, Inc.

General Information—Pulp and Paper Industry*

Definitions of Commonly Used Terms:

Fiber(s): Cellulosic cell structures derived from the original plantlife source or from previously manufactured paper products; normally considered as water insoluble.

Pulp: A composite mixture of cellulosic fibers constituting the basic material used for paper making.

Stock: A designation of pulp (fibers) in process flow. In this Section, the terms "stock" or "paper stock" denote pulp (fibers) and water mixtures or suspensions. This usage excludes the presence of non-cellulosic materials such as fillers or dissolved solids.

Consistency: Equivalent to the terms "suspended solids" or "insoluble solids." In this Section, "consistency" is defined as the fiber or pulp content expressed as a weight percentage of a paper stock, pulp slurry, or pulp cake (fiber-water mixtures).

Oven Dry: Abbreviated as OD and signifying a moisture-free condition of pulp (fibers).

Air Dry: Abbreviated as AD and denoting an assumed moisture content of 10%, on a wet weight basis, for a pulp (fibers).

$$AD \text{ value} = 1.11 \times OD \text{ value}$$

$$OD \text{ value} = 0.90 \times AD \text{ value}$$

Tons Per Day: Pulp mill production rate, generally expressed as tons of OD or AD pulp per day or 24 hours. The production rate can be calculated as follows:

Short Tons of Pulp per Day

$$= (\text{Stock Flow in US GPM}) (C) (0.06)$$

Where: C = stock consistency expressed as a percentage

0.06 = derived constant

* Courtesy of IMPCO Division, Ingersoll-Rand Company, Nashua, N.H. 03060.

Notes: (1) Use OD consistency value to obtain OD pulp production rate.

Use AD consistency value to obtain AD pulp production rate.

(2) The equation constant, C, was derived by use of water density value of 8.34 lb/U.S. gallon, the density value at 55°F; therefore, the equation is accurate only at stock consistencies of 0.1% or less, and at a stock temperature of 55°F.

Solutions of the production rate equation for a normal range of stock flow and consistencies are shown on the chart on page 3-109.

Example: What is the flow in US GPM of 5.0% OD consistency stock equivalent to a production rate of 100 short tons of OD pulp per day?

Solution: Locate 100 TPD value on Y-axis and follow horizontal line until it intersects the 5.0% consistency line. Follow vertical line from the point of intersection to the X-axis and read 333 US GPM as the stock flow equivalent.

Note: Chart can be used for either OD or AD values but not for mixed values.

Weight and Volume Relationships for Cellulose Fiber-Water Suspensions

The accompanying Tables (1, 2, 3 and 4) indicate weight and volume relationships for cellulose fiber-water suspensions.

The appropriate values given in Tables 2, 3 and 4 were calculated to reflect stock density change with change in pulp (fiber) content of the stock. An equation, shown below, was derived to enable calculation of stock density at any given stock consistency.

$$\text{Stock Density (lb/gal)} = (8.34) + (3.33 \times \% \text{ cons.})$$

Where: 8.34 = lb water in US Gal. @ 55°F
       3.33 = rate of change factor
    % Cons. = % OD Stock consistency, expressed as a decimal.

Commonly required weight-volume relationships are listed in Tables 1, 2, 3 and 4 along with values calculated using the equations shown in Table 1. Constants used are:

$$(1) \quad 1.388 = \frac{2000 \text{ lb/short ton}}{1440 \text{ minutes/day}}$$

$$(2) \quad 7.48 = {}^*\text{U.S. Gallons/Cubic Foot}$$

$$(3) \quad 8.34 = {}^{**}\text{lb/U.S. Gallon of water @ 55°F}$$
(corresponding to 62.39 lb per cu ft.)

In using the equations in Table 1 the values for Column E should be determined first, then proceed alphabetically starting with Column B.

Table 1.
Explanation of Equations Used

$A = \%$ O.D. consistency	A	Lb of O.D. fiber in 100 lbs of stock. % O.D. cons.
$B = \dfrac{1.388}{E}$	B	Gal of stock per min per ton of O.D. fiber per 24 hours
$C = E \times 7.48$	C	Lb of O.D. fiber in 1 cu ft of stock
$D = \dfrac{1}{E \times 7.48} = \dfrac{1}{C}$	D	Cu ft of stock having 1 lb of O.D. fiber
$E = \dfrac{A}{100} \times L$	E	Lb of O.D. fiber in 1 gal of stock
$F = \dfrac{1}{\frac{A}{100} \times L} = \dfrac{1}{E}$	F	Gal of stock having 1 lb of O.D. fiber
$G = \dfrac{1.388}{E \times 7.48} = \dfrac{1.388}{C}$	G	Cu ft of stock per min per ton of O.D. fiber per 24 hours
$H = \dfrac{1.388 \times L}{E}$	H	Lb of stock per min per ton of O.D. fiber per 24 hours
$I = \dfrac{100}{A} - 1$	I	Lb of water per lb of O.D. fiber
$J = \left\lvert \dfrac{100}{A} - 1 \right\rvert \times \dfrac{1}{8.34} = \dfrac{I}{8.34}$	J	Gal of water per lb of O.D. fiber
$K = \left\lvert \dfrac{100}{A} - 1 \right\rvert \times \dfrac{2000}{8.34} = \dfrac{I \times 2000}{8.34}$	K	Gal of water per ton of O.D. fiber
$L = 8.34 + \left\lvert 3.33 \times \dfrac{A}{100} \right\rvert$	L	Lb total wt per gal of stock

Weight-Volume Relationships

Table 2—Weight and Volume Relationships for Cellulose Fiber-water Suspensions

Based on oven dry (OD) fiber

Range 0.000% to 1.60%

% Cons / Lb of OD fiber in 100 lb of stock	Gal of stock per min per ton of OD fiber per 24 hours	Lb of OD fiber in 1 cu ft of stock	Cu ft of stock having 1 lb of OD fiber	Lbs of OD fiber in 1 gal of stock	Gal of stock having 1 lb of OD fiber	Cu ft of stock per min per ton of OD fiber per 24 hours	Lbs of stock per min per ton of OD fiber per 24 hours	Lbs of water per lb of OD fiber	Gal of water per lb of OD fiber	Gal of water per ton of OD fiber	Lb total wt per gal of stock
.000											
0.05	330.5	0.0314	31.9	.0042	238	44.2	2757	1999	240	479377	8.34
0.10	173.5	0.0598	16.9	.008	125	23.2	1447	999	120	239568	8.34
0.20	83.1	0.127	7.87	.017	58.8	10.9	682	499	59.8	119664	8.35
0.30	55.5	0.187	5.35	.025	40.0	7.42	464	332	39.8	79617	8.35
0.40	41.6	0.247	4.05	.033	30.3	5.62	351	249	29.9	59713	8.35
.50	33.2	0.313	3.20	.042	23.9	4.44	278	199	23.9	47722	8.36
.55	30.2	0.344	2.91	.046	21.8	4.04	253	181	21.7	43406	8.36
.60	27.7	0.375	2.67	.050	19.9	3.70	231	166	19.9	39808	8.36
.65	25.6	0.406	2.46	.054	18.4	3.42	214	153	18.3	36691	8.36
.70	23.7	0.438	2.29	.058	17.1	3.17	198	142	17.1	34053	8.36
.75	22.1	0.469	2.13	.0627	16.0	3.00	185	132	15.9	31655	8.36
.80	20.7	0.500	2.00	.067	15.0	2.77	174	124	14.9	29736	8.37
.85	19.5	0.532	1.88	.0711	14.1	2.61	163	117	14.0	28058	8.37
.90	18.4	0.563	1.78	.0753	13.3	2.47	154	110	13.2	26379	8.37
.95	17.5	0.595	1.68	.0795	12.6	2.34	146	104	12.5	24940	8.37
1.00	16.6	0.626	1.60	.0837	12.0	2.22	139	99	11.9	23741	8.37
1.10	15.1	0.689	1.45	.0922	10.9	2.01	126	90	10.8	21583	8.38
1.20	13.8	0.751	1.33	.1006	9.95	1.85	116	82.3	9.87	19736	8.38
1.30	12.8	0.814	1.23	.109	9.18	1.70	107	75.9	9.10	18202	8.38
1.40	11.8	0.877	1.14	.117	8.53	1.58	99.2	70.4	8.45	16883	8.38
1.50	11.0	0.941	1.06	.126	7.95	1.48	92.5	65.7	7.87	15756	8.39

* Basis U.S. Gallons.
** Basis temperature of approximately 55°F.

Table 3—Weight and Volume Relationships for Cellulose Fiber-water Suspensions

Weight-Volume Relationships

Based on oven dry (OD) fiber   Range 1.60% to 5.00%

% Cons — Lb of OD fiber in 100 lb of stock	Gal of stock per min per ton of OD fiber per 24 hours	Lbs of OD fiber in 1 cu ft of stock	Cu ft of stock having 1 lb of OD fiber	Lbs of OD fiber in 1 gal of stock	Gal of stock having 1 lb of OD fiber	Cu ft of stock per min per ton of OD fiber per 24 hours	Lb of stock per min per ton of OD fiber per 24 hours	Lb of water per lb of OD fiber	Gal of water per lb of OD fiber	Gal of water per ton of OD fiber	Lb total wt per gal of stock
1.60	10.3	1.0038	.996	.134	7.45	1.38	86.7	61.5	7.37	14748	8.39
1.70	9.73	1.0666	.938	.143	7.01	1.30	81.7	57.8	6.93	13861	8.39
1.80	9.19	1.130	.885	.151	6.62	1.23	77.1	54.6	6.54	13094	8.40
1.90	8.70	1.193	.838	.160	6.27	1.16	73.1	51.6	6.19	12374	8.40
2.00	8.26	1.256	.796	.168	5.95	1.10	69.4	49.0	5.88	11751	8.40
2.20	7.51	1.383	0.723	.185	5.41	1.00	63.2	44.5	5.33	10672	8.41
2.40	6.88	1.510	0.662	.202	4.95	0.919	57.9	40.7	4.88	9760	8.42
2.60	6.34	1.637	0.611	.219	4.57	0.848	53.4	37.5	4.49	8993	8.42
2.80	5.88	1.765	0.567	.236	4.24	0.787	49.6	34.7	4.16	8321	8.43
3.00	5.49	1.892	0.528	.253	3.95	0.733	46.3	32.3	3.88	7746	8.44
3.25	5.06	2.05	0.487	.274	3.65	0.676	42.7	29.8	3.57	7146	8.44
3.50	4.69	2.21	0.452	.296	3.38	0.628	39.7	27.6	3.31	6619	8.45
3.75	4.38	2.37	0.422	.317	3.15	0.585	37.0	25.7	3.08	6163	8.46
4.00	4.10	2.53	0.395	.339	2.95	0.548	34.7	24.0	2.88	5755	8.47
4.25	3.85	2.69	0.371	.360	2.78	0.515	32.7	22.5	2.70	5396	8.48
4.50	3.64	2.85	0.350	.382	2.62	0.486	30.9	21.2	2.54	5084	8.48
4.75	3.44	3.02	0.332	.403	2.48	0.460	29.2	20.1	2.40	4820	8.49
5.00	3.27	3.18	0.315	.425	2.35	0.437	27.8	19.0	2.28	4556	8.50

3

Weight-Volume Relationships

Table 4—Weight and Volume Relationships for Cellulose Fiber-water Suspensions

% Cons (Lb of OD fiber in 100 lb of stock)	Gal of stock per min per ton of OD fiber per 24 hours	Lb of OD fiber in 1 cu ft of stock	Cu ft of stock having 1 lb of OD fiber	Lbs of OD fiber in 1 gal of stock	Gal of stock having 1 lb of OD fiber	Cu ft of stock per min per ton of OD fiber per 24 hours	Lb of stock per min per ton of OD fiber per 24 hours	Lb of water per lb of OD fiber	Gal of water per lb of OD fiber	Gal of water per ton of OD fiber	Lb total wt per gal of stock
		Based on oven dry (OD) fiber						Range 5%–30% consistency			
5.00	3.27	3.18	0.315	0.425	2.35	0.437	27.8	19.0	2.28	4556	8.50
5.25	3.11	3.34	0.299	0.447	2.24	0.416	26.5	18.1	2.16	4341	8.51
5.50	2.97	3.50	0.286	0.468	2.14	0.396	25.3	17.2	2.06	4125	8.52
5.75	2.83	3.67	0.273	0.490	2.04	0.379	24.2	16.4	1.97	3933	8.53
6.00	2.71	3.83	0.261	0.512	1.95	0.363	23.1	15.7	1.88	3765	8.53
6.25	2.60	3.99	0.251	0.534	1.87	0.348	22.2	15.0	1.80	3597	8.54
6.50	2.50	4.16	0.241	0.556	1.80	0.334	21.4	14.4	1.72	3453	8.55
6.75	2.40	4.32	0.232	0.577	1.73	0.321	20.6	13.8	1.66	3309	8.56
7.00	2.32	4.48	0.223	0.599	1.67	0.310	19.8	13.3	1.59	3189	8.57
7.25	2.23	4.65	0.215	0.621	1.61	0.299	19.2	12.8	1.53	3070	8.57
7.50	2.16	4.81	0.208	0.644	1.55	0.288	18.5	12.3	1.48	2950	8.58
7.75	2.09	4.98	0.201	0.666	1.50	0.279	17.9	11.9	1.43	2854	8.59
8.00	2.02	5.14	0.194	0.688	1.45	0.270	17.4	11.5	1.38	2758	8.60
8.50	1.90	5.48	0.183	0.732	1.37	0.253	16.3	10.8	1.29	2590	8.62
9.00	1.79	5.81	0.172	0.777	1.29	0.239	15.4	10.1	1.21	2422	8.63
9.50	1.69	6.14	0.163	0.821	1.22	0.226	14.6	9.53	1.14	2285	8.65
10.00	1.60	6.48	0.154	0.866	1.15	0.214	13.9	9.00	1.08	2158	8.67
10.50	1.52	6.82	0.147	0.912	1.10	0.204	13.2	8.52	1.02	2043	8.68
11.00	1.45	7.16	0.140	0.957	1.05	0.194	12.6	8.09	0.970	1940	8.70
11.50	1.39	7.50	0.133	1.00	0.998	0.185	12.1	7.70	0.923	1847	8.72
12.00	1.33	7.84	0.128	1.05	0.954	0.177	11.6	7.33	0.879	1758	8.74
13	1.22	8.53	0.117	1.14	0.877	0.163	10.7	6.69	0.802	1604	8.77
14	1.13	9.22	0.109	1.23	0.812	0.151	9.92	6.14	0.737	1472	8.80
15	1.05	9.92	0.101	1.33	0.754	0.140	9.25	5.67	0.680	1360	8.84
16	0.978	10.6	0.0942	1.42	0.704	0.131	8.68	5.25	0.630	1259	8.88
17	0.917	11.3	0.0883	1.51	0.661	0.123	8.17	4.88	0.585	1170	8.91
18	0.862	12.0	0.0831	1.61	0.621	0.115	7.72	4.56	0.546	1094	8.95
19	0.814	12.8	0.0784	1.71	0.586	0.109	7.31	4.26	0.511	1022	8.98
20	0.770	13.5	0.0741	1.80	0.555	0.103	6.94	4.00	0.480	959.2	9.02
22	0.694	15.0	0.0668	2.00	0.500	0.0928	6.31	3.55	0.425	851.3	9.09
24	0.631	16.5	0.0608	2.20	0.455	0.0843	5.78	3.17	0.380	760.2	9.17
26	0.578	18.0	0.0557	2.40	0.416	0.0772	5.34	2.85	0.341	683.5	9.25
28	0.532	19.5	0.0512	2.61	0.383	0.0711	4.96	2.57	0.308	616.3	9.32
30	0.492	21.1	0.0474	2.82	0.355	0.0658	4.63	2.33	0.280	558.8	9.40

Pulp and Paper Data
Relationship of Pulp Production Rate to Stock Flow
At Various Stock Consistencies
(Tons of Pulp per 24 Hours Versus U.S. G.P.M.)

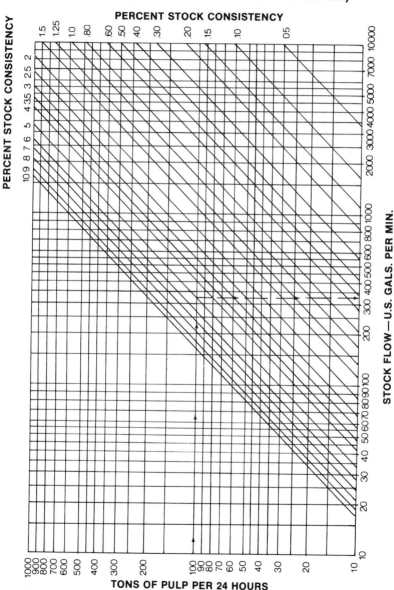

Note: Use OD % Consistency with Tons of OD Pulp.
Use AD % Consistency with Tons of AD Pulp.

Friction of Water
Head Losses Through Valves and Fittings

Head losses (h_f) through valves, fittings, sudden contractions and enlargements, entrance and exit losss can be expressed in terms of the velocity head ($V^2/2g$) by using the applicable resistance coefficient (K) in the equations:

$$h_f = K \frac{V^2}{2g} = K(0.0155)V^2 = K \frac{(0.00259)\text{gpm}^2}{d^4}$$

Select applicable (K) from tables on pages 3-111 to 3-117; select (V) for average velocity in pipe of diameter required to accommodate fitting; see examples on page 3-119.

A second method of expressing head losses (h_f) through valves and fittings etc. is in terms of the equivalent length of straight pipe that will produce the same loss as calculated by the Darcy-Weisbach equation for straight pipe. (See table on page 3-120).

The applicable equations are:

$$h_f = \left(f \frac{L}{D} \right) \frac{V^2}{2g} \; ; \quad K = f \frac{L}{D} \; ; \quad L = \frac{KD}{f}$$

where
- d = pipe diameter—inches
- D = pipe diameter in feet
- f = friction factor (from chart, Page 3-11) for zone of complete turbulence.
- g = gravitational constant—32.174 ft/sec²
- h_f = head loss in feet of liquid
- K = resistance coefficient (from tables on pages 3-111 to 3-120) is based on test data, or extrapolated from test data; and depends on design, size and type of fitting.
- L = friction loss in pipe fittings in terms of equivalent length in feet of straight pipe (See table page 3-120).
- V = average velocity in pipe of diameter required to accommodate fitting—ft/sec.

From the above one can solve for (L) and L/D ratio using the value of K from the tables and selecting f for the zone of complete turbulence.

A third method of expressing head losses, particularly for control valves, is in terms of a flow coefficient C_v. This is defined as the flow of liquid at 60°F in gallons per minute at a pressure drop of one pound per square inch across the valve. The relationship of C_v and K is shown by the following formulas.

$$C_v = \frac{29.9 \times d^2}{\sqrt{K}} \text{ and } K = \frac{894 \times d^4}{(C_v)^2}$$

The tables on pages 3-111 to 3-119 list K values for schedule 40 pipe in sizes up to and including 24″ and are based on flows for complete turbulence.

Since the K values between pipe sizes are close, it is reasonable to interpolate between sizes if they do not correspond to schedule 40 diameters.

For K values for pipes larger than 24″ it is suggested that the 24″ value be used.

The above text and tables on pages 3-111 to 3-120 are based on material in Crane Co. Technical Paper No. 410*. Reference to this paper is suggested for more complete review of this subject.

* It should be noted that there is considerable variation in published values of resistance coefficient K for different valves and fittings.

Friction of Water (Continued)
Friction Loss in Pipe Fittings

Resistance coefficient K $\left(\text{use in formula } h_f = K\dfrac{V^2}{2g} \right)$

Note: Fittings are standard with full openings.

Fitting	L/D	Nominal pipe size											
		1/2	3/4	1	1 1/4	1 1/2	2	2 1/2–3	4	6	8–10	12–16	18–24
		K value											
Gate Valves	8	0.22	0.20	0.18	0.18	0.15	0.15	0.14	0.14	0.12	0.11	0.10	**0.10**
Globe Valves	340	9.2	8.5	7.8	7.5	7.1	6.5	6.1	5.8	5.1	4.8	4.4	**4.1**
Angle Valves	55	1.48	1.38	1.27	1.21	1.16	1.05	0.99	0.94	0.83	0.77	0.72	**0.66**
Angle Valves	150	4.05	3.75	3.45	3.30	3.15	2.85	2.70	2.55	2.25	2.10	1.95	**1.80**
Ball Valves	3	0.08	0.08	0.07	0.07	0.06	0.06	0.05	0.05	0.05	0.04	0.04	**0.04**

Calculated from data in Crane Co. Technical Paper No. 410.

3

Note: Fittings are standard with full openings.

Friction of Water (Continued)
Friction Losses in Pipe Fittings

Resistance coefficient K $\left(\text{use in formula } h_f = K \dfrac{V^2}{2g} \right)$

Fitting	L/D	1/2	3/4	1	1¼	1½	2	2½-3	4	6	8-10	12-16	18-24
								K value					
Butterfly Valve							0.86	0.81	0.77	0.68	0.63	0.35	0.30
Plug Valve straightway	18	0.49	0.45	0.41	0.40	0.38	0.34	0.32	0.31	0.27	0.25	0.23	0.22
Plug Valve 3-way thru-flo	30	0.81	0.75	0.69	0.66	0.63	0.57	0.54	0.51	0.45	0.42	0.39	0.36
Plug Valve branch-flo	90	2.43	2.25	2.07	1.98	1.89	1.71	1.62	1.53	1.35	1.26	1.17	1.08
Standard elbow 90°	30	0.81	0.75	0.69	0.66	0.63	0.57	0.54	0.54	0.45	0.42	0.39	0.36
Standard elbow 45°	16	0.43	0.40	0.37	0.35	0.34	0.30	0.29	0.27	0.24	0.22	0.21	0.19
Standard elbow long radius 90°	16	0.43	0.40	0.37	0.35	0.34	0.30	0.29	0.27	0.24	0.22	0.21	0.19

Nominal pipe size

Calculated from data in Crane Co. Technical Paper No. 410

Friction of Water *(Continued)*
Friction Losses in Pipe Fittings

Resistance coefficient K $\left(\text{use in formula } h_f = K \dfrac{V^2}{2g} \right)$

Note: Fittings are standard with full openings.

Fitting	Type of bend	L/D	½	¾	1	1¼	1½	2	2½–3	4	6	8–10	12–16	18–24
									K value					
Close Return Bend		50	1.35	1.25	1.15	1.10	1.05	0.95	0.90	0.85	0.75	0.70	0.65	0.60
Standard Tee	thru flo	20	0.54	0.50	0.46	0.44	0.42	0.38	0.36	0.34	0.30	0.28	0.26	0.24
	thru branch	60	1.62	1.50	1.38	1.32	1.26	1.14	1.08	1.02	0.90	0.84	0.78	0.72
90° Bends, Pipe bends, flanged elbows, butt welded elbows	r/d = 1	20	0.54	0.50	0.46	0.44	0.42	0.38	0.36	0.34	0.30	0.28	0.26	0.24
	r/d = 2	12	0.32	0.30	0.28	0.26	0.25	0.23	0.22	0.20	0.18	0.17	0.16	0.14
	r/d = 3	12	0.32	0.30	0.28	0.26	0.25	0.23	0.22	0.20	0.18	0.17	0.16	0.14
	r/d = 4	14	0.38	0.35	0.32	0.31	0.29	0.27	0.25	0.24	0.21	0.20	0.18	0.17
	r/d = 6	17	0.46	0.43	0.39	0.37	0.36	0.32	0.31	0.29	0.26	0.24	0.22	0.20
	r/d = 8	24	0.65	0.60	0.55	0.53	0.50	0.46	0.43	0.41	0.36	0.34	0.31	0.29
	r/d = 10	30	0.81	0.75	0.69	0.66	0.63	0.57	0.54	0.51	0.45	0.42	0.39	0.36
	r/d = 12	34	0.92	0.85	0.78	0.75	0.71	0.65	0.61	0.58	0.51	0.48	0.44	0.41
	r/d = 14	38	1.03	0.95	0.87	0.84	0.80	0.72	0.68	0.65	0.57	0.53	0.49	0.46
	r/d = 16	42	1.13	1.05	0.97	0.92	0.88	0.80	0.76	0.71	0.63	0.59	0.55	0.50
	r/d = 18	46	1.24	1.15	1.06	1.01	0.97	0.87	0.83	0.78	0.69	0.64	0.60	0.55
	r/d = 20	50	1.35	1.25	1.15	1.10	1.05	0.95	0.90	0.85	0.75	0.70	0.65	0.60
Mitre Bends	α = 0°	2	0.05	0.05	0.05	0.04	0.04	0.04	0.04	0.03	0.03	0.03	0.03	0.02
	α = 15°	4	0.11	0.10	0.09	0.09	0.08	0.08	0.07	0.07	0.06	0.06	0.05	
	α = 30°	8	0.22	0.20	0.18	0.18	0.17	0.15	0.14	0.14	0.12	0.11	0.10	0.10
	α = 45°	15	0.41	0.38	0.35	0.33	0.32	0.29	0.27	0.26	0.23	0.21	0.20	0.18
	α = 60°	25	0.68	0.63	0.58	0.55	0.53	0.48	0.45	0.43	0.38	0.35	0.33	0.30
	α = 75°	40	1.09	1.00	0.92	0.88	0.84	0.76	0.72	0.68	0.60	0.56	0.52	0.48
	α = 90°	60	1.62	1.50	1.38	1.32	1.26	1.14	1.08	1.02	0.90	0.84	0.78	0.72

Calculated from data in Crane Co. Technical Paper No. 410.

3

Friction of Water (Continued)
Friction Losses in Pipe Fittings

Resistance coefficient K $\left(\text{use in formula } h_f = K \dfrac{V^2}{2g}\right)$

Note: Fittings are standard with full port openings.

Fitting stop-check valves	L/D	Minimum velocity for full disc lift — general ft/sec†	Minimum velocity for full disc lift — water ft/sec	1/2	3/4	1	1¼	1½	2	2½-3	4	6	8-10	12-16	18-24
										K value*					
	400	55 √V	6.96	10.8	10	9.2	8.8	8.4	7.5	7.2	6.8	6.0	5.6	5.2	4.8
	200	75 √V	9.49	5.4	5	4.6	4.4	4.2	3.8	3.6	3.4	3.0	2.8	2.6	2.4
	350	60 √V	7.59	9.5	8.8	8.1	7.7	7.4	6.7	6.3	6.0	5.3	4.9	4.6	4.2
	300	60 √V	7.59	8.1	7.5	6.9	6.6	6.3	5.7	5.4	5.1	4.5	4.2	3.9	3.6
	55	140 √V	17.7	1.5	1.4	1.3	1.2	1.2	1.1	1.0	.94	.83	.77	.72	.66

Nominal pipe size

Calculated from data in Crane Co. Technical Paper No. 410.

Friction of Water *(Continued)*
Friction Loss in Pipe Fittings

Resistance coefficient K $\left(\text{use in formula } h_f = K\,\dfrac{V^2}{2g}\right)$

Note: Fittings are standard with full port openings.

Fitting	L/D	Minimum velocity for full disc lift — general ft/sec†	Minimum velocity for full disc lift — water ft/sec	Nominal pipe size — K value* ½	¾	1	1¼	1½	2	2½–3	4	6	8–10	12–16	18–24
Swing check valve	100	35 √V̄	4.43	2.7	2.5	2.3	2.2	2.1	1.9	1.8	1.7	1.5	1.4	1.3	1.2
	50	48 √V̄	6.08	1.4	1.3	1.2	1.1	1.1	1.0	0.9	0.9	.75	.70	.65	.6
Lift check valve	600	40 √V̄	5.06	16.2	15	13.8	13.2	12.6	11.4	10.8	10.2	9.0	8.4	7.8	7.2
	55	140 √V̄	17.7	1.5	1.4	1.3	1.2	1.2	1.1	1.0	.94	.83	.77	.72	.66
Tilting disc check valve	5°	80 √V̄	10.13						.76	.72	.68	.60	.56	.39	.24
	15°	30 √V̄	3.80						2.3	2.2	2.0	1.8	1.7	1.2	.72
Foot valve with strainer poppet disc	420	15 √V̄	1.90	11.3	10.5	9.7	9.3	8.8	8.0	7.6	7.1	6.3	5.9	5.5	5.0
Foot valve with strainer hinged disc	75	35 √V̄	4.43	2.0	1.9	1.7	1.7	1.7	1.4	1.4	1.3	1.1	1.1	1.0	.90

Calculated from data in Crane Co. Technical Paper No. 410.
* These K values for flow giving full disc lift. K values are higher for low flows giving partial disc lift.
† In these formulas, V, is specific volume—ft³/lb.

Friction of Water *(Continued)*
Friction Loss in Pipe Fittings

Resistance coefficient $\left(\text{use in formula } h_f = K \dfrac{V^2}{2g}\right)$

Fitting	Description	All pipe sizes
		K value
Pipe exit	projecting sharp edged rounded	1.0
Pipe entrance	inward projecting	0.78
Pipe entrance flush	sharp edged	0.5
	r/d = 0.02	0.28
	r/d = 0.04	0.24
	r/d = 0.06	0.15
	r/d = 0.10	0.09
	r/d = 0.15 & up	0.04

From Crane Co. Technical Paper 410.

Friction of Water (Continued)

Friction Loss Due to Change in Pipe Size—Feet of Liquid
Loss of head in ft of liquid
Based on velocity in smaller pipe

Sudden Enlargements

Velocity of d₁ fps	\(d_1/d_2\)								
	0.9	0.8	0.7	0.6	0.5	0.4	0.3	0.2	0.1
2	.00	.01	.02	.03	.03	.04	.05	.06	.06
3	.01	.02	.04	.06	.08	.10	.12	.13	.14
4	.01	.03	.06	.10	.14	.17	.21	.23	.24
5	.01	.05	.10	.16	.22	.27	.32	.36	.38
6	.02	.07	.15	.23	.31	.39	.46	.51	.55
7	.03	.10	.20	.31	.43	.53	.63	.70	.75
8	.04	.13	.26	.41	.56	.70	.83	.92	.97
9	.05	.16	.33	.52	.70	.88	1.04	1.16	1.23
10	.06	.20	.40	.64	.87	1.09	1.29	1.43	1.52
12	.08	.29	.58	.92	1.25	1.57	1.86	2.06	2.19
15	.13	.45	.91	1.43	1.96	2.45	2.90	3.22	3.43
20	.22	.80	1.62	2.55	3.48	4.35	5.16	5.72	6.09
25	.35	1.26	2.53	3.98	5.44	6.80	8.06	8.94	9.52
30	.50	1.82	3.64	5.73	7.83	9.79	11.6	12.9	13.7
40	.90	3.23	6.46	10.2	13.9	17.4	20.6	22.9	24.4
K value	.036	.13	.26	.41	.56	.70	.83	.92	.98

Sudden Contractions

\(d_1/d_2\)										Velocity of d₁ fps
0.1	0.2	0.3	0.4	0.5	0.6	0.7	0.8	0.9		
.03	.03	.03	.03	.02	.02	.02	.01	.01		2
.07	.07	.06	.06	.05	.04	.03	.03	.01		3
.12	.12	.11	.10	.09	.08	.06	.04	.02		4
.19	.19	.18	.16	.15	.12	.10	.07	.04		5
.28	.27	.26	.23	.21	.18	.14	.10	.05		6
.38	.37	.35	.32	.29	.24	.19	.14	.07		7
.50	.48	.46	.42	.38	.32	.25	.18	.09		8
.63	.60	.56	.53	.48	.40	.31	.23	.12		9
.77	.75	.71	.65	.59	.50	.38	.28	.15		10
1.12	1.07	1.03	.94	.85	.72	.56	.40	.21		12
1.75	1.68	1.61	1.47	1.33	1.12	.87	.63	.33		15
3.10	2.98	2.86	2.61	2.36	1.99	1.55	1.12	.59		20
4.86	4.66	4.47	4.08	3.69	3.11	2.43	1.75	.92		25
6.99	6.71	6.43	5.87	5.31	4.48	3.50	2.52	1.32		30
12.4	11.9	11.4	10.4	9.45	7.96	6.22	4.48	2.36		40
.50	.48	.46	.42	.38	.32	.25	.18	.095		K value

For sudden enlargements $K = \left(1 - \dfrac{d_1^2}{d_2^2}\right)^2$

For sudden contractions $K = 0.5\left(1 - \dfrac{d_1^2}{d_2^2}\right)$

Calculated from formula $h_f = K \dfrac{V^2}{2g}$

Example: Assume $d_1 = 6''$; $d_2 = 10''$; velocity $d_1 = 10$ fps; $\dfrac{d_1}{d_2} = 0.60$

From chart: for sudden enlargements: $h_f = 0.64$ feet
from sudden contractions: $h_f = 0.50$ feet

Friction of Water *(Continued)*
Formulas for Calculating "K" Factors
for Sudden and Gradual Contractions and Enlargements

(K values are for velocity in the small pipe)

Gradual Contraction (Based on velocity in small pipe)

1) $\theta < 45°$ $K = 0.8 \sin \dfrac{\theta}{2} \left(1 - \dfrac{d_1^2}{d_2^2} \right)$

2) $\theta > 45° < 180°$ $K = 0.5 \left(1 - \dfrac{d_1^2}{d_2^2} \right) \sqrt{\sin \dfrac{\theta}{2}}$

Gradual Enlargement (Based on velocity in small pipe)

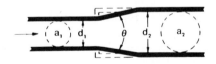

3) $\theta < 45°$ $K = 2.6 \sin \dfrac{\theta}{2} \left(1 - \dfrac{d_1^2}{d_2^2} \right)^2$

4) $\theta > 45° < 180°$ $K = \left(1 - \dfrac{d_1^2}{d_2^2} \right)^2$

Substitute above values of K in formula $h_f = K \dfrac{V^2}{2g}$ If desired,

areas can be used instead of diameters in which case substitute

$\dfrac{a_1}{a_2}$ for $\dfrac{d_1^2}{d_2^2}$ and $\left(\dfrac{a_1}{a_2} \right)^2$ for $\left(\dfrac{d_1}{d_2} \right)^4$

Friction of Water
Friction Loss in Pipe Fittings

Resistance coefficient K $\left(\text{use in formula } h_f = K \dfrac{V^2}{2g} \right)$

The K factors in the table below are given for use in making estimates of friction loss for fittings not covered in the preceding pages.

Type of fitting	K value
Disk or wobble meter	3.4 to 10
Rotary meter (star or cog-wheel piston)	10
Reciprocating piston meter	15
Turbine wheel (double-flow) meter	5 to 7.5
Bends having corrugated inner radius	1.3 to 1.6 times value for smooth bend

3

Example: Determine L (Friction loss in pipe fittings in terms of equivalent length in feet of straight pipe). Assume a 6″ angle valve— Schedule 40 pipe size. Select K from table on page 3-111; select D and f for schedule 40 pipe from table below where D is pipe diameter in feet.

Pipe size inches sch. 40	D Feet	f	Pipe size inches sch. 40	D Feet	f	Pipe size inches sch. 40	D Feet	f	Pipe size inches	D Feet	f
½	0.0518	0.027	2½	0.2058	0.018	10	0.835	0.014	24	1.8857	0.012
			3	0.2557	0.018	12	0.9948	0.013	30*	2.3333	0.011
¾	0.0687	0.025	4	0.3355	0.017	14	1.0937	0.013	36*	2.8333	0.011
1	0.0874	0.023	5	0.4206	0.016	16	1.250	0.013	42*	3.3333	0.010
1¼	0.115	0.022	6	0.5054	0.015	18	1.4063	0.012	48*	3.8333	0.010
1½	0.1342	0.021	8	0.6651	0.014	20	1.5678	0.012			
2	0.1723	0.019									

Based on 1″ thick wall.

Solution: For angle valve in 6″ pipe

K from page 3-111 = 2.25; D = 0.5054; f = 0.015

$$L = \frac{KD}{f} = \frac{2.25 \times 0.5054}{0.015} = 75.8 \text{ ft.}$$—equivalent length of straight

pipe. (this is shown in the table on page 3-120)

For an example not covered in the table on page 3-120, take a 4″ plug valve with flow through branch (From page 3-112; K = 1.53)

$$L = \frac{KD}{f} = \frac{1.53 \times 0.3355}{0.017}$$

$$= 30.2 \text{ ft.}$$—equivalent length of straight pipe.

Friction loss of water in pipe fittings in terms of equivalent length—(L)—feet of straight pipe

Nominal pipe size	Actual inside diameter inches d	Friction factor f	Gate valve full open	90° elbow	Long radius 90° or 45° std elbow	Std tee thru flow	Std tee branch flow	Close return bend	Swing check valve full open	Angle valve full open	Globe valve full open	Butterfly valve	90° Welding elbow r/d = 1	90° Welding elbow r/d = 2	Mitre bend 45°	Mitre bend 90°
½	.622	.027	.41	1.55	.83	1.04	3.11	2.59	5.18	7.78	17.6					
¾	.824	.025	.55	2.06	1.10	1.37	4.12	3.43	6.86	10.3	23.3					
1	1.049	.023	.70	2.62	1.40	1.75	5.25	4.37	8.74	13.1	29.7					
1¼	1.380	.022	.92	3.45	1.84	2.30	6.90	5.75	11.5	17.3	39.1					
1½	1.610	.021	1.07	4.03	2.15	2.68	8.05	6.71	13.4	20.1	45.6					
2	2.067	.019	1.38	5.17	2.76	3.45	10.3	8.61	17.2	25.8	58.6	7.75	3.45	2.07	2.58	10.3
2½	2.469	.018	1.65	6.17	3.29	4.12	12.3	10.3	20.6	30.9	70.0	9.26	4.12	2.47	3.08	12.3
3	3.068	.018	2.04	7.67	4.09	5.11	15.3	12.8	25.5	38.4	86.9	11.5	5.11	3.07	3.84	15.3
4	4.026	.017	2.68	10.1	5.37	6.71	20.1	16.8	33.6	50.3	114	15.1	6.71	4.03	5.03	20.1
5	5.047	.016	3.36	12.6	6.73	8.41	25.2	21.0	42.1	63.1	143	18.9	8.41	5.05	6.31	25.2
6	6.065	.015	4.04	15.2	8.09	10.1	30.3	25.3	50.5	75.8	172	22.7	10.1	6.07	7.58	30.3
8	7.981	.014	5.32	20.0	10.6	13.3	39.9	33.3	33.3	99.8	226	29.9	13.3	7.98	9.98	39.9
10	10.02	.014	6.68	25.1	13.4	16.7	50.1	41.8	41.8	125	284	29.2	16.7	10.0	12.5	50.1
12	11.938	.013	7.96	29.8	15.9	19.9	59.7	49.7	49.7	149	338	34.8	19.9	11.9	14.9	59.7
14	13.124	.013	8.75	32.8	17.5	21.8	65.6	54.7	54.7	164	372	38.3	21.8	13.1	16.4	65.6
16	15.00	.013	10.0	37.5	20.0	25.0	75.0	62.5	62.5	188	425	31.3	25.0	15.0	18.8	75.0
18	16.876	.012	11.3	42.2	22.5	28.1	84.4	70.3	70.3	210	478	35.2	28.1	16.9	21.1	84.4
20	18.814	.012	12.5	47.0	25.1	31.4	94.1	78.4	78.4	235	533	39.2	31.4	18.8	23.5	94.1
24	22.628	.012	15.1	56.6	30.2	37.7	113	94.3	94.3	283	641	47.1	37.7	22.6	28.3	113
30	28	.011	18.7	70	37.3	46.7	140	117					46.7	28	35	140
36	34	.011	22.7	85	45.3	56.7	170	142					56.7	34	43	170
42	40	.010	26.7	100	53.3	66.7	200	167					66.7	40	50	200
48	46	.010	30.7	115	61.3	76.7	230	192					76.7	46	58	230
L/D			8	30	16	20	60	50	½ to 6 =100, 24 to 48 =50	150	340		20	12	15	60

Calculated from data in Crane Co.—Technical Paper 410. $K = f\dfrac{L}{D}$; $f = \dfrac{KD}{L}$; $L = \dfrac{KD}{f}$ where D is inside pipe diameter in feet.

Friction of Water *(Continued)*
Resistance of Valves and Fittings to Flow
of Fluids in Equivalent Length of Pipe

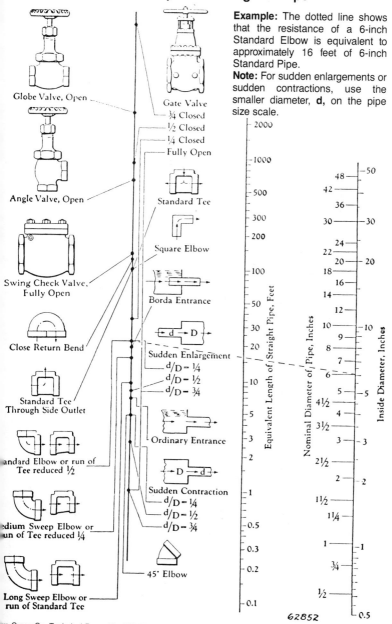

Example: The dotted line shows that the resistance of a 6-inch Standard Elbow is equivalent to approximately 16 feet of 6-inch Standard Pipe.

Note: For sudden enlargements or sudden contractions, use the smaller diameter, **d,** on the pipe size scale.

Globe Valve, Open

Angle Valve, Open

Swing Check Valve, Fully Open

Close Return Bend

Standard Tee Through Side Outlet

andard Elbow or run of Tee reduced ½

dium Sweep Elbow or un of Tee reduced ¼

Long Sweep Elbow or run of Standard Tee

Gate Valve
¾ Closed
½ Closed
¼ Closed
Fully Open

Standard Tee

Square Elbow

Borda Entrance

Sudden Enlargement
d/D = ¼
d/D = ½
d/D = ¾

Ordinary Entrance

Sudden Contraction
d/D = ¼
d/D = ½
d/D = ¾

45° Elbow

2000
1000
500
300
200
100
50
30
20
10
5
3
2
1
0.5
0.3
0.2
0.1

Equivalent Length of Straight Pipe, Feet

Nominal Diameter of Pipe, Inches
48
42
36
30
24
22
20
18
16
14
12
10
9
8
7
6
5
4½
4
3½
3
2½
2
1½
1¼
1
¾
½

Inside Diameter, Inches
50
30
20
10
5
3
2
1
0.5

62852

m Crane Co. Technical Paper No. 409. Data based on the above chart are satisfactory for most applications; for
e detailed data and information refer to pages 3-110 to page 3-120 which are based on Crane Co. Technical Paper
410.

Friction Losses—Valves and Fittings—Viscous Liquids

Very little reliable test data on losses through Valves and Fittings for viscous liquids is available. In the absence of meaningful data some engineers assume the flow is turbulent and use the equivalent length method; i.e. where friction losses through valves and fittings are expressed in terms of equivalent length of straight pipe (see pages 3-120 and 3-121). Calculations made on the basis of turbulent flow will give safe results since friction losses for turbulent flow are higher than for laminar (viscous) flow.

Miscellaneous Formulas

Discharge of fluid through valves and fittings

$$\text{gal per min} = 19.65 \, d^2 \sqrt{\frac{h_L}{K}}$$

This equation may be used for determining the flow in a system if K is the sum of all the resistances in the system including entrance and exit losses.

Where: d = pipe diameter—inches
h_L = friction loss in feet of liquid
K = sum of all resistance in the system including entrance and exit losses.

$$\text{Velocity (fps)} = \frac{0.4085 \, \text{gpm}}{d^2(\text{in.})}$$

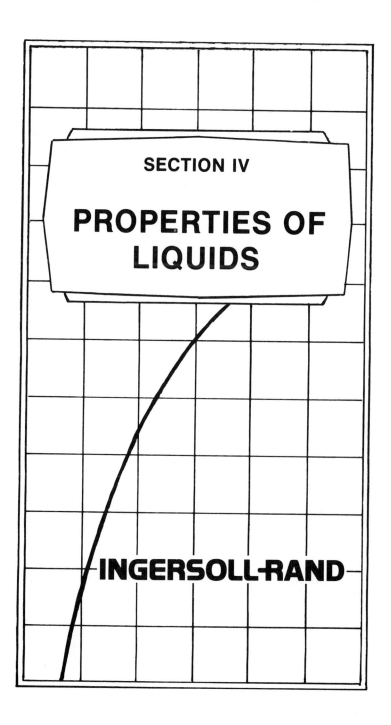

SECTION IV

PROPERTIES OF LIQUIDS

INGERSOLL-RAND

4

CONTENTS OF SECTION 4

Properties of Liquids

PROPERTIES OF LIQUIDS

Density Information

The *DENSITY* of a liquid is the amount of mass of that liquid (lb, kg, g) contained in a unit of volume (ft^3, gal., m^3, cm^3, etc.). Thus, the units of density are lb/ft^3, lb/gal., kg/m^3, g/cm^3, etc.

Because gravity exerts a force called "weight" on a given mass, the terms "weight density" or gravity of a liquid are often used.*

The *SPECIFIC GRAVITY* of a liquid is its density *relative* to that of water; i.e., its density divided by that of water. The water temperature for this purpose is usually 60°F (15.6°C) where its density is 0.9991 g/cm^3 (Page 4-4).

For some purposes a water temperature of 39.2°F (4°C) is used as a base of reference which is its point of maximum density, namely 1.000 g/cm^3; for other purposes a water temperature of 68°F (20°C) may be selected as a base of reference. The base temperature of 60°F (15.6°C) is often specified together with that of the liquid whose specific gravity is involved. Thus, 140°F water with a density of 0.9832 g/cm^3 has a specific gravity at 140°/60°F of 0.9841 (= 0.9832/0.9991).

It can be seen that the specified gravity of a liquid is about numerically equal to its density in g/cm^3. Measuring methods have led to other density units, such as degrees API or degrees Baume, which are related to specific gravity through the formulas and tables on the following pages.

SPECIFIC WEIGHT as used in various equations in this data book is the weight in lb per cu ft. The specific weight of water at 60°F (15.6°C) is 62.3714 lb/ft^3; and at 68°F (20°C) it is 62.3208 lb/ft^3. For other temperatures proper specific weight values should be used (see page 4-4); also for further discussion refer back to page 2-3.

---

* The density definition involves strictly mass. Weight and mass are numerically equal at earth sea level in the usual English system of units (where lb is properly distinguished as lb_{mass} or lb_{force}). Systems that *derive* either the mass or force unit in terms of the other via Newton's second law of motion—expressed as F = ma—(such as the International (SI) System) do not have this numerical equality, but also do not need the gravitational constant g_0 = 32.174 (lb_{mass}/lb_{force}) ft/sec^2 in calculations involving fluid motion. If the lb_{mass}-lb_{force} system is used, F = ma must be replaced by $F = \dfrac{1}{g_0}$ ma. Because of this, the factor m/g_0 (= 0.0311 × m in lb_{mass}) per unit volume is sometimes called mass density, even though the unit of density expressed as lb_{mass} per unit volume is also a "mass density". See pp. 8-3 to 8-7.

Note: g_0 is gravitational constant at sea level—32.174 ft/sec^2.

Properties of Water at Various Temperatures

Temp F	Pressure of saturated vapor lb/in² abs	Specific volume		Density specific wt.		Conversion factor ft/lb/in²	Kinematic viscosity centistokes	Temperature	
		ft³/lb	gal/lb	lb/ft³	*g/cm³			°F	°C
32	0.08859	0.016022	0.1199	62.414	0.9998	2.307	1.79	32	0
33	0.09223	0.016021	0.1198	62.418	0.9999	2.307	1.75	33	0.6
34	0.09600	0.016021	0.1198	62.418	0.9999	2.307	1.72	34	1.1
35	0.09991	0.016020	0.1198	62.420	0.9999	2.307	1.68	35	1.7
36	0.10395	0.016020	0.1198	62.420	0.9999	2.307	1.66	36	2.2
37	0.10815	0.016020	0.1198	62.420	0.9999	2.307	1.63	37	2.8
38	0.11249	0.016019	0.1198	62.425	1.0000	2.307	1.60	38	3.3
39	0.11698	0.016019	0.1198	62.425	1.0000	2.307	1.56	39	3.9
40	0.12163	0.016019	0.1198	62.425	1.0000	2.307	1.54	40	4.4
41	0.12645	0.016019	0.1198	62.426	1.0000	2.307	1.52	41	5
42	0.13143	0.016019	0.1198	62.426	1.0000	2.307	1.49	42	5.
43	0.13659	0.016019	0.1198	62.426	1.0000	2.307	1.47	43	6.
44	0.14192	0.016019	0.1198	62.426	1.0000	2.307	1.44	44	6.
45	0.14744	0.016020	0.1198	62.42	0.9999	2.307	1.42	45	7
46	0.15314	0.016020	0.1198	62.42	0.9999	2.307	1.39	46	7
47	0.15904	0.016021	0.1198	62.42	0.9999	2.307	1.37	47	8
48	0.16514	0.016021	0.1198	62.42	0.9999	2.307	1.35	48	8
49	0.17144	0.016022	0.1198	62.41	0.9998	2.307	1.33	49	9.
50	0.17796	0.016023	0.1199	62.41	0.9998	2.307	1.31	50	10
51	0.18469	0.016023	0.1199	62.41	0.9998	2.307	1.28	51	10
52	0.19165	0.016024	0.1199	62.41	0.9997	2.307	1.26	52	11
53	0.19883	0.016025	0.1199	62.40	0.9996	2.308	1.24	53	11
54	0.20625	0.016026	0.1199	62.40	0.9996	2.308	1.22	54	12
55	0.21392	0.016027	0.1199	62.39	0.9995	2.308	1.20	55	12
56	0.22183	0.016028	0.1199	62.39	0.9994	2.308	1.19	56	13
57	0.23000	0.016029	0.1199	62.39	0.9994	2.308	1.17	57	13
58	0.23843	0.016031	0.1199	62.38	0.9993	2.308	1.16	58	14
59	0.24713	0.016032	0.1199	62.38	0.9992	2.309	1.14	59	15
60	0.25611	0.016033	0.1199	62.37	0.9991	2.309	1.12	60	15
62	0.27494	0.016036	0.1200	62.36	0.9989	2.309	1.09	62	16
64	0.29497	0.016039	0.1200	62.35	0.9988	2.310	1.06	64	17
66	0.31626	0.016043	0.1200	62.33	0.9985	2.310	1.03	66	18
68	0.33889	0.016046	0.1200	62.32	0.9983	2.311	1.00	68	20
70	0.36292	0.016050	0.1201	62.31	0.9981	2.311	0.98	70	21
75	0.42964	0.016060	0.1201	62.27	0.9974	2.313	0.90	75	23
80	0.50683	0.016072	0.1202	62.22	0.9967	2.314	0.85	80	26
85	0.59583	0.016085	0.1203	62.17	0.9959	2.316	0.81	85	29
90	0.69813	0.016099	0.1204	62.12	0.9950	2.318	0.76	90	32
95	0.81534	0.016144	0.1205	62.06	0.9941	2.320	0.72	95	35
100	0.94924	0.016130	0.1207	62.00	0.9931	2.323	0.69	100	3
110	1.2750	0.016165	0.1209	61.98	0.9910	2.328	0.61	110	4.
120	1.6927	0.016204	0.1212	61.71	0.9886	2.333	0.57	120	48
130	2.2230	0.016247	0.1215	61.56	0.9860	2.340	0.51	130	5.
140	2.8892	0.016293	0.1219	61.38	0.9832	2.346	0.47	140	60
150	3.7184	0.016343	0.1223	61.19	0.9802	2.353	0.44	150	6
160	4.7414	0.016395	0.1226	60.99	0.9771	2.361	0.41	160	7
170	5.9926	0.016451	0.1231	60.79	0.9737	2.369	0.38	170	7
180	7.5110	0.016510	0.1235	60.57	0.9703	2.377	0.36	180	8
190	9.340	0.016572	0.1240	60.34	0.9666	2.386	0.33	190	8

* Approximately numerically equal to specific gravity basis temperature reference of 39.2°F (4°C).
Calculated from data in ASME Steam Tables.

Note: For complete Steam Tables see pages 5-7 through 5-24.

Properties of Water at Various Temperatures (*Continued*)

Temp F	Pressure of saturated vapor lb/in² abs	Specific volume		Density specific wt.		Conversion factor ft/lb/in²	Kinematic viscosity centistokes	Temperature	
		ft³/lb	gal/lb	lb/ft³	*g/cm³			°F	°C
200	11.526	0.016637	0.1245	60.11	0.9628	2.396	0.31	200	93.3
210	14.123	0.016705	0.1250	59.86	0.9589	2.406	0.29	210	98.9
212	14.696	0.016719	0.1251	59.81	0.9580			212	100.0
220	17.186	0.016775	0.1255	59.61	0.9549	2.416		220	104.4
230	20.779	0.016849	0.1260	59.35	0.9507	2.426		230	110
240	24.968	0.016926	0.1266	59.08	0.9464	2.437		240	115.6
250	29.825	0.017006	0.1272	58.80	0.9420	2.449	0.24	250	121.1
260	35.427	0.017089	0.1278	58.52	0.9374	2.461		260	126.7
270	41.856	0.017175	0.1285	58.22	0.9327	2.473		270	132.2
280	49.200	0.017264	0.1291	57.92	0.9279	2.486		280	137.8
290	57.550	0.01736	0.1299	57.60	0.9228	2.500		290	143.3
300	67.005	0.01745	0.1305	57.31	0.9180	2.513	0.20	300	148.9
310	77.667	0.01755	0.1313	56.98	0.9128	2.527		310	154.4
320	89.643	0.01766	0.1321	56.63	0.9071	2.543		320	160
330	103.045	0.01776	0.1329	56.31	0.9020	2.557		330	165.6
340	117.992	0.01787	0.1337	55.96	0.8964	2.573		340	171.1
350	134.604	0.01799	0.1346	55.59	0.8904	2.591	0.17	350	176.7
360	153.010	0.01811	0.1355	55.22	0.8845	2.608		360	182.2
370	173.339	0.01823	0.1364	54.84	0.8787	2.625		370	187.8
380	195.729	0.01836	0.1374	54.47	0.8725	2.644		380	193.3
390	220.321	0.01850	0.1384	54.05	0.8659	2.664		390	198.9
400	247.259	0.01864	0.1394	53.65	0.8594	2.684	0.15	400	204.4
410	276.694	0.01878	0.1404	53.25	0.8530	2.704		410	392.2
420	308.780	0.01894	0.1417	52.80	0.8458	2.727		420	215.6
430	343.674	0.01909	0.1428	52.38	0.8391	2.749		430	221.1
440	381.54	0.01926	0.1441	51.92	0.8317	2.773		440	226.7
450	422.55	0.01943	0.1453	51.47	0.8244	2.798	0.14	450	232.2
460	466.87	0.01961	0.1467	50.99	0.8169	2.824		460	237.8
470	514.67	0.01980	0.1481	50.51	0.8090	2.851		470	243.3
480	566.15	0.02000	0.1496	50.00	0.8010	2.880		480	248.9
490	621.48	0.02021	0.1512	49.48	0.7926	2.910		490	254.4
500	680.86	0.02043	0.1528	48.95	0.7841	2.942	0.13	500	260
510	744.47	0.02067	0.1546	48.38	0.7750	2.976		510	265.6
520	812.53	0.02091	0.1564	47.82	0.7661	3.011		520	271.1
530	885.23	0.02118	0.1584	47.21	0.7563	3.050		530	276.7
540	962.79	0.02146	0.1605	46.60	0.7465	3.090		540	282.2
550	1045.43	0.02176	0.1628	45.96	0.7362	3.133	0.12	550	287.8
560	1133.38	0.02207	0.1651	45.31	0.7258	3.178		560	293.3
570	1226.88	0.02242	0.1677	44.60	0.7145	3.228		570	298.9
580	1326.17	0.02279	0.1705	43.88	0.7029	3.281		580	304.4
590	1431.5	0.02319	0.1735	43.12	0.6908	3.339		590	310
600	1543.2	0.02364	0.1768	42.30	0.6776	3.404	0.12	600	315.6
610	1661.6	0.02412	0.1804	41.46	0.6641	3.473		610	321.1
620	1786.9	0.02466	0.1845	40.55	0.6496	3.551		620	326.6
630	1919.5	0.02526	0.1890	39.59	0.6342	3.637		630	332.2
640	2059.9	0.02595	0.1941	38.54	0.6173	3.737		640	337.8
650	2203.4	0.02674	0.2000	37.40	0.5991	3.851		650	343.3
670	2532.2	0.02884	0.2157	34.67	0.5554	4.153		670	354.4
690	2895.7	0.03256	0.2436	30.71	0.4920	4.689		690	365.6
700	3094.3	0.03662	0.2739	27.31	0.4374	5.273		700	371.1
705.47	3208.2	0.05078	0.3799	19.69	0.3155	7.312		705.47	374.15

* Approximately numerically equal to specific gravity basis temperature reference of 39.2°F (4°C). Calculated from data in ASME Steam Tables.

Pounds per gallon and specific gravities corresponding to degrees API at 60°F

$$\text{Formula—sp gr} = \frac{141.5}{131.5 + {}^\circ\text{API}}$$

Deg API	Tenths of Degrees									
	0	1	2	3	4	5	6	7	8	9
10	8.328	8.322	8.317	8.311	8.305	8.299	8.293	8.287	8.282	8.276
	1.0000	.9993	.9986	.9979	.9972	.9965	.9958	.951	.9944	.9937
11	8.270	8.264	8.258	8.252	8.246	8.241	8.235	8.229	8.223	8.218
	.9930	.9923	.9916	.9909	.9902	.9895	.9888	.9881	.9874	.9868
12	8.212	8.206	8.201	8.195	8.189	8.183	8.178	8.172	8.166	8.161
	.9861	.9854	.9847	.9840	.9833	.9826	.9820	.9813	.9806	.9799
13	8.155	8.150	8.144	8.138	8.132	8.127	8.122	8.116	8.110	8.105
	.9792	.9786	.9779	.9772	.9765	.9759	.9752	.9745	.9738	.9732
14	8.099	8.093	8.088	8.082	8.076	8.071	8.066	8.061	8.055	8.049
	.9725	.9718	.9712	.9705	.9698	.9692	.9685	.9679	.9672	.9665
15	8.044	8.038	8.033	8.027	8.021	8.016	8.011	8.006	8.000	7.995
	.9659	.9652	.9646	.9639	.9632	.9626	.9619	.9613	.9606	.9600
16	7.989	7.984	7.978	7.973	7.967	7.962	7.956	7.951	7.946	7.940
	.9593	.9587	.9580	.9574	.9567	.9561	.9554	.9548	.9541	.9535
17	7.935	7.930	7.925	7.919	7.914	7.909	7.903	7.898	7.893	7.887
	.9529	.9522	.9516	.9509	.9503	.9497	.9490	.9484	.9478	.9471
18	7.882	7.877	7.871	7.866	7.861	7.856	7.851	7.846	7.841	7.835
	.9465	.9459	.9452	.9446	.9440	.9433	.9427	.9421	.9415	.9408
19	7.830	7.825	7.820	7.814	7.809	7.804	7.799	7.793	7.788	7.783
	.9402	.9396	.9390	.9383	.9377	.9371	.9365	.9358	.9352	.9346
20	7.778	7.773	7.768	7.762	7.757	7.752	7.747	7.742	7.737	7.732
	.9340	.9334	.9328	.9321	.9315	.9309	.9303	.9297	.9291	.9285
21	7.727	7.722	7.717	7.711	7.706	7.701	7.696	7.691	7.686	7.681
	.9279	.9273	.9267	.9260	.9254	.9248	.9242	.9236	.9230	.9224
22	7.676	7.671	7.666	7.661	7.656	7.651	7.646	7.641	7.636	7.632
	.9218	.9212	.9206	.9200	.9194	.9188	.9182	.9176	.9170	.9165
23	7.627	7.622	7.617	7.612	7.607	7.602	7.597	7.592	7.587	7.583
	.9159	.9153	.9147	.9141	.9135	.9129	.9123	.9117	.9111	.9106
24	7.578	7.573	7.568	7.563	7.558	7.554	7.549	7.544	7.539	7.534
	.9100	.9094	.9088	.9082	.9076	.9071	.9065	.9059	.9053	.9047
25	7.529	7.524	7.519	7.514	7.509	7.505	7.500	7.495	7.491	7.486
	.9042	.9036	.9030	.9024	.9018	.9013	.9007	.9001	.8996	.8990
26	7.481	7.476	7.427	7.467	7.462	7.458	7.453	7.448	7.443	7.438
	.8984	.8978	.8973	.8967	.8961	.8956	.8950	.8944	.8939	.8933
27	7.434	7.429	7.424	7.420	7.415	7.410	7.406	7.401	7.397	7.392
	.8927	.8922	.8916	.8911	.8905	.8899	.8894	.8888	.8883	.8877
28	7.387	7.383	7.378	7.373	7.368	7.364	7.360	7.355	7.350	7.346
	.8871	.8866	.8860	.8855	.8849	.8844	.8838	.8833	.8827	.8822
29	7.341	7.337	7.332	7.328	7.323	7.318	7.314	7.309	7.305	7.300
	.8816	.8811	.8805	.8800	.8794	.8789	.8783	.8778	.8772	.8767
30	7.296	7.291	7.287	7.282	7.278	7.273	7.268	7.264	7.259	7.255
	.8762	.8756	.8751	.8745	.8740	.8735	.8729	.8724	.8718	.8713
31	7.251	7.246	7.242	7.238	7.233	7.228	7.224	7.219	7.215	7.211
	.8708	.8702	.8679	.8692	.8686	.8681	.8676	.8670	.8665	.8660
32	7.206	7.202	7.198	7.193	7.188	7.184	7.180	7.176	7.171	7.167
	.8654	.8649	.8644	.8639	.8633	.8628	.8623	.8618	.8612	.8607
33	7.163	7.158	7.153	7.149	7.145	7.141	7.137	7.132	7.128	7.123
	.8602	.8597	.8591	.8536	.8581	.8576	.8571	.8565	.8560	.8555
34	7.119	7.115	7.111	7.106	7.102	7.098	7.093	7.089	7.085	7.081
	.8550	.8545	.8540	.8534	.8529	.8524	.8519	.8514	.8509	.8504
35	7.076	7.072	7.067	7.063	7.059	7.055	7.051	7.047	7.042	7.038
	.8498	.8493	.8488	.8483	.8478	.8473	.8468	.8463	.8458	.8453
36	7.034	7.030	7.026	7.022	7.018	7.013	7.009	7.005	7.001	6.997
	.8448	.8443	.8438	.8433	.8428	.8423	.8418	.8412	.8408	.8403
37	6.993	6.989	6.985	6.980	6.976	6.972	6.968	6.964	6.960	6.955
	.8398	.8393	.8388	.8383	.8378	.8373	.8368	.8363	.8358	.8353
38	6.951	6.947	6.943	6.939	6.935	6.930	6.926	6.922	6.918	6.914
	.8348	.8343	.8338	.8333	.8328	.8324	.8319	.8314	.8309	.8304
39	6.910	6.906	6.902	6.898	6.894	6.890	6.886	6.882	6.878	6.874
	.8299	.8294	.8289	.8285	.8280	.8275	.8270	.8265	.8260	.8256
40	6.870	6.866	6.862	6.858	6.854	6.850	6.846	6.842	6.838	6.834
	.8251	.8246	.8241	.8236	.8232	.8227	.8222	.8217	.8212	.8208
41	6.830	6.826	6.822	6.818	6.814	6.810	6.806	6.802	6.798	6.794
	.8203	.8198	.8193	.8189	.8184	.8178	.8174	.8170	.8165	.8160

Pounds per gallon and specific gravities corresponding to degrees API at 60°F (*Continued*)

Deg API	Tenths of Degrees									
	0	1	2	3	4	5	6	7	8	9
42	6.790	6.786	6.782	6.779	6.775	6.771	6.767	6.763	6.759	6.756
	.8155	.8151	.8146	.8142	.8137	.8132	.8128	.8123	.8118	.8114
43	6.752	6.748	6.744	6.740	6.736	6.732	6.728	6.724	6.720	6.716
	.8109	.8104	.8100	.8095	.8090	.8086	.8081	.8076	.8072	.8067
44	6.713	6.709	6.705	6.701	6.697	6.694	6.690	6.686	6.682	6.679
	.8063	.8058	.8054	.8049	.8044	.8040	.8035	.8031	.8026	.8022
45	6.675	6.671	6.667	6.663	6.660	6.656	6.652	6.648	6.645	6.641
	.8017	.8012	.8008	.8003	.7999	.7994	.7990	.7985	.7981	.7976
46	6.637	6.633	6.630	6.626	6.622	6.618	6.615	6.611	6.607	6.604
	.7972	.7967	.7963	.7958	.7954	.7949	.7945	.7941	.7936	.7932
47	6.600	6.596	6.592	6.589	6.585	6.582	6.578	6.574	6.571	6.567
	.7927	.7923	.7918	.7914	.7909	.7905	.7901	.7896	.7892	.7887
48	6.563	6.560	6.556	6.552	6.548	6.545	6.541	6.537	6.534	6.530
	.7883	.7879	.7874	.7870	.7865	.7861	.7857	.7852	.7848	.7844
49	6.526	6.523	6.520	6.516	6.512	6.509	6.505	6.501	6.498	6.494
	.7839	.7835	.7831	.7826	.7822	.7818	.7813	.7809	7805	.7800
50	6.490	6.487	6.484	6.480	6.476	6.473	6.469	6.466	6.462	6.459
	.7796	.7792	.7788	.7783	.7779	.7775	.7770	.7766	.7762	.7758
51	6.455	6.451	6.448	6.445	6.441	6.437	6.434	6.430	6.427	6.423
	.7753	.7749	.7745	.7741	.7736	.7732	.7728	.7724	.7720	.7715
52	6.420	6.416	6.413	6.410	6.406	6.402	6.399	6.396	6.392	6.389
	.7711	.7707	.7703	.7699	.7694	.7690	.7686	.7682	.7678	.7674
53	6.385	6.381	6.378	6.375	6.371	6.368	6.365	6.360	6.357	6.354
	.7669	.7665	.7661	.7657	.7653	.7649	.7645	.7640	.7636	.7632
54	6.350	6.347	6.344	6.340	6.337	6.334	6.330	6.326	6.323	6.320
	.7628	.7624	.7620	.7616	.7612	.7608	.7603	.7599	.7595	.7591
55	6.316	6.313	6.310	6.306	6.303	6.300	6.296	6.293	6.290	6.287
	.7587	.7583	.7579	.7575	.7571	.7567	.7563	.7559	.7555	.7551
56	6.283	6.280	6.276	6.273	6.270	6.266	6.263	6.259	6.256	6.253
	.7547	.7543	.7539	.7535	.7531	.7527	.7523	.7519	.7515	.7511
57	6.249	6.246	6.243	6.240	6.236	6.233	6.229	6.226	6.223	6.219
	.7507	.7503	.7499	.7495	.7491	.7487	.7483	.7479	.7475	.7471
58	6.216	6.213	6.209	6.206	6.203	6.199	6.196	6.193	6.190	6.187
	.7467	.7463	.7459	.7455	.7451	.7447	.7443	.7440	.7436	.7432
59	6.184	6.180	6.177	6.174	6.170	6.167	6.164	6.161	6.158	6.154
	.7428	.7424	.7420	.7416	.7412	.7408	.7405	.7401	.7397	.7393
60	6.151	6.148	6.144	6.141	6.138	6.135	6.132	6.129	6.125	6.122
	.7389	.7385	.7381	.7377	.7374	.7370	.7366	.7362	.7358	.7354
61	6.119	6.116	6.113	6.109	6.106	6.103	6.100	6.097	6.094	6.090
	.7351	.7347	.7343	.7339	.7335	.7332	.7328	.7324	.7320	.7316
62	6.087	6.084	6.081	6.078	6.075	6.072	6.068	6.065	6.062	6.059
	.7313	.7309	.7305	.7301	.7298	.7294	.7290	.7286	.7283	.7279
63	6.056	6.053	6.050	6.047	6.044	6.040	6.037	6.034	6.031	6.028
	.7275	.7271	.7268	.7264	.7260	.7256	.7253	.7249	.7245	.7242
64	6.025	6.022	6.019	6.016	6.013	6.010	6.007	6.004	6.000	5.997
	.7238	.7234	.7230	.7227	.7223	.7219	.7216	.7212	.7208	.7205
65	5.994	5.991	5.988	5.985	5.982	5.979	5.976	5.973	5.970	5.967
	.7201	.7197	.7194	.7190	.7186	.7183	.7179	.7175	.7172	.7168
66	5.964	5.961	5.958	5.955	5.952	5.949	5.946	5.943	5.940	5.937
	.7165	.7161	.7157	.7154	.7150	.7146	.7143	.7139	.7136	.7132
67	5.934	5.931	5.928	5.925	5.922	5.919	5.916	5.913	5.910	5.907
	.7128	.7125	.7121	.7118	.7114	.7111	.7107	.7013	.7100	.7096
68	5.904	5.901	5.898	5.895	5.892	5.889	5.886	5.883	5.880	5.877
	.7093	.7089	.7086	.7082	.7079	.7075	.7071	.7068	.7064	.7061
69	5.874	5.871	5.868	5.866	5.863	5.860	5.857	5.854	5.851	5.848
	.7057	.7054	.7050	.7047	.7043	.7040	.7036	.7033	.7029	.7026
70	5.845	5.842	5.839	5.836	5.833	5.831	5.828	5.825	5.823	5.820
	.7022	.7019	.7015	.7012	.7008	.7005	.7001	.6998	.6995	.6991
71	5.817	5.814	5.811	5.808	5.805	5.802	5.799	5.796	5.793	5.791
	.6988	.6984	.6981	.6977	.6974	.6970	.6967	.6964	.6960	.6957
72	5.788	5.785	5.782	5.779	5.776	5.773	5.771	5.768	5.765	5.762
	.6952	.6950	.6946	.6943	.6940	.6936	.6933	.6929	.6926	.6923
73	5.759	5.757	5.754	5.751	5.748	5.745	5.743	5.740	5.737	5.734
	.6919	.6916	.6913	.6909	.6906	.6902	.6899	.6896	.6892	.6889
74	5.731	5.728	5.726	5.723	5.720	5.718	5.715	5.712	5.709	5.706
	.6886	.6882	.6879	.6876	.6872	.6869	.6866	.6862	.6859	.6856

4

Pounds per gallon and specific gravities corresponding to degrees API at 60°F (*Continued*)

Deg API	Tenths of Degrees									
	0	1	2	3	4	5	6	7	8	9
75	5.703	5.701	5.698	5.695	5.693	5.690	5.687	5.685	5.682	5.679
	.6852	.6849	.6846	.6842	.6839	.6836	.6832	.6829	.6826	.6823
76	5.676	5.673	5.671	5.668	5.665	5.662	5.660	5.657	5.654	5.652
	.6819	.6816	.6813	.6809	.6806	.6803	.6800	.6796	.6793	.6790
77	5.649	5.646	5.643	5.641	5.638	5.635	5.632	5.630	5.627	5.624
	.6787	.6783	.6780	.6777	.6774	.6770	.6767	.6764	.6761	.6757
78	5.622	5.619	5.617	5.614	5.611	5.608	5.606	5.603	5.600	5.598
	.6754	.6751	.6748	.6745	.6741	.6738	.6735	.6732	.6728	.6725
79	5.595	5.592	5.590	5.587	5.584	5.582	5.579	5.577	5.574	5.571
	.6722	.6719	.6716	.6713	.6709	.6706	.6703	.6700	.6697	.6693
80	5.568	5.566	5.563	5.561	5.558	5.556	5.553	5.550	5.548	5.545
	.6690	.6687	.6684	.6681	.6678	.6675	.6671	.6668	.6665	.6662
81	5.542	5.540	5.537	5.534	5.532	5.529	5.526	5.524	5.522	5.519
	.6659	.6656	.6653	.6649	.6646	.6643	.6640	.6637	.6634	.6631
82	5.516	5.514	5.511	5.508	5.506	5.503	5.501	5.498	5.496	5.493
	.6628	.6625	.6621	.6618	.6615	.6612	.6609	.6606	.6603	.6600
83	5.491	5.489	5.486	5.483	5.480	5.477	5.475	5.472	5.470	5.467
	.6597	.6594	.6591	.6588	.6584	.6581	.6578	.6575	.6572	.6569
84	5.465	5.462	5.460	5.458	5.455	5.453	5.450	5.448	5.445	5.443
	.6566	.6563	.6560	.6557	.6554	.6551	.6548	.6545	.6542	.6539
85	5.440	5.437	5.435	5.432	5.430	5.427	5.425	5.422	5.420	5.417
	.6536	.6533	.6530	.6527	.6524	.6521	.6518	.6515	.6512	.6509
86	5.415	5.412	5.410	5.407	5.405	5.402	5.400	5.397	5.395	5.392
	.6506	.6503	.6500	.6497	.6494	.6491	.6488	.6485	.6482	.6479
87	5.390	5.387	5.385	5.382	5.380	5.377	5.375	5.372	5.370	5.367
	.6476	.6473	.6470	.6467	.6464	.6461	.6458	.6455	.6452	.6449
88	5.365	5.363	5.361	5.358	5.356	5.353	5.351	5.348	5.346	5.343
	.6446	.6444	.6441	.6438	.6435	.6432	.6429	.6426	.6423	.6420
89	5.341	5.338	5.336	5.334	5.331	5.329	5.326	5.324	5.321	5.319
	.6417	.6414	.6411	.6409	.6406	.6403	.6400	.6397	.6394	.6391
90	5.316	5.314	5.312	5.310	5.307	5.305	5.302	5.300	5.297	5.295
	.6388	.6385	.6382	.6380	.6377	.6374	.6371	.6368	.6365	.6362
91	5.293	5.291	5.288	5.286	5.283	5.281	5.278	5.276	5.274	5.271
	.6360	.6357	.6354	.6351	.6348	.6345	.6342	.6340	.6337	.6334
92	5.269	5.266	5.264	5.262	5.260	5.257	5.254	5.252	5.250	5.248
	.6331	.6328	.6325	.6323	.6320	.6317	.6314	.6311	.6309	.6306
93	5.245	5.243	5.241	5.238	5.236	5.234	5.232	5.229	5.227	5.225
	.6303	.6300	.6297	.6294	.6292	.9289	.6286	.6283	.6281	.6278
94	5.222	5.220	5.217	5.215	5.213	5.211	5.208	5.206	5.204	5.201
	.6275	.6272	.6269	.6267	.6264	.6261	.6258	.6256	.6253	.6250
95	5.199	5.196	5.194	5.192	5.190	5.187	5.185	5.183	5.180	5.179
	.6247	.6244	.6242	.6239	.6236	.6233	.6231	.6228	.6225	.6223
96	5.176	5.174	5.172	5.170	5.167	5.164	5.162	5.160	5.158	5.156
	.6220	.6217	.6214	.6212	.6209	.6206	.6203	.6201	.6198	.6195
97	5.154	5.151	5.149	5.146	5.144	5.142	5.140	5.138	5.136	5.133
	.6193	.6190	.6187	.6184	.6182	.6179	.6176	.6174	.6171	.6168
98	5.131	5.129	5.126	5.124	5.122	5.120	5.118	5.116	5.113	5.111
	.6166	.6163	.6160	.6158	.6155	.6152	.6150	.6147	.6144	.6141
99	5.109	5.107	5.104	5.102	5.100	5.098	5.096	5.093	5.091	5.089
	.6139	.6136	.6134	.6131	.6128	.6126	.6123	.6120	.6118	.6115
100	5.086	5.09	5.09	5.08	5.08	5.08	5.08	5.07	5.07	5.07
	.6112	.6110	.6107	.6104	.6102	.6099	.6097	.6094	.6091	.6089
101	5.07	5.07	5.06	5.06	5.06	5.06	5.06	5.05	5.05	5.05
	.6086	.6083	.6081	.6078	.6076	.6073	.6070	.6068	.6065	.6063
102	5.05	5.04	5.04	5.04	5.04	5.04	5.03	5.03	5.03	5.03
	.6060	.6058	.6055	.6052	.6050	.6047	.6044	.6042	.6039	.6037
103	5.02	5.02	5.02	5.02	5.02	5.01	5.01	5.01	5.01	5.01
	.6034	.6032	.6029	.6026	.6024	.6021	.6019	.6016	.6014	.6011
104	5.00	5.00	5.00	5.00	4.99	4.99	4.99	4.99	4.99	4.98
	.6008	.6006	.6003	.6001	.5998	.5996	.5993	.5991	.5988	.5986
105	4.98	4.98	4.98	4.98	4.97	4.97	4.97	4.97	4.97	4.96
	.5983	.5981	.5978	.5976	.5973	.5970	.5968	.5965	.5963	.5960
106	4.96	4.96	4.96	4.95	4.95	4.95	4.95	4.95	4.94	4.94
	.5958	.5955	.5953	.5950	.5948	.5945	.5943	.5940	.5938	.5935
107	4.94	4.94	4.94	4.93	4.93	4.93	4.93	4.93	4.92	4.92
	.5933	.5930	.5928	.5925	.5923	.5921	.5918	.5916	.5913	.5911

Pounds per gallon and specific gravities corresponding to degrees API at 60°F (*Continued*)

Deg API	0	1	2	3	4	5	6	7	8	9
					Tenths of Degrees					
108	4.92	4.92	4.92	4.91	4.91	4.91	4.91	4.91	4.90	4.90
	.5908	.5906	.5903	.5901	.5898	.5896	.5893	.5891	.5888	.5886
109	4.90	4.90	4.90	4.89	4.89	4.89	4.89	4.89	4.88	4.88
	.5884	.5881	.5879	.5876	.5874	.5871	.5869	.5867	.5864	.5862
110	4.88	4.88	4.87	4.87	4.87	4.87	4.87	4.86	4.86	4.86
	.5859	.5857	.5854	.5852	.5850	.5847	.5845	.5842	.5840	.5837
111	4.86	4.86	4.85	4.85	4.85	4.85	4.85	4.84	4.84	4.84
	.5835	.5833	.5830	.5828	.5825	.5823	.5821	.5818	.5816	.5813
112	4.84	4.84	4.83	4.83	4.83	4.83	4.83	4.82	4.82	4.82
	.5811	.5909	.5806	.5804	.5802	.5799	.5797	.5794	.5792	.5790
113	4.82	4.82	4.82	4.81	4.81	4.81	4.81	4.81	4.80	4.80
	.5787	.5785	.5783	.5780	.5778	.5776	.5773	.5771	.5768	.5766
114	4.80	4.80	4.80	4.79	4.79	4.79	4.79	4.79	4.78	4.78
	.5764	.5761	.5759	.5757	.5754	.5752	.5750	.5747	.5745	.5743
115	4.78	4.78	4.78	4.77	4.77	4.77	4.77	4.77	4.76	4.76
	.5740	.5738	.5736	.5733	.5731	.5729	.5726	.5724	.5722	.5719
116	4.76	4.76	4.76	4.76	4.75	4.75	4.75	4.75	4.75	4.74
	.5717	.5715	.5713	.5710	.5708	.5706	.5703	.5701	.5699	.5696
117	4.74	4.74	4.74	4.74	4.73	4.73	4.73	4.73	4.73	4.73
	.5694	.5692	.5690	.5687	.5685	.5683	.5680	.5678	.5676	.5674
118	4.72	4.72	4.72	4.72	4.72	4.71	4.71	4.71	4.71	4.71
	.5671	.5669	.5667	.5665	.5662	.5660	.5658	.5655	.5653	.5651
119	4.70	4.70	4.70	4.70	4.70	4.69	4.69	4.69	4.69	4.69
	.5649	.5646	.5644	.5642	.5640	.5637	.5635	.5633	.5631	.5628
120	4.69	4.68	4.68	4.68	4.68	4.68	4.67	4.67	4.67	4.67
	.5626	.5624	.5622	.5620	.5617	.5615	.5613	.5611	.5608	.5606
121	4.67	4.67	4.66	4.66	4.66	4.66	4.66	4.65	4.65	4.65
	.5604	.5602	.5600	.5597	.5595	.5593	.5591	.5588	.5586	.5584
122	4.65	4.65	4.64	4.64	4.64	4.64	4.64	4.64	4.63	4.63
	.5582	.5580	.5577	.5575	.5573	.5571	.5569	.5566	.5564	.5562
123	4.63	4.63	4.63	4.62	4.62	4.62	4.62	4.62	4.62	4.61
	.5560	.5558	.5556	.5553	.5551	.5549	.5547	.5545	.5542	.5540
124	4.61	4.61	4.61	4.61	4.61	4.60	4.60	4.60	4.60	4.60
	.5538	.5536	.5534	.5532	.5530	.5527	.5525	.5523	.5521	.5519
125	4.59	4.59	4.59	4.59	4.59	4.59	4.58	4.58	4.58	4.58
	.5517	.5514	.5512	.5510	.5508	.5506	.5504	.5502	.5499	.5497
126	4.58	4.57	4.57	4.57	4.57	4.57	4.57	4.56	4.56	4.56
	.5495	.5493	.5491	.5489	.5487	.5484	.5482	.5480	.5478	.5476
127	4.56	4.56	4.56	4.55	4.55	4.55	4.55	4.55	4.54	4.54
	.5474	.5472	.5470	.5468	.5465	.5463	.5461	.5459	.5457	.5455
128	4.54	4.54	4.54	4.54	4.53	4.53	4.53	4.53	4.53	4.53
	.5453	.5451	.5449	.5446	.5444	.5442	.5440	.5438	.5436	.5434
129	4.52	4.52	4.52	4.52	4.52	4.51	4.51	4.51	4.51	4.51
	.5432	.5430	.5428	.5426	.5424	.5421	.5419	.5417	.5415	.5413
130	4.51	4.50	4.50	4.50	4.50	4.50	4.50	4.49	4.49	4.49
	.5411	.5409	.5407	.5405	.5403	.5401	.5399	.5397	.5395	.5393
131	4.49	4.49	4.49	4.48	4.48	4.48	4.48	4.48	4.48	4.47
	.5390	.5388	.5386	.5384	.5382	.5380	.5378	.5376	.5374	.5372
132	4.47	4.47	4.47	4.47	4.47	4.46	4.46	4.46	4.46	4.46
	.5370	.5368	.5366	.5364	.5362	.5360	.5358	.5356	.5354	.5352
133	4.46	4.45	4.45	4.45	4.45	4.45	4.45	4.44	4.44	4.44
	.5350	.5348	.5346	.5344	.5342	.5340	.5338	.5336	.5334	.5332
134	4.44	4.44	4.44	4.43	4.43	4.43	4.43	4.43	4.43	4.42
	.5330	.5328	.5326	.5324	.5322	.5320	.5318	.5316	.5314	.5312
135	4.42	4.42	4.42	4.42	4.42	4.41	4.41	4.41	4.41	4.41
	.5310	.5308	.5306	.5304	.5302	.5300	.5298	.5296	.5294	.5292
136	4.41	4.40	4.40	4.40	4.40	4.40	4.40	4.39	4.39	4.39
	.5290	.5288	.5286	.5284	.5282	.5280	.5278	.5276	.5274	.5272
137	4.39	4.39	4.39	4.38	4.38	4.38	4.38	4.38	4.38	4.37
	.5270	.5268	.5266	.5264	.5262	.5260	.5258	.5256	.5254	.5252
138	4.37	4.37	4.37	4.37	4.37	4.36	4.36	4.36	4.36	4.36
	.5250	.5249	.5247	.5245	.5243	.5241	.5239	.5237	.5235	.5233
139	4.36	4.35	4.35	4.35	4.35	4.35	4.35	4.35	4.34	4.34
	.5231	.5229	.5227	.5225	.5223	.5221	.5219	.5218	.5216	.5214

Values from 10.0 to 100.0 API from tables published by American Petroleum Institute.
Values above 100.0 API calculated by Ingersoll-Rand Co.

Physical Properties of Calcium Chloride (CaCl₂) and Sodium Chloride (NaCl)

| Calcium chloride | | | | | Note | Sodium chloride | | | | | |
Degrees Baume 60°F	Specific gravity 60°/60°F	Degrees Salometer 60°F	% CaCl₂ by weight	Freezing point °F		Specific gravity 60°/60°F	Degrees Baume 60°F	Degrees Salometer 60°F	% NaCl by weight	Lb NaCl per gallon solution	Freezing point °F
0	1.000	0	0	32.	Commercial CaCl₂ is available in several degrees of hydration	1.000	0	0	0	0	32.0
1.	1.007	4	1	31.1		1.007	1.04	3.8	1	0.084	30.5
2.1	1.015	8	2	30.4		1.015	2.07	7.6	2	0.169	29.3
3.4	1.024	12	3	29.5		1.022	3.08	11.4	3	0.256	27.8
4.5	1.032	16	4	28.6		*1.029	4.08	15.2	4	0.344	26.6
5.7	1.041	22	5	27.7	It also picks up moisture from the atmosphere.	1.036	5.07	18.9	5	0.433	25.2
6.8	1.049	26	6	26.6		1.044	6.07	22.7	6	0.523	23.9
8.	1.058	32	7	25.5		1.051	7.06	26.5	7	0.617	22.5
9.1	1.067	36	8	24.3		1.059	8.01	30.3	8	0.708	21.2
10.2	1.076	40	9	22.8		1.066	8.97	33.9	9	0.802	19.9
11.4	1.085	44	10	21.3	Solutions should therefore, be made by reference to hydrometer reading.	1.073	9.90	37.5	10	0.897	18.7
12.5	1.094	48	11	19.7		1.081	10.86	41.3	11	0.994	17.4
13.5	1.103	52	12	18.1		1.089	11.80	42.2	12	1.092	16.0
14.6	1.112	58	13	16.3		1.096	12.73	49.2	13	1.190	14.7
15.6	1.121	62	14	14.3		1.104	13.64	53.0	14	1.289	13.
16.8	1.131	68	15	12.2		1.111	14.54	56.8	15	1.389	12.2
17.8	1.140	72	16	10.		1.119	15.46	60.6	16	1.495	11.0
19.	1.151	76	17	7.5		1.127	16.37	64.4	17	1.602	9.8
20.	1.160	80	18	4.6		1.135	17.27	68.2	18	1.710	8.5
21.	1.169	84	19	1.7		1.143	18.16	71.9	19	1.819	7.3
22.	1.179	88	20	-1.4		1.151	19.03	75.5	20	1.928	6.1
23.	1.188	92	21	-4.9		1.159	19.92	79.1	21	2.037	5.0
24.	1.198	96	22	-8.6		1.168	20.80	83.0	22	2.147	3.9
25.	1.208	100	23	-11.6		1.176	21.68	86.9	23	2.266	2.8
26.	1.218	104	24	-17.1		1.184	22.54	90.9	24	2.376	1.7
27.	1.229	108	25	-21.8		1.192	23.39	94.7	25	2.488	+0.5
28.	1.239	112	26	-27.		1.201	24.27	98.5	26	2.610	-1.1
29.	1.250	116	27	-32.6		1.204	24.60	100.	26.395	2.661	-1.6
30.	1.261	120	28	-39.2							
31.	1.272	124	29	-46.2							
32.	1.283	128	30	-54.4							

Temperature correction 1° Salometer to every 7½°F added to reading for temperatures above 60°F; subtracted below.
* Specific gravity of sea water.

PROPERTIES OF LIQUIDS

Specific Gravity of Caustic Soda Solutions
15°C (59°F) by Lunge

Specific gravity	Degrees Baumé	Degrees Twaddell	Per cent NaOH	Per cent Na²O	One gallon contains	
					pounds NaOH	pounds Na²O
1.007	1.0	1.4	0.61	0.47	0.051	0.039
1.014	2.0	2.8	1.20	0.93	0.101	0.079
1.022	3.1	4.4	2.00	1.55	0.170	0.132
1.029	4.1	5.8	2.70	2.10	0.232	0.180
1.036	5.1	7.2	3.35	2.60	0.289	0.225
1.045	6.2	9.0	4.00	3.10	0.345	0.268
1.052	7.2	10.4	4.64	3.60	0.407	0.316
1.060	8.2	12.0	5.29	4.10	0.467	0.362
1.067	9.1	13.4	5.87	4.55	0.522	0.405
1.075	10.1	15.0	6.55	5.08	0.587	0.455
1.083	11.1	16.6	7.31	5.67	0.660	0.512
1.091	12.1	18.2	8.00	6.20	0.728	0.564
1.100	13.2	20.0	8.68	6.73	0.796	0.617
1.108	14.1	21.6	9.42	7.30	0.870	0.674
1.116	15.1	23.2	10.06	7.80	0.936	0.726
1.125	16.1	25.0	10.97	8.50	1.029	0.797
1.134	17.1	26.8	11.84	9.18	1.119	0.868
1.142	18.0	28.4	12.64	9.80	1.203	0.933
1.152	19.1	30.4	13.55	10.50	1.301	1.008
1.162	20.2	32.4	14.37	11.14	1.392	1.079
1.171	21.2	34.2	15.13	11.73	1.477	1.145
1.180	22.1	36.0	15.91	12.33	1.565	1.213
1.190	23.1	38.0	16.77	13.00	1.664	1.290
1.200	24.2	40.0	17.67	13.70	1.768	1.371
1.210	25.2	42.0	18.58	14.40	1.874	1.453
1.220	26.1	44.0	19.58	15.18	1.992	1.554
1.231	27.2	46.2	20.59	15.96	2.113	1.638
1.241	28.2	48.2	21.42	16.76	2.216	1.734
1.252	29.2	50.4	22.64	17.55	2.363	1.832
1.263	30.2	52.6	23.67	18.35	2.492	1.932
1.274	31.2	54.8	24.81	19.23	2.635	2.042
1.285	32.2	57.0	25.80	20.00	2.764	2.143
1.297	33.2	59.4	26.83	20.80	2.901	2.249
1.308	34.1	61.6	27.80	21.55	3.032	2.350
1.320	35.2	64.0	28.83	22.35	3.173	2.460
1.332	36.1	66.4	29.93	23.20	3.324	2.576
1.345	37.2	69.0	31.22	24.20	3.501	2.714
1.357	38.1	71.4	32.47	25.17	3.673	2.848
1.370	39.2	74.0	33.69	26.12	3.848	2.983
1.383	40.2	76.6	34.96	27.10	4.031	3.125
1.397	41.2	79.4	36.25	28.10	4.222	3.273
1.410	42.2	82.0	37.47	29.05	4.405	3.415
1.424	43.2	84.8	38.80	30.08	4.606	3.571
1.438	44.2	87.6	39.99	31.00	4.794	3.716
1.453	45.2	90.6	41.41	32.10	5.016	3.888
1.468	46.2	93.6	42.83	33.20	5.242	4.063
1.483	47.2	96.6	44.38	34.40	5.487	4.253
1.498	48.2	99.6	46.15	35.70	5.764	4.459
1.514	49.2	102.8	47.60	36.90	6.008	4.658
1.530	50.2	106.0	49.02	38.00	6.253	4.847

4

United States Standard Baume Scales

Relations between Baume degrees and specific gravity
Liquids heavier than water

$$\text{Formula—sp gr} = \frac{145}{145 - °\text{Baume}}$$

Baume degrees	Sp Gr 60°–60°F	Baume degrees	Sp Gr 60°–60°F	Baume degrees	Sp Gr 60°–60°F	Baume degrees	Sp Gr 60°–60°F
0	1.00000	20	1.16000	40	1.38095	60	1.70588
1	1.00694	21	1.16935	41	1.39423	61	1.72619
2	1.01399	22	1.17886	42	1.40777	62	1.74699
3	1.02113	23	1.18852	43	1.42157	63	1.76829
4	1.02837	24	1.19835	44	1.43564	64	1.79012
5	1.03571	25	1.20833	45	1.45000	65	1.81250
6	1.04317	26	1.21849	46	1.46465	66	1.83544
7	1.05072	27	1.22881	47	1.47959	67	1.85897
8	1.05839	28	1.23932	48	1.49485	68	1.88312
9	1.06618	29	1.25000	49	1.51042	69	1.90789
10	1.07407	30	1.26087	50	1.52632	70	1.93333
11	1.08209	31	1.27193	51	1.54255	71	1.95946
12	1.09023	32	1.28319	52	1.55914	72	1.98630
13	1.09848	33	1.29464	53	1.57609	73	2.01389
14	1.10687	34	1.30631	54	1.59341	74	2.04225
15	1.11538	35	1.31818	55	1.61111	75	2.07143
16	1.12403	36	1.33028	56	1.62921	76	2.10145
17	1.13281	37	1.34259	57	1.64773	77	2.13235
18	1.14173	38	1.35514	58	1.66667	78	2.16418
19	1.15079	39	1.36792	59	1.68605	79	2.19697

Liquids lighter than water

$$\text{Formula—sp gr} = \frac{140}{130 + °\text{Baume}}$$

Baume degrees	Sp Gr	Baume degrees	Sp Gr	Baume degrees	Sp Gr	Baume degrees	Sp Gr
10	1.00000	30	0.87500	50	0.77778	70	0.70000
11	.99291	31	.86957	51	.77348	71	.69652
12	.98592	32	.86420	52	.76923	72	.69307
13	.97902	33	.85890	53	.76503	73	.68966
14	.97222	34	.85366	54	.76087	74	.68627
15	.96552	35	.84848	55	.75676	75	.68293
16	.95890	36	.84337	56	.75269	76	.67961
17	.95238	37	.83832	57	.74866	77	.67633
18	.94595	38	.83333	58	.74468	78	.67308
19	.93960	39	.82840	59	.74074	79	.66986
20	.93333	40	.82353	60	.73684	80	.66667
21	.92715	41	.81871	61	.73298	81	.66351
22	.92105	42	.81395	62	.72917	82	.66038
23	.91503	43	.80925	63	.72539	83	.65728
24	.90909	44	.80460	64	.72165	84	.65421
25	.90323	45	.80000	65	.71795	85	.65117
26	.89744	46	.79545	66	.71428	86	.64815
27	.89172	47	.79096	67	.71066	87	.64516
28	.88608	48	.78652	68	.70707	88	.64220
29	.88050	49	.78212	69	.70352	89	.63927

From Circular No. 59 Bureau of Standards.

Specific Gravities of Sugar Solutions

Per cent sugar (degrees Balling's or Brix) with corresponding specific gravity and degrees Baume. Temperature 60°F

Per cent sugar Balling's or Brix 60°F – 15.56°C	Specific gravity 60°/60°F	Degrees Baume 60°F	Per cent sugar Balling's or Brix 60°F – 15.56°C	Specific gravity 60°/60°F	Degrees Baume 60°F	Per cent sugar Balling's or Brix 60°F – 15.6°C	Specific gravity 60°/60°F	Degrees Baume 60°F
0	1.0000	0.00	34	1.1491	18.81	68	1.3384	36.67
1	1.0039	0.56	35	1.1541	19.36	69	1.3447	37.17
2	1.0078	1.13	36	1.1591	19.90	70	1.3509	37.66
3	1.0118	1.68	37	1.1641	20.44	71	1.3573	38.17
4	1.0157	2.24	38	1.1692	20.98	72	1.3636	38.66
5	1.0197	2.80	39	1.1743	21.52	73	1.3700	39.16
6	1.0238	3.37	40	1.1794	22.06	74	1.3764	39.65
7	1.0278	3.93	41	1.1846	22.60	75	1.3829	40.15
8	1.0319	4.49	42	1.1898	23.13	76	1.3894	40.64
9	1.0360	5.04	43	1.1950	23.66	77	1.3959	41.12
10	1.0402	5.60	44	1.2003	24.20	78	1.4025	41.61
11	1.0443	6.15	45	1.2057	24.74	79	1.4091	42.10
12	1.0485	6.71	46	1.2110	25.26	80	1.4157	42.58
13	1.0528	7.28	47	1.2164	25.80	81	1.4224	43.06
14	1.0570	7.81	48	1.2218	26.32	82	1.4291	43.54
15	1.0613	8.38	49	1.2273	26.86	83	1.4359	44.02
16	1.0657	8.94	50	1.2328	27.38	84	1.4427	44.49
17	1.0700	9.49	51	1.2384	27.91	85	1.4495	44.96
18	1.0744	10.04	52	1.2439	28.43	86	1.4564	45.44
19	1.0788	10.59	53	1.2496	28.96	87	1.4633	45.91
20	1.0833	11.15	54	1.2552	29.48	88	1.4702	46.37
21	1.0878	11.70	55	1.2609	30.00	89	1.4772	46.84
22	1.0923	12.25	56	1.2667	30.53	90	1.4842	47.31
23	1.0968	12.80	57	1.2724	31.05	91	1.4913	47.77
24	1.1014	13.35	58	1.2782	31.56	92	1.4984	48.23
25	1.1060	13.90	59	1.2841	32.08	93	1.5055	48.69
26	1.1107	14.45	60	1.2900	32.60	94	1.5126	49.14
27	1.1154	15.00	61	1.2959	33.11	95	1.5198	49.59
28	1.1201	15.54	62	1.3019	33.63	96	1.5270	50.04
29	1.1248	16.19	63	1.3079	34.13	97	1.5343	59.49
30	1.1296	16.63	64	1.3139	34.64	98	1.5416	50.94
31	1.1345	17.19	65	1.3200	35.15	99	1.5489	51.39
32	1.1393	17.73	66	1.3261	35.66	100	1.5563	51.93
33	1.1442	18.28	67	1.3323	36.16			

The above table is from the determinations of Dr. F. Plato, and has been adopted as standard by the United States Bureau of Standards.

4

Specific Gravity and Temperature Relations
of Petroleum (Approximate)

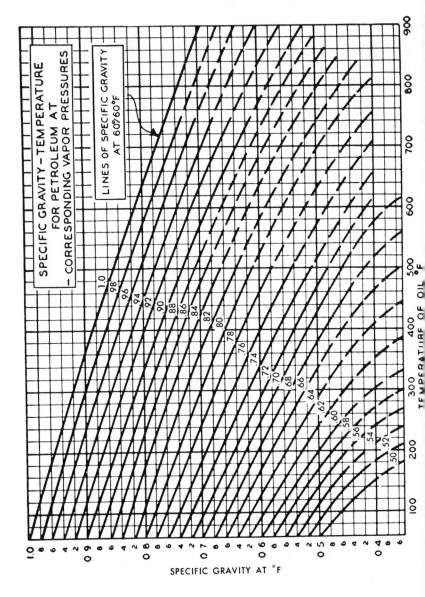

Specific Gravity—Referred to water at 60°F.
Example: oil with sp. gr. of 0.82 at 60°F will have sp. gr. of 0.64 at 500°F.

Courtesy of Hydraulic Institute.

Specific Gravity of Hydrocarbons

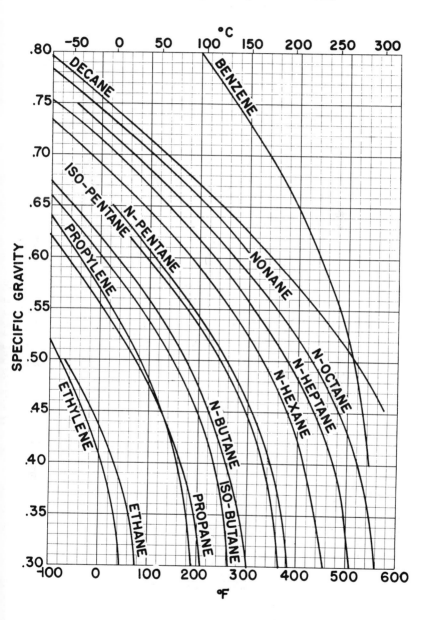

Drawn by Ingersoll-Rand based on data from Gas Processors & Suppliers Assn.

Specific Gravity—Miscellaneous Liquids

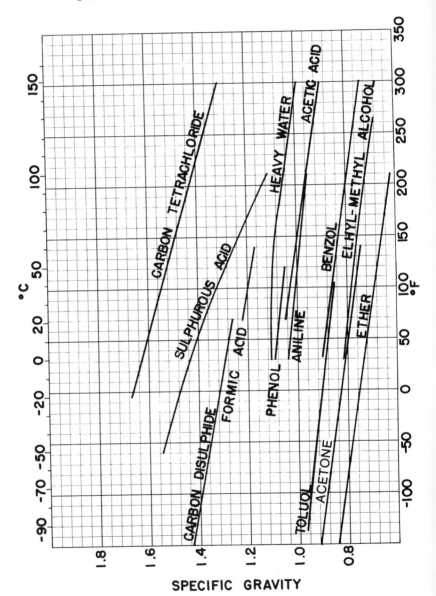

Drawn by Ingersoll-Rand based on data from various chemical handbooks.

Specific Gravity at 60°F of Aqueous Solutions

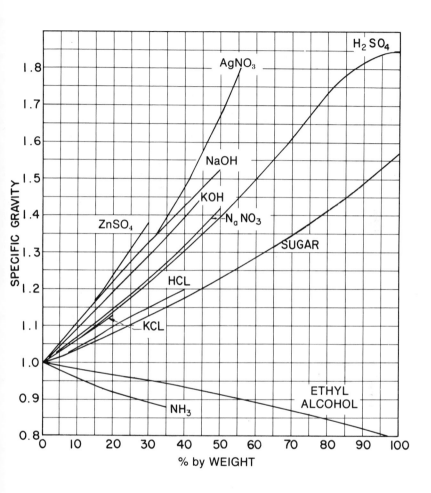

SPECIFIC GRAVITY

% by WEIGHT

Drawn by Ingersoll-Rand based on data from various chemical handbooks.

Specific Gravity of Refrigerant Liquids

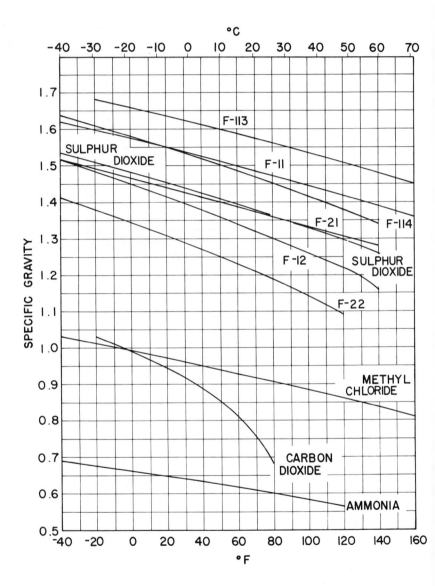

Drawn by Ingersoll-Rand based on data from various refrigerant handbooks.

Vapor Pressure of Gasolines

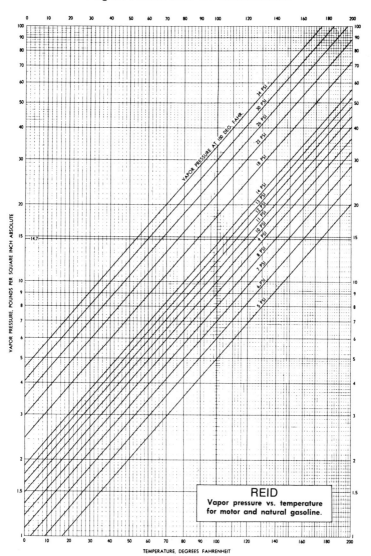

To determine the gage working pressure of a vessel to store any natural gasoline:

1. Determine the maximum liquid surface temperature reached or likely to be reached by the liquid during the period of storage.
2. The vertical temperature line intersects the Reid vapor pressure line for the liquid being considered at a definite point.
3. From the curve determine the initial vapor pressure in pounds absolute at the left hand side horizontally from the intersection mentioned in "2."
4. From the initial vapor pressure in pounds absolute subtract 14.7. The result is the gage working pressure of the vessel required to store that liquid, without evaporation loss.

Vapor Pressure of Hydrocarbons

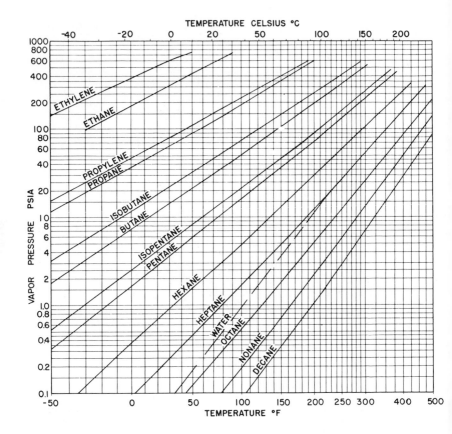

Drawn by Ingersoll-Rand based on data from various sources.

Vapor Pressure of Various Liquids

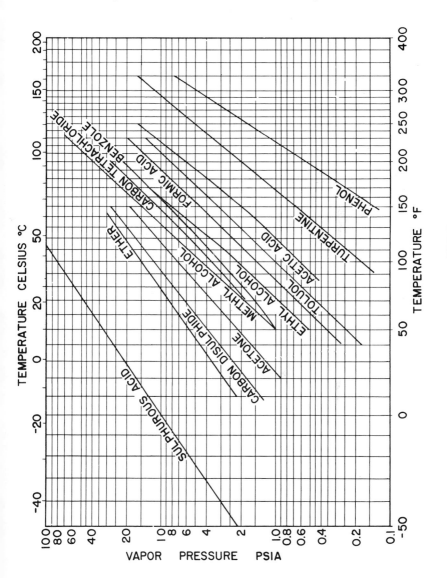

Drawn by Ingersoll-Rand based on data from various sources.

Vapor Pressure of Refrigerant Liquids

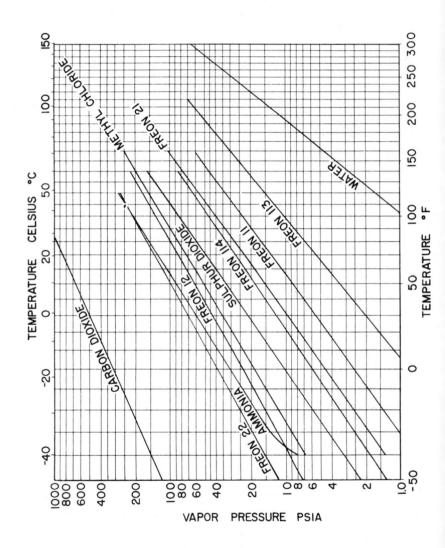

Drawn by Ingersoll-Rand based on data from various refrigerant handbooks.

PROPERTIES OF LIQUIDS

Viscosity—General Information

The viscosity of a fluid (liquid or gas) is that property which offers resistance to flow due to the existence of internal friction within the fluid. This resistance to flow, expressed as a coefficient of dynamic (or absolute) viscosity is the force required to move a unit area a unit distance.

There are two basic viscosity parameters; i.e. (1) dynamic (or absolute) viscosity; and (2) kinematic viscosity. These two parameters are related since the kinematic viscosity may be obtained by dividing the dynamic viscosity by the mass density. (See note on page 4-3 for definition of mass density.)

(1) The unit of *dynamic* (or *absolute*) viscosity in the *English* system is measured in pound seconds per square foot which is numerically identical with the slug per foot second. The unit of *dynamic* viscosity in *metric* measure is the dyne-second per square centimeter called the poise, which is numerically identical with the gram per centimeter-second. It is usually more convenient to express numerical values in centipoises such that 100 centipoises equal one poise.

The dimensions of dynamic (or absolute) viscosity are: force $\dfrac{\text{time}}{\text{length}^2}$

(2) Since the Darcy-Weisbach and Colebrook relationships (see page 3-3) are based on using a Reynolds number which varies inversely with the *kinematic* viscosity and which is obtained by dividing the dynamic (absolute) viscosity by the mass density, it is usual practice to use units of kinematic viscosity which have the dimensions of:

$$\frac{\text{length}^2}{\text{time}}$$

The unit of kinematic viscosity in English measure is the square foot per second. The unit of kinematic viscosity in metric measure is the square centimeter per second called the stoke. It is usually more convenient to express numerical values in centistokes such that 100 centistokes equal one stoke.

When English system units are used in converting from dynamic to kinematic viscosity the density $\dfrac{w}{g}$ (or mass density), rather than the specific gravity must be used where w is the weight in lb/ft³ and g is the acceleration of gravity (32.174 ft/sec²).

When the metric system terms centipoises and centistokes are used the density is numerically equal to the specific gravity.

The relationship between the dynamic and kinematic viscosity units with their proper dimensions must be carefully considered so that the correct parameters will be used as required in friction loss and other calculations.

Various types of instruments are available to determine viscosity, the one most widely used being the Saybolt viscometer which measures the time in seconds required for a liquid to flow from a filled container of specified dimensions through one of two orifices in the bottom of the container.

The term SSU (Seconds Saybolt Universal) refers to the time required for the smaller of the two orifices, and the term SSF (Seconds Saybolt Furol) the time required for the larger orifice. The smaller orifice (SSU) being used for the lighter oils and the larger orifice (SSF) for the heavy oils. The efflux time in seconds is converted empirically to kinematic viscosity in other units.

The various viscosity relationships and conversions are given on the following pages.

Approximate Viscosity Conversions

Seconds Saybolt Universal SSU	Kinematic viscosity		Seconds Saybolt Furol SSF	Seconds Red-wood 1 Stand-ard	Seconds Red-wood 2 Ad-miralty	Degrees Engler	Degrees Barbey	Kine-matic centi-stokes
	centistokes	ft²/sec						
31	1.0	0.00001076		29		1.00	6200	1.0
31.5	1.13	0.00001216		29.4		1.01	5486	1.13
32	1.81	0.00001948		29.8		1.08	3425	1.81
32.6	2.00	0.00002153		30.2		1.10	3100	2.00
33	2.11	0.00002271		30.6		1.11	2938	2.11
34	2.40	0.00002583		31.3		1.14	2583	2.40
35	2.71	0.00002917		32.1		1.17	2287	2.71
36	3.00	0.00003229		32.9		1.20	2066	3.00
38	3.64	0.00003918		33.7		1.26	1703	3.64
39.2	4.00	0.00004306		35.5		1.30	1550	4.00
40	4.25	0.00004575		36.2	5.10	1.32	1459	4.25
42	4.88	0.00005253		38.2	5.25	1.36	1270	4.88
42.4	5.00	0.00005382		38.6	5.28	1.37	1240	5.00
44	5.50	0.00005920		40.6	5.39	1.40	1127	5.50
45.6	6.00	0.00006458		41.8	5.51	1.43	1033	6.00
46	6.13	0.00006598		42.3	5.54	1.44	1011	6.13
46.8	7.00	0.00007535		43.1	5.60	1.48	885	7.00
50	7.36	0.00007922		44.3	5.83	1.58	842	7.36
52.1	8.00	0.00008611		46.0	6.03	1.64	775	8.00
55	8.88	0.00009558		48.3	6.30	1.73	698	8.88
55.4	9.00	0.00009688		48.6	6.34	1.74	689	9.00
58.8	10.00	0.0001076		51.3	6.66	1.83	620	10.00
60	10.32	0.0001111		52.3	6.77	1.87	601	10.32
65	11.72	0.0001262		56.7	7.19	2.01	529	11.72
70	13.08	0.0001408		60.9	7.60	2.16	474	13.08
75	14.38	0.0001548		65.1	8.02	2.37	431	14.38
80	15.66	0.0001686		69.2	8.44	2.45	396	15.66
85	16.90	0.0001819		73.4	8.87	2.59	367	16.90
90	18.12	0.0001950		77.6	9.30	2.73	342	18.12
95	19.32	0.0002080		81.6	9.71	2.88	321	19.32
100	20.52	0.0002209		85.6	10.12	3.02	302	20.52
120	25.15	0.0002707		102	11.88	3.57	246	25.15
140	29.65	0.0003191		119	13.63	4.11	209	29.65
160	34.10	0.0003670		136	15.39	4.64	182	34.10
180	38.52	0.0004146		153	17.14	5.12	161	38.52
200	42.95	0.0004623		170	18.90	5.92	144	42.95
300	64.6	0.0006953	32.7	253	28.0	8.79	96	64.6
400	86.2	0.0009278	42.4	338	37.1	11.70	71.9	86.2
500	108.0	0.001163	52.3	423	46.2	14.60	57.4	108.0
600	129.4	0.001393	62.0	507	55.3	17.50	47.9	129.4
700	151.0	0.001625	72.0	592	64.6	20.44	41.0	151.0
800	172.6	0.001858	82.0	677	73.8	23.36	35.9	172.6
900	194.2	0.002090	92.1	762	83.0	26.28	31.9	194.2
1000	215.8	0.002323	102.1	846	92.3	29.20	28.7	215.8

4

Approximate Viscosity Conversions (Continued)

Seconds Saybolt Universal SSU	Kinematic viscosity		Seconds Saybolt Furol SSF	Seconds Red-wood 1 Stand-ard	Seconds Red-wood 2 Ad-miralty	Degrees Engler	Degrees Barbey	Kine-matic centi-stokes
	centistokes	ft²/sec						
1200	259.0	0.002788	122	1016	111	35.1	23.9	259.0
1400	302.3	0.003254	143	1185	129	40.9	20.5	302.3
1600	345.3	0.003717	163	1354	148	46.7	18.0	345.3
1800	388.5	0.004182	183	1524	166	52.6	15.6	388.5
2000	431.7	0.004647	204	1693	185	58.4	14.4	431.7
2500	539.4	0.005806	254	2115	231	73.0	11.5	539.4
3000	647.3	0.006967	305	2538	277	87.6	9.6	647.3
3500	755.2	0.008129	356	2961	323	102	8.21	755.2
4000	863.1	0.009290	408	3385	369	117	7.18	863.1
4500	970.9	0.01045	458	3807	415	131	6.39	970.9
5000	1078.8	0.01161	509	4230	461	146	5.75	1078.8
6000	1294.6	0.01393	610	5077	553	175	4.78	1294.6
7000	1510.3	0.01626	712	5922	646	204	4.11	1510.3
8000	1726.1	0.01858	814	6769	738	234	3.59	1726.1
9000	1941.9	0.02092	916	7615	830	263	3.19	1941.9
10000	2157.6	0.02322	1018	8461	922	292	2.87	2157.6
15000	3236.5	0.03483	1526	12692		438	1.92	3236.5
20000	4315.3	0.04645	2035	16923		584	1.44	4315.3

Viscosity relationships

$$\text{Kinematic viscosity (centistokes)} = \frac{\text{absolute viscosity (centipoises)}}{\text{density (g/cm}^3)^*}$$

$$\text{ft}^2/\text{sec} = \text{centistokes} \times 1.07639 \times 10^{-5}$$

$$\text{centistokes} = \text{ft}^2/\text{sec} \times 92903.4$$

Approximate viscosity conversions

$$\text{ft}^2/\text{sec (50-100 SSU)} = \text{SSU} \times 2.433 \times 10^{-6} - .00210/\text{SSU}$$
$$\text{ft}^2/\text{sec (100-350 SSU)} = \text{SSU} \times 2.368 \times 10^{-6} - .00145/\text{SSU}$$
$$\text{ft}^2/\text{sec (over 350 SSU)} = \text{SSU (taken at 100°F)} \times 2.3210 \times 10^{-6}$$
$$\text{centistokes (50-100 SSU)} = \text{SSU} \times 0.226 - 205.3/\text{SSU}$$
$$\text{centistokes (100-350 SSU)} = \text{SSU} \times 0.220 - 147.7/\text{SSU}$$
$$\text{centistokes (over 350 SSU)} = \text{SSU (taken at 100°F or 37.8°C)} \times 0.21576$$
$$\text{centistokes (over 350 SSU)} = \text{SSU (taken at 210°F or 98.9°C)} \times 0.21426$$
$$\text{centistokes (over 500 SSF)} = \text{SSF (taken at 122°F or 50°C)} \times 2.120$$
$$\text{centistokes (over 300 Redwood \#1)} = \text{Redwood \#1 (Standard)} \times 0.255$$
$$\text{centistokes (over 50 Redwood \#2)} = \text{Redwood \#2 (Admiralty)} \times 2.3392$$
$$\text{centistokes (over 18 Engler)} = \text{Engler} \times 7.389$$
$$\text{centistokes (over 20 Stormer)} = \text{Stormer} \times 2.802$$
$$\text{centistokes (over 1.0 Demler \#10)} = \text{Demler \#10} \times 31.506$$
$$\text{centistokes (over 1.3 Demler \#1)} = \text{Demler \#1} \times 3.151$$
$$\text{centistokes (over 14 Parlin \#20)} = \text{Parlin Cup \#20} \times 61.652$$
$$\text{centistokes (over 230 Ford \#4)} = \text{Ford Cup \#4} \times 3.753$$
$$\text{centistokes} = 6200 \text{ Barbey}$$

* Usually same as specific gravity.

PROPERTIES OF LIQUIDS

Viscosity—Unit Conversions

Kinematic Viscosity

Multiply	by	to obtain
ft^2/sec	92903.04	centistokes
ft^2/sec	0.092903	sq meters/sec
sq meters/sec	10.7639	ft^2/sec
sq meters/sec	1000000.0	centistokes
centistokes	0.000001	sq meters/sec
centistokes	0.0000107639	ft^2/sec

See previous page for conversions in SSU, Redwood, etc.

Absolute or Dynamic Viscosity

lbf-sec/ft^2	47880.26	centipoises
lbf-sec/ft^2	47.8803	Pascal-sec
centipoises	0.000102	kg-sec/sq meter
centipoises	0.0000208854	lbf-sec/sq ft*
centipoises	0.001	Pascal-sec
Pascal-sec	0.0208854	lbf-sec/sq ft
Pascal-sec	1000	centipoises

* Sometimes absolute viscosity is given in terms of pounds mass. In this case—
centipoises × 0.000672 = lbm/ft sec.

Absolute to Kinematic Viscosity

centipoises	1/density (g/cm^3)	centistokes
centipoises	0.00067197/density (lb/ft^3)	ft^2/sec
lbf-sec/ft^2	32.174/density (lb/ft^3)	ft^2/sec
kg-sec/m^2	9.80665/density (kg/m^3)	sq meters/sec
Pascal-sec	1000/density (g/cm^3)	centistokes

Kinematic to Absolute Viscosity

centistokes	density (g/cm^3)	centipoises
sq meters/sec	0.10197 × density (kg/m^3)	kg-sec/sq meter
ft^2/sec	0.03108 × density (lb/ft^3)	lbf-sec/ft^2
ft^2/sec	1488.16 × density (lb/ft^3)	centipoises
centistokes	0.001 × density (g/cm^3)	Pascal-sec
sq meters/sec	1000 × density (g/cm^3)	Pascal-sec

4

Viscosity of Crankcase Oils

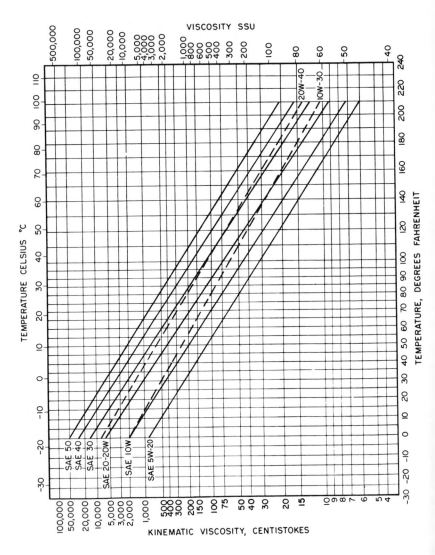

Drawn by Ingersoll-Rand based on data from Texaco, Inc.

Viscosity of Turbine Oils

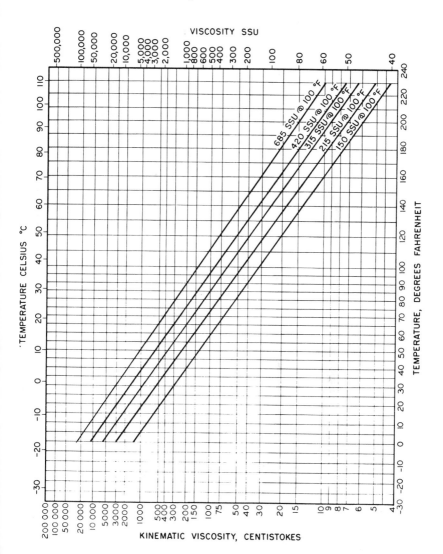

Drawn by Ingersoll-Rand based on data from Texaco, Inc.

Viscosity of Fuel Oils

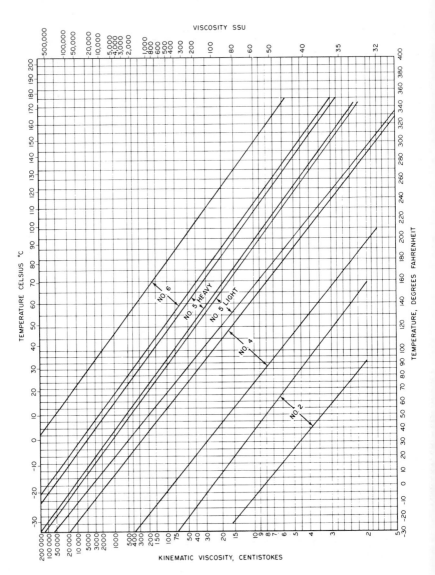

Drawn by Ingersoll-Rand based on data from Texaco, Inc.

Viscosity—Temperature Relations of Petroleum Oils

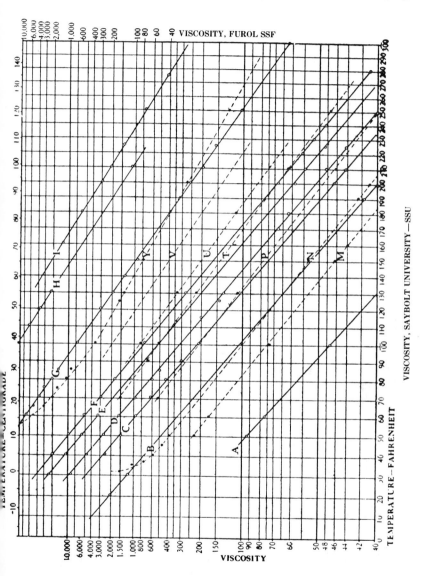

This chart may be used to determine the viscosity of an oil at any temperature provided its viscosity at two temperatures is known.

The lines on this chart show viscosities of representative oils.

Note: This chart is similar to ASTM tentative standard D341-32T which has a somewhat wider viscosity and temperature range.

Courtesy of Texaco, Inc.

Viscosity of Miscellaneous Liquids

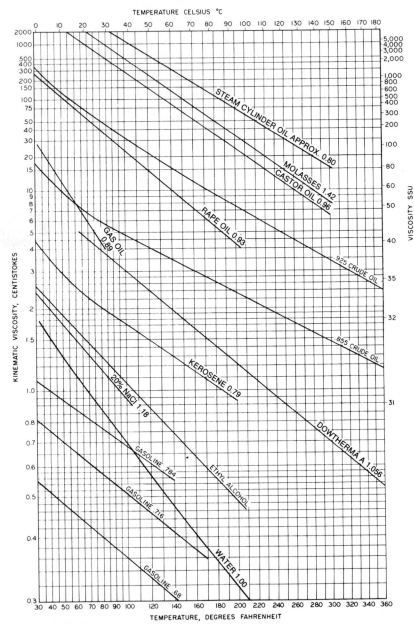

Specific gravities shown are for 60°F (15.6°C)

Drawn by Ingersoll-Rand based on data from various sources.

Viscosity of Refrigerant Liquids

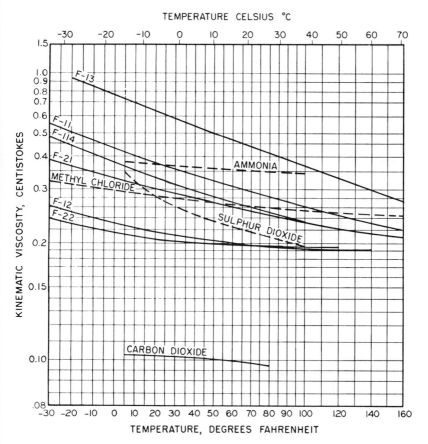

Drawn by Ingersoll-Rand based on data from various refrigerant handbooks.

Viscosity of Sucrose Solutions

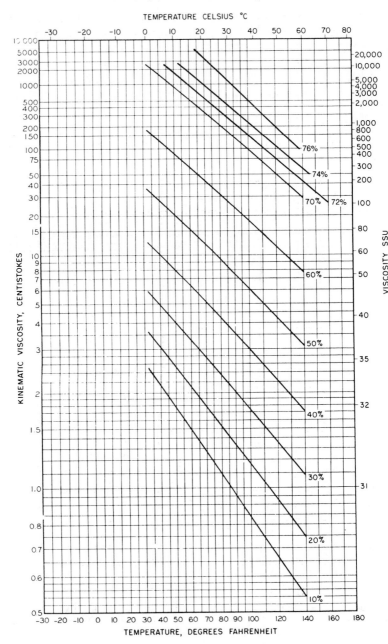

Drawn by Ingersoll-Rand based on data from various sugar handbooks.

Viscosity Blending Chart

Many liquids designated by such names as asphalt, molasses, oil, varnish, etc., are actually blends or cut-backs and have lower viscosities than the unblended liquids of the same name. On Fig below, let oil, A, have the higher viscosity and oil, B, the lower viscosity. Mark the viscosity of A and B on the right and left hand scales, respectively, and draw a straight line connecting the two as shown. The viscosity of any blend of A and B will be shown by the intersection of the vertical line representing the percentage composition and the line thus drawn. Viscosities of oils A & B must be plotted at the same temperature.

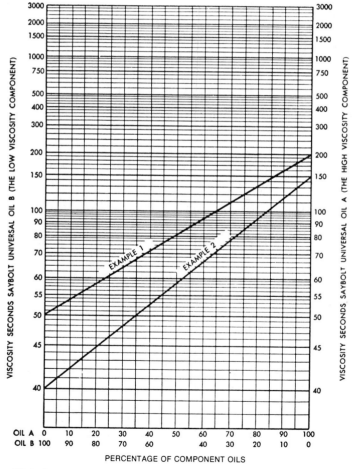

Courtesy of Hydraulic Institute.

Petroleum Temperature-volume Relations

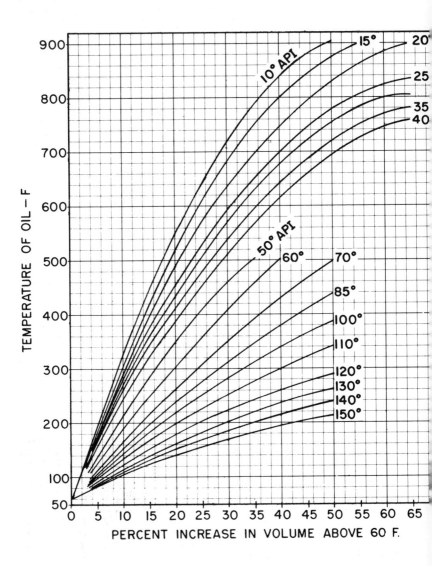

Courtesy of Hydraulic Institute.

Specific Gravity and Viscosity of Liquids

Liquid	Boiling point at atm press	Specific gravity			Viscosity			
		Temp		based on water = 1 at 60°F	Temp			
		°F	°C		°F	°C	centistokes	SSU
Acetaldehyde CH₃CHO	69F 20.8C	61 68	16.1 20	0.788 0.762	61 68	16.1 20	0.305 0.295	36
Acetic acid—5% = vinegar CH₃COOH		59	15	1.006				
10%		59	15	1.014	59	15	1.35	31.7
50%		59	15	1.061	59	15	2.27	33
80%		59	15	1.075	59	15	2.85	35
Conc.-glacial	244F 118C	59	15	1.055	59	15	1.34	31.7
Acetic acid anhydride (CH₃COO)₂O	139C	59	15	1.087	59	15	0.88	
Acetone CH₃COCH₃ ..	133F 50.5C	68	20	0.792	68 77	20 25	0.41	
Alcohol allyl	207F 97.2C	68	20	0.855	68 104	20 40	1.60 0.90 cp	31.8
butyl-n	243F 117C	68 158	20 70	0.81 0.78	68 158	20 70	3.64 1.17	38 31.5
ethyl (grain) C₂H₅OH	172F 78.3C	68 104	20 40	0.789 0.772	68 100	20 37.8	1.52 1.2	31.7 31.5
methyl (wood) CH₃OH	151F 64.7C	68	20	0.79	59 32	15 0	0.74 1.04	
propyl	207F 97.5C	68 32	20 0	0.804 0.817	68 122	20 50	2.8 1.4	35 31.7
Aluminum sulphate— 36% sol		60	15.6	1.055	68	20	1.41	31.7
Ammonia	−33.5C	0	−17.8	0.662	0	−17.8	0.30	
Aniline	363F 184.4C	68 32	20 0	1.022 1.035	68 50	20 10	4.37 6.4	40 46.4
Asphalt, blended RC-0, MC-0, SC-0 ..		60	15.6	1.0+	77 100	25 37.8	159–324 60–108	737–1.5M 280–500
RC-1, MC-1, SC-1 ..		60	15.6	1.0+	100 122	37.8 50	518–1080 159–324	2.4M–5M 737–1500
RC-2, MC-2, SC-2 ..		60	15.6	1.0+	122 140	50 60	518–1080 215–430	2.4M–5M 1M–2M
RC-3, MC-3, SC-3 ..		60	15.6	1.0+	122 140	50 60	1295–2805 540–1080	6M–13M 2.5M–5M
RC-4, MC-4, SC-4 ..		60	15.6	1.0+	140 180	60 82.8	1725–4315 270–540	8M–20M 1.25M–2.5M
RC-5, MC-5, SC-5 ‹.		60	15.6	1.0+	140 180	60 82.8	6040–18340 647–1295	28M–85M 3M–6M
RS-1, MS-1, SS-1 ...		60	15.6	1.0+	77 100	25 37.8	33–216 19–75	155–1M 90–350
Asphalt emulsions Fed #1		60	15.6	1.0+	77 100	25 37.8	215–1510 75–367	1M–7M 350–1700
Fed #2, V, VI		60	15.6	1.0+	77 100	25 37.8	33–216 19–75	155–1000 90–350

Based on material from the Hydraulic Institute with additions by Ingersoll-Rand.

4

Specific Gravity and Viscosity of Liquids (Continued)

Liquid	Boiling point at atm press	Specific gravity			Viscosity			
		Temp		based on water = 1 at 60°F	Temp		centistokes	SSU
		°F	°C		°F	°C		
Automotive crankcase oils SAE-5W		60	15.6	.88–.94	0	−17.8	1295 max	6M–max
SAE 10W		60	15.6	.88–.94	0	−17.8	1295–2590	6M–12M
SAE 20W		60	15.6	.88–.94	0	−17.8	2590–10350	12M–48M
SAE 20		60	15.6	.88–.94	210	98.9	5.7–9.6	45–58
SAE 30		60	15.6	.88–.94	210	98.9	9.6–12.9	58–70
SAE 40		60	15.6	.88–.94	210	98.9	12.9–16.8	70–85
SAE 50		60	15.6	.88–.94	210	98.9	16.8–22.7	85–110
Automotive gear oils SAE 75W		60	15.6	.88–.94	210	98.9	4.2 min	40 min
SAE 80W		60	15.6	.88–.94	210	98.9	7.0 min	49 min
SAE 85W		60	15.6	.88–.94	210	98.9	11.0 min	63 min
SAE 90		60	15.6	.88–.94	210	98.9	14–25	74–120
SAE 140		60	15.6	.88–.94	210	98.9	25–43	120–200
SAE 150		60	15.6	.88–.94	210	98.9	43 min	200 min
Beer		60	15.6	1.01	68	20	1.8	32(est)
Benzene (Benzol) C_6H_6 ...	176F 80.4C	32 60	0 15.6	0.899 0.885	32 68	0 20	1.00 0.744	31
Bone oil		60	15.6	0.918	130 212	54.4 100	47.5 11.6	220 65
Boric acid, sat. H_3BO_3		46.4 59	8 15	1.014 1.025				
Brine see sodium choride and calcium chloride ...								
Bromine	142F 58.8C	68 32	20 0	2.9	68	20	0.34	
Butane-n	31.1F −0.5C	60	15.6	0.584	−50 30	−1.1	0.52 0.35	
Butyric acid n	316F 162.5C	68	20	0.959	68 32	20 0	1.61 2.3cp	31.8
Calcium chloride 5%		65	18.3	1.040	65	18.3	1.156	
25%		60	15.6	1.23	60	15.6	4.0	39
Carbolic acid (phenol) ...	360F 182.2C	65	18.3	1.08	65 194	18.3 90	11.83 1.26cp	65

Specific Gravity and Viscosity of Liquids (Continued)

Liquid	Boiling point at atm press	Specific gravity			Viscosity			
		Temp		based on water = 1 at 60°F	Temp			
		°F	°C		°F	°C	centistokes	SSU
Carbon tetrachloride CCl₄	170F 76.7C	68 100	20 37.8	1.594	68 100	20 37.8	0.612 0.53	
Carbon disulphide CS₂	115F 46.2C	32 68	0 20	1.293 1.263	32 68	0 20	0.33 0.298	
Castor oil		68 104	20 40	0.96 0.95	100 130	37.8 54.4	259–325 98–130	1200–1500 450–600
China wood oil		60	15.6	0.943	69 100	20.6 37.8	308.5 125.5	1425 580
Chloroform	142F 61.2C	68 140	20 60	1.489 1.413	68 140	20 60	0.38 0.35	
Cocoanut oil		60	15.6	0.925	100 130	37.8 54.4	29.8–31.6 14.7–15.7	140–148 76–80
Cod oil		60	15.6	0.928	100 130	37.8 54.4	32.1 19.4	150 95
Corn oil		60	15.6	0.924	130 212	54.4 100	28.7 8.6	135 54
Corn starch solutions 22 Baume		60	15.6	1.18	70 100	21.1 37.8	32.1 27.5	150 130
24 Baume		60	15.6	1.20	70 100	21.1 37.8	129.8 95.2	600 440
25 Baume		60	15.6	1.21	70 100	21.1 37.8	303 173.2	1400 800
Cotton seed oil		60	15.6	.88–.93	100 130	37.8 54.4	37.9 20.6	176 100
Creosote		60	15.6	1.04–1.10	60 130	15.6 54.4		
Crude oil 48° API		60 130	15.6 54.4	0.79 0.76	60 130	15.6 54.4	3.8 1.6	39 31.8
40° API		60 130	15.6 54.4	0.825 0.805	60 130	15.6 54.4	9.7 3.5	55.7 38
35.6 API		60 130	15.6 54.4	0.847 0.824	60 130	15.6 54.4	17.8 4.9	88.4 42.3
32.6 API		60 130	15.6 54.4	0.862 0.84	60 130	15.6 54.4	23.2 7.1	110 46.8
Salt Creek		60 130	15.6 54.4	0.843 0.82	60 130	15.6 54.4	77 6.1	45.6
Decane-n	343F 173C	68	20	0.73	0 100	−17.8 37.8	2.36 1.001	34 31
Diethylene glycol		60	15.6	1.12	70	21.1	32	149.7
Diethyl ether	94.4F	68	20	0.714	68	20	0.32	
Diesel fuel oils 2D		60	15.6	.82–.95	100 130	37.8 54.4	2–6 1.–3.97	32.6–45.5 –39
3D		60	15.6	.82–.95	100 130	37.8 54.4	6–11.75 3.97–6.78	45.5–65 39–48
4D		60	15.6	.82–.95	100 130	37.8 54.4	29.8 max 13.1 max	140 max 70 max
5D		60	15.6	.82–.95	122 160	50 71.1	86.6 max 35.2 max	400 max 165 max
Ethyl acetate CH₃COOC₂H₅	171F 77.2C	59 68	15 20	0.907 0.90	59 68	15 20	0.4 0.49	
Dowtherm	494.3°	77	25°C	1.056	77	25		

Specific Gravity and Viscosity of Liquids (Continued)

Liquid	Boiling point at atm press	Specific gravity			Viscosity			
		Temp		based on water = 1 at 60°F	Temp			
		°F	°C		°F	°C	centistokes	SSU
Ethyl bromide C_2H_5Br	101F 77.2C	59	15	1.45	68	20	0.27	
Ethylene bromide	269F 131.7C	68	20	2.18	68	20	0.787	
Ethylene chloride	183F 837C	68	20	1.246	68	20	0.668	
Ethylene glycol ..		60	15.6	1.125	70	21.1	17.8	88.4
Formic acid 10%		68	20	1.025	68	20	1.04	31
50%		68	20	1.121	68	20	1.2	31.5
80%		68	20	1.186	68	20	1.4	31.7
Conc.		60	15.6	1.221	68 77	20 25	1.48 1.57cp	31.7
Freon −11		70	21.1	1.49	70	21.1	0.21	
−12		70	21.1	1.33	70	21.1	0.27	
−21		70	21.1	1.37	70	21.1	1.45	31.7
Furfurol	161.7C	68	20	1.159	68 77	20 25	1.45 1.49cp	31.7
Fuel oils 1		60	15.6	.82−.95	70 100	21.1 37.8	2.39−4.28 −2.69	34−40 32−35
2		60	15.6	.82−.95	70 100	21.1 37.8	3.0−7.4 2.11−4.28	36−50 33−40
3		60	15.6	.82−.95	70 100	21.1 37.8	2.69−5.84 2.06−3.97	35−45 32.8−39
5A		60	15.6	.82−.95	70 100	21.1 37.8	7.4−26.4 4.91−13.7	50−125 42−72
5B		60	15.6	.82−.95	70 100	21.1 37.8	26.4− 13.6−67.1	125− 72−310
6		60	15.6	.82−.95	122 160	50 71.1	97.4−660 37.5−172	450−3M 175−780
Gas oils		60	15.6	0.89	70 100	21.1 37.8	13.9 7.4	73 50
Gasolines a		60	15.6	0.74	60 100	15.6 37.8	0.88 0.71	
b		60	15.6	0.72	60 100	15.6 37.8	0.64	
c		60	15.6	0.68	60 100	15.6 37.8	0.46 0.40	
Glycerine 100%	554F	68	20	1.260	68.6 100	20.3 37.8	648 176	2950 813
50% water		68	20	1.13	68 140	20 60	5.29 1.85cp	43
Glucose		60	15.6	1.35−1.44	100 150	37.8 65.6	7.7M−22M 880−2420	35M−100M 4M−11M
Heptane-n	209.2F 98.4C	60	15.6	0.688	0 100	−17.8 37.8	0.928 0.511	
Hexane-n	155.7F 68.7C	60	15.6	0.664	0 100	−17.8 37.8	0.683 0.401	

PROPERTIES OF LIQUIDS

Specific Gravity and Viscosity of Liquids (Continued)

Liquid	Boiling point at atm press	Specific gravity			Viscosity			
		Temp		based on water = 1 at 60°F	Temp			
		°F	°C		°F	°C	centistokes	SSU
Honey					100	37.8	73.6	340
Industrial lubricants								
Turbine oils								
685 . . . . SSU at 100°F . . .					60 200	15.6 93.3	647 14.5	3000 77
420 . . . . SSU					60 200	15.6 93.3	367 11	1700 63
315 . . . . SSU					60 200	15.6 93.3	259 8	1200 52
215 . . . . SSU					60 200	15.6 93.3	151 7.3	700 48
150 . . . . SSU					60 200	15.6 93.3	99 6	460 45.5
Machine lubricants								
# 8				.88–.94	100 130	37.8 54.4	23–34 13–18	112–160 70–90
#10				.88–.94	100 130	37.8 54.4	34–72 18–25	160–235 90–120
#20				.88–.94	100 130	37.8 54.4	72–83 25–39	235–385 120–185
#30				.88–.94	100 130	37.8 54.4	75–119 39–55	350–550 185–255
Cutting oils								
#1					100 130	37.8 54.4	30–40 17–23	140–190 86–110
#2					100 130	37.8 54.4	40–46 23–26	190–220 110–125
Ink, printers		60	15.6	1.0–1.4	100 130	37.8 54.4	550–2200 238–660	2500–10M 1100–3M
Insulating oil					70 100	21.1 37.8	24.1 max 11.75 max	115 max 65 max
Kerosene		60	15.6	.78–.82	68	20	2.71	35
Jet Fuel (av)	325F	60	15.6	.82	−30	−34.4	7.9	52
Lard		60	15.6	0.96	100 130	37.8 54.4	62.1 34.3	287 160
Lard oil		60	15.6	.91–.93	100 130	37.8 54.4	41–47.5 23.4–27.1	190–220 112–128
Linseed oil		60	15.6	.92–.94	100 130	37.8 54.4	30.5 18.94	143 93
Mercury	675.1F 356.9C	60	15.6	13.57	70 100	21.1 37.8	0.118 0.11	

4

Specific Gravity and Viscosity of Liquids (Continued)

Liquid	Boiling point at atm press	Specific gravity			Viscosity			
		Temp		based on water = 1 at 60°F	Temp			
		°F	°C		°F	°C	centistokes	SSU
Methyl acetate	135F 57.2C	68	20	0.93	68 104	20 40	0.44 0.32cp	
Methyl iodide	108F 42.6C	68	20	2.28	68 104	20 40	0.213 0.42cp	
Menhadden oil		60	15.6	0.93	100 130	37.8 54.4	29.8 18.2	140 90
Milk		60	15.6	1.02–1.05	68	20	1.13	31.5
Molasses A, first		60	15.6	1.40–1.46	100 130	37.8 54.4	281–5070 151–1760	1300–23500 700–8160
B, second		60	15.6	1.43–1.48	100 130	37.8 54.4	1410–13.2M 660–3.3M	6535–61180 3058–15294
C, blackstrap		60	15.6	1.46–1.49	100 130	37.8 54.4	2630–55M 1320–16.5M	12190–255M 6120–76.5M
Naphthalene	424F 218C	68	20	1.145	176 212	80 100	0.9 0.78cp	
Neatsfoot oil........		60	15.6	0.917	100 130	37.8 54.4	49.7 27.5	230 130
Nitrobenzene	412F 210.9C	68 59	20 15	1.203 1.205	68	20	1.67	31.8
Nonane-n	302F 150.7C	60 68	15.6 20	0.7218 0.718	0 100	−17.8 37.8	1.728 0.807	32
Octane-n	258F 125.6C	60	15.6	0.7069	0 100	−17.8 37.8	1.266 0.645	31.7
Olive oil	(570)F (300)C	60	15.6	.91–.92	100 130	37.8 54.4	43.2 24.1	200
Palm oil		60	15.6	0.924	100 130	37.8 54.4	47.8 26.4	
Peanut oil		60	15.6	0.92	100 130	37.8 54.4	42 23.4	200
Pentane-n	96.9F 36C	32 60	0 15.6	0.650 0.631	0 80	−17.8 26.7	0.508 0.342	
Petrolatum		60	15.6	0.83	130 160	54.4 71.1	20.5 15	100 77
Petroleum ether		60	15.6	0.64	60	15.6	31(est)	1.1
Propionic acid	286F	68	20	0.99	32 68	0 20	1.52cp 1.13	31.5
Propylene glycol		68	20	1.038	70	21.1	52	241
Quenching oil (typical)		60	15.6	.86–.89			100–120	20.5–25

Specific Gravity and Viscosity of Liquids (Continued)

Liquid	Boiling point at atm press	Specific gravity			Viscosity			
		Temp		based on water = 1 at 60°F	Temp			
		°F	°C		°F	°C	centistokes	SSU
Rapeseed oil		68	20	0.92	100	37.8	54.1	250
					130	54.4	31	145
Rosin oil		60	15.6	0.98	100	37.8	324.7	1500
					130	54.4	129.9	600
Rosin (wood)		60	15.6	1.09 avg	100	37.8	216–11M	1M–50M
					200	93.3	108–4400	500–20M
Sesame seed oil		60	15.6	0.923	100	37.8	39.6	184
					130	54.4	23	110
Sodium chloride 5%		39	3.9	1.037	68	20	1.097	31.1
25%		39	3.9	1.196	60	15.6	2.4	34
		60	15.6	1.19				
Sodium hydroxide (caustic soda) 20%		60	15.6	1.22	65	18.3	4.0	39.4
30%		60	15.6	1.33	65	18.3	10.0	58.1
40%		60	15.6	1.43	65	18.3		110.1
Soya bean oil		60	15.6	.924–.928	100	37.8	35.4	165
					130	54.4	19.64	96
Sperm oil		60	15.6	1.35–1.44	100	37.8	21–23	110
					130	54.4	15.2	78
Sugar solutions Corn syrup 86.4 Brix		60	15.6	1.459	100	37.8	180Mcp	
					180	82.2	1750cp	
84.4 Brix		60	15.6	1.445	100	37.8	48Mcp	
					180	82.2	800cp	
82.3 Brix		60	15.6	1.431	100	37.8	17Mcp	
					180	82.2	380cp	
80.3 Brix		60	15.6	1.418	100	37.8	6900cp	
					180	82.2	230cp	
78.4 Brix		60	15.6	1.405	100	37.8	3200cp	
					180	82.2	160cp	
Sugar solutions Sucrose 60 Brix		60	15.6	1.29	70	21.1	49.7	230
					100	37.8	18.7	92
64 Brix		60	15.6	1.31	70	21.1	95.2	440
					100	37.8	31.6	148
68 Brix		60	15.6	1.338	70	21.1	216.4	1000
					100	37.8	59.5	275

4

Specific Gravity and Viscosity of Liquids (Continued)

Liquid	Boiling point at atm press	Specific gravity			Viscosity			
		Temp		based on water = 1 at 60°F	Temp		centistokes	SSU
		°F	°C		°F	°C		
72 Brix		60	15.6	1.36	70 100	21.1 37.8	595 138.6	2700 640
74 Brix		60	15.6	1.376	70 100	21.1 37.8	1210 238	5500 1100
76 Brix		60	15.6	1.39	70 100	21.1 37.8	2200 440	10000 2000
Sulphur	444.6C							
Sulphuric acid 100%		68	20	1.839	68 140	20 60	14.6 7.2cp	76
95%		68	20	1.839	68	20	14.5	75
60%		68	20	1.50	68	20	4.4	41
20%		68	20	1.14				
Tar, coke oven		60	15.6	1.12+	70 100	21.1 37.8	600–1760 141–308	3M–8M 650–1400
Tar, gas house		60	15.6	1.16–1.30	70 100	21.1 37.8	3300–66M 440–4400	15M–300M 2M–20M
Tar, pine		60	15.6	1.06+	100 132	37.8 55.6	559 108.2	2500 500
Tar, road— RT-2		60	15.6	1.07+	122 212	50 100	43.2–64.9 8.8–10.2	200–300 55–60
RT-4		60	15.6	1.08+	122 212	50 100	86.6–154 11.6–14.3	400–700 65–70
RT-6		60	15.6	1.09+	122 212	50 100	216–440 16.8–26.2	1M–2M 85–125
RT-8		60	15.6	1.13+	122 212	50 100	660–1760 31.8–48.3	3M–8M 150–225
RT-10		60	15.6	1.14+	122 212	50 100	4.4M–13.2M 53.7–86.6	20M–60M 250–400
RT-12		60	15.6	1.15+	122 212	50 100	25M–75M 108–173	114M–456M 500–800
Toluene	231F 110.6C	68	20	0.866	68 140	20 60	0.68 0.38cp	
Trielhylene glycol ...		68	20	1.125	70	21.1	40	185.7
Turpentine	320F	60	15.6	.86–.87	100 130	37.8 54.4	86.6–95.2 39.9–44.3	400–440 185–205
Varnish, spar		60	15.6	0.9	68 100	20 37.8	313 143	1425 650

Specific Gravity and Viscosity of Liquids (Continued)

Liquid	Boiling point at atm press	Specific gravity			Viscosity			
		Temp		based on water = 1 at 60°F	Temp		centistokes	SSU
		°F	°C		°F	°C		
Water distilled		60	15.6	1.00	68	20	1.0038	31
fresh		60	15.6	1.0	60 130	15.6 54.4	1.13 0.55	31.5
sea		60	15.6	1.03			1.15	31.5
Whale oil		60	15.6	0.925	100 130	37.8 54.4	35–39.6 19.9–23.4	163–184 97–112
Xylene-o	287F 142.7C	68	20	0.87	68 104	20 40	0.93 0.623cp	

Centrifugal pump performance with viscous liquids

Since pump performance characteristic curves are basis water, corrections (per charts in *Fig 4-2 and 4-3) must be applied when handling viscous liquids. The following two examples will illustrate the use of these charts.

Example A—performance correction:

Given: Characteristic curve (Fig 4-1) page 4-46 for pump handling water at normal temperature (see page 4-46, 4-47 and 4-48).

Problem: Determine the approximate performance curve for oil having a specific gravity of 0.90 and viscosity of 1000 SSU (216 centistokes).

From water curve in Fig 4-1 note that capacity at best efficiency point ($1.0 \times Q_n$) is 750 gpm. Tabulate gpm for $0.6 \times Q_n$, $0.8 \times Q_n$, $1.0 \times Q_n$ and $1.20 \times Q_n$ for water as in table following Fig 4-1; read heads and efficiencies from the water curve at these values of gpm and tabulate as shown. Entering the chart (Fig 4-3) at 750 gpm go vertically to the head in feet (100′) and horizontally to 1000 SSU and vertically to the correction factors, reading one value for C_Q and C_E and four values for C_H and tabulate as shown. Multiplying the tabulated water values by these factors will give the corrected values for operation with the viscous liquid. Corrected head and efficiency curves may be plotted using these points; approximate brake horsepower and curve

*NOTE: Figures 4-1 to 4-3 appear on pages 4-46 to 4-48.

can be determined by use of the formula:

$$\text{Estimated bhp (viscous)} = \frac{\text{capacity (viscous)} \times \text{head (viscous) sp gr}}{3960 \times \text{Efficiency (viscous)}}$$

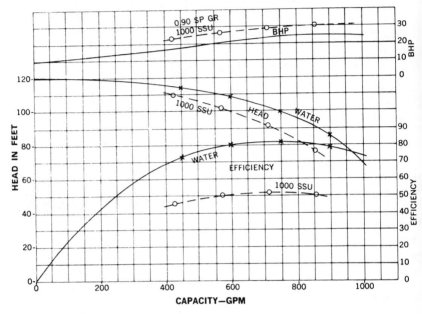

Fig. 4-1 Sample performance chart

Courtesy of Hydraulic Institute.

Sample Calculations				
	$0.6 \times Q_{NW}$	$0.8 \times Q_{NW}$	$1.0 \times Q_{NW}$	$1.2 \times Q_{NW}$
Water capacity (Q_w) gpm	450	600	750	900
Water head (H_w) ft	114	108	100	86
Water efficiency (E_w) %	72.5	80	82	79.5
Viscosity of liquid SSU	1000 SSU	1000 SSU	1000 SSU	1000 SSU
C_Q—from chart	0.95	0.95	0.95	0.95
C_H—from chart	0.96	0.94	0.92	0.89
C_E—from chart	0.635	0.635	0.635	0.635
Viscous capacity—$Q_w \times C_Q$ gpm ..	427	570	712	855
Viscous head—$H_w \times C_H$ ft	109.5	101.5	92	76.5
Viscous efficiency—$E_w \times C_E$ %	46.0	50.8	52.1	50.5
Specific gravity of liquid	0.90	0.90	0.90	0.90
bhp viscous	23.1	25.9	28.6	29.4

Viscosity Corrections for Small Pumps (Continued)
Between 10 to 100 GPM

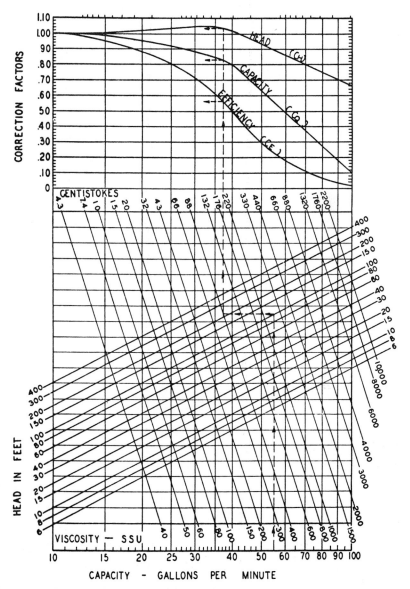

Fig. 4-2 Performance correction chart.
(Correction factors apply to Best Efficiency Point only)

Viscosity Corrections for Large Pumps (Continued)
Above 100 GPM

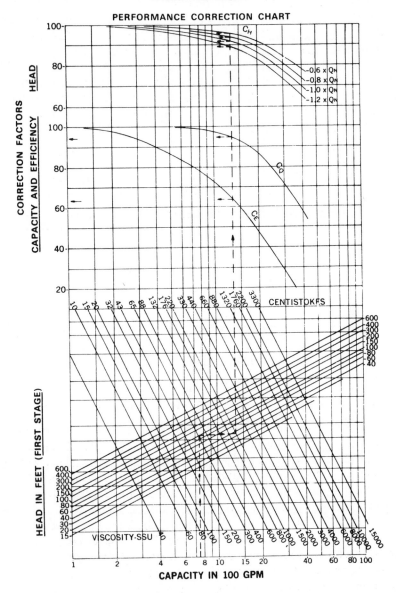

Fig. 4-3 Performance correction chart

Courtesy of Hydraulic Institute.

Example B—selecting a pump:

Selecting a pump for viscous liquids is the reverse of correcting for water performance; i.e. take the desired design conditions and divide by the applicable correction factors to obtain the equivalent design conditions on water. For example: select a pump to deliver 750 gpm at 100 ft when handling a liquid having a viscosity of 1000 SSU and specific gravity of 0.90 at pumping temperature. Enter chart at 750 gpm and follow the same procedure as in Example A except for this calculation use C_H from curve marked $1.0 \times Q_n$ (capacity at best efficiency point—bep)

$$C_Q = 0.95 \qquad C_E = 0.64 \qquad C_H \text{ for } ``1.0 \times Q_n" = 0.92$$

Equivalent water conditions obtained by dividing the viscous conditions by the above correction factors will be 790 gpm and 108.7 ft.

If the pump selected for these equivalent water conditions has a water efficiency of 81% the viscous efficiency will be 0.64×0.81 or about 52%.

$$\text{Estimated bhp} = \frac{750 \times 100 \times 0.90}{3960 \times 0.52} = 32.8$$

Note: Correction charts are approximate and apply only to Centrifugal pumps of conventional design with open or closed impellers and adequate suction head to force liquid into impeller; not good for axial or mixed flow pumps or non-uniform liquids.

Correction factors for flows 100 gpm and below (Fig. 4-2) are basis (bep).

For a more detailed discussion of these correction factors reference should be made to the Hydraulic Institute Standards.

Pump performance on stock (for friction loss see page 3-88)

Since pump performance curves are based on tests with water at normal temperatures (60°F to 70°F), there will be a reduction in head, capacity and efficiency when handling stock, and corrections (depending on consistency) must be applied to the water performance. These corrections (applied to the head and capacity at the best efficiency point (bep) will be approximately 0.725 for 6% stock; 0.825 for 5.5%; 0.90 for 5.0%; 0.94 for 4.5%; 0.98 for 4.0%; and 1.0 for 3.5% and less.

The brake horsepower (bhp) of a pump delivering stock at the corrected head and capacity will be approximately the same as if it were delivering water at the bep. Therefore, the approximate efficiency of the pump on stock can be determined by calculating its hydraulic horsepower at the corrected head and capacity and dividing by the bhp.

Pumps handling stock with entrained air must be given special consideration (consult with manufacturer).

Slurry Information

The abrasive nature of some slurries is clearly a consideration in selecting and designing slurry pumps. Excessive wear of wetted pump parts due to abrasion has limited operational life in some instances to two weeks. Abrasive wear is inconclusive and difficult to predict even though many studies on wear testers have been performed. Abrasive considerations are the abrading mineral itself, abrasive hardness, particle velocity, density, directions, sharpness, shape, size and corrosiveness.

Pump components exposed to abrasion, i.e. impellers, casings and suction covers, are made from abrasion resistant materials such as Ni-hard and rubber.

Experience has shown that for abrasive handling pumps, the pump RPM should be kept as low as possible. A guideline in showing the effect of RPM on wear is the relation that wear will vary approximately as the cube of the RPM—wear α RPM³. Hence since RPM is related to pump developed pressure, high head applications will wear much more rapidly than lower heads. Also, it can generally be seen that pump part hardness is inversely proportional to abrasive wear—wear α 1/BHN;* and wear also varies directly with particle concentration—wear α C_v.

Both synthetic and natural rubbers are used in slurry pumps for their superior abrasion and corrosion resistance. Their abrasion resistance exceeds Ni-hard or other metals when the particles are small and round. Sharp and hard solids with high energy are unsuitable for rubber application because they can cut the rubber material. The dampening effect of rubber is low for impact angles greater than 20°. Also, rubber is generally unsuitable for applications with heads over 150' and where particle size exceeds ¼ inch. Wear resistant metals such as Ni-hard are used on more coarse and harder slurries.

Metal/Rubber Slurry Pump Selection Criteria

Use Metal-lined Pump:	*Use Rubber-lined Pump:*
Solids greater than ¼ in.	Solids less than ¼ in.
PH greater than 4.5	PH less than 6.0
Abrasive service above 100 ft head	Abrasive service below 100 ft head
Temperatures to 250°F	Non-abrasive service below 100 ft/sec—impeller peripheral speed
Hydrocarbon based slurries	
	Temperatures below 150°F

* Brinell hardness number

Sediment Terminology
Scale of Particle Sizes

Tyler screen mesh per inch	U.S. standard mesh per inch	Inches	Microns	Class
		1.3–2.5	33,000–63,500	Very Coarse Gravel
		.6–1.3	15,200–33,000	Coarse Gravel
2.5		.321	8,000	Medium Gravel
5	5	.157	4,000	Fine Gravel
9	10	.079	2,000	Very Fine Gravel
16	18	.039	1,000	Very Coarse Sand
32	35	.0197	500	Coarse Sand
60	60	.0098	250	Medium Sand
115	120	.0049	125	Fine Sand
250	230	.0024	62	Very Fine Sand
400		.0015	37	Coarse Silt
		.0006–.0012	16–31	Medium Silt
			8–16	Fine Silt
			4–8	Very Fine Silt
			2–4	Coarse Clay
			1–2	Medium Clay
			.5–1	Fine Clay

4

Mohs Scale of Hardness, Modified
(Trans. Am. Electrochem Society, 1933)

Mineral or Material	Mohs Hardness	
Talc	1	Soft to Medium
Gypsum, Kaolin Clay, Anthracite	2	
Calc Spar, Gray Cast Iron	3	
Fluor Spar	4	
Apatite	5	
Orthoclase or Periclase	6	Medium to Hard
Vitreous Pure Silica	7	
Quartz, Stellite	8	
Topaz	9	
Garnet	10	Hard to Very Hard
Fused Zirconia, Tantalum Carbide	11	
Fused Alumina, Tungsten Carbide	12	
Silicon Carbide	13	
Boron Carbide	14	
Diamond	15	

Hardness of Common Minerals

Soft	Medium	Hard	Very Hard
Asbestos Rock	Limestone	Granite	Iron Ore (taconite)
Gypsum Rock	Dolomite	Quartzite	Granite
Slate	Sandstone	Iron Ore	Granite Gravel
Talc	Coal	Trap Rock	
Soft Limestone		Gravel	

Slurry rheology, viscosity

Terms:

Rheology—study of deformation and flow of substances.

Fluid—a substance which undergoes continuous deformation when subjected to shear stress.

Consistency (apparent viscosity)—a slurry's resistance to deformation when subjected to shear stress. This term is applied to differentiate from absolute viscosity which is used in conjunction with Newtonian fluids.

Kinematic viscosity—absolute viscosity (consistency) divided by the mass density* of the fluid.

Fluidity—inverse of viscosity.

Plasticity—property of a fluid which requires a definite yield stress to produce a continuous flow.

Rigidity—consistency of a plastic fluid in terms of stress beyond the yield.

Newtonian fluid—a fluid whose viscosity is constant and is independent of shear rate, and where shear rate is linearly proportional to shear stress. (water, oil, etc).

Non-Newtonian (complex) fluid—a fluid whose consistency is a function of shear stress, and the shear rate—shear stress relationship is non-linear.

For either Newtonian or Non-Newtonian fluids, viscosity (or consistency is the rate of shear (flow) per unit shearing stress (force causing flow).

$$\tau = \mu \; dv/dy$$

τ = Tangential Shearing Stress (force)
μ = Viscosity (consistency)
dv/dy = Shear rate (velocity gradient)

Types of Non-Newtonian fluids:

Bingham-plastic fluids—a fluid where no flow occurs until a definite yield point is reached. This yield stress is necessary to overcome static friction of the fluid particles. Most slurry mixtures used in pipeline transportation exhibit Bingham plastic characteristics.

Pseudo-plastic fluids—substances with no definite yield stress which exhibit a decrease in consistency with increasing shear rate.

Dilatant (inverted plastic) fluids—a fluid which exhibits an increase

---

* mass density = weight ÷ acceleration of gravity.

in consistency with increasing shear rate. These fluids have the property of increasing their volume when stirred. Examples are starch in water, quicksands and beach sands.

Thixotropic fluids—a fluid which exhibits a decrease in consistency with time to a minimum value at any shear rate. It will break down when stirred but rebuild itself after a given time. Examples are drilling muds, gypsum in water, paint.

Typical flow diagrams (rheogram) for various fluids:

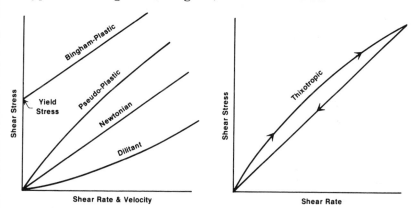

NOTE: Shear stress is proportional to pressure or total head; shear rate is proportional to velocity or flow.

Useful formulas for solids and slurries:

$$S_L = \text{Specific gravity of liquid}$$
$$S_s = \text{Specific gravity of solids}$$
$$S_m = \text{Specific gravity of slurry mixture}$$
$$C_v = \text{Percent solid concentration by volume}$$
$$C_w = \text{Percent solid concentration by weight}$$

(1) $$C_v = \frac{S_m - S_L}{S_s - S_L}$$

(2) $$C_w = \frac{C_v \times S_s}{S_m}$$

(3) $$S_m = C_v (S_s - S_L) + S_L$$

(4) $$S_m = \frac{S_L}{1 - \dfrac{C_w(S_s - S_L)}{S_s}}$$

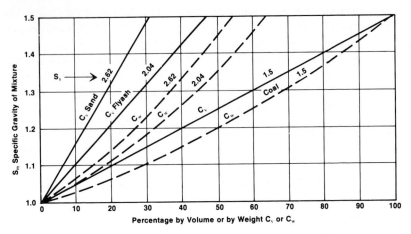

From Centrifugal Pumps by A. J. Stepanoff with permission of John Wiley & Sons.

Critical Carrying Velocity of Slurries in Pipes

As a slurry is conveyed by turbulent flow in a pipe, particles have a tendency to settle. The critical velocity of a slurry flow in a pipe is that velocity below which particles start forming a sliding bed on the bottom of the pipe which will cause the flow to become unstable and the pipe will eventually clog. General slurry pipeline practice is to design the pipe velocity to exceed the critical velocity by at least 30 percent.

This velocity will depend upon pipe diameter, solids concentration and the properties of the fluid and solid particles.

Extended studies have been done on critical speeds of slurry mixtures. One typical study done by Durand with sand-water suspensions gives the relationship:

$$V_c = F_1[2gD(S_s - 1)]^{1/2}$$

Where D = inside pipe diameter—ft
$\quad\quad S_s$ = specific gravity of solids
$\quad\quad V_c$ = critical carrying velocity—ft/sec
$\quad\quad g$ = acceleration of gravity—ft/sec²
$\quad\quad F_1$ = an experimental coefficient dependent upon grain size and concentration and approximate equals 1.34 above .05 in. particle size. NOTE: That this coefficient is for sand-water mixtures to 15 percent concentration by weight.

In general slurry pipeline practice, to prevent settlement in the pipeline, hydraulic conditions should ensure turbulent flow.

As a very approximate guide for slurries with particle sizes under 50 microns, a minimum velocity in the range of 4 to 7 ft. per second second is required, provided this velocity gives turbulent conditions. For larger particle size slurries (over 150 microns) and volume concentrations up to 15 percent, a rough guide for minimum velocity is 14 times the square root of pipe diameter (ft.), (Durand's equation).

There is no general method or formula to determine the critical velocity of all slurry combinations, therefore, if a precise critical velocity is required, results should be obtained by experimentation.

Slurry Head Correction—Pipe Friction Loss

For a given solid throughput and pipe diameter, the lowest pressure loss is obtained at the transition between laminar and turbulent flow. Although this minimum pressure loss is also the most economical running point (power per pound of solids), the operating velocity must be kept above this critical carrying velocity.

As with critical carrying velocities, many extensive studies have been done with pressure gradients of solid mixtures. Again, a general purpose formula for all slurries is impractical to predict. However, certain guidelines can be followed.

When the slurry contains particles under 150 microns and the concentration of these particles is low, and the fluid velocity is high enough to ensure uniform particle distribution in the pipe—under these circumstances, the slurry behaves as a *Newtonian liquid and

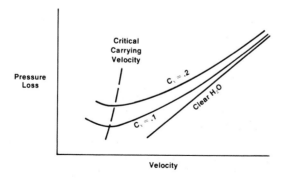

A typical pressure loss vs. velocity relationship.

* For Newtonian Liquid definition
see page 1-5.

the pressure loss is the same as the water friction loss which can be calculated from the friction loss charts in a previous section. (Pages 3-3 to 3-48)

Friction loss is also dependent on pipe roughness. In slurry pipeline design, a rough pipe design will yield a higher pressure loss capability. Using a "C"* factor pipe of 100 will result in a pressure loss capability about 100% greater than design with a clean-steel pipe, however "C"* values of 140 are not uncommon with certain types of slurries.

Although slurry-pipe friction can be higher than water or Newtonian fluids, many slurries have negligible head correction and can be treated with a correction very nearly the same as clear water. Avoid large corrections, unless tested, since overcapacity can cause pump problems.

In calculating and/or estimating pipe friction losses for slurries, it has been common practice, for many years, to use the Hazen and Williams empirical formula discussed on pages 3-7 and 3-8. This formula is convenient to use and experience has shown, that with the selection of the proper friction factor "C" will produce reliable results.

Both the Darcy and Hazen-Williams formulas can be used for slurry pumping with appropriate experience correction factors. The Hazen-Williams formula is more convenient in that "C" values can be associated with given slurries and extrapolated from the friction factor tables, using corrections for various "C" factors shown on page 3-8.

With reference to pump performance, most slurries have little affect on performance except for density; allowance, however, should be made for pump wear to maintain plant production.

---

* Friction factor in Hazen and Williams formula. "C" of 140 is for new steel pipe.

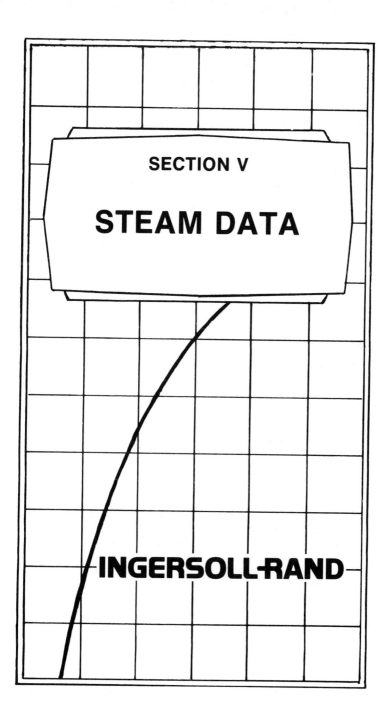

SECTION V

STEAM DATA

INGERSOLL-RAND

5

CONTENTS OF SECTION 5

Steam Data

Steam Data Notes

Steam is the term usually applied to the vapor-phase of water when this phase is reached by boiling water. The term vapor describes the gaseous state of any substance, below its critical condition, from which it can be reduced to a liquid by compression. But water vapor is usually thought of only in a mixture with air, while the word steam has a much broader meaning. In a certain range of (low) pressures, the terms steam and water vapor are used interchangeably.

"Boiling point" is the temperature at which a liquid boils—that is, changes rapidly and violently into vapor, (or steam, if the liquid is water), through the application of heat. When the pressure exerted upon the liquid is 760 mm Hg or 14.696 lb per sq in abs., the boiling point of water is 212°F or 100°C. The temperature at which water boils varies, however, with the pressure; water may actually boil at freezing temperature (32°F) provided the pressure is held down to .0885 lb per sq in; on the other hand its maximum boiling temperature (the critical temperature), is approximately 705°F, under a pressure of some 3200 lb per sq in.

Steam, or water vapor, is invisible. Only through partial condensation does it appear as a mist. Steam may exist either in saturated form, while in contact with water, or as superheated steam, after separation from the water from which it was generated and further heating. Saturated steam may be dry or wet; in the latter case it carries free moisture and the amount of moisture determines the "quality" of the steam. The exhaust from a steam turbine or engine is usually wet steam. The temperature of dry—or wet saturated steam at a given pressure is the same and is determined entirely by the absolute pressure. If the pressure is maintained, the temperature will remain constant as condensation proceeds. Removal of heat produces condensation.

Superheated steam behaves like a gas; when compressed, its temperature rises; when heated at constant pressure its volume increases, when heated at constant volume its pressure rises, etc. Its condition is usually indicated by the "degrees of superheat" above the saturation temperature, and by its pressure.

1 cu ft of water, evaporated at 212°F and 14.696 lb per sq in absolute pressure, becomes 1606 cu ft of dry-saturated steam.

1 cu ft of steam weighs 0.03731 lb, and 1 lb of steam occupies 26.80 cu ft, at a pressure of 14.696 lb per sq in absolute and a temperature of 212°F.

5

1 cu ft of dry air weighs 0.08073 lb, and 1 lb of dry air occupies 12.387 cu ft at pressure of 14.696 lb per sq in absolute and a temperature of 32°F.

The amount of heat required to transform a liquid into its vapor, the temperature remaining constant, is called the latent heat of vaporization. The value of the latent heat varies with the pressure under which the liquid is caused to vaporize.

The latent heat of vaporization of water to steam is 970.3 Btu per lb at atmospheric pressure.

The Btu (British thermal unit) is equivalent to 778.0 ft-lb, which is the heat energy required to raise the temperature of 1 lb of water 1°F in the range from 32 to 212°F. In the metric system use is made of the term calorie (cal) or gram-calorie which is the heat required to raise the temperature of 1 gram of water 1°C within the range 0 to 100°C. The kilogram-calorie or large calorie is 1000 gram-calories. In modern practice the Joule is used as a measure of energy. It is equivalent to 0.7376 ft-lb.

The output of a steam generating plant is often expressed in pounds of steam delivered per hour. Since the steam output may vary in temperature and pressure, the boiler capacity is more completely expressed as the heat transferred in Btu per hour. Boiler capacity is usually expressed as kilo Btu (kB)/hour which is 1000 Btu/hour, or mega Btu (mB)/hour which is 1,000,000 Btu/hour.

An older expression of boiler capacity is boiler horsepower. It is equivalent to 34.5 lb of water evaporated per hr at standard atmospheric pressure and 212°F. It is equivalent to 33,475 Btu/hr.

*ENTHALPY—(Heat Content) is the sum of the internal and external energies of a substance.
*ENTROPY—is a measure of the unavailability of energy in a substance.
*For more details reference to MARKS Handbook is suggested.

Mollier Diagram for Steam

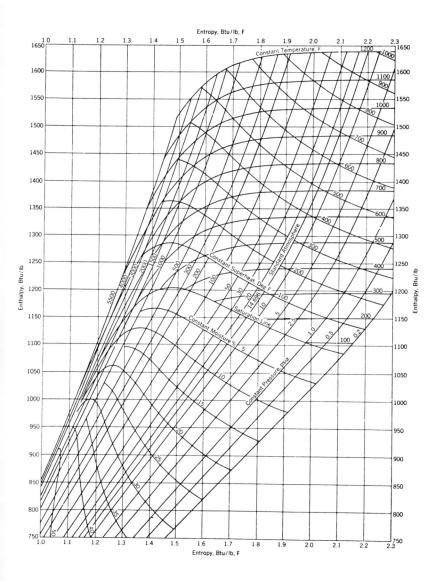

Pressure-enthalpy Chart for Steam

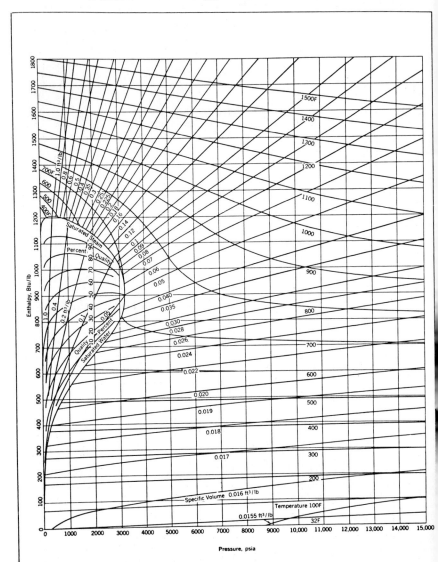

Courtesy of Babcock Wilcox.

Properties of Saturated Steam—Temperature Table

Temp F	Absolute Pressure			Vacuum in Hg ref to 29.921 in bar. at 32F	Specific volume sat vap ft³/lbm V_g	Total heat or enthalpy Btu/lb		
	in Hg	mm Hg	lb/in²			water h_f	evap h_{fg}	steam h_g
32	0.1803	4.581	0.08859	29.741	3304.7	−0.0179	1075.5	1075.5
32.018	0.1805	4.585	0.08865	29.741	3302.4	0.0003	1075.5	1075.5
33	0.1878	4.77	0.09223	29.734	3180.7	0.989	1074.9	1075.9
34	0.1955	4.96	0.09600	29.726	3061.9	1.996	1074.4	1076.4
35	0.203	5.17	0.09991	29.718	2948.1	3.002	1073.8	1076.8
36	0.212	5.38	0.10395	29.710	2839.0	4.008	1073.2	1077.2
37	0.220	5.59	0.10815	29.701	2734.4	5.013	1072.7	1077.7
38	0.229	5.82	0.11249	29.692	2634.2	6.018	1072.1	1078.1
39	0.238	6.05	0.11698	29.683	2538.0	7.023	1071.5	1078.5
40	0.248	6.29	0.12163	29.674	2445.8	8.027	1071.0	1079.0
41	0.257	6.54	0.12645	29.664	2357.3	9.031	1070.4	1079.4
42	0.268	6.80	0.13143	29.654	2274.4	10.035	1069.8	1079.9
43	0.278	7.06	0.13659	29.643	2191.0	11.038	1069.3	1080.3
44	0.289	7.34	0.14192	29.632	2112.8	12.041	1068.7	1080.7
45	0.300	7.62	0.14744	29.621	2037.8	13.044	1068.1	1081.2
46	0.312	7.92	0.15314	29.610	1965.7	14.047	1067.6	1081.6
47	0.324	8.22	0.15904	29.597	1896.5	15.049	1067.0	1082.1
48	0.336	8.54	0.16514	29.585	1830.0	16.051	1066.4	1082.5
49	0.349	8.87	0.17144	29.572	1766.2	17.053	1065.9	1082.9
50	0.362	9.20	0.17796	29.559	1704.8	18.054	1065.3	1083.4
51	0.376	9.55	0.18469	29.545	1645.9	19.056	1064.7	1083.8
52	0.390	9.91	0.19165	29.531	1589.2	20.057	1064.2	1084.2
53	0.405	10.28	0.19883	29.516	1534.8	21.058	1063.6	1084.7
54	0.420	10.67	0.20625	29.501	1482.4	22.058	1063.1	1085.1
55	0.436	11.06	0.21392	29.486	1432.0	23.059	1062.5	1085.6
56	0.452	11.47	0.22183	29.470	1383.6	24.059	1061.9	1086.0
57	0.468	11.89	0.23000	29.453	1337.0	25.060	1061.4	1086.4
58	0.485	12.33	0.23843	29.436	1292.2	26.060	1060.8	1086.9
59	0.503	12.78	0.24713	29.418	1249.1	27.060	1060.2	1087.3
60	0.521	13.24	0.25611	29.400	1207.6	28.060	1059.7	1087.7
61	0.540	13.72	0.26538	29.381	1167.6	29.059	1059.1	1088.2
62	0.560	14.22	0.27494	29.362	1129.2	30.059	1058.5	1088.6
63	0.580	14.73	0.28480	29.341	1092.1	31.058	1058.0	1089.0
64	0.601	15.25	0.29497	29.321	1056.5	32.058	1057.4	1089.5
65	0.622	15.80	0.30545	29.299	1022.1	33.057	1056.9	1089.9
66	0.644	16.36	0.31626	29.277	989.0	34.056	1056.3	1090.4
67	0.667	16.93	0.32740	29.255	957.2	35.055	1055.7	1090.8
68	0.690	17.53	0.33889	29.231	926.5	36.054	1055.2	1091.2
69	0.714	18.14	0.35073	29.207	896.9	37.053	1054.6	1091.7
70	0.739	18.77	0.36292	29.182	868.4	38.052	1054.0	1092.1
71	0.765	19.42	0.37549	29.157	840.9	39.050	1053.5	1092.5
72	0.791	20.09	0.38844	29.130	814.3	40.049	1052.9	1093.0
73	0.818	20.78	0.40177	29.103	788.8	41.048	1052.4	1093.4
74	0.846	21.49	0.41550	29.075	764.1	42.046	1051.8	1093.8
75	0.875	22.22	0.42964	29.047	740.3	43.045	1051.2	1094.3
76	0.904	22.97	0.44420	29.017	717.4	44.043	1050.7	1094.7
77	0.935	23.75	0.45919	28.986	695.2	45.042	1050.1	1095.1
78	0.966	24.54	0.47461	28.955	673.9	46.040	1049.5	1095.6
79	0.999	25.37	0.49049	28.923	653.2	47.038	1049.0	1096.0

5

Properties of Saturated Steam—Temperature Table (*cont.*)

Temp F	Absolute Pressure			Vacuum in Hg ref to 29.921 in bar. at 32F	Specific volume sat vap ft³/lbm V_g	Total heat or enthalpy Btu/lb		
	in Hg	mm Hg	lb/in²			water h_f	evap h_{fg}	steam h_g
80	1.032	26.21	0.50683	28.889	633.3	48.037	1048.4	1096.4
81	1.066	27.08	0.52364	28.855	614.1	49.035	1047.8	1096.9
82	1.101	27.97	0.54093	28.820	595.6	50.033	1047.3	1097.3
83	1.138	28.89	0.55872	28.784	577.6	51.031	1046.7	1097.7
84	1.175	29.84	0.57702	28.746	560.3	52.029	1046.1	1098.2
85	1.213	30.81	0.59583	28.708	543.6	53.027	1045.6	1098.6
86	1.253	31.81	0.61518	28.669	527.5	54.026	1045.0	1099.0
87	1.293	32.84	0.63507	28.628	511.9	55.024	1044.4	1099.5
88	1.335	33.90	0.65551	28.587	496.8	56.022	1043.9	1099.9
89	1.377	34.99	0.67653	28.544	432.2	57.020	1043.3	1100.3
90	1.421	36.10	0.69813	28.500	468.1	58.018	1042.7	1100.8
91	1.467	37.25	0.72032	28.455	454.5	59.016	1042.2	1101.2
92	1.513	38.43	0.74313	28.408	441.3	60.014	1041.6	1101.6
93	1.561	39.64	0.76655	28.361	428.6	61.012	1041.0	1102.1
94	1.610	40.89	0.79062	28.312	416.3	62.010	1040.5	1102.5
95	1.660	42.165	0.81534	28.261	404.4	63.008	1039.9	1102.9
96	1.712	43.478	0.84072	28.210	392.9	64.006	1039.3	1103.3
97	1.765	44.826	0.86679	28.157	381.7	65.005	1038.8	1103.8
98	1.819	46.210	0.89356	28.102	370.9	66.003	1038.2	1104.2
99	1.875	47.631	0.92103	28.046	360.5	67.001	1037.6	1104.6
100	1.933	49.090	0.94924	27.989	350.4	67.999	1037.1	1105.1
101	1.992	50.586	0.97818	27.930	340.6	68.997	1036.5	1105.5
102	2.052	52.123	1.00789	27.869	331.1	69.995	1035.9	1105.9
103	2.114	53.700	1.03838	27.807	322.0	70.993	1035.4	1106.3
104	2.178	55.317	1.06965	27.743	313.1	71.992	1034.8	1106.8
105	2.243	56.976	1.10174	27.678	304.5	72.990	1034.2	1107.2
106	2.310	58.681	1.1347	27.611	296.18	73.99	1033.6	1107.6
107	2.379	60.424	1.1684	27.542	288.11	74.99	1033.1	1108.1
108	2.504	62.213	1.2030	27.417	280.30	75.98	1032.5	1108.5
109	2.522	64.049	1.2385	27.400	272.72	76.98	1031.9	1108.9
110	2.596	65.936	1.2750	27.325	265.39	77.98	1031.4	1109.3
111	2.672	67.865	1.3123	27.249	258.28	78.98	1030.8	1109.8
112	2.750	69.841	1.3505	27.172	251.38	79.98	1030.2	1110.2
113	2.830	71.873	1.3898	27.092	244.70	80.98	1029.6	1110.6
114	2.911	73.947	1.4299	27.001	238.22	81.97	1029.1	1111.0
115	2.995	76.078	1.4711	26.926	231.94	82.97	1028.5	1111.5
116	3.081	78.260	1.5133	26.840	225.85	83.97	1027.9	1111.9
117	3.169	80.499	1.5566	26.752	219.94	84.97	1027.3	1112.3
118	3.259	82.790	1.6009	26.662	214.21	85.97	1026.8	1112.7
119	3.352	85.138	1.6463	26.569	208.66	86.97	1026.2	1113.2
120	3.446	87.538	1.6927	26.475	203.26	87.97	1025.6	1113.6
121	3.543	89.999	1.7403	26.378	198.03	88.96	1025.0	1114.0
122	3.643	92.523	1.7891	26.279	192.95	89.96	1024.5	1114.4
123	3.744	95.103	1.8390	26.177	188.03	90.96	1023.9	1114.9
124	3.848	97.746	1.8901	26.073	183.24	91.96	1023.3	1115.3
125	3.956	100.47	1.9428	25.966	178.60	92.96	1022.7	1115.7
126	4.064	103.22	1.9959	25.858	174.09	93.96	1022.2	1116.1
127	4.175	106.05	2.0507	25.746	169.72	94.96	1021.6	1116.5
128	4.289	108.95	2.1068	25.632	165.47	95.96	1021.0	1117.0
129	4.406	111.92	2.1642	25.515	161.34	96.96	1020.4	1117.4

Absolute pressures in inches Hg, millimeters Hg, and vacuum in inches Hg calculated by Ingersoll-Rand.

Properties of Saturated Steam—Temperature Table (*cont.*)

Temp F	Absolute Pressure in Hg	mm Hg	lb/in²	Vacuum in Hg ref to 29.921 in bar. at 32F	Specific volume sat vap ft³/lbm V_g	water h_f	evap h_{fg}	steam h_g
130	4.526	114.96	2.2230	25.395	157.33	97.96	1019.8	1117.8
131	4.648	118.06	2.2830	25.273	153.44	98.95	1019.3	1118.2
132	4.773	121.25	2.3445	25.148	149.66	99.95	1018.7	1118.6
133	4.902	124.50	2.4074	25.020	145.98	100.95	1018.1	1119.1
134	5.032	127.82	2.4717	24.889	142.41	101.95	1017.5	1119.5
135	5.166	131.23	2.5375	24.755	138.94	102.95	1016.9	1119.9
136	5.303	134.70	2.6047	24.618	135.57	103.95	1016.4	1120.3
137	5.443	138.26	2.6735	24.478	132.29	104.95	1015.8	1120.7
138	5.586	141.89	2.7438	24.335	129.11	105.95	1015.2	1121.1
139	5.773	145.61	2.8157	24.188	126.01	106.95	1014.6	1121.6
140	5.882	149.41	2.8892	24.039	123.00	107.95	1014.0	1122.0
141	6.035	153.30	2.9643	23.886	120.07	108.95	1013.4	1122.4
142	6.192	157.27	3.0411	23.730	117.22	109.95	1012.9	1122.8
143	6.351	161.32	3.1195	23.570	114.45	110.95	1012.3	1123.2
144	6.515	165.47	3.1997	23.407	111.76	111.95	1011.7	1123.6
145	6.681	169.71	3.2816	23.240	109.14	112.95	1011.1	1124.0
146	6.852	174.04	3.3653	23.069	106.59	113.95	1010.5	1124.5
147	7.026	178.46	3.4508	22.895	104.11	114.95	1009.9	1124.9
148	7.204	182.97	3.5381	22.718	101.70	115.95	1009.3	1125.3
149	7.385	187.58	3.6273	22.536	99.35	116.95	1008.7	1125.7
150	7.571	192.30	3.7184	22.351	97.07	117.95	1008.2	1126.1
151	7.760	197.11	3.8114	22.161	94.84	118.95	1007.6	1126.5
152	7.954	202.02	3.9065	21.968	92.68	119.95	1007.0	1126.9
153	8.151	207.04	4.0035	21.770	90.57	120.95	1006.4	1127.3
154	8.353	212.16	4.1025	21.569	88.52	121.95	1005.8	1127.7
155	8.559	217.39	4.2036	21.363	86.52	122.95	1005.2	1128.2
156	8.769	222.73	4.3068	21.153	84.57	123.95	1004.6	1128.6
157	8.983	228.18	4.4122	20.938	82.68	124.95	1004.0	1129.0
158	9.202	233.74	4.5197	20.719	80.83	125.96	1003.4	1129.4
159	9.426	239.41	4.6294	20.496	79.04	126.96	1002.8	1129.8
160	9.654	245.20	4.7414	20.678	77.29	127.96	1002.2	1130.2
161	9.886	251.11	4.8556	20.035	75.58	128.96	1001.6	1130.6
162	10.123	257.14	4.9722	19.798	73.92	129.96	1001.0	1131.0
163	10.366	263.28	5.0911	19.556	72.30	130.96	1000.4	1131.4
164	10.613	269.56	5.2124	19.309	70.72	131.96	999.8	1131.8
165	10.864	275.96	5.3361	19.057	69.18	132.96	999.2	1132.2
166	11.121	282.48	5.4623	18.800	67.68	133.97	998.6	1132.6
167	11.384	289.14	5.5911	18.538	66.22	134.97	998.0	1133.0
168	11.651	295.93	5.7223	18.271	64.80	135.97	997.4	1133.4
169	11.923	302.85	5.8562	17.998	63.41	136.97	996.8	1133.8
170	12.201	309.91	5.9926	17.720	62.06	137.97	996.2	1134.2
171	12.484	317.10	6.1318	17.437	60.74	138.98	995.6	1134.6
172	12.773	324.44	6.2736	17.148	59.45	139.98	995.0	1135.0
173	13.068	331.92	6.4182	16.854	58.19	140.98	994.4	1135.4
174	13.368	339.54	6.5656	16.554	56.97	141.98	993.8	1135.8
175	13.674	347.31	6.7159	16.248	55.77	142.99	993.2	1136.2
176	13.985	355.23	6.8690	15.936	54.61	143.99	992.6	1136.6
177	14.303	363.30	7.0250	15.618	53.47	144.99	992.0	1137.0
178	14.627	371.52	7.1840	15.295	52.36	145.99	991.4	1137.4
179	14.957	379.90	7.3460	14.965	51.28	147.00	990.8	1137.8

Properties of Saturated Steam—Temperature Table (*cont.*)

Temp F	Absolute Pressure			Vacuum in Hg ref to 29.921 in bar. at 32F	Specific volume sat vap ft³/lbm V_g	Total heat or enthalpy Btu/lb		
	in Hg	mm Hg	lb/in²			water h_f	evap h_{fg}	steam h_g
180	15.293	388.42	7.5110	14.629	50.225	148.00	990.2	1138.2
181	15.635	397.12	7.679	14.287	49.194	149.00	989.6	1138.6
182	15.983	405.96	7.850	13.939	48.189	150.01	989.0	1139.0
183	16.339	415.01	8.025	13.582	47.207	151.01	988.4	1139.4
184	16.701	424.22	8.203	13.220	46.249	152.01	987.8	1139.8
185	17.070	433.58	8.384	12.851	45.313	153.02	987.1	1140.2
186	17.445	443.09	8.568	12.477	44.400	154.02	986.5	1140.5
187	17.827	452.81	8.756	12.094	43.508	155.02	985.9	1140.9
188	18.216	462.69	8.947	11.705	42.638	156.03	985.3	1141.3
189	18.611	472.72	9.141	11.310	41.787	157.03	984.7	1141.7
190	19.016	483.02	9.340	10.905	40.957	158.04	984.1	1142.1
191	19.426	493.41	9.541	10.496	40.146	159.04	983.5	1142.5
192	19.845	504.06	9.747	10.076	39.354	160.05	982.8	1142.9
193	20.271	514.87	9.956	9.651	38.580	161.05	982.2	1143.3
194	20.702	525.84	10.168	9.219	37.824	162.05	981.6	1143.7
195	21.144	537.06	10.385	8.777	37.086	163.06	981.0	1144.0
196	21.592	548.43	10.605	8.329	36.364	164.06	980.4	1144.4
197	22.050	560.07	10.830	7.871	35.659	165.07	979.7	1144.8
198	22.514	571.86	11.058	7.407	34.970	166.08	979.1	1145.2
199	22.987	583.86	11.290	6.935	34.297	167.08	978.5	1145.6
200	23.467	596.06	11.526	6.454	33.639	168.09	977.9	1146.0
201	23.956	608.48	11.766	5.966	32.996	169.09	977.2	1146.3
202	24.456	621.15	12.011	5.467	32.367	170.10	976.6	1146.7
203	24.960	633.97	12.259	4.962	31.752	171.10	976.0	1147.1
204	25.475	647.05	12.512	4.447	31.151	172.11	975.4	1147.5
205	26.000	660.40	12.770	3.921	30.564	173.12	974.7	1147.9
206	26.531	673.89	13.031	3.390	29.989	174.12	974.1	1148.2
207	27.073	687.65	13.297	2.848	29.428	175.13	973.5	1148.6
208	27.625	701.67	13.568	2.297	28.878	176.14	972.8	1149.0
209	28.185	715.89	13.843	1.737	28.341	177.14	972.2	1149.4
210	28.755	730.37	14.123	1.167	27.816	178.15	971.6	1149.7
211	29.333	745.05	14.407	0.588	27.302	179.16	970.9	1150.1
212	29.921	760.00	14.696	0.000	26.799	180.17	970.3	1150.5

Tables on pages 5-7 to 5-10 reproduced by permission from ASME Steam Tables© 1967 by American Society of Mechanical Engineers. All rights reserved.

Absolute pressures in inches Hg, millimeters Hg, and vacuum in inches Hg calculated by Ingersoll-Rand.

Properties of Saturated Steam—Temperature Table (*cont.*)

Temp F	Abs press lb/in²	Specific volume ft³/lbm V_g	Enthalpy, Btu/lbm			Entropy, Btu/lbm × F		Temp F
			Sat liquid h_f	Evap h_{fg}	Sat vapor h_g	Sat liquid s_f	Sat vapor s_g	
212	14.696	26.799	180.17	970.3	1150.5	0.3121	1.7568	212
213	14.990	26.307	181.17	969.7	1150.8	0.3136	1.7552	213
214	15.289	25.826	182.18	969.0	1151.2	0.3151	1.7536	214
215	15.592	25.355	183.19	968.4	1151.6	0.3166	1.7520	215
216	15.901	24.894	184.20	967.8	1152.0	0.3181	1.7505	216
220	17.186	23.148	188.23	965.2	1153.4	0.3241	1.7442	220
224	18.556	21.545	192.27	962.6	1154.9	0.3300	1.7380	224
228	20.015	20.073	196.31	960.0	1156.3	0.3359	1.7320	228
232	21.567	18.718	200.35	957.4	1157.8	0.3417	1.7260	232
236	23.216	17.471	204.40	954.8	1159.2	0.3476	1.7201	236
240	24.968	16.321	208.45	952.1	1160.6	0.3533	1.7142	240
244	26.826	15.260	212.50	949.5	1162.0	0.3591	1.7085	244
248	28.796	14.281	216.56	946.8	1163.4	0.3649	1.7028	248
252	30.883	13.375	220.62	944.1	1164.7	0.3706	1.6972	252
256	33.091	12.538	224.69	941.4	1166.1	0.3763	1.6917	256
260	35.427	11.762	228.76	938.6	1167.4	0.3819	1.6862	260
264	27.894	11.042	232.83	935.9	1168.7	0.3876	1.6808	264
268	40.500	10.375	236.91	933.1	1170.0	0.3932	1.6755	268
272	43.249	9.755	240.99	930.3	1171.3	0.3987	1.6702	272
276	46.147	9.180	245.08	927.5	1172.5	0.4043	1.6650	276
280	49.200	8.6439	249.2	924.6	1173.8	0.4098	1.6599	280
284	52.414	8.1453	253.3	921.7	1175.0	0.4154	1.6548	284
288	55.795	7.6807	257.4	918.8	1176.2	0.4208	1.6498	288
292	59.350	7.2475	261.5	915.9	1177.4	0.4263	1.6449	292
296	63.084	6.8433	265.6	913.0	1178.6	0.4317	1.6400	296
300	67.005	6.4658	269.7	910.0	1179.7	0.4372	1.6351	300
304	71.119	6.1130	273.8	907.0	1180.9	0.4426	1.6303	304
308	75.433	5.7830	278.0	904.0	1182.0	0.4479	1.6256	308
312	79.953	5.4742	282.1	901.0	1183.1	0.4533	1.6209	312
316	84.688	5.1849	286.3	897.9	1184.1	0.4586	1.6162	316
320	89.643	4.9138	290.4	894.8	1185.2	0.4640	1.6116	320
324	94.826	4.6595	294.6	891.6	1186.2	0.4692	1.6071	324
328	100.245	4.4208	298.7	888.5	1187.2	0.4745	1.6025	328
332	105.907	4.1966	302.9	885.3	1188.2	0.4798	1.5981	332
336	111.820	3.9859	307.1	882.1	1189.1	0.4850	1.5936	336
340	117.992	3.7878	311.3	878.8	1190.1	0.4902	1.5892	340
344	124.430	3.6013	315.5	875.5	1191.0	0.4954	1.5849	344
348	131.142	3.4258	319.7	872.2	1191.9	0.5006	1.5806	348
352	138.138	3.2603	323.9	868.9	1192.7	0.5058	1.5763	352
356	145.424	3.1044	328.1	865.5	1193.6	0.5110	1.5721	356
360	153.010	2.9573	332.3	862.1	1194.4	0.5161	1.5678	360
364	160.903	2.8184	336.5	858.6	1195.2	0.5212	1.5637	364
368	169.113	2.6873	340.8	855.1	1195.9	0.5263	1.5595	368
372	177.648	2.5633	345.0	851.6	1196.7	0.5314	1.5554	372
376	186.517	2.4462	349.3	848.1	1197.4	0.5365	1.5513	376
380	195.729	2.3353	353.6	844.5	1198.0	0.5416	1.5473	380
384	205.294	2.2304	357.9	840.8	1198.7	0.5466	1.5432	384
388	215.220	2.1311	362.2	837.2	1199.3	0.5516	1.5392	388
392	225.516	2.0369	366.5	833.4	1199.9	0.5567	1.5352	392
396	236.193	1.9477	370.8	829.7	1200.4	0.5617	1.5313	396

5

Properties of Saturated Steam—Temperature Table (cont.)

Temp F	Abs press lb/in²	Specific volume ft³/lbm V_g	Enthalpy, Btu/lbm			Entropy, Btu/lbm × F		Temp F
			Sat liquid h_f	Evap h_{fg}	Sat vapor h_g	Sat liquid s_f	Sat vapor s_g	
400	247.259	1.8630	375.1	825.9	1201.0	0.5667	1.5274	400
404	258.725	1.7827	379.4	822.0	1201.5	0.5717	1.5234	404
408	270.600	1.7064	383.8	818.2	1201.9	0.5766	1.5195	408
412	282.894	1.6340	388.1	814.2	1202.4	0.5816	1.5157	412
416	295.617	1.5651	392.5	810.2	1202.8	0.5866	1.5118	416
420	308.78	1.4997	396.9	806.2	1203.1	0.5915	1.5080	420
424	322.39	1.4374	401.3	802.2	1203.5	0.5964	1.5042	424
428	336.46	1.3782	405.7	798.0	1203.7	0.6014	1.5004	428
432	351.00	1.3218	410.1	793.9	1204.0	0.6063	1.4966	432
436	366.03	1.2681	414.6	789.7	1204.2	0.6112	1.4928	436
440	381.54	1.21687	419.0	785.4	1204.4	0.6161	1.4890	440
444	397.56	1.16806	423.5	781.1	1204.6	0.6210	1.4853	444
448	414.09	1.12152	428.0	776.7	1204.7	0.6259	1.4815	448
452	431.14	1.07711	432.5	772.3	1204.8	0.6308	1.4778	452
456	448.73	1.03472	437.0	767.8	1204.8	0.6356	1.4741	456
460	466.87	0.99424	441.5	763.2	1204.8	0.6405	1.4704	460
464	485.56	0.95557	446.1	758.6	1204.7	0.6454	1.4667	464
468	504.83	0.91862	450.7	754.0	1204.6	0.6502	1.4629	468
472	524.67	0.88329	455.2	749.3	1204.5	0.6551	1.4592	472
476	545.11	0.84950	459.9	744.5	1204.3	0.6599	1.4555	476
480	566.15	0.81717	464.5	739.6	1204.1	0.6648	1.4518	480
484	587.81	0.78622	469.1	734.7	1203.8	0.6696	1.4481	484
488	610.10	0.75658	473.8	729.7	1203.5	0.6745	1.4444	488
492	633.03	0.72820	478.5	724.6	1203.1	0.6793	1.4407	492
496	656.61	0.70100	483.2	719.5	1202.7	0.6842	1.4370	496
500	680.86	0.67492	487.9	714.3	1202.2	0.6890	1.4333	500
504	705.78	0.64991	492.7	709.0	1201.7	0.6939	1.4296	504
508	731.40	0.62592	497.5	703.7	1201.1	0.6987	1.4258	508
512	757.72	0.60289	502.3	698.2	1200.5	0.7036	1.4221	512
516	784.76	0.58079	507.1	692.7	1199.8	0.7085	1.4183	516
520	312.53	0.55956	512.0	687.0	1199.0	0.7133	1.4146	520
524	841.04	0.53916	516.9	681.3	1198.2	0.7182	1.4108	524
528	870.31	0.51955	521.8	675.5	1197.3	0.7231	1.4070	528
532	900.34	0.50070	526.8	669.6	1196.4	0.7280	1.4032	532
536	931.17	0.48257	531.7	663.6	1195.4	0.7329	1.3993	536
540	962.79	0.46513	536.8	657.5	1194.3	0.7378	1.3954	540
544	995.22	0.44834	541.8	651.3	1193.1	0.7427	1.3915	544
548	1028.49	0.43217	546.9	645.0	1191.9	0.7476	1.3876	548
552	1062.59	0.41660	552.0	638.5	1190.6	0.7525	1.3837	552
556	1097.55	0.40160	557.2	632.0	1189.2	0.7575	1.3797	556
560	1133.38	0.38714	562.4	625.3	1187.7	0.7625	1.3757	560
564	1170.10	0.37320	567.6	618.5	1186.1	0.7674	1.3716	564
568	1207.72	0.35975	572.9	611.5	1184.5	0.7725	1.3675	568
572	1246.26	0.34678	578.3	604.5	1182.7	0.7775	1.3634	572
576	1285.74	0.33426	583.7	597.2	1180.9	0.7825	1.3592	576
580	1326.2	0.32216	589.1	589.9	1179.0	0.7876	1.3550	580
584	1367.7	0.31048	594.6	582.4	1176.9	0.7927	1.3507	584
588	1410.0	0.29919	600.1	574.7	1174.8	0.7998	1.3464	588
592	1453.3	0.28827	605.7	566.8	1172.6	0.8030	1.3420	592
596	1497.8	0.27770	611.4	558.8	1170.2	0.8082	1.3375	596

Properties of Saturated Steam—Temperature Table (cont.)

Temp F	Abs press lb/in²	Specific volume ft³/lbm V_g	Enthalpy, Btu/lbm			Entropy, Btu/lbm × F		Temp F
			Sat liquid h_f	Evap h_{fg}	Sat vapor h_g	Sat liquid s_f	Sat vapor s_g	
600	1543.2	0.26747	617.1	550.6	1167.7	0.8134	1.3330	600
604	1589.7	0.25757	622.9	542.2	1165.1	0.8187	1.3284	604
608	1637.3	0.24796	628.8	533.6	1162.4	0.8240	1.3238	608
612	1686.1	0.23865	634.8	524.7	1159.5	0.8294	1.3190	612
616	1735.9	0.22960	640.8	515.6	1156.4	0.8348	1.3141	616
620	1786.9	0.22081	646.9	506.3	1153.2	0.8403	1.3092	620
624	1839.0	0.21226	653.1	496.6	1149.6	0.8458	1.3041	624
628	1892.4	0.20394	659.5	486.7	1146.1	0.8514	1.2988	628
632	1947.0	0.19583	665.9	476.4	1142.2	0.8571	1.2934	632
636	2002.8	0.18792	672.4	465.7	1138.1	0.8628	1.2879	636
640	2059.9	0.18021	679.1	454.6	1133.7	0.8686	1.2821	640
644	2118.3	0.17269	685.9	443.1	1129.0	0.8746	1.2761	644
648	2178.1	0.16534	692.9	431.1	1124.0	0.8806	1.2699	648
652	2239.2	0.15816	700.0	418.7	1118.7	0.8868	1.2634	652
656	2301.7	0.15115	707.4	405.7	1113.1	0.8931	1.2567	656
660	2365.7	0.14431	714.9	392.1	1107.0	0.8995	1.2498	660
664	2431.1	0.13757	722.9	377.1	1100.6	0.9064	1.2425	664
668	2498.1	0.13087	731.5	362.1	1093.5	0.9137	1.2347	668
672	2566.6	0.12424	740.2	345.7	1085.9	0.9212	1.2266	672
676	2636.8	0.11769	749.2	328.5	1077.6	0.9287	1.2179	676
680	2708.6	0.11117	758.5	310.1	1068.5	0.9365	1.2086	680
684	2782.1	0.10463	768.2	290.2	1058.4	0.9447	1.1984	684
688	2857.4	0.09799	778.8	268.2	1047.0	0.9535	1.1872	688
692	2934.5	0.09110	790.5	243.1	1033.6	0.9634	1.1744	692
696	3013.4	0.08370	804.4	212.8	1017.2	0.9749	1.1591	696
700	3094.3	0.07519	822.4	172.7	995.2	0.9901	1.1390	700
701	3114.9	0.07271	828.2	159.8	988.0	0.9949	1.1326	701
702	3135.5	0.06997	835.0	144.7	979.7	1.0006	1.1252	702
703	3156.3	0.06684	843.2	126.4	969.6	1.0076	1.1163	703
704	3177.2	0.06300	854.2	102.0	956.2	1.0169	1.1046	704
704.5	3187.8	0.06055	861.9	85.3	947.2	1.0234	1.0967	704.5
705.0	3198.3	0.05730	873.0	61.4	934.4	1.0329	1.0856	705.0
705.47	3208.2	0.05078	906.0	0.0	906.0	1.0612	1.0612	705.47

Any pressure may be expressed in a number of different units by using the following conversion formulas.

1 standard atmosphere = 14.696 lb/sq in absolute
1 standard atmosphere = 29.9213 inches Hg (at 32°F—0°C)
1 standard atmosphere = 34.00 ft water (at 75°F—23.9°C)
1 standard atmosphere = 76 cm or 760 mm Hg (at 0°C—32°F)
1 pound per square inch = 2.036 inches Hg (at 32°F—0°C)
1 pound per square inch = 27.763 inches water (at 75°F—23.9°C)
1 inch Hg (at 32°F) = .491 pounds per square inch.
1 inch Hg = 25.4 millimeters Hg
1 kg cm² = 14.223 lb/sq in
1 pound per sq. in. = 6.895 kilopascals

5

Properties of Saturated Steam—Pressure; In Hg Abs

Absolute pressure in Hg	Temp °F	Sp vol cu ft/lb	Absolute pressure in Hg	Temp °F	Sp vol cu ft/lb	Absolute pressure in Hg	Temp °F	Sp vol cu ft/lb
.05	5.43	11200.	.50	58.80	1256.5	1.00	79.03	652.3
.06	9.03	9400.	.51	59.35	1233.6	1.01	79.33	646.4
.07	12.11	8300.	.52	59.90	1210.9	1.02	79.64	640.4
.08	14.83	7250.	.53	60.43	1189.5	1.03	79.94	634.4
.09	17.24	6500.	.54	60.96	1168.3	1.04	80.23	628.7
			.55	61.48	1148.4	1.05	80.52	623.1
.10	19.44	5860.	.56	62.00	1128.6	1.06	80.81	617.5
.11	21.42	5320.	.57	62.49	1110.2	1.07	81.10	612.0
.12	23.25	4960.	.58	62.99	1091.9	1.08	81.39	606.7
.13	24.94	4520.	.59	63.47	1074.6	1.09	81.67	601.4
.14	26.53	4210.						
			.60	63.96	1057.3	1.10	81.95	596.2
.15	28.00	3950.	.61	64.43	1041.0	1.11	82.23	591.2
.16	29.39	3730.	.62	64.90	1024.9	1.12	82.51	586.2
.17	30.72	3500.	.63	65.35	1009.7	1.13	82.78	581.3
.18	31.96	3310.	.64	65.81	994.7	1.14	83.06	576.5
			.65	66.26	980.3	1.15	83.33	571.8
			.66	66.70	966.3	1.16	83.60	567.1
			.67	67.13	952.5	1.17	83.87	562.5
			.68	67.56	939.4	1.18	84.13	558.1
.1803	32.00	3306.	.69	67.99	926.3	1.19	84.39	553.7
.19	33.28	3147.						
.20	34.56	2997.	.70	68.40	914.0	1.20	84.65	549.3
.21	35.78	2861.	.71	68.82	901.7	1.21	84.91	544.9
.22	36.96	2736.	.72	69.23	889.9	1.22	85.17	540.7
.23	38.09	2624.	.73	69.63	878.4	1.23	85.43	536.6
.24	39.18	2520.	.74	70.03	867.1	1.24	85.68	532.5
.25	40.23	2424.	.75	70.43	856.1	1.25	85.93	528.4
.26	41.23	2336.	.76	70.81	845.5	1.26	86.18	524.5
.27	42.22	2253.	.77	71.20	835.1	1.27	86.43	520.6
.28	43.17	2177.	.78	71.58	825.0	1.28	86.68	516.7
.29	44.08	2106.	.79	71.96	815.1	1.29	86.92	512.9
.30	44.96	2039.	.80	72.33	805.6	1.30	87.17	509.2
.31	45.83	1976.8	.81	72.70	796.2	1.31	87.41	505.6
.32	46.67	1917.9	.82	73.06	786.9	1.32	87.65	502.0
.33	47.48	1863.0	.83	73.42	778.0	1.33	87.89	498.4
.34	48.28	1810.9	.84	73.78	769.2	1.34	88.12	494.9
.35	49.05	1761.6	.85	74.13	760.7	1.35	88.36	491.5
.36	49.80	1715.3	.86	74.48	752.4	1.36	88.59	488.1
.37	50.53	1671.1	.87	74.83	744.1	1.37	88.83	484.7
.38	51.25	1629.9	.88	75.17	736.2	1.38	89.06	481.3
.39	51.96	1590.0	.89	75.51	728.4	1.39	89.28	478.1
.40	52.64	1553.0	.90	75.85	720.7	1.40	89.51	474.9
.41	53.31	1517.0	.91	76.18	713.2	1.41	89.74	471.7
.42	53.98	1482.0	.92	76.51	705.9	1.42	89.97	468.5
.43	54.62	1449.9	.93	76.83	698.7	1.43	90.19	465.4
.44	55.25	1418.5	.94	77.15	691.7	1.44	90.41	462.4
.45	55.88	1388.4	.95	77.47	684.8	1.45	90.63	459.4
.46	56.48	1360.0	.96	77.79	678.1	1.46	90.85	456.4
.47	57.08	1332.3	.97	78.11	671.4	1.47	91.07	453.5
.48	57.66	1306.2	.98	78.42	665.0	1.48	91.29	450.6
.49	58.24	1280.9	.99	78.73	658.7	1.49	91.50	447.8

Sp vol for temp below 32°F are approximate.

Values from .05 to .18 in Hg reproduced by permission from Chemical Engineers Handbook by John
Perry, published by McGraw-Hill Book Co., Inc.

Values from .1803 to 29.92 in Hg calculated graphically by Ingersoll-Rand Co. by permission of the author
and publisher from data in "Thermodynamic Properties of Steam" by Keenan and Keyes.

Properties of Saturated Steam—Pressure; In Hg Abs

(Continued)

Absolute pressure in Hg	Temp °F	Sp vol cu ft/lb	Absolute pressure in Hg	Temp °F	Sp vol cu ft/lb	Absolute pressure in Hg	Temp °F	Sp vol cu ft/lb
1.50	91.72	445.0	2.00	101.14	339.3	2.50	108.71	274.9
1.51	91.93	442.2	2.01	101.31	337.7	2.51	108.84	273.9
1.52	92.14	439.5	2.02	101.47	336.1	2.52	108.98	272.9
1.53	92.35	436.8	2.03	101.64	334.5	2.53	109.12	271.9
1.54	92.56	434.1	2.04	101.80	333.0	2.54	109.25	270.9
1.55	92.77	431.4	2.05	101.97	331.4	2.55	109.39	269.9
1.56	92.98	428.7	2.06	102.13	329.9	2.56	109.52	268.9
1.57	93.19	426.2	2.07	102.30	328.4	2.57	109.66	267.9
1.58	93.39	423.7	2.08	102.46	326.9	2.58	109.79	266.9
1.59	93.60	421.2	2.09	102.62	325.4	2.59	109.92	266.0
1.60	93.80	418.7	2.10	102.78	324.0	2.60	110.06	265.0
1.61	94.00	416.2	2.11	102.94	322.5	2.61	110.19	264.0
1.62	94.20	413.8	2.12	103.10	321.1	2.62	110.32	263.1
1.63	94.40	411.4	2.13	103.25	319.7	2.63	110.46	262.2
1.64	94.60	409.0	2.14	103.41	318.3	2.64	110.59	261.2
1.65	94.80	406.6	2.15	103.57	316.9	2.65	110.72	260.3
1.66	95.01	404.3	2.16	103.73	315.5	2.66	110.85	259.4
1.67	95.20	402.0	2.17	103.88	314.1	2.67	110.98	258.4
1.68	95.39	399.8	2.18	104.04	312.8	2.68	111.11	257.5
1.69	95.59	397.6	2.19	104.19	311.5	2.69	111.24	256.6
1.70	95.78	395.4	2.20	104.34	310.2	2.70	111.37	255.8
1.71	95.97	393.2	2.21	104.50	308.8	2.71	111.49	254.9
1.72	96.16	391.1	2.22	104.65	307.5	2.72	111.62	254.0
1.73	96.35	389.0	2.23	104.80	306.2	2.73	111.75	253.1
1.74	96.54	386.9	2.24	104.95	304.9	2.74	111.88	252.2
1.75	96.72	384.8	2.25	105.11	303.6	2.75	112.01	251.4
1.76	96.91	382.7	2.26	105.26	302.4	2.76	112.13	250.5
1.77	97.10	380.7	2.27	105.41	301.1	2.77	112.26	249.7
1.78	97.28	378.7	2.28	105.55	299.9	2.78	112.38	248.8
1.79	97.46	376.7	2.29	105.70	298.7	2.79	112.51	248.0
1.80	97.65	374.7	2.30	105.85	297.4	2.80	112.63	247.2
1.81	97.83	372.7	2.31	106.00	296.2	2.81	112.76	246.3
1.82	98.01	370.8	2.32	106.15	295.0	2.82	112.88	245.5
1.83	98.19	368.9	2.33	106.29	293.8	2.83	113.01	244.7
1.84	98.37	367.0	2.34	106.44	292.7	2.84	113.13	243.9
1.85	98.55	365.2	2.35	106.58	291.5	2.85	113.25	243.1
1.86	98.73	363.3	2.36	106.73	290.3	2.86	113.37	242.3
1.87	98.91	361.4	2.37	106.87	289.1	2.87	113.50	241.5
1.88	99.09	359.6	2.38	107.02	287.9	2.88	113.62	240.7
1.89	99.26	357.9	2.39	107.16	286.8	2.89	113.74	239.9
1.90	99.44	356.1	2.40	107.31	285.7	2.90	113.86	239.1
1.91	99.61	354.4	2.41	107.45	284.6	2.91	113.98	238.3
1.92	99.78	352.6	2.42	107.59	283.5	2.92	114.11	237.5
1.93	99.96	350.8	2.43	107.73	282.4	2.93	114.23	236.8
1.94	100.13	349.1	2.44	107.87	281.3	2.94	114.35	236.0
1.95	100.30	347.5	2.45	108.01	280.2	2.95	114.46	235.3
1.96	100.47	345.8	2.46	108.15	279.2	2.96	114.58	234.5
1.97	100.64	344.1	2.47	108.29	278.1	2.97	114.70	233.8
1.98	100.81	342.5	2.48	108.43	277.0	2.98	114.82	233.0
1.99	100.97	340.9	2.49	108.57	276.0	2.99	114.94	232.2

Values from .05 to .18 in Hg reproduced by permission from Chemical Engineers Handbook by John H. Perry, published by McGraw-Hill Book Co., Inc.

Values from .1803 to 29.92 in Hg calculated graphically by Ingersoll-Rand Co. by permission of the authors and publisher from data in "Thermodynamic Properties of Steam" by Keenan and Keyes.

5

Properties of Saturated Steam—Pressure; In Hg Abs

(Continued)

Absolute pressure in Hg	Temp °F	Sp vol cu ft/lb	Absolute pressure in Hg	Temp °F	Sp vol cu ft/lb	Absolute pressure in Hg	Temp °F	Sp vol cu ft/lb
3.00	115.06	231.5	4.20	127.22	168.8	12.00	169.3	63.0
3.05	115.64	228.0	4.30	128.10	165.1	12.50	171.1	60.7
3.10	116.22	224.5	4.40	128.95	161.5	13.00	172.8	58.5
3.15	116.79	221.2	4.50	129.79	158.2	13.50	174.4	56.5
3.20	117.35	217.9	4.60	130.61	155.0	14.00	176.1	54.6
3.25	117.90	214.8	4.70	131.42	151.8	14.50	177.6	52.8
3.30	118.45	211.8	4.80	132.22	148.9	15.00	179.1	51.1
3.35	118.99	208.8	4.90	133.00	146.0	16.00	182.1	48.1
3.40	119.52	205.9	5.00	133.8	143.3	17.00	184.8	45.5
3.45	120.04	203.0	5.50	137.4	131.0	18.00	187.5	43.1
3.50	120.56	200.3	6.00	140.8	120.7	19.00	190.0	41.0
3.55	121.07	197.7	6.50	143.9	112.0	20.00	192.4	39.1
3.60	121.58	195.1	7.00	146.9	104.5	21.00	194.7	37.3
3.65	122.08	192.6	7.50	149.6	97.9	22.00	196.9	35.7
3.70	122.57	190.1	8.00	152.2	92.2	23.00	199.0	34.3
3.75	123.06	187.7	8.50	154.7	87.0	24.00	201.1	32.9
3.80	123.55	185.4	9.00	157.1	82.5	25.00	203.1	31.7
3.85	124.02	183.2	9.50	159.3	78.4	26.00	205.0	30.6
3.90	124.49	181.0	10.00	161.5	74.8	27.00	206.9	29.5
3.95	124.97	178.8	10.50	163.6	71.4	28.00	208.7	28.5
4.00	125.42	176.7	11.00	165.5	68.4	29.00	210.4	27.6
4.10	126.33	172.6	11.50	167.4	65.6	29.92	212.0	26.8

Values from .05 to 0.1803 in Hg reproduced by permission from Chemical Engineers Handbook by John H. Perry, published by McGraw-Hill Book Co., Inc.

Values from 0.1803 to 29.92 in Hg calculated graphically by Ingersoll-Rand Co. by permission of the authors and publisher from data in "Thermodynamic Properties of Steam" by Keenan and Keyes.

For correction of observed vacuum and barometer to standard condition see pages 7-5 to 7-10.

Properties of Saturated Steam—Pressure; mm Hg Abs

Absolute pressure mm Hg	Temp °F	Sp vol cu ft/lb	Absolute pressure mm Hg	Temp °F	Sp vol cu ft/lb	Absolute pressure mm Hg	Temp °F	Sp vol cu ft/lb
1.5	8.73	9700.	25.0	78.55	662.3	50.0	100.61	344.4
2.0	14.50	7300.	25.5	79.15	650.0	50.5	100.94	341.2
2.5	19.09	5920.	26.0	79.74	638.2	51.0	101.27	338.0
3.0	22.91	4950.	26.5	80.33	626.8	51.5	101.60	334.9
3.5	26.19	4250.	27.0	80.90	615.8	52.0	101.92	331.9
4.0	29.05	3780.	27.5	81.46	605.3	52.5	102.24	328.9
4.5	31.62	3380.	28.0	82.02	594.9	53.0	102.56	326.0
			28.5	82.56	585.2	53.5	102.88	323.1
			29.0	83.10	575.6	54.0	103.19	320.2
			29.5	83.63	566.5	54.5	103.50	317.5
4.579	32.00	3306.	30.0	84.16	557.5	55.0	103.81	314.8
5.0	34.17	3042.	30.5	84.67	549.0	55.5	104.12	312.1
5.5	36.55	2779.	31.0	85.19	540.5	56.0	104.41	309.5
6.0	38.77	2558.	31.5	85.68	532.4	56.5	104.72	306.9
6.5	40.82	2372.	32.0	86.18	524.6	57.0	105.02	304.4
7.0	42.75	2211.	32.5	86.66	516.9	57.5	105.31	301.9
7.5	44.55	2070.4	33.0	87.15	509.5	58.0	105.61	299.5
8.0	46.25	1946.8	33.5	87.62	502.4	58.5	105.90	297.1
8.5	47.86	1838.0	34.0	88.09	495.4	59.0	106.19	294.7
9.0	49.37	1741.8	34.5	88.55	488.6	59.5	106.47	292.4
9.5	50.83	1654.4						
10.0	52.21	1576.1	35.0	89.01	482.0	60.0	106.76	290.1
10.5	53.55	1504.7	35.5	89.46	475.6	60.5	107.05	287.8
11.0	54.82	1439.8	36.0	89.91	469.3	61.0	107.33	285.6
11.5	56.05	1380.1	36.5	90.34	463.3	61.5	107.61	283.4
12.0	57.22	1326.0	37.0	90.78	457.4	62.0	107.88	281.2
12.5	58.36	1275.8	37.5	91.21	451.7	62.5	108.16	279.1
13.0	59.45	1229.5	38.0	91.63	446.1	63.0	108.43	277.0
13.5	60.51	1186.2	38.5	92.05	440.6	63.5	108.71	274.9
14.0	61.54	1146.1	39.0	92.47	435.3	64.0	108.98	272.9
14.5	62.54	1108.6	39.5	92.88	430.0	64.5	109.24	270.9
15.0	63.50	1073.6	40.0	93.29	425.0	65.0	109.51	269.0
15.5	64.44	1040.7	40.5	93.69	420.0	65.5	109.77	267.1
16.0	65.35	1009.8	41.0	94.09	415.1	66.0	110.04	265.2
16.5	66.24	980.8	41.5	94.48	410.4	66.5	110.30	263.3
17.0	67.10	953.5	42.0	94.87	405.8	67.0	110.56	261.4
17.5	67.94	927.7	42.5	95.26	401.4	67.5	110.82	259.6
18.0	68.76	903.3	43.0	95.64	397.0	68.0	111.07	257.8
18.5	69.56	880.4	43.5	96.11	392.7	68.5	111.33	256.0
19.0	70.34	858.5	44.0	96.39	388.4	69.0	111.58	254.3
19.5	71.11	837.5	44.5	96.76	384.2	69.5	111.83	252.6
20.0	71.85	817.8	45.0	97.13	380.3	70.0	112.08	250.9
20.5	72.59	798.9	45.5	97.49	376.4	70.5	112.33	249.2
21.0	73.31	780.9	46.0	97.85	372.6	71.0	112.58	247.5
21.5	74.01	763.6	46.5	98.21	368.8	71.5	112.82	245.9
22.0	74.69	747.3	47.0	98.56	365.1	72.0	113.06	244.3
22.5	75.36	731.7	47.5	98.91	361.4	72.5	113.31	242.7
23.0	76.03	716.4	48.0	99.26	357.9	73.0	113.55	241.1
23.5	76.67	702.1	48.5	99.60	354.4	73.5	113.79	239.6
24.0	77.31	688.3	49.0	99.94	351.0	74.0	114.03	238.1
24.5	77.94	674.9	49.5	100.28	347.7	74.5	114.26	236.6

Sp vol for temp below 32°F are approximate.
 Values from 1.5 to 4.579 mm Hg calculated from data in Chemical Engineers Handbook by John H. Perry, published by McGraw-Hill Book Co., Inc.
 Values from 4.579 to 760 mm Hg calculated graphically by Ingersoll-Rand Co. by permission of the authors and publisher from data in "Thermodynamic Properties of Steam" by Keenan and Keyes.

5

Properties of Saturated Steam—Pressure; mm Hg Abs (*cont.*)

Absolute pressure mm Hg	Temp °F	Sp vol cu ft/lb	Absolute pressure mm Hg	Temp °F	Sp vol cu ft/lb	Absolute pressure mm Hg	Temp °F	Sp vol cu ft/lb
75.0	114.50	235.1	101.0	125.21	177.7	135.0	136.1	135.3
76.0	114.97	232.1	102.0	125.57	176.0	140.0	137.5	130.7
77.0	115.43	229.3	103.0	125.93	174.4	145.0	138.8	126.5
78.0	115.89	226.5	104.0	126.28	172.8	150.0	140.2	122.6
79.0	116.34	223.8	105.0	126.64	171.3	175.0	146.2	106.1
80.0	116.78	221.2	106.0	126.99	169.8	200.0	151.6	93.6
81.0	117.23	218.6	107.0	127.33	168.3	225.0	156.4	83.8
82.0	117.66	216.1	108.0	127.68	166.8	250.0	160.8	75.9
83.0	118.10	213.7	109.0	128.02	165.4	275.0	164.9	69.4
84.0	118.52	211.3	110.0	128.36	164.0	300.0	168.6	64.0
85.0	118.95	209.0	111.0	128.70	162.6	325.0	172.1	59.4
86.0	119.36	206.7	112.0	129.03	161.2	350.0	175.3	55.4
87.0	119.78	204.4	113.0	129.36	159.9	375.0	178.4	51.9
88.0	120.20	202.2	114.0	129.69	158.6	400.0	181.5	48.7
89.0	120.60	200.1	115.0	130.02	157.3	450.0	186.7	43.8
90.0	121.01	198.0	116.0	130.34	156.0	500.0	191.6	39.7
91.0	121.40	158.0	117.0	130.66	154.7	550.0	196.1	36.3
92.0	121.80	194.0	118.0	130.99	153.5	600.0	200.3	33.4
93.0	122.19	192.0	119.0	131.30	152.3	650.0	204.2	30.9
94.0	122.58	190.0	120.0	131.62	151.1	700.0	207.9	28.9
95.0	122.97	188.2	121.0	131.93	149.9	760.0	212.0	26.8
96.0	123.35	186.4	122.0	132.24	148.8			
97.0	123.73	184.6	123.0	132.55	147.7			
98.0	124.10	182.8	124.0	132.85	146.5			
99.0	124.47	181.1	125.0	133.16	145.4			
100.0	124.84	179.4	130.0	134.7	140.2			

Values from 1.5 to 4.579 mm Hg calculated from data in Chemical Engineers Handbook by John H. Perry, published by McGraw-Hill Book Co., Inc.

Values from 4.579 to 760 mm Hg calculated graphically by Ingersoll-Rand Co. by permission of the authors and publisher from data in "Thermodynamic properties of Steam" by Keenan and Keyes.

Properties of Saturated Steam—Pressure Table

Abs press lb/in²	Temp °F	Specific volume ft³/lbm		Enthalpy btu/lbm		Entropy btu/lbm × F		Abs press lb/in²
		Water v_f	Steam v_g	Water h_f	Steam h_g	Water s_f	Steam s_g	
.08865	32.018	0.016022	3302.4	0.0003	1075.5	0.0000	2.1872	.08865
0.25	59.323	0.016032	1235.5	27.382	1067.4	0.0542	2.0967	0.25
0.50	79.586	0.016071	641.5	47.623	1096.3	0.0925	2.0370	0.50
1.0	101.74	0.016136	333.60	69.73	1105.8	0.1326	1.9781	1.0
3.0	141.47	0.016300	118.73	109.42	1122.6	0.2009	1.8864	3.0
6.0	170.05	0.016451	61.984	138.03	1134.2	0.2474	1.8294	6.0
10.0	193.21	0.016592	38.420	161.26	1143.3	0.2836	1.7879	10.0
14.696	212.00	0.016719	26.799	180.17	1150.5	0.3121	1.7568	14.696
15.0	213.03	0.016726	26.290	181.21	1150.9	0.3137	1.7552	15.0
20.0	227.96	0.016834	20.087	196.27	1156.3	0.3358	1.7320	20.0
25.0	240.07	0.016927	16.301	208.52	1160.6	0.3535	1.7141	25.0
30.0	250.34	0.017009	13.744	218.9	1164.1	0.3682	1.6995	30.0
35.0	259.29	0.017083	11.896	228.0	1167.1	0.3809	1.6872	35.0
40.0	267.25	0.017151	10.4965	236.1	1169.8	0.3921	1.6765	40.0
45.0	274.44	0.017214	9.3988	243.5	1172.0	0.4021	1.6671	45.0
50.0	281.02	0.017274	8.5140	250.2	1174.1	0.4112	1.6586	50.0
55.0	287.08	0.017329	7.7850	256.4	1175.9	0.4196	1.6510	55.0
60.0	292.71	0.017383	7.1736	262.2	1177.6	0.4273	1.6440	60.0
65.0	297.98	0.017433	6.6533	267.6	1179.1	0.4344	1.6375	65.0
70.0	302.93	0.017482	6.2050	272.7	1180.6	0.4411	1.6316	70.0
75.0	307.61	0.017529	5.8144	277.6	1181.9	0.4474	1.6260	75.0
80.0	312.04	0.017573	5.4711	282.1	1183.1	0.4534	1.6208	80.0
85.0	316.26	0.017617	5.1669	286.5	1184.2	0.4590	1.6159	85.0
90.0	320.28	0.017659	4.8953	290.7	1185.3	0.4643	1.6113	90.0
95.0	324.13	0.017700	4.6514	294.7	1186.2	0.4694	1.6069	95.0
100.0	327.82	0.017740	4.4310	298.5	1187.2	0.4743	1.6027	100
105.0	331.37	0.01778	4.2309	302.2	1188.0	0.4790	1.5988	105
110.	334.79	0.01782	4.0306	305.8	1188.9	0.4834	1.5950	110
115.	338.08	0.01785	3.8813	309.3	1189.6	0.4877	1.5913	115
120.	341.27	0.01789	3.7275	312.6	1190.4	0.4919	1.5879	120
125.	344.35	0.01792	3.5857	315.8	1191.1	0.4959	1.5845	125
130.	347.33	0.01796	3.4544	319.0	1191.7	0.4998	1.5813	130
135.	350.23	0.01799	3.3325	322.0	1192.4	0.5035	1.5782	135
140.	353.04	0.01803	3.2010	325.0	1193.0	0.5071	1.5752	140
145.	355.77	0.01806	3.1130	327.8	1193.5	0.5107	1.5723	145
150.	358.43	0.01809	3.0139	330.6	1194.1	0.5141	1.5695	150
160.	363.55	0.01815	2.8366	336.1	1195.1	0.5206	1.5641	160
170.	368.42	0.01821	2.6738	341.2	1196.0	0.5269	1.5591	170
180.	373.08	0.01827	2.5312	346.2	1196.9	0.5328	1.5543	180
190.	377.53	0.01833	2.4030	350.9	1197.6	0.5384	1.5498	190
200.	381.80	0.01839	2.2873	355.5	1198.3	0.5438	1.5454	200
210.	385.91	0.01844	2.18217	359.9	1199.0	0.5490	1.5413	210
220.	389.88	0.01850	2.08629	364.2	1199.6	0.5540	1.5374	220
230.	393.70	0.01855	1.99846	368.3	1200.1	0.5588	1.5336	230
240.	397.39	0.01860	1.91769	372.3	1200.6	0.5634	1.5299	240
250.	400.97	0.01865	1.84317	376.1	1201.1	0.5679	1.5264	250
260.	404.44	0.01870	1.77418	379.9	1201.5	0.5722	1.5230	260
270.	407.80	0.01875	1.71013	383.6	1201.9	0.5764	1.5197	270

5

Properties of Saturated Steam—Pressure Table (cont.)

Abs press lb/in²	Temp °F	Specific volume ft³/lbm		Enthalpy btu/lbm		Entropy btu/lbm × F		Abs press lb/in²
		Water v_f	Steam v_g	Water h_f	Steam h_g	Water s_f	Steam s_g	
280	411.07	0.01880	1.65049	387.1	1202.3	0.5805	1.5166	280
290	414.25	0.01885	1.59482	390.6	1202.6	0.5844	1.5135	290
300	417.35	0.01889	1.54274	394.0	1202.9	0.5882	1.5105	300
310	420.36	0.01894	1.49390	397.3	1203.2	0.5920	1.5076	310
320	423.31	0.01899	1.44801	400.5	1203.4	0.5956	1.5048	320
330	426.18	0.01903	1.40480	403.7	1203.6	0.5991	1.5021	330
340	428.99	0.01908	1.36405	406.8	1203.8	0.6026	1.4994	340
350	431.73	0.01912	1.32554	409.8	1204.0	0.6059	1.4968	350
360	434.41	0.01917	1.28910	412.8	1204.1	0.6092	1.4943	360
380	439.61	0.01925	1.22177	418.6	1204.4	0.6156	1.4894	380
400	444.60	0.01934	1.16095	424.2	1204.6	0.6217	1.4847	400
450	456.28	0.01954	1.03179	437.3	1204.8	0.6360	1.4738	450
500	467.01	0.01975	0.92762	449.5	1204.7	0.6490	1.4639	500
550	476.94	0.01994	0.84177	460.9	1204.3	0.6611	1.4547	550
600	486.20	0.02013	0.76975	471.7	1203.7	0.6723	1.4461	600
650	494.89	0.02032	0.70843	481.9	1202.8	0.6828	1.4381	650
700	503.08	0.02050	0.65556	491.6	1201.8	0.6928	1.4304	700
750	510.84	0.02069	0.60949	500.9	1200.7	0.7022	1.4232	750
800	518.21	0.02087	0.56896	509.8	1199.4	0.7111	1.4163	800
850	525.24	0.02105	0.53302	518.4	1198.0	0.7197	1.4096	850
900	531.95	0.02123	0.50091	526.7	1196.4	0.7279	1.4032	900
950	538.39	0.02141	0.47205	534.7	1194.7	0.7358	1.3970	950
1000	544.58	0.02159	0.44596	542.6	1192.9	0.7434	1.3910	1000
1100	556.28	0.02695	0.40058	557.5	1189.1	0.7578	1.3794	1100
1200	567.19	0.02232	0.36245	571.9	1184.8	0.7714	1.3683	1200
1300	577.42	0.02269	0.32991	585.6	1180.2	0.7843	1.3577	1300
1400	587.07	0.02307	0.30178	598.8	1175.3	0.7966	1.3474	1400
1500	596.20	0.02346	0.27719	611.7	1170.1	0.8085	1.3373	1500
1600	604.87	0.02387	0.25545	624.2	1164.5	0.8199	1.3274	1600
1700	613.13	0.02428	0.23607	636.5	1158.6	0.8309	1.3176	1700
1800	621.02	0.02472	0.21861	648.5	1152.3	0.8417	1.3079	1800
1900	628.56	0.02517	0.20278	660.4	1145.6	0.8522	1.2981	1900
2000	635.80	0.02565	0.18831	672.1	1138.3	0.8625	1.2881	2000
2100	642.76	0.02615	0.17501	683.8	1130.5	0.8727	1.2780	2100
2200	649.45	0.02669	0.16272	695.5	1122.2	0.8828	1.2676	2200
2300	655.89	0.02727	0.15133	707.2	1113.2	0.8929	1.2569	2300
2400	662.11	0.02790	0.14076	719.0	1103.7	0.9031	1.2460	2400
2500	668.11	0.02859	0.13068	731.7	1093.3	0.9139	1.2345	2500
2600	673.91	0.02938	0.12110	744.5	1082.0	0.9247	1.2250	2600
2700	679.53	0.03029	0.11194	757.3	1069.7	0.9356	1.2097	2700
2800	684.96	0.03134	0.10305	770.7	1055.8	0.9468	1.1958	2800
2900	690.22	0.03264	0.09420	785.1	1039.8	0.9588	1.1803	2900
3000	695.33	0.03428	0.08500	801.8	1020.3	0.9728	1.1619	3000
3100	700.28	0.03681	0.07452	824.0	993.3	0.9914	1.1373	3100
3200	705.08	0.04472	0.05663	875.5	931.6	1.0351	1.0832	3200
3208.2	705.47	0.05078	0.05078	906.0	906.0	1.0612	1.0612	3208.2

Properties of Superheated Steam

Abs press lb/in² (sat temp-F)		Sat water	Sat steam	Temperature—degrees Fahrenheit						
				300	400	500	600	700	800	900
1 (101.74)	sh			198.26	298.26	398.26	498.26	598.26	698.26	798.26
	v	0.01614	333.6	452.3	511.9	571.5	631.1	690.7	750.3	809.8
	h	69.73	1105.8	1195.7	1241.8	1288.6	1336.1	1384.5	1433.7	1483.8
	s	0.1326	1.9781	2.1152	2.1722	2.2237	2.2708	2.3144	2.3551	2.3934
5 (162.24)	sh			137.76	237.76	337.76	437.36	537.76	637.76	737.76
	v	0.01641	73.53	90.24	102.24	114.21	126.15	138.08	150.01	161.94
	h	130.20	1131.1	1194.8	1241.3	1288.2	1335.9	1384.3	1433.6	1483.7
	s	0.2349	1.8443	1.9369	1.9943	2.0460	2.0932	2.1369	2.1776	2.2159
10 (193.21)	sh			106.79	206.79	306.79	406.79	506.79	606.79	706.79
	v	0.01659	38.42	44.98	51.03	57.04	63.03	69.00	74.98	80.94
	h	161.26	1143.3	1193.7	1240.6	1287.8	1335.5	1384.0	1433.4	1483.5
	s	0.2836	1.7879	1.8593	1.9173	1.9692	2.0166	2.0603	2.1011	2.1394
14.696 (212.00)	sh			88.00	188.00	288.00	388.00	488.00	588.00	688.00
	v	0.0167	26.799	30.52	33.963	38.77	42.86	46.93	51.00	55.06
	h	180.17	1150.5	1192.6	1239.9	1287.4	1335.2	1383.8	1433.2	1483.4
	s	0.3121	1.7568	1.8158	1.8720	1.9265	1.9739	2.0177	2.0585	2.0969
20 (227.96)	sh			72.04	172.04	272.04	372.04	472.04	572.04	672.04
	v	0.01683	20.087	22.356	25.428	28.457	31.466	34.465	37.458	40.447
	h	196.27	1156.3	1191.4	1239.2	1286.9	1334.9	1383.5	1432.9	1483.2
	s	0.3358	1.7320	1.7805	1.8397	1.8921	1.9397	1.9836	2.0244	2.0628
40 (267.25)	sh			32.75	132.75	232.75	332.75	432.75	532.75	632.75
	v	0.01715	10.497	11.036	12.624	14.165	15.685	17.195	18.699	20.199
	h	236.14	1169.8	1186.6	1236.4	1285.0	1333.6	1382.5	1432.1	1482.5
	s	0.3921	1.6765	1.6992	1.7608	1.8143	1.8624	1.9065	1.9476	1.9860
60 (292.71)	sh			7.29	107.29	207.29	307.29	407.29	507.29	607.29
	v	0.1738	7.174	7.257	8.354	9.400	10.425	11.438	12.446	13.450
	h	262.21	1177.6	1181.6	1233.5	1283.2	1332.3	1381.5	1431.3	1481.8
	s	0.4273	1.6440	1.6492	1.7134	1.7681	1.8168	1.8612	1.9024	1.9410
80 (312.04)	sh				87.96	187.96	287.96	387.96	487.96	587.96
	v	0.01757	5.471		6.218	7.018	7.794	8.560	9.319	10.075
	h	282.15	1183.1		1230.5	1281.3	1330.9	1380.5	1430.5	1481.1
	s	0.4534	1.6208		1.6790	1.7349	1.7842	1.8289	1.8702	1.9089
100 (327.82)	sh				72.18	172.18	272.18	372.18	472.18	572.18
	v	0.01774	4.431		4.935	5.588	6.216	6.833	7.443	8.050
	h	298.54	1187.2		1227.4	1279.3	1329.6	1379.5	1429.7	1480.4
	s	0.4743	1.6027		1.6516	1.7088	1.7586	1.8036	1.8451	1.8839
120 (341.27)	sh				58.73	158.73	258.73	358.73	458.73	558.73
	v	0.01789	3.7275		4.0786	4.6341	5.1637	5.6813	6.1928	6.7006
	h	312.58	1190.4		1224.1	1277.4	1328.2	1378.4	1428.8	1479.8
	s	0.4919	1.5879		1.6286	1.6872	1.7376	1.7829	1.8246	1.8635
140 (353.04)	sh				46.96	146.96	246.96	346.96	446.96	546.96
	v	0.01803	3.2190		3.4661	3.9526	4.4119	4.8588	5.2995	5.7364
	h	324.96	1193.0		1220.8	1275.3	1326.8	1377.4	1428.0	1479.1
	s	0.5071	1.5752		1.6085	1.6686	1.7196	1.7652	1.8071	1.8461
160 (363.55)	sh				36.45	136.45	236.45	336.45	436.45	536.45
	v	0.01815	2.8336		3.0060	3.4413	3.8480	4.2420	4.6295	5.0132
	h	336.07	1195.1		1217.4	1273.3	1325.4	1376.4	1427.2	1478.4
	s	0.5206	1.5641		1.5906	1.6522	1.7039	1.7499	1.7919	1.8383

Tables on pages 5-21 to 5-24 reproduced from ASME Steam Tables© 1967 by The American Society of Mechanical Engineers. All rights reserved.

*sh = superheat; v = specific volume in ft³/lb; h = total heat in Btu/lb; s = entropy in Btu/°F/lb.

5

Properties of Superheated Steam (*cont.*)

Abs press lb/in² (sat temp-F)		Sat water	Sat steam	Temperature—degrees Fahrenheit						
				600	700	800	900	1000	1200	1400
180 (373.08)	sh			226.92	326.92	426.92	526.92	626.92	826.92	1026.92
	p	0.01827	2.5312	3.4093	3.7621	4.1084	4.4508	4.7907	5.4697	6.1363
	h	346.19	1196.9	1324.0	1375.3	1426.3	1477.7	1529.7	1635.9	1745.3
	s	0.5328	1.5543	1.6900	1.7362	1.7784	1.8176	1.8545	1.9227	1.9849
200 (381.80)	sh			218.20	318.20	418.20	518.20	618.20	818.20	1018.20
	v	0.01839	2.2873	3.0583	3.3783	3.6915	4.0008	4.3077	4.9165	5.5209
	h	355.51	1198.3	1322.6	1374.3	1425.5	1477.0	1529.1	1635.4	1745.0
	s	0.5438	1.5454	1.6773	1.7293	1.7663	1.8057	1.8426	1.9109	1.9732
220 (389.88)	sh			210.12	310.12	410.12	510.12	610.12	810.12	1010.12
	v	0.01850	2.0863	2.7710	3.0642	3.3504	3.6327	3.9125	4.4671	5.0173
	h	364.17	1199.6	1321.2	1373.2	1427.7	1476.3	1528.5	1635.0	1744.7
	s	0.5540	1.5374	1.6658	1.7128	1.7553	1.7948	1.8318	1.9002	1.9625
240 (397.39)	sh			202.61	302.61	402.61	502.61	602.61	802.61	1002.61
	v	0.01860	1.9177	2.5316	2.8024	3.0661	3.3259	3.5831	4.0926	4.5977
	h	372.27	1200.6	1319.7	1372.1	1423.8	1475.6	1527.9	1634.6	1744.3
	s	0.5634	1.5299	1.6552	1.7025	1.7452	1.7848	1.8219	1.8904	1.9528
260 (404.44)	sh			195.56	295.56	395.56	495.56	595.59	795.56	955.56
	v	0.01870	1.7742	2.3289	2.5808	2.8256	3.0663	3.3044	3.7758	4.2427
	h	379.90	1201.5	1318.2	1371.1	1423.0	1474.9	1527.3	1634.2	1744.0
	s	0.5722	1.5230	1.6453	1.6930	1.7359	1.7756	1.8128	1.8814	1.9439
280 (411.07)	sh			188.93	288.93	388.93	488.93	588.93	788.93	988.93
	v	0.01880	1.6505	2.1551	2.3909	2.6194	2.8437	3.0655	3.5042	3.9384
	h	387.12	1202.3	1316.8	1370.9	1422.1	1474.2	1526.8	1633.8	1743.7
	s	0.5805	1.5166	1.6361	1.6841	1.7273	1.7671	1.8043	1.8730	1.9356
300 (417.35)	sh			182.65	282.65	382.65	482.65	582.65	782.65	982.65
	v	0.01889	1.5427	2.0044	2.2263	2.4407	2.6509	2.8585	3.2688	3.6746
	h	393.99	1202.9	1315.2	1368.9	1421.3	1473.6	1526.2	1633.3	1743.4
	s	0.5882	1.5105	1.6274	1.6758	1.7192	1.7591	1.7964	1.8652	1.9278
350 (431.73)	sh			168.27	268.27	368.27	468.27	568.27	768.27	968.27
	v	0.01922	1.3255	1.7028	1.8970	2.0832	2.2652	2.4445	2.7980	3.1471
	h	409.83	1204.0	1311.4	1366.2	1419.2	1471.8	1524.7	1632.3	1742.6
	s	0.6059	1.4968	1.6077	1.6571	1.7009	1.7411	1.7787	1.8477	1.9105
400 (444.60)	sh			155.40	255.40	355.40	455.40	555.40	755.40	955.40
	v	0.01934	1.1610	1.4763	1.6490	1.8151	1.9759	2.1339	2.4450	2.7515
	h	424.17	1204.6	1307.4	1363.4	1417.0	1470.1	1523.9	1631.2	1741.9
	s	0.6217	1.4847	1.5901	1.6406	1.6850	1.7255	1.7632	1.8325	1.8955
500 (467.01)	sh			132.99	232.99	332.99	432.99	532.99	732.99	932.99
	v	0.01975	0.9276	1.1584	1.3037	1.4397	1.5708	1.6992	1.9507	2.1977
	h	449.52	1204.7	1299.1	1357.7	1412.7	1466.6	1520.3	1629.1	1740.0
	s	0.6490	1.4639	1.5595	1.6123	1.6578	1.6990	1.7371	1.8069	1.8657
600 (486.20)	sh			113.80	213.80	313.80	413.80	513.80	713.80	913.80
	v	0.02013	0.7697	0.9456	1.0726	1.1892	1.3008	1.4093	6.6261	1.8284
	h	471.70	1203.7	1290.3	1351.8	1408.3	1463.0	1517.4	1627.0	1738.8
	s	0.6723	1.4461	1.5329	1.5884	1.6351	1.6769	1.7155	1.7859	1.8494
700 (503.08)	sh			96.92	196.92	296.92	396.92	496.92	696.92	896.92
	v	0.02050	0.6556	0.7928	0.5072	1.0102	1.1078	1.2023	1.3858	1.5647
	h	491.61	1201.8	1281.0	1345.6	1403.7	1459.4	1514.4	1624.8	1737.2
	s	0.6928	1.4304	1.5090	1.5673	1.6154	1.6580	1.6970	1.7679	1.8318

*sh = superheat; v = specific volume in ft³/lb; h = total heat in Btu/lb; s = entropy in Btu/°F/lb.

Properties of Superheated Steam (*cont.*)

Abs press lb/in² (sat temp-F)		Sat water	Sat steam	Temperature—degrees Fahrenheit						
				700	800	900	1000	1200	1400	1500
800 (518.21)	sh			181.79	281.79	381.79	481.79	681.79	881.79	981.79
	v	0.02087	0.5690	0.7828	0.8759	0.9631	1.0470	1.2093	1.3669	1.4446
	h	509.81	1199.4	1339.3	1399.1	1455.8	1511.4	1622.7	1735.7	1792.9
	s	0.7111	1.4163	1.5484	1.5980	1.6413	1.6807	1.7522	1.8164	1.8464
900 (531.95)	sh			168.05	268.05	368.05	468.05	668.05	868.05	968.05
	v	0.02123	0.5009	0.6858	0.7713	0.8504	0.9262	1.0720	1.2131	1.2825
	h	526.70	1196.4	1332.7	1394.4	1452.2	1508.5	1620.6	1734.1	1791.6
	s	0.7279	1.4032	1.5311	1.5822	1.6263	1.6662	1.7382	1.8028	1.8329
1000 (544.58)	sh			155.42	255.42	355.42	455.42	655.42	855.42	955.42
	v	0.02159	0.4460	0.6080	0.6875	0.7603	0.8295	0.9622	1.0901	1.1529
	h	542.55	1192.9	1325.9	1389.6	1448.5	1505.4	1618.4	1732.5	1790.3
	s	0.7434	1.3910	1.5149	1.5677	1.6126	1.6530	1.7256	1.7905	1.8207
1200 (567.19)	sh			132.81	232.81	332.81	432.81	632.81	832.81	932.81
	v	0.02232	0.3624	0.4905	0.5615	0.6250	0.6845	0.7974	0.9055	0.9584
	h	571.85	1184.8	1311.5	1379.7	1440.9	1499.4	1614.2	1729.4	1787.6
	s	0.7714	1.3683	1.4851	1.5415	1.5883	1.6298	1.7035	1.7691	1.7996
1400 (587.07)	sh			112.93	212.93	312.93	412.93	612.93	812.93	912.93
	v	0.02307	0.3018	0.4059	0.4712	0.5282	0.5809	0.6798	0.7737	0.8195
	h	598.83	1175.3	1296.1	1369.3	1433.2	1493.2	1609.9	1726.3	1785.0
	s	0.7966	1.3474	1.4575	1.5182	1.5670	1.6096	1.6845	1.7508	1.7815
1600 (604.87)	sh			95.13	195.13	295.13	395.13	595.13	795.13	895.13
	v	0.02387	0.2555	0.3415	0.4032	0.4555	0.5031	0.5915	0.6748	0.7153
	h	624.20	1164.5	1279.4	1358.5	1425.2	1486.9	1605.6	1723.2	1782.3
	s	0.8199	1.3274	1.4312	1.4968	1.5478	1.5916	1.6678	1.7347	1.7657
1800 (621.02)	sh			78.98	178.98	278.98	378.98	578.98	778.98	878.93
	v	0.02472	0.2186	0.2906	0.3500	0.3988	0.4426	0.5229	0.5980	0.6343
	h	648.49	1152.3	1261.1	1347.2	1417.1	1480.6	1601.2	1720.1	1779.7
	s	0.8417	1.3079	1.4054	1.4768	1.5302	1.5753	1.6528	1.7204	1.7516
2000 (642.76)	sh			64.20	164.20	264.20	364.20	564.20	764.20	864.20
	v	0.02565	0.1883	0.2488	0.3072	0.3534	0.3942	0.4680	0.5365	0.5695
	h	672.11	1138.3	1240.9	1335.4	1408.7	1474.1	1596.9	1717.0	1771.1
	s	0.8625	1.2881	1.3794	1.4578	1.5138	1.5603	1.6391	1.7075	1.7389
2500 (668.11)	sh			31.89	131.89	231.89	331.89	531.89	731.89	831.89
	v	0.02859	0.1307	0.1681	0.2293	0.2712	0.3068	0.3692	0.4259	0.4529
	h	731.71	1093.3	1176.7	1303.4	1386.7	1457.5	1585.9	1709.2	1770.4
	s	0.9139	1.2345	1.3076	1.4129	1.4766	1.5269	1.6094	1.6796	1.7116
3000 (695.31)	sh			4.67	104.67	204.67	304.67	504.67	704.67	804.67
	v	0.03428	0.0850	0.0982	0.1759	0.2161	0.2484	0.3033	0.3522	0.3753
	h	801.84	1020.3	1060.5	1267.0	1363.2	1440.2	1574.8	1701.4	1763.8
	s	0.9728	1.1619	1.1966	1.3692	1.4429	1.4976	1.5841	1.6561	1.6888
3500	v				0.1364	0.1764	0.2066	0.2563	0.2995	0.3198
	n				1224.6	1338.2	1422.2	1563.6	1693.6	1757.2
	s				1.3242	1.4112	1.4709	1.5618	1.6358	1.6691
4000	v				0.1052	0.1463	0.1752	0.2210	0.2601	0.2783
	h				1174.3	1311.6	1403.6	1552.2	1685.7	1750.6
	s				1.2754	1.3807	1.4461	1.5417	1.6177	1.6516

Tables on pages 5-21 to 5-24 reproduced from ASME Steam Tables© 1967 by The American Society of Mechanical Engineers. All Rights Reserved.

*sh = superheat; v = specific volume in ft³/lb; h = total heat in Btu/lb; s = entropy in Btu/°F/lb.

5

Properties of Superheated Steam (*cont.*)

Abs press lb/in² (sat temp-F)		750	800	900	1000	1100	1200	1300	1400	1500
						Temperature—degrees Fahrenheit				
5000	v	0.0338	0.0591	0.1038	0.1312	0.1529	0.1718	0.1890	0.2050	0.2203
	h	854.9	1042.9	1252.9	1364.6	1452.1	1529.1	1600.9	1670.0	1737.4
	s	1.0070	1.1593	1.3207	1.4001	1.4582	1.5061	1.5481	1.5863	1.6216
6000	v	0.0298	0.0397	0.0757	0.1020	0.1221	0.1391	0.1544	0.1684	0.1817
	h	822.9	945.1	1188.8	1323.6	1422.3	1505.9	1582.0	1654.2	1724.2
	s	0.9758	1.0746	1.2615	1.3574	1.4229	1.4748	1.5194	1.5593	1.5960
7000	v	0.0279	0.0334	0.0573	0.0816	0.1004	0.1160	0.1298	0.1424	0.1542
	h	806.9	901.8	1124.9	1281.7	1392.2	1482.6	1563.1	1638.6	1711.1
	s	0.9582	1.0350	1.2005	1.3171	1.3904	1.4466	1.4938	1.5355	1.5735
8000	v	0.0267	0.0306	0.0465	0.0671	0.0845	0.0989	0.1115	0.1230	0.1338
	h	796.5	879.1	1074.3	1241.0	1362.2	1459.6	1544.5	1623.1	1698.1
	s	0.9455	1.0122	1.1613	1.2798	1.3603	1.4208	1.4705	1.5140	1.5533
9000	v	0.0258	0.0288	0.0402	0.0568	0.0724	0.0858	0.0975	0.1081	0.1179
	h	789.3	864.7	1037.6	1204.1	1333.0	1437.1	1526.3	1607.9	1685.3
	s	0.9354	0.9964	1.1285	1.2468	1.3323	1.3970	1.4492	1.4944	1.5349
10,000	v	0.0251	0.0276	0.0362	0.0495	0.0633	0.0757	0.0865	0.0963	0.1054
	h	783.8	854.5	1011.3	1172.6	1305.3	1415.3	1508.6	1593.1	1672.8
	s	0.9270	0.9842	1.1039	1.2185	1.3065	1.3749	1.4295	1.4763	1.5180
11,000	v	0.0245	0.0267	0.0335	0.0443	0.0562	0.0676	0.0776	0.0868	0.0952
	h	799.5	846.9	992.1	1146.3	1280.2	1394.4	1491.5	1578.7	1660.6
	s	0.9196	0.9742	1.0851	1.1945	1.2833	1.3544	1.4112	1.4595	1.5023
12,000	v	0.0241	0.0260	0.0317	0.0405	0.0508	0.0610	0.0704	0.0790	0.0869
	h	776.1	841.0	977.8	1124.5	1258.0	1374.7	1475.1	1564.9	1648.8
	s	0.9131	0.9657	1.0701	1.1742	1.2627	1.3353	1.3941	1.4438	1.4877
13,000	v	0.0236	0.0253	0.0302	0.0376	0.0466	0.0558	0.0645	0.0725	0.0799
	h	773.5	836.3	966.8	1106.7	1238.5	1356.5	1459.4	1551.6	1637.4
	s	0.9073	0.9582	1.0578	1.1571	1.2445	1.3179	1.3781	1.4291	1.4741
14,000	v	0.0233	0.0248	0.0291	0.0354	0.0432	0.0515	0.0595	0.0670	0.0740
	h	771.3	832.6	958.0	1092.3	1221.4	1340.2	1444.4	1538.8	1626.5
	s	0.9019	0.9515	1.0473	1.1426	1.2282	1.3021	1.3641	1.4153	1.4612
15,000	v	0.0230	0.0244	0.0282	0.0337	0.0405	0.0479	0.0552	0.0624	0.0690
	h	769.6	829.5	950.9	1080.6	1206.8	1326.0	1430.3	1526.4	1615.9
	s	0.8970	0.9455	1.0382	1.1302	1.2139	1.2880	1.3491	1.4022	1.4491

Tables on pages 5-21 to 5-24 reproduced from ASME Steam Tables⁵ 1967 by The American Society of Mechanical Engineers. All rights reserved.

*sh = superheat; v = specific volume in ft³/lb; h = total heat in Btu/lb; s = entropy in Btu/°F/lb.

STEAM DATA

Theoretical Steam Rates, Condensing for Engines and Turbines
lb per hp-hr

Initial temp °F	Exhaust pressure—in Hg abs									
	3.0	2.5	2.0	1.5	1.0	3.0	2.5	2.0	1.5	1.0
	150 lb gage 365.8°F saturated steam					175 lb gage 377.4°F saturated steam				
365.8	8.35	8.13	7.85	7.53	7.14	....	....	....	....	....
377.4	....	....	....	....	....	8.11	7.89	7.64	7.34	6.97
400	8.17	7.95	7.67	7.36	6.99	8.00	7.78	7.52	7.23	6.87
450	7.92	7.70	7.44	7.15	6.78	7.74	7.53	7.29	7.01	6.66
500	7.67	7.45	7.22	6.93	6.68	7.50	7.30	7.07	6.80	6.46
550	7.42	7.22	6.98	6.72	6.38	7.25	7.07	6.84	6.59	6.27
600	7.18	6.98	6.76	6.51	6.18	7.02	6.84	6.63	6.39	6.08
650	6.95	6.76	6.55	6.31	6.00	6.79	6.62	6.43	6.19	5.90
700	6.72	6.53	6.34	6.11	5.82	6.58	6.41	6.23	6.00	5.72
	200 lb gage 387.8°F saturated steam					250 lb gage 406°F saturated steam				
387.8	7.92	7.71	7.46	7.19	6.84	....	....	....	....	....
406.0	....	....	....	....	....	7.62	7.43	7.20	6.95	6.62
450	7.61	7.41	7.17	6.90	6.57	7.39	7.20	6.99	6.74	6.43
500	7.35	7.16	6.95	6.68	6.37	7.15	6.97	6.76	6.52	6.22
550	7.12	6.94	6.73	6.48	6.18	6.92	6.75	6.55	6.32	6.04
600	6.90	6.72	6.52	6.29	5.99	6.69	6.53	6.35	6.13	5.85
650	6.67	6.51	6.32	6.10	5.81	6.49	6.33	6.15	5.94	5.68
700	6.46	6.30	6.12	5.91	5.64	6.28	6.13	5.96	5.76	5.51
750	6.25	6.10	5.93	5.73	5.47	6.08	5.94	5.77	5.58	5.34
	300 lb gage 421.7°F saturated steam					400 lb gage 448.1°F saturated steam				
421.7	7.39	7.21	7.01	6.76	6.47	....	....	....	....	....
448.1	....	....	....	....	....	7.07	6.91	6.72	6.50	6.23
450	7.23	7.06	6.86	6.62	6.33	....	....	....	....	....
500	6.99	6.83	6.63	6.40	6.12	6.78	6.63	6.46	6.25	5.98
550	6.76	6.61	6.42	6.20	5.93	6.63	6.40	6.23	6.04	5.79
600	6.55	6.40	6.21	6.01	5.75	6.34	6.19	6.03	5.84	5.60
650	6.33	6.20	6.02	5.82	5.58	6.13	5.99	5.84	5.66	5.43
700	6.14	5.99	5.84	5.65	5.41	5.94	5.81	5.67	5.49	5.26
750	5.94	5.81	5.66	5.48	5.25	5.75	5.63	5.49	5.32	5.11
800	5.76	5.63	5.49	5.31	5.09	5.57	5.45	5.32	5.16	4.96
850	5.57	5.45	5.32	5.15	4.94	5.40	5.28	5.16	5.01	4.82
	600 lb gage 488.8°F saturated steam					800 lb gage 520.3°F saturated steam				
600	6.10	5.98	5.83	5.66	5.45	....	....	....	....	....
650	5.90	5.78	5.64	5.47	5.27	5.78	5.67	5.54	5.38	5.19
700	5.70	5.59	5.46	5.30	5.10	5.58	5.47	5.35	5.20	5.01
750	5.52	5.41	5.29	5.14	4.94	5.39	5.28	5.17	5.03	4.85
800	5.35	5.24	5.12	4.98	4.80	5.21	5.12	5.01	4.87	4.70
850	5.18	5.08	4.97	4.83	4.65	5.05	4.96	4.85	4.73	4.57
900	5.02	4.93	4.82	4.69	4.52	4.89	4.80	4.70	4.58	4.43
950	4.86	4.78	4.67	4.55	4.39	4.74	4.66	4.57	4.45	4.30
1000	4.71	4.63	4.53	4.42	4.27	4.60	4.53	4.43	4.32	4.18

5

Theoretical Steam Rates, Condensing for Engines and Turbines

lb per hp-hr

Initial temp °F	Exhaust pressure—in Hg abs									
	3.0	2.5	2.0	1.5	1.0	3.0	2.5	2.0	1.5	1.0
	1000 lb gage 546.4°F saturated steam					1200 lb gage 568.8°F saturated steam				
700	5.51	5.41	5.28	5.15	4.97	....	....	....	....	....
750	5.31	5.21	5.10	4.97	4.80	5.27	5.17	5.07	4.94	4.77
800	5.14	5.04	4.93	4.81	4.65	5.08	4.99	4.89	4.77	4.62
850	4.97	4.88	4.78	4.65	4.50	4.91	4.83	4.73	4.61	5.46
900	4.81	4.73	4.63	4.52	4.37	4.76	4.67	4.58	4.47	4.33
950	4.67	4.59	4.49	4.38	4.24	4.61	4.53	4.44	4.33	4.20
1000	4.52	4.45	4.36	4.26	4.12	5.47	4.39	4.31	4.21	4.08

Theoretical Steam Rates, Non-Condensing

lb per hp-hr

100 lb gage, 337.9°F saturated steam

Exhaust press lb/sq in gage	Initial temperature, °F									
	337.9	350	400	450	500	550	600	650	700	750
	Initial superheat, °F									
	0	12.1	62.1	112	162	212	262	312	362	412
0	16.9	16.8	16.2	15.6	15.0	14.3	13.6	12.9	12.3	11.8
5	19.4	19.3	18.6	17.8	17.0	16.2	15.3	14.6	13.9	13.3
10	22.0	21.8	21.0	20.1	19.1	18.1	17.2	16.3	15.6	14.9
15	24.7	24.5	23.6	22.4	21.2	20.2	19.1	18.2	17.3	16.6
20	27.7	27.4	26.3	25.1	23.7	22.4	23.2	20.2	19.3	18.4
25	31.0	30.7	29.4	27.9	26.2	24.8	26.5	22.5	21.4	20.5
30	34.6	34.3	32.8	30.9	29.1	27.6	21.2	24.9	23.8	22.7
35	38.7	38.4	36.7	34.4	32.4	30.6	29.1	27.8	26.5	25.3
40	43.4	43.0	41.1	38.5	36.3	34.3	32.6	31.1	29.6	28.2
45	48.9	48.5	46.2	43.2	40.6	38.5	36.6	34.9	33.4	31.8
50	....	....	52.3	48.9	46.1	43.5	41.3	39.5	37.6	35.8
55	....	....	....	....	52.5	49.7	47.2	45.0	42.8	40.9
60	....	....	....	....	....	....	....	51.9	49.5	47.2

Theoretical Steam Rates, Non-Condensing
for Engines and Turbines—lb per hp-hr
150 lb gage, 365.8°F saturated steam

Exhaust press lb/sq in gage	Initial temperature, °F									
	365.8	400	450	500	550	600	650	700	750	800
	Initial superheat, F									
	0	34.2	84.2	134	184	234	284	334	384	434
0	14.4	14.1	13.6	13.1	12.5	12.0	11.5	11.0	10.5	10.0
5	16.2	15.7	15.1	14.6	13.9	13.3	12.7	12.1	11.5	11.0
10	17.9	17.4	16.7	16.0	15.3	14.6	13.8	13.2	12.6	12.1
15	19.6	19.1	18.3	17.5	16.6	15.8	15.0	14.3	13.7	13.1
20	21.3	20.8	19.9	19.0	18.0	17.1	16.2	15.5	14.8	14.1
25	23.2	22.6	21.6	20.5	19.4	18.4	17.5	16.7	15.9	15.3
30	25.0	24.4	23.3	22.1	20.9	19.2	18.8	18.0	17.2	16.4
35	27.1	26.4	25.2	23.8	22.5	21.3	20.2	19.3	18.5	17.7
40	29.3	28.5	27.1	25.6	24.2	23.0	21.8	20.8	19.9	19.0
45	31.7	30.8	29.3	27.7	26.0	24.7	23.5	22.3	21.4	20.5
50	34.3	33.3	31.6	29.7	28.0	26.5	25.2	24.0	22.9	22.0
60	40.2	39.0	36.8	34.6	32.6	30.9	29.3	28.0	26.8	25.6
70	47.3	45.8	43.2	40.5	38.2	36.2	34.3	32.8	31.4	30.1
80	....	....	51.2	48.1	45.3	42.9	40.8	38.8	37.2	35.6
90	....	....	....	....	....	51.7	49.2	47.0	44.9	43.0

200 lb gage, 387.8°F saturated steam

Exhaust press lb/sq in gage	Initial temperature, °F									
	387.8	400	450	500	550	600	650	700	750	800
	Initial superheat, °F									
	0	12.2	62.2	112	162	212	262	312	262	412
0	13.1	13.0	12.5	12.0	11.5	11.1	10.6	10.2	9.7	9.3
5	14.4	14.3	13.7	13.2	12.7	12.1	11.6	11.1	10.6	10.1
10	15.7	15.6	15.0	14.3	13.8	13.2	12.5	12.0	11.4	10.9
15	17.0	16.9	16.2	15.5	14.9	14.1	13.5	12.8	12.2	11.7
20	18.3	18.1	17.4	16.6	15.9	15.1	14.4	13.7	13.1	12.5
25	19.6	19.4	18.6	17.8	17.0	16.1	15.3	14.6	13.9	13.3
30	20.9	20.8	19.9	19.0	18.0	17.1	16.2	15.4	14.7	14.1
35	22.3	22.1	22.1	20.2	19.1	18.1	17.2	16.3	15.6	15.0
40	23.8	23.6	22.5	21.4	20.3	19.2	18.2	17.3	16.5	15.8
50	26.8	26.5	25.3	24.1	22.7	21.4	20.4	19.4	18.5	17.7
60	30.1	29.9	28.5	27.0	25.4	24.1	22.8	21.7	20.7	19.8
70	34.0	33.8	32.0	30.2	28.4	26.9	25.5	24.3	23.2	22.2
80	38.3	38.0	36.1	33.9	31.9	30.2	28.6	27.3	26.0	24.9
90	43.5	43.1	40.9	38.3	35.9	34.0	32.3	30.7	29.3	28.1
100	49.6	49.2	46.5	43.3	40.7	38.5	36.6	34.8	33.3	31.8
110	....	....	....	49.4	46.5	44.1	41.8	39.8	38.0	36.5

5

Theoretical Steam Rates, Non-Condensing
for Engines and Turbines
250 lb gage, 406.0°F saturated steam

Exhaust press lb/sq in gage	Initial temperature, °F									
	406	450	500	550	600	650	700	750	800	850
	Initial superheat, °F									
	0	44	94	144	194	244	294	344	394	444
0	12.1	11.7	11.3	10.9	10.4	10.0	9.6	9.2	8.8	8.5
5	13.3	12.8	12.3	11.8	11.4	10.9	10.4	10.0	9.6	9.2
10	14.4	13.9	13.3	12.8	12.3	11.7	11.2	10.7	10.2	9.8
15	15.4	14.9	14.3	13.7	13.1	12.5	11.9	11.4	10.9	10.4
20	16.5	15.9	15.3	14.6	13.9	13.2	12.6	12.0	11.5	11.0
25	17.5	16.9	16.2	15.4	14.7	14.0	13.3	12.7	12.1	11.6
30	18.5	17.9	17.1	16.3	15.5	14.7	14.0	13.4	12.8	12.2
40	20.7	19.9	19.0	18.1	17.2	16.3	15.5	14.7	14.1	13.5
50	22.9	22.1	21.0	19.9	18.9	17.9	17.0	16.2	15.5	14.6
60	25.3	24.4	23.2	21.9	20.7	19.6	18.6	17.8	17.0	16.3
70	27.9	26.8	25.4	24.0	22.7	21.5	20.4	19.5	18.6	17.8
80	30.7	29.5	27.9	26.3	24.8	23.6	22.4	21.3	20.4	19.5
90	33.8	32.5	30.7	28.8	27.2	25.8	24.5	23.3	22.3	21.4
100	37.3	35.8	33.8	31.7	29.8	28.3	26.9	25.6	24.5	23.5
120	45.7	43.7	41.0	38.5	36.3	34.4	32.7	31.2	29.8	28.6

300 lb gage, 421.7°F saturated steam

Exhaust press lb/sq in gage	Initial temperature, °F									
	421.7	450	500	550	600	650	700	750	800	850
	Initial superheat, °F									
	0	28.3	78.3	128	178	228	278	328	378	428
0	11.5	11.2	10.8	10.4	10.0	9.6	9.2	8.9	8.5	8.2
5	12.5	12.2	11.7	11.3	10.8	10.4	10.0	9.6	9.1	8.8
10	13.5	13.2	12.6	12.1	11.6	11.1	10.6	10.2	9.7	9.3
15	14.4	14.0	13.4	12.9	12.3	11.8	11.3	10.8	10.3	9.9
20	15.3	14.9	14.3	13.7	13.1	12.5	11.9	11.3	10.8	10.4
30	17.0	16.5	15.8	15.1	14.4	13.7	13.1	12.5	11.9	11.4
40	18.7	18.3	17.4	16.6	15.8	15.0	14.3	13.6	13.0	12.4
50	20.5	20.0	19.1	18.1	17.3	16.3	15.5	14.8	14.1	13.5
60	22.4	21.8	20.7	19.7	18.7	17.7	16.8	16.0	15.3	14.6
80	26.5	25.7	24.5	23.1	21.8	20.6	19.6	18.7	17.9	17.1
100	31.2	30.2	28.7	27.0	25.4	24.1	22.8	21.8	20.8	19.9
120	36.6	35.6	33.5	31.5	29.7	28.1	26.8	25.5	24.4	23.3
140	43.5	42.2	39.7	37.1	35.0	33.1	31.4	30.1	28.7	27.4
160	52.3	50.4	47.2	44.1	41.6	39.4	37.3	35.6	34.2	32.6
180	....	....	....	....	50.5	47.7	45.3	43.1	41.3	39.6

Theoretical Steam Rates, Non-Condensing (Continued)
for Engines and Turbines
400 lb gage, 448.1°F saturated steam

Exhaust press lb/sq in gage	Initial temperature, °F									
	448.1	500	550	600	650	700	750	800	850	900
	Initial superheat, °F									
	0	51.9	102	152	202	252	302	352	402	452
0	10.6	10.2	9.8	9.4	9.0	8.7	8.4	8.0	7.7	7.4
5	11.5	11.0	10.5	10.1	9.7	9.3	8.9	8.6	8.2	7.9
10	12.2	11.7	11.2	10.8	10.3	9.9	9.5	9.1	8.7	8.4
20	13.7	13.0	12.5	11.9	11.4	10.9	10.4	10.0	9.6	9.2
30	15.0	14.3	13.7	13.1	12.5	11.9	11.4	10.8	10.4	9.9
40	16.3	15.6	14.8	14.1	13.5	12.8	12.2	11.7	11.2	10.7
50	17.6	16.8	16.0	15.2	14.5	13.8	13.1	12.5	11.9	11.4
60	18.9	18.0	17.2	16.3	15.5	14.7	14.0	13.3	12.8	12.2
80	21.7	20.6	19.6	18.5	17.5	16.6	15.8	15.1	14.4	13.8
100	24.7	23.4	22.2	20.9	19.7	18.7	17.8	17.0	16.2	15.6
120	27.9	26.5	25.0	23.5	22.2	21.0	20.0	19.1	18.2	17.5
140	31.6	29.9	28.1	26.4	24.9	23.6	22.4	21.4	20.5	19.6
160	35.8	33.8	31.7	29.7	28.0	26.5	25.2	24.1	23.0	22.1
180	40.7	38.4	35.8	33.5	31.7	30.0	28.5	27.2	26.0	25.0
200	46.6	43.7	40.6	38.1	36.0	34.1	32.4	30.9	29.6	28.4

600 lb gage, 488.8°F saturated steam

Exhaust press lb/sq in gage	Initial temperature, °F									
	575	600	650	700	750	800	850	900	950	1000
	Initial superheat, °F									
	86.2	111	161	211	261	311	361	411	461	511
0	8.9	8.7	8.4	8.1	7.8	7.5	7.2	6.9	6.7	6.4
10	10.0	9.8	9.4	9.1	8.7	8.3	8.0	7.7	7.4	7.1
20	11.0	10.8	10.3	9.9	9.5	9.1	8.7	8.3	8.0	7.7
30	11.9	11.6	11.1	10.6	10.1	9.7	9.3	8.9	8.5	8.2
40	12.8	12.4	11.9	11.3	10.8	10.3	9.9	9.4	9.1	8.7
50	13.5	13.2	12.6	12.0	11.4	10.9	10.4	10.0	9.6	9.2
60	14.3	14.0	13.3	12.7	12.1	11.5	11.0	10.5	10.0	9.7
80	15.9	15.5	14.7	14.0	13.3	12.6	12.0	11.5	11.0	10.6
100	17.5	17.1	16.2	15.3	14.5	13.8	13.1	12.6	12.1	11.6
125	18.3	19.0	18.0	17.0	16.1	15.3	14.6	14.0	13.4	12.8
150	21.8	21.1	19.9	18.7	17.8	16.9	16.1	15.4	14.8	14.2
175	24.1	23.4	21.9	20.6	19.6	18.7	17.8	17.0	16.3	15.7
200	26.8	25.9	24.1	22.8	21.6	20.5	19.6	18.7	18.0	17.3
250	32.7	31.6	29.5	27.8	26.3	25.0	23.9	22.9	22.0	21.1
300	40.5	39.0	36.5	34.4	32.5	31.0	29.6	28.3	27.1	26.1

5

Pages 5-25 to 5-29 calculated from "Theoretical Steam Rate Tables" by J. H. Keenan and F. G. Keyes, published by American Society of Mechanical Engineers.

Approximate Turbine Efficiency*—Rankine Cycle
3600 rpm

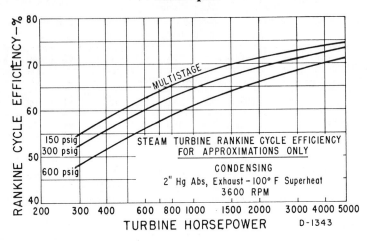

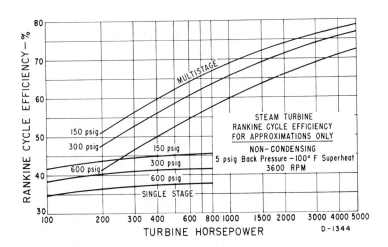

Theoretical Steam Rate Formulas

$$TSR = \frac{2545}{\Delta H}$$

$$\text{Steam flow (lb/hr)} = \frac{TSR \times hp}{\text{corrected efficiency}}$$

TSR = theoretical steam rate—lb/hp-hr

ΔH = difference in enthalpy between inlet and exhaust steam (isentropic)

* Corrections for superheat and speed on next page.

Corrections to Rankine Cycle Efficiency Curves
Superheat Corrections

Type of turbine	Single-stage	Multi-stage	
	Non-condensing	Non-condensing	Condensing
Correction method	Add or subtract to or from RCE	Multiply	Multiply
Superheat			
0°F	add 0.6	0.963	0.977
100°F	—	1.000	1.000
200°F	Subtract 0.6	1.012	1.018
300°F	Subtract 1.2	1.015	1.034

Speed Correction Multiplier for Speeds Other Than 3600 rpm Multi-stage Turbines Only

	Non-condensing				Condensing			
RPM	3000	5000	7500	10,000	3600	5000	7500	10,000
BHP								
500	1.000	1.030	1.036	1.018	1.000	1.000	1.000	1.000
1000	1.000	1.013	1.006	0.982	1.000	1.000	1.000	1.000
2000	1.000	1.001	0.980	0.940	1.000	1.000	1.000	0.957
3000	1.000	0.997	0.968	0.920	1.000	1.000	0.984	0.929
5000	1.000	0.994	0.959	0.902	1.000	1.000	0.955	0.895

5

EFFICIENCY

Page 5-30 gives approximate Rankine cycle efficiencies (RCE) for single-stage and multi-stage turbines at various ratings and steam pressures. These data may be used only for rough estimating. There is considerable variance between manufacturers for a given rating and condition, some offering a higher efficiency, some lower, depending upon how the conditions match a particular size or design.

Although very large turbines are used for certain types of drives, a limit of 5000 hp has been chosen for these data since it was felt this encompassed the majority of drives where such data would be used. It is to be expected that larger units would have higher efficiencies. For example, a 25,000 hp, 3600 rpm turbine at 600 psig, 750°F and 5″ Hg abs. exhaust, would have an efficiency of about 82%.

"Single-stage turbines often operate at some back pressure. The curves are based on 5 psig back pressure. For back pressures to 50 psig multiply RCE from the curves by a correction factor equal to:

$$\text{corr. Factor} = 1 + \frac{0\text{--}25 \ (\text{back pressure} - 5)}{100}$$

where the back pressure is in psig."

Condensing turbines show a small increase in RCE for higher absolute exhaust pressure (lower vacuums), but it is not significant for the purpose of these curves.

Gas or Vapor Flow

For flow problems involving gas or vapor the Darcy formulae are:

$$R = \frac{DVp}{32.174\ u} = \frac{dV}{12\ v} = \frac{6.32\ W}{dz} = \frac{22735\ Qp}{dz} = \frac{378.9\ qp}{dz}$$

$$h_w = 0.002745\ \frac{fLV^2 s_a}{d}$$

$$h_p = 0.001295\ \frac{fLV^2}{dw} = \frac{fLV^2 p}{24\ gd} = \frac{43.53\ fLQ^2 p}{pd^5}$$

$$h_p = \frac{0.01209\ fLq^2 p}{d^5} = \frac{0.00000336\ fLW^2}{pd^5}$$

Symbols

D = internal pipe dia—ft
d = internal pipe dia—in
f = friction factor (page 3-11)
g = acceleration due to gravity
    —32.174 ft/sec^2
h_w = pressure drop
    —inches of water
h_p = pressure drop—psi
L = length of pipe—ft
p = density at temp and press
    of flow conditions—lb/ft^3
q = flow—cfm—ft^3/min
Q = flow—cfs—ft^3/sec
R = Reynolds number
s_a = specific gravity of gas (air = 1)
u = absolute viscosity = lbf-sec/ft^2
V = velocity of flow—(ft/sec)
v = kinematic viscosity (ft^2/sec)
W = flow—lb/hr
w = specific volume—ft^3/lb
z = absolute viscosity—centipoises

The Darcy formula can not be applied indiscriminately to vapor or gas flow because it does not take into account the affect compressibility has on velocity and density.

1. When h_p is less than 10% of upstream pressure, reasonable accuracy is obtained. Base p and V on either upstream or downstream conditions.

2. When h_p is between 10 and 40% of upstream pressure, reasonable accuracy is obtained by using p and V based on an average of upstream and downstream conditions.

3. When h_p is over 40% of upstream pressure divide the total length into shorter sections and add the pressure drops for each section.

FRICTION OF STEAM IN PIPES
Use of tables and charts, pages 5-34 to 5-37 and 5-39

Example —

Given a flow of 30,000 lb/hr of steam at 125 lb/in² gage and 100°F of superheat through 955 feet of 8-inch pipe with two 90° elbows and one gate valve. What is the friction loss?

Solution —

- Steam at 125 lb/in² gage pressure will be approximately 125 + 15 atmospheric pressure = 140 lb/in² absolute pressure.
- From the table on page 5-19, the temperature of 140 lb/in² steam without superheat is 353°F.
- The total temperature with superheat is 353 + 100 = 453°F.
- From the table on page 5-39, the length of pipe equivalent to the friction loss through two 90° elbows is 2 × 20 = 40 ft and the equivalent length for a gate valve is 5.32 ft. The total equivalent length of pipe is 955 + 40 + 5.32 = 1000 ft.
- Enter the table on page 5-34 at 125 lb/in² gage pressure and 450°F total heat, finding a correction factor of 2.641.
- Divide the steam flow of 30,000 lb/hr by 2.641 which gives an equivalent flow of 11,359 lb/hr for use in the chart.
- Now enter the chart on page 5-37 at 11,359 lb/hr. Run vertically to the line for 8-inch pipe and then horizontally to the right, reading a friction loss or pressure drop of 0.005 lb/in² per ft. For 1000 equivalent feet of pipe the friction loss is 1000 × 0.005 = 5 lb/in².

Flow of Steam Conversion Factors

The chart on pages 5-36 to 5-37 is based on ½ lb gage pressure saturated steam. At increased pressures and temperatures steam pipe will carry load as indicated in chart times (×) conversion factor below, with drop as indicated in chart. To simplify the use of the chart it is suggested that the steam loads in question be corrected by dividing same by proper factor below. Then apply corrected load directly to low pressure chart. See example, page 5-33.

Pressure lb gage	Sat temp	Total temperatures—°F																		
		300	350	400	450	500	550	600	650	700	750	800	850	900	950	1000	1050	1100	1150	1200
½	1.000	0.938	0.908	0.880	0.855	0.832	0.811	0.792	0.773	0.756	0.740	0.725	0.712	0.698	0.686	0.674	0.663	0.658	0.642	0.632
5	1.129	1.069	1.034	1.003	0.974	0.948	0.924	0.901	0.881	0.861	0.843	0.826	0.810	0.795	0.781	0.767	0.754	0.742	0.731	0.719
10	1.255	1.199	1.159	1.124	1.091	1.062	1.035	1.010	0.987	0.965	0.945	0.925	0.907	0.891	0.875	0.859	0.845	0.831	0.818	0.806
15	1.368	1.317	1.273	1.233	1.198	1.165	1.135	1.108	1.082	1.058	1.036	1.015	0.995	0.977	0.959	0.942	0.927	0.911	0.897	0.884
20	1.472	1.426	1.378	1.335	1.296	1.260	1.228	1.198	1.170	1.144	1.120	1.097	1.076	1.056	1.037	1.019	1.002	0.986	0.970	0.955
25	1.567	1.528	1.475	1.429	1.387	1.349	1.314	1.282	1.252	1.224	1.198	1.174	1.151	1.130	1.109	1.090	1.071	1.054	1.038	1.022
30	1.657	1.624	1.567	1.517	1.473	1.432	1.395	1.361	1.329	1.299	1.272	1.246	1.222	1.199	1.177	1.157	1.137	1.119	1.101	1.084
35	1.742	1.715	1.655	1.602	1.554	1.511	1.472	1.435	1.402	1.371	1.341	1.314	1.289	1.264	1.241	1.220	1.199	1.180	1.161	1.143
40	1.822	1.803	1.738	1.682	1.631	1.586	1.545	1.506	1.471	1.438	1.408	1.379	1.352	1.327	1.303	1.280	1.258	1.238	1.218	1.200
45	1.898	1.887	1.818	1.759	1.706	1.658	1.614	1.574	1.537	1.503	1.471	1.441	1.413	1.386	1.361	1.337	1.315	1.293	1.273	1.253
50	1.972	1.968	1.895	1.832	1.777	1.727	1.681	1.640	1.601	1.565	1.532	1.500	1.471	1.443	1.417	1.392	1.369	1.346	1.325	1.305
60	2.110	..	2.042	1.973	1.912	1.858	1.808	1.763	1.721	1.683	1.647	1.613	1.581	1.551	1.523	1.496	1.471	1.447	1.424	1.402
70	2.238	..	2.180	2.105	2.039	1.981	1.927	1.879	1.834	1.793	1.754	1.718	1.684	1.652	1.622	1.594	1.567	1.541	1.517	1.494
80	2.360	..	2.311	2.230	2.159	2.097	2.040	1.988	1.941	1.897	1.856	1.817	1.781	1.748	1.716	1.686	1.657	1.630	1.604	1.579
90	2.474	..	2.437	2.349	2.274	2.207	2.147	2.092	2.042	1.995	1.952	1.912	1.874	1.838	1.804	1.773	1.743	1.714	1.687	1.661
100	2.584	..	2.558	2.464	2.384	2.313	2.249	2.192	2.138	2.090	2.044	2.002	1.962	1.924	1.889	1.856	1.824	1.794	1.766	1.739
125	2.837	..	..	2.734	2.641	2.560	2.488	2.424	2.364	2.309	2.259	2.211	2.167	2.125	2.086	2.049	2.014	1.981	1.950	1.920
150	3.070	..	..	2.985	2.880	2.789	2.709	2.637	2.571	2.511	2.455	2.403	2.355	2.310	2.267	2.226	2.188	2.152	2.118	2.085
175	3.285	..	..	3.222	3.104	3.002	2.914	2.836	2.764	2.698	2.638	2.582	2.530	2.481	2.435	2.391	2.350	2.311	2.274	2.238
200	3.487	..	..	3.450	3.316	3.205	3.108	3.023	2.946	2.875	2.810	2.749	2.694	2.641	2.592	2.545	2.501	2.459	2.420	2.382
225	3.678	..	..	3.669	3.520	3.398	3.293	3.201	3.118	3.042	2.968	2.908	2.848	2.793	2.740	2.690	2.644	2.600	2.558	2.518
250	3.859	..	..	..	3.717	3.583	3.470	3.370	3.282	3.201	3.128	3.060	2.996	2.936	2.881	2.829	2.780	2.733	2.689	2.647
275	4.033	..	..	..	3.907	3.762	3.640	3.534	3.440	3.354	3.276	3.204	3.137	3.075	3.017	2.962	2.910	2.861	2.814	2.770
300	4.200	..	..	..	4.093	3.935	3.804	3.691	3.591	3.501	3.419	3.343	3.273	3.207	3.146	3.088	3.034	2.983	2.934	2.888
350	4.517	..	..	..	4.454	4.269	4.119	3.992	3.880	3.780	3.689	3.606	3.529	3.458	3.391	3.328	3.269	3.214	3.162	3.111

Flow of Steam Conversion Factors (Continued)

Pressure lb gage	Sat temp	300	350	400	450	500	550	600	650	700	750	800	850	900	950	1000	1050	1100	1150	1200
400	4.816				4.806	4.589	4.419	4.276	4.152	4.043	3.944	3.854	3.770	3.693	3.621	3.553	3.491	3.431	3.374	3.320
450	5.099					4.900	4.707	4.548	4.413	4.293	4.186	4.088	3.998	3.915	3.838	3.766	3.698	3.634	3.574	3.517
500	5.370					5.205	4.986	4.810	4.659	4.532	4.416	4.311	4.215	4.127	4.045	3.968	3.896	3.828	3.764	3.704
550	5.630					5.506	5.259	5.064	4.902	4.762	4.638	4.526	4.424	4.330	4.243	4.161	4.086	4.014	3.946	3.882
600	5.883					5.806	5.526	5.312	5.136	4.892	4.852	4.732	4.624	4.525	4.433	4.347	4.267	4.192	4.121	4.053
650	6.127					6.107	5.790	5.554	5.363	5.201	5.059	4.932	4.818	4.713	4.616	4.526	4.442	4.363	4.289	4.218
700	6.365						6.052	5.792	5.585	5.411	5.260	5.126	5.005	4.895	4.793	4.698	4.611	4.528	4.451	4.377
750	6.597						6.312	6.025	5.802	5.616	5.456	5.314	5.187	5.071	4.965	4.865	4.774	4.687	4.606	4.530
800	6.825						6.574	6.258	6.016	5.817	5.647	5.498	5.364	5.242	5.132	5.028	4.933	4.842	4.759	4.679
850	7.048						6.837	6.488	6.227	6.014	5.835	5.677	5.537	5.410	5.295	5.187	5.087	4.994	4.906	4.824
900	7.267						7.103	6.718	6.435	6.209	6.019	5.853	5.707	5.574	5.454	5.341	5.238	5.141	5.051	4.965
950	7.484						7.375	6.947	6.642	6.400	6.200	6.026	5.872	5.734	5.609	5.492	5.385	5.285	5.191	5.102
1000	7.696							7.175	6.846	6.588	6.376	6.194	6.034	5.890	5.760	5.638	5.528	5.424	5.327	5.236
1050	7.908							7.406	7.049	6.775	6.551	6.360	6.193	6.043	5.908	5.783	5.669	5.561	5.461	5.367
1100	8.117							7.638	7.252	6.960	6.725	6.525	6.351	6.194	6.055	5.924	5.807	5.692	5.593	5.496
1150	8.326							7.873	7.455	7.144	6.896	6.686	6.505	6.343	6.198	6.064	5.942	5.828	5.722	5.622
1200	8.532							8.112	7.657	7.327	7.065	6.846	6.657	6.489	6.339	6.201	6.075	5.957	5.849	5.746
1250	8.736							8.355	7.859	7.508	7.233	7.004	6.807	6.633	6.477	6.335	6.204	6.084	5.973	5.867
1300	8.941							8.605	8.063	7.689	7.399	7.160	6.955	6.775	6.614	6.468	6.333	6.209	6.095	5.936
1350	9.143							8.859	8.269	7.870	7.565	7.314	7.101	6.915	6.749	6.598	6.460	6.332	6.215	6.103
1400	9.347							9.125	8.475	8.049	7.728	7.467	7.246	7.053	6.882	6.726	6.584	6.454	6.333	6.219
1450	9.549							9.402	8.684	8.230	7.892	7.619	7.389	7.190	7.013	6.853	6.707	6.573	6.450	6.333
1500	9.750								8.893	8.408	8.053	7.768	7.530	7.324	7.142	6.977	6.827	6.690	6.564	6.444
1600	10.156								9.326	8.771	8.376	8.066	7.810	7.591	7.397	7.223	7.066	6.921	6.788	6.662
1700	10.564								9.775	9.135	8.698	8.361	8.088	7.852	7.647	7.463	7.297	7.147	7.007	6.877
1800	10.977								10.252	9.506	9.020	8.654	8.358	8.109	7.891	7.699	7.525	7.366	7.221	7.085
1900	11.397								10.760	9.885	9.343	8.945	8.628	8.363	8.133	7.930	7.748	7.581	7.431	7.288
2000	11.822								11.321	10.272	9.669	9.234	8.893	8.612	8.370	8.158	7.966	7.793	7.636	7.488
2100	12.262								11.964	10.672	9.996	9.523	9.159	8.858	8.603	8.381	8.181	8.000	7.837	7.683
2200	12.707									11.091	10.329	9.813	9.421	9.103	8.834	8.600	8.392	8.204	8.034	7.875

Total temperatures—°F

Steam flow chart and tables are reproduced with permission from ITT Grinnel book of Piping Design and Engineering.

5

Friction Loss for Steam

**Based on ½ lb gage pressure. See page 5-34
to convert to other pressures**

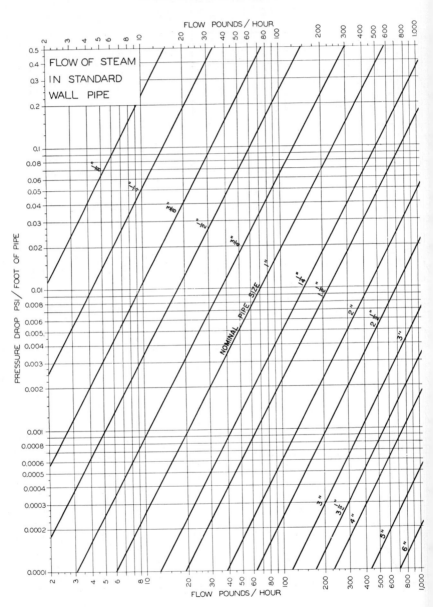

Friction Loss of Steam (Continued)

**Based on ½ lb gage pressure. See page 5-34
to convert to other pressures**

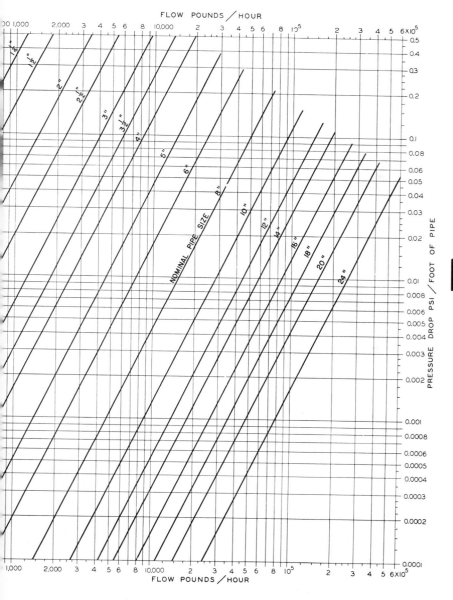

Low Pressure Steam Flow
lb per hr based on 100 ft per sec velocity

Absolute press in in. Hg.

Pipe			.50	.75	1.00	1.25	1.50	2.00	2.50	3.00	3.50	4.00	5.00	6.00	8.00	10.00	29.920
Nom size	Area* sq ft																
1½	.01414		4	6	8	10	11	15	19	22	25	29	36	42	55	68	190
2	.02331		7	10	13	16	19	25	31	36	42	47	59	70	91	112	313
2½	.03326		10	14	18	23	27	35	44	52	60	68	84	99	130	160	447
3	.05132		15	22	28	35	42	54	67	80	92	105	129	153	200	247	689
4	.08840		25	37	49	60	72	94	116	137	159	180	222	264	345	426	1188
5	.13900		40	58	77	95	112	147	182	216	250	283	349	414	543	669	1867
6	.20070		57	84	111	137	162	213	263	312	361	409	504	598	784	966	2696
8	.34720		99	146	192	237	281	368	455	540	624	707	872	1035	1356	1672	4664
10	.54790		157	230	302	373	443	581	717	852	985	1116	1377	1634	2140	2638	7360
12	.78540		225	330	433	535	635	833	1028	1221	1411	1600	1973	2342	3068	3782	10551
14	.95750		274	403	528	652	775	1016	1254	1488	1721	1951	2406	2855	3740	4610	12862
16	1.26800		363	533	700	864	1026	1346	1660	1971	2279	2583	3186	3781	4953	6105	17033
18	1.62300		465	682	896	1106	1313	1722	2125	2523	2916	3307	4078	4840	6339	7814	21802
20	2.02100		579	850	1115	1377	1635	2145	2646	3141	3632	4117	5078	6026	7894	9731	27149
24	2.94800		845	1240	1627	2008	2385	3128	3860	4582	5297	6006	7407	8791	11514	14194	39601
30	4.66600		1337	1962	2575	3179	3775	4951	6109	7253	8385	9506	11724	13913	18225	22466	62680
36	6.77700		1942	2849	3740	4617	5483	7191	8873	10534	12178	13807	17028	20208	26470	32630	91038
42	9.28100		2659	3902	5121	6323	7509	9848	12152	14426	16677	18909	23319	27675	36250	44686	124675
48	12.17700		3489	5120	6719	8296	9852	12921	15944	18928	21881	24809	30595	36310	47561	58629	163578
54	15.46600		4431	6503	8534	10537	12513	16411	20250	24040	27792	31510	38859	46117	60408	74465	207760
60	19.14700		5485	8051	10565	13045	15491	20318	25070	29762	34406	39009	48108	57094	74785	92188	257208
66	23.22100		6653	9764	12814	15821	18788	24641	30404	36095	41727	47309	58344	69242	90967	111804	311936
72	27.68800		7932	11642	15278	18864	22402	29381	36253	43038	49754	56410	69568	82562	108145	133311	371942

* Area denotes transverse internal area of pipe { sizes up to 12" Schedule 40 pipe / sizes above 12" are Std. wt. pipe (.375 wall)

Friction Loss in Pipe Fittings in Terms of Equivalent Length—Feet of Straight Pipe

Nominal pipe size	Actual inside diameter d	Friction factor f	Gate valve full open	90° elbow	45° elbow	Std tee thru flow	Std tee branch flow	Close return bend	Swing check valve full open	Angle valve full open	Globe valve full open	Butterfly valve	90° Welding elbow r/d = 1	90° Welding elbow r/d = 2	Mitre bend 45	Mitre bend 90
½	.622	.027	.41	1.55	.83	1.04	3.11	2.59	5.18	7.78	17.6					
¾	.824	.025	.55	2.06	1.10	1.37	4.12	3.43	6.86	10.3	23.3					
1	1.049	.023	.70	2.62	1.40	1.75	5.25	4.37	8.74	13.1	29.7					
1¼	1.380	.022	.92	3.45	1.84	2.30	6.90	5.75	11.5	17.3	39.1					
1½	1.610	.021	1.07	4.03	2.15	2.68	8.05	6.71	13.4	20.1	45.6					
2	2.067	.019	1.38	5.17	2.76	3.45	10.3	8.61	17.2	25.8	58.6		3.45	2.07	2.58	10.3
2½	2.469	.018	1.65	6.17	3.29	4.12	12.3	10.3	20.6	30.9	70.0		4.12	2.47	3.08	12.3
3	3.068	.018	2.04	7.67	4.09	5.11	15.3	12.8	25.5	38.4	86.9		5.11	3.07	3.84	15.3
4	4.026	.017	2.68	10.1	5.37	6.71	20.1	16.8	33.6	50.3	114		6.71	4.03	5.03	20.1
5	5.047	.016	3.36	12.6	6.73	8.41	25.2	21.0	42.1	63.1	143		8.41	5.05	6.31	25.2
6	6.065	.015	4.04	15.2	8.09	10.1	30.3	25.3	50.5	75.8	172	7.75	10.1	6.07	7.58	30.3
8	7.981	.014	5.32	20.0	10.6	13.3	39.9	33.3	33.3	99.8	226	9.26	13.3	7.98	9.98	39.9
10	10.02	.014	6.68	25.1	13.4	16.7	50.1	41.8	41.8	125	284	11.5	16.7	10.0	12.5	50.1
12	11.938	.013	7.96	29.8	15.9	19.9	59.7	49.7	49.7	149	338	15.1	19.9	11.9	14.9	59.7
14	13.124	.013	8.75	32.8	17.5	21.8	65.6	54.7	54.7	164	372	18.9	21.8	13.1	16.4	65.6
16	15.00	.013	10.0	37.5	20.0	25.0	75.0	62.5	62.5	188	425	22.7	25.0	15.0	18.8	75.0
18	16.876	.012	16.9	42.2	22.5	28.1	84.4	70.3	70.3	210	478	29.9	28.1	16.9	21.1	84.4
20	18.814	.012	12.5	47.0	25.1	31.4	94.1	78.4	78.4	235	533	29.2	31.4	18.8	23.5	94.1
24	22.628	.012	15.1	56.6	30.2	37.7	113	94.3	94.3	283	641	34.8	37.7	22.6	28.3	113
30	28	.011	18.7	70	37.3	46.7	140	117				38.3	46.7	28	35	140
36	34	.011	22.7	85	45.3	56.7	170	142				31.3	56.7	34	43	170
42	40	.010	26.7	100	53.3	66.7	200	167				35.2	66.7	40	50	200
48	46	.010	30.7	115	61.3	76.7	230	192				39.2	76.7	46	58	230
L/D			8	30	16	20	60	50	½ to 6 = 100, 24 to 48 = 50	150	340		20	12	15	60

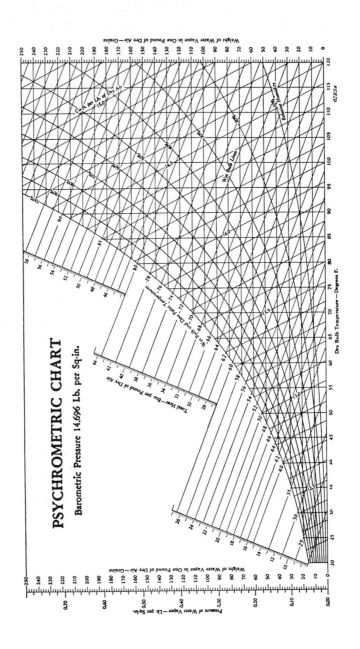

PSYCHROMETRIC CHART

Barometric Pressure 14,696 Lb. per Sq-in.

Psychrometric Chart
Examples showing use of chart on page 5-40

CONDITIONS: 95° dry-bulb and 75° wet-bulb

Relative humidity: At intersection of 75° wet-bulb and 95° dry-bulb the relative humidity is read directly on the curved lines as 40 per cent.

Dew point: At intersection of 75° wet-bulb and 95° dry-bulb lines, the dew point is read directly on horizontal temperature lines as 67°.

Vapor pressure: At intersection of 75° wet-bulb and 95° dry-bulb lines, pass in horizontal direction to left of chart and on scale read the vapor pressure as 0.33 lb per sq in abs.

Vapor pressure in inches, Hg (at 32°F) = 2.036 × lb/sq in abs.

Vapor pressure in millimeters, Hg (at 32°F) = 51.71 × lb/sq in abs.

Total heat above 0° in mixture per lb of dry air: From where wet-bulb line joins saturation line, follow 75° wet-bulb line upward to its intersection with slanting scale at left of chart read 38.5 Btu per lb of dry air saturated with moisture. The use of this scale to obtain total heat in the mixture at any wet-bulb temperature is a great convenience, as the number of Btu required to heat the mixture and humidify, as well as the refrigeration required to cool and dehumidify the mixture, can be obtained by taking the difference in total heat before and after treatment of the mixture.

Grains of moisture per lb of dry air: From intersection of 95° dry-bulb and 75° wet-bulb temperature lines follow horizontal line to right and read directly 99 grains of moisture per lb.

Cu ft of mixture per lb of dry air: At intersection of 75° wet-bulb and 95° dry-bulb lines read directly on diagonal lines 14.29 cu ft per lb, which is the specific volume.

5

Requirements in U.S. gpm for Boiler Feeding

Boiler hp	gpm	lb per hr	Boiler hp	gpm	lb per hr
50	4	1,725	2,500	172	86,250
75	5	2,587	3,000	207	103,500
100	7	3,450	3,500	242	120,750
150	10	5,175	4,000	276	138,000
175	12	6,037	4,500	310	155,250
200	14	6,900	5,000	345	172,500
225	16	7,762	10,000	689	345,000
250	17	8,625	15,000	1,034	517,500
275	19	9,487	20,000	1,387	690,000
300	21	10,350	25,000	1,723	862,500
350	24	12,075	35,000	2,413	1,207,500
400	28	13,800	40,000	2,759	1,380,000
500	34	17,250	45,000	3,102	1,550,000
750	53	25,875	50,000	3,447	1,725,000
1,000	69	34,500	60,000	4,136	2,070,000
1,500	104	51,750	80,000	5,515	2,760,000
2,000	138	69,000	100,000	6,894	3,450,000

Note: (a) gpm is given to the nearest whole number.

(b) The above water quantities are based on 34.5 lb of water evaporated per hour from and at 212 deg F. The weight of one gallon of water is taken as being equal to 8.34 lb at 60 deg F. Intermediate water quantities in gal per min are obtainable by multiplying the boiler hp by .069.

(c) In selecting boiler feed pumps, the fact that boilers are often run two or three hundred percent of rating should be taken into consideration. The above figures are of the actual boiler horsepower developed.

(d) Boiler feed pumps should have pressure in excess of the boiler rated pressure in order to compensate for frictional losses, entrance losses, regulating valve losses, and normal static head. These should be specified for a particular installation. However, for estimating purposes, the following are fair values:

Boiler Pressure	Boiler Feed Pump Discharge Pressure
200	250
400	475
800	925
1200	1350
1600	1920
2000	2400
2400	2880
3000	3600

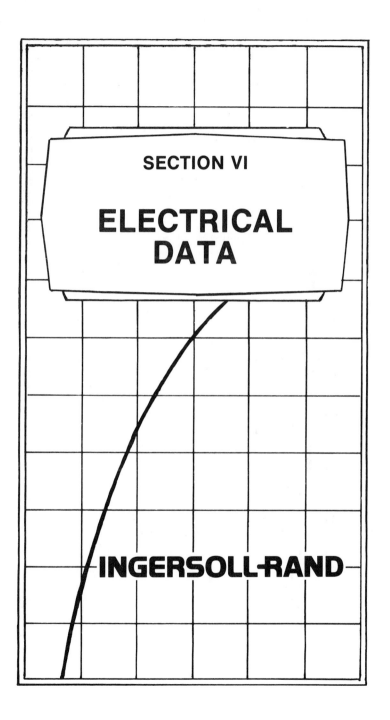

SECTION VI

ELECTRICAL
DATA

INGERSOLL-RAND

CONTENTS OF SECTION 6

Electrical Data

Electrical Data

Volt (E) is the unit of electric pressure or electromotive force. It is the potential which will produce a current of 1 ampere through a resistance of 1 ohm.

Ampere (I) is the unit of electrical current (coulombs per sec)

Ohm (R) is the unit of electrical resistance—volts/ampere.

Watts (W) and *Kilowatts* (KW) are units of electric power.

Kilovolt-amperes (KVA) is a measurement of apparent electric power.

Kilowatt hour (Kwhr) is a unit of electrical energy or work performed.

Joule (J) metric unit of energy = watt per sec.

1 Kwhr = 2,655,000 ft-lb = 1.341 hp-hr = 3413 Btu = 3,600,000 joules

Ohm Law Relationships (direct current)

$$E = IR = W/I = \sqrt{WR} \qquad W = I^2R = E^2/R = EI$$
$$I = E/R = W/E = \sqrt{W/R} \qquad R = E/I = W/I^2 = E^2/W$$

Electrical Formulas Symbols as above; plus

    eff = efficiency (expressed as a decimal)
    pf = power factor (expressed as a decimal)
    hp = horsepower output

Required	Direct current	Alternating current Single-phase	Alternating current 3-phase*
Kva		$\dfrac{IE}{1000}$	$\dfrac{1.73\,IE}{1000}$
Kilowatts	$\dfrac{IE}{1000}$	$\dfrac{IE(pf)}{1000}$	$\dfrac{1.73\,IE(pf)}{1000}$
Horsepower (output)	$\dfrac{IE(eff)}{746}$	$\dfrac{IE(eff)(pf)}{746}$	$\dfrac{1.73\,IE(eff)(pf)}{746}$
Joules	$\dfrac{IE}{sec}$	$\dfrac{IE(eff)(pf)}{sec}$	$\dfrac{1.73\,IE(eff)(pf)}{sec}$
Amperes (hp known)	$\dfrac{746(hp)}{E(eff)}$	$\dfrac{746(hp)}{E(eff)(pf)}$	$\dfrac{746(hp)}{1.73\,E(eff)(pf)}$
Amperes (kw known)	$\dfrac{1000\,kw}{E}$	$\dfrac{1000\,kw}{E(pf)}$	$\dfrac{1000\,kw}{1.73\,E(pf)}$
Amperes (kva known)		$\dfrac{1000\,kva}{E}$	$\dfrac{1000\,kva}{1.73\,E}$

* For 3-phase systems E is measured line to line and I is phase current.

6

Motor selection

Motors operate successfully where voltage variation does not exceed 10 percent above or below normal or where frequency variation does not exceed 5% above or below normal. The sum of the voltage and frequency variation should not exceed 10%.

It should be noted that such variations will affect the operating characteristics, such as full load and starting current, starting and breakdown torque, efficiency and power factor.

Standard motors are available to meet a wide variety of conditions. In addition, special motors may be built to meet unusual conditions.*

It is wise to go to the motor manufacturer with the conditions of operation.

Information required will include:

· Voltage and frequency of current (including probable variations in frequency and voltage).
· Horsepower requirement of the driven machine.
· Whether the load is continuous, intermittent or varying.
· The operating speed or speeds.
· Method of starting the motor.
· Type of motor enclosure—such as drip-proof, splash-proof, totally enclosed, weather protection, explosion proof, dust-ignition proof or other enclosure.
· The ambient or surrounding temperature.
· Altitude of operation.
· Any special conditions of heat, moisture, explosive, dust laden, or chemical laden atmosphere.
· Type of connection to driven machine. (direct, belted, geared, etc.)
· Transmitted bearing load to the motor. (overhung load, thrust, etc.)

Torque

Torque is the turning effort caused by a force acting normal to a radius at a set distance from the axis of rotation. It can be expressed in lb-ft (lb at a radius of 1 ft). The full-load torque of a motor is:

$$\text{Full-load torque} = \frac{5250 \times \text{hp}}{\text{rpm}}$$

The locked rotor or starting torques are given in the tables on page 6-6 and 6-7. Above 250 hp the locked rotor torques are normally

* See page 6-11.

70% of full load torque for 3600 rpm motors and 80% for 1800 rpm motors.

It is important to check the starting and accelerating torque requirements of the driven machine in order that a motor may be selected with adequate torque.

Manufacturers can build motors with special torque characteristics if required.

Motor speeds

The synchronous speed of AC motors is determined by the number of poles and frequency.

$$\text{Synchronous speed} = \frac{120 \times f}{p} \text{ where}$$

f = frequency in Hertz (Hz)-(cycles)
p = number of poles

Induction motors will have full-load speeds 2% to 5% below the synchronous speed.

D-C motors have full-load base speeds when hot of 500, 850, 1150, 1750, 2500 and 3500 rpm. In general the % slip decreases as motor horsepower increases.

See speed chart on page 6-16

6

Typical Efficiencies of Low Voltage (230/460) Three-Phase Motors

3600 and 1800 rpm

Horse-power	Induction motors			Synchronous motors—unity pf		
	Full load	¾ load	½ load	Full load	¾ load	½ load
1–2	76	75	71			
3–5	80	80	77			
10–25	85	85	82			
25–50	87	87	86	87	83	75
75–100	90.5	91	90.5	89.5	88.5	84
125–200	91.5	92	91	87	80	80.5
201–500	92–93.4	91.8–93.4	90–91.5	93–95.3	92.7–95	91–93.2
501–1500	93–94.8	93–94.8	91–93	95–96.2	95–95.9	93–95.2

Typical Motor Characteristics

Single-phase—60 Hertz

| Horse-power | Approx full load rpm | Amperes—230 volt | | NEMA code letter | Approx torque—lb-ft | | |
		Typical full load	NEMA locked rotor (max)		Full load	Locked rotor (min)	Breakdown full-load (min)
½	3530	3.5	25	N	0.75	2.3	2.0
	1730	4.0		L	1.52	5.3	3.6
	1140	5.5		K	2.30	6.3	5.2
¾	3520	4.8	35	L	1.12	3.1	2.8
	1735	5.5		K	2.27	7.4	5.2
	1135	7.3		L	3.47	8.0	6.9
1	3520	6.0	35	K	1.49	3.8	3.6
	1725	7.3			3.04	9.0	6.8
	1155	8.4			4.55	9.5	9.2
1½	3500	8.4	50	J	2.25	4.5	4.6
	1715	10.4			4.59	12.5	10.1
	1150	12.5			6.85	13.0	13.8
2	3495	10.8	65	J	3.00	5.5	6.0
	1745	12.0			6.02	16.0	13.0
	1155	15.2			9.09	16.0	18.0
3	3510	15.6	90	H	4.49	7.5	8.6
	1730	17.0			9.10	22	19.0
	1155	17.5			13.6	23	25.8
5	3500	22	135	G	7.5	11	13.5
	1740	23			15.0	33	30.0
	1145	22			22.9	33	40.5
7½	3500	31	200	G	11.2	16	20.0
	1750	30			22.5	45	45.0
10	3530	42	260	G	14.9	20	27.0
	1750	45			30.0	52.5	60.0

Three-phase—60 Hertz (NEMA design B)

| Horse-power | Approx full load rpm | Amperes—460 volt | | NEMA code letter | Approx torque—lb-ft | | |
		Typical full load	NEMA locked rotor (max)		Full load	Locked rotor (min)	Breakdown full-load (min)
1	3510	1.6	15	N	1.50	3.00	4.5
	1750	1.8			3.03	8.33	9.09
	1140	1.9			4.60	7.82	12.2
1½	3455	2.2	20	M	2.27	3.97	5.68
	1735	2.3			4.58	11.5	12.8
	1160	2.6			6.79	11.2	17.0
2	3495	2.8	25	L	3.00	5.1	7.2
	1725	3.1			6.09	14.3	16.4
	1155	3.3			9.09	14.5	21.8
3	3475	4.1	32	K	4.50	7.2	10.4
	1755	4.6			8.97	19.3	22.4
	1155	4.8			13.6	21.1	31.3

Typical Motor Characteristics (Continued)

		Amperes—460 volt			Approx torque lb-ft		
Horse-power	Approx full load speed	Typical full load	NEMA locked rotor max	NEMA code letter	Full load	(Starting) Locked rotor (min)	Breakdown full-load (min)
5	3500	6.7	46.0	J	7.5	11.3	16.1
	1745	7.1			15.0	27.5	33.8
	1155	8.1			22.7	34.1	48.8
7½	3510	10.3	63.5	H	11.1	15.5	22.2
	1740	10.4			22.6	39.6	48.6
	1165	11.2			33.7	50.6	69.1
10	3515	13.2	81.0	H	14.9	20.1	29.8
	1740	13.6			30.1	49.7	60.2
	1160	15.3			45.3	68.0	90.6
15	3505	20.1	116	G	22.4	29.1	44.8
	1750	21.1			45.0	72.0	90.0
	1170	21.3			67.1	93.9	134
20	3540	25.7	145	F	24.7	32.1	49.4
	1755	26.2		G	59.8	89.7	119.6
	1170	26.5		G	89.5	120.8	179.0
25	3540	31.3	182.5	F	37.1	48.2	74.2
	1760	31.6		G	74.4	111.6	148.8
	1175	33.9		F	111.8	150.9	223.6
30	3545	32.0	217.5	F	44.4	57.7	88.8
	1760	37.5		G	89.3	134.0	178.6
	1175	39.8		G	134.0	181.0	268
40	3550	47.8	290	G	59.2	80.0	118.4
	1770	54.4		F	118.5	166.0	237.0
	1175	52.5		G	179.5	242.0	359.0
50	3555	60.4	362	F	73.9	88.7	147.8
	1770	64.8		G	147.9	207	295.8
	1170	64.0		G	223.0	301	446.0
60	3555	72.5	435	G	88.6	106	177.2
	1775	75.5			177.0	248	354
	1175	80.0			267.0	347	534
75	3560	86.5	542	G	110.5	116	221
	1780	91.0			222.0	311	444
	1175	96.0			333.0	450	666
100	3550	113	725	G	147.0	154	294
	1775	119			296.0	370	592
	1180	122			444.0	555	888
125	3560	147	907	G	184	184	368
	1780	151			369	406	738
	1175	154			558	698	1116
150	3560	171	1085	G	221	221	442
	1775	172			444	488	888
	1175	188			668	802	1336
200	3560	230	1450	G	294	294	588
	1775	226			444	444	888
	1175	241			890	1063	1780
250	3560	284	1825	G	268	188	469
	1775	280			738	738	1476
	1180	296			1111	. . . .	. . . .
300	3560	335	2200	G	442	309	773
	1775	337			887	710	1552
350	3560	384	2550	G	516	361	903
	1760	406			1042	834	1823
400	3555	435	2900		591	414	
	1760	470			1189	951	

From General Electric and National Electrical Code.

Approx Full Load Current of Electric Motors

Three-phase—AC motors						Direct current motors				
Horse-power	Amperes					Horse-power	Amperes			
	115 V	230 V	460 V	575 V	2300 V		90 V	180 V	240 V	550 V
½	4.0	2.0				½	6.8	3.4	2.7	—
¾	5.6	2.8				¾	9.6	4.8	3.8	—
1	7.2	3.6	1.8	1.4		1	12.2	6.1	4.7	1.8
1½	10.4	5.2	2.6	2.1		1½		8.3	6.6	2.6
2	13.6	6.8	3.4	2.7		2		10.8	8.5	3.4
3		9.6	4.8	3.9		3		16	12.2	5.0
5		15.2	7.6	6.1		5		27	20	8.2
7½		22	11	9		7½		—	29	12
10		28	14	11		10		—	38	16
15		42	21	17		15			56	23
20		54	27	22		20			74	31
25		68	34	27		25			92	38
30		80	40	32		30			110	46
40		104	52	41		40			146	61
50		130	65	52		50			180	75
60		154	77	62	16	60			215	90
75			96	77	20	75			268	111
100			124	99	26	100			357	148
125			156	125	31	125			443	184
150			180	144	37	150				220
200			240	192	49	200				295

Single-phase—AC motors			Synchronous type AC motors unity power factor*				
Horse-power	Amperes		Horse-power	Amperes			
	115 V	230 V		220 V	440 V	550 V	2300 V
¼	5.8	2.9	25	54	27	22	
½	9.8	4.9	30	65	33	26	
¾	13.8	6.9	40	86	43	35	
1	16	8	50	108	54	44	—
1½	20	10	60	128	64	51	12
2	24	12	75	161	81	65	15
3	34	17	100	211	106	85	20
5	56	28	125	264	132	106	25
7½	80	40	150	—	158	127	30
10	100	50	200		210	168	40

From 1975 National Electrical Code—Tables 430–147, 148, 150. For motors running at normal speeds with normal torque characteristics. Motors built for low speed or high torque may require more current.
* For synchronous motors with 0.90 or 0.80 power factor multiply current shown by 1.1 and 1.25 respectively.

Motor Wiring

Not more than 3 conductors in raceway, cable or direct burial
Based on ambient temperature of 30C (86F)

Horse-power	Approx full-load current, amps		Minimum wire size, type THW or RHW AWG		Branch circuit protection average setting— amps		Horse-power
	×1.0	×1.25	Cu	Al	Fuse	Breaker	
115 volt—Single-phase Induction Motors							
½	9.8	12.3	14	12	30	15	½
¾	13.8	17.3	12	10	40	30	¾
1	16	20	12	10	45	30	1
1½	20	25	10	10	60	30	1½
2	24	30	10	8	80	30	2
3	34	42.5	8	6	110	50	3
5	56	70	4	3	150	100	5
7½	80	100	3	1	225	100	7½
10	100	125	1	2/0	300	150	10
230 volt—Single-phase Induction Motors							
½	4.9	6.1	14	12	15	15	½
¾	6.9	8.6	14	12	20	15	¾
1	8	10	14	12	20	15	1
1½	10	12.5	14	12	30	15	1½
2	12	15	14	12	35	15	2
3	17	21.3	10	10	50	30	3
5	28	35	8	8	80	50	5
7½	40	50	6	6	110	50	7½
10	50	62.5	6	4	150	100	10
230 volt—Three-phase Squirrel-Cage Induction Motors							
1	3.6	4.5	14	12	15	15	1
1½	5.2	6.5	14	12	15	15	1½
2	6.8	8.5	14	12	20	15	2
3	9.6	12	14	12	30	15	3
5	15.2	19	12	10	45	30	5
7½	22	27.5	10	8	60	30	7½
10	28	35	8	8	80	50	10
15	42	52.5	6	4	125	50	15
20	54	67.5	4	3	150	100	20
25	68	85	4	2	200	100	25
30	80	100	3	1	225	100	30
40	104	130	1	2/0	300	150	40
50	130	162.5	2/0	4/0	350	150	50
60	154	192.5	3/0	250 MCM	400	225	60

6

Table from General Electric, based on section 430-22 and Table 430-147 from National Electric Code.

Column entitled ×1.25 multiplies full load current by 1.25 to aid in selecting motor branch circuit conductors.

Wire size based on conductors having 75C insulation.

Motor Wiring (Continued)

Not more than 3 conductors in a conduit, cable or raceway
Based on ambient temperature of 30C (86F)

Horse-power	Approx full-load current, amps		Minimum wire size type THW or RHW AWG		Branch circuit protection average setting— amps		Horse-power
	×1.0	×1.25	Cu	Al	Fuse	Breaker	
460 volts—Three-phase Squirrel Cage Motors							
1	1.8	2.3	14	12	15	15	1
1½	2.6	3.3	14	12	15	15	1½
2	3.4	4.3	14	12	15	15	2
3	4.8	6	14	12	15	15	3
5	7.6	9.5	14	12	25	15	5
7½	11	13.8	14	12	35	15	7½
10	14	17.5	12	10	45	30	10
15	21	26.3	10	8	60	30	15
20	27	33.8	8	8	80	50	20
25	34	42.5	8	6	110	50	25
30	40	50	6	6	150	50	30
40	52	65	6	4	175	100	40
50	65	81.3	4	2	200	100	50
60	77	96.3	3	1	225	100	60
75	96	120	1		300		75
100	124	155	2/0		350		100
125	156	195	3/0		400		125
150	180	225	4/0				150
200	240	300	350				200

Table from General Electric, based on section 430-22 and Table 430-147 from National Electric Code.

Column entitled ×1.25 multiplies full load current by 1.25 to aid in selecting motor branch circuit conductors.

Wire size based on conductors having 75C insulation.

Motor Branch Circuit Protection Devices

Maximum rating or setting

Type of motor	Percent of full-load current			
	Non-time delay fuse	Dual element (time-delay) fuse	Instantaneous type breaker	Inverse time breaker
Single-phase, all types				
No code letter	300	175	700	250
All AC single-phase, and poly-phase squirrel cage and synchronous* motors with full-voltage, resistor reactor starting				
No code letter and codes F to V	300	175	700	250
Code letters B to E	250	175	700	200
Code letter A	150	150	700	150
All AC squirrel cage and synchronous* motors with auto transformer starting				
Not more than 30 amps—no code letter	250	175	700	200
Over 30 amps—no code letter	200	175	700	200
Over 30 amps—codes F to V	250	175	700	200
Over 30 amps—codes B to E	200	175	700	200
Over 30 amps—codes A	150	150	700	150
High-reactance squirrel cage motor				
Not more than 30 amps—no code	250	175	700	250
Over 30 amps—no code	200	175	700	200
Wound-rotor				
No code letter	150	150	700	150
Direct-current motors				
Not more than 50 hp—no code	150	150	250	150
Over 50 hp—no code	150	150	175	150

From National Electric Code—1975.
* Synchronous motors of the low-torque, low-speed type (usually 450 rpm or lower) which start unloaded do not require a fuse rating or circuit-breaker setting in excess of 200 percent of full-load current. Such motors are often used to drive reciprocating compressors, pumps, etc.

6

Wet and Canned Type Motors

Motors are available, or can be designed and built, of either the "canned" type or "wet" motor type when seal-less or wet motor gland-less type pump and motor assemblies may be required due to difficult stuffing box packing problems.

Toxic liquids at high pressures and temperatures may require a hermetically sealed "canned" type pump and motor assembly.

For water at high pressure and temperatures such as on boiler circulating service it may be desirable to use a "wet" motor glandless type pump and motor assembly.

In all cases where unusual or difficult pump problems may be involved the pump manufacturer should be consulted.

Properties of Conductors

Size AWG MCM	Area Cir mils	Concentric lay conductors		Bare conductors		DC resistance ohms/M ft at 25°C (77°F)		
		No. wires	Diam each wire inches	Diam inches	Area sq inches	Copper		Alumi-num
						Bare	Tin'd	
18	1620			.0403	.0013	6.51	6.79	10.7
16	2580			.0508	.0020	4.10	4.26	6.72
14	4110			.0641	.0032	2.57	2.68	4.22
12	6530			.0808	.0051	1.62	1.68	2.66
10	10380			.1019	.0081	1.018	1.06	1.67
8	16510			.1285	.0130	.6404	.659	1.05
6	26240	7	.0612	.184	.027	.410	.427	.674
4	41740	7	.0772	.232	.042	.259	.269	.424
3	52620	7	.0867	.260	.053	.205	.213	.336
2	66360	7	.0974	.292	.067	.162	.169	.266
1	83690	19	.0664	.332	.087	.129	.134	.211
0	105600	19	.0745	.372	.109	.102	.106	.168
00	133100	19	.0837	.418	.137	.0811	.0843	.133
000	167800	19	.0940	.470	.173	.0642	.0668	.105
0000	211600	19	.1055	.528	.219	.0509	.0525	.0836
250	250000	37	.0822	.575	.260	.0431	.0449	.0708
300	300000	37	.0900	.630	.312	.0360	.0374	.0590
350	350000	37	.0973	.681	.364	.0308	.0320	.0505
400	400000	37	.1040	.728	.416	.0270	.0278	.0442
500	500000	37	.1162	.813	.519	.0216	.0222	.0354
600	600000	61	.0992	.893	.626	.0180	.0187	.0295
700	700000	61	.1071	.964	.730	.0154	.0159	.0253
750	750000	61	.1109	.998	.782	.0144	.0148	.0236
800	800000	61	.1145	1.030	.833	.0135	.0139	.0221
900	900000	61	.1215	1.090	.933	.0120	.0123	.0197
1000	1000000	61	.1280	1.150	1.039	.0108	.0111	.0177
1250	1250000	91	.1172	1.289	1.305	.00863	.00888	.0142
1500	1500000	91	.1284	1.410	1.561	.00719	.00740	.0118
1750	1750000	127	.1174	1.526	1.829	.00616	.00634	.0101
2000	2000000	127	.1255	1.630	2.087	.00539	.00555	.00885

The resistance values given in the last three columns are applicable only to direct current. When conductors larger than No. 4/0 are used with alternating current the multiplying factors on page 6-13 should be used to compensate for skin effect.

Multiplying Factors for Converting Resistance to 60-Hertz AC Resistance

These apply to table on page 6-12

	Multiplying factor			
	For nonmetallic sheathed cables in air or nonmetallic conduit		For metallic sheathed cables or all cables in metallic raceways	
Size	Copper	Aluminum	Copper	Aluminum
Up to 3 AWG	1.	1.	1.	1.
2	1.	1.	1.01	1.00
1	1.	1.	1.01	1.00
0	1.001	1.000	1.02	1.00
00	1.001	1.001	1.03	1.00
000	1.002	1.001	1.04	1.01
0000	1.004	1.002	1.05	1.01
250 MCM	1.005	1.002	1.06	1.02
300 MCM	1.006	1.003	1.07	1.02
350 MCM	1.009	1.004	1.08	1.03
400 MCM	1.011	1.005	1.10	1.04
500 MCM	1.018	1.007	1.13	1.06
600 MCM	1.025	1.010	1.16	1.08
700 MCM	1.034	1.013	1.19	1.11
750 MCM	1.039	1.015	1.21	1.12
800 MCM	1.044	1.017	1.22	1.14
1000 MCM	1.067	1.026	1.30	1.19
1250 MCM	1.102	1.040	1.41	1.27
1500 MCM	1.142	1.058	1.53	1.36
1750 MCM	1.185	1.079	1.67	1.46
2000 MCM	1.233	1.100	1.82	1.56

6

Allowable Current-carrying Capacities (Amperes) of Insulated Copper Conductors

Not more than three conductors in raceway cable or direct burial (Based on ambient temprature of 30C (86F)

Size AWG or MCM	Temperature rating of conductor					
	60C 140F	75C 167F	85–90 C 185–194 F	110C 230F	125C 257F	200C 392F
	Types of insulation					
	RUW T TW UF	RH RHW RUH THW THWN XHHW USE	MI V AVB TA, SA TBS RHH THHN XHHW	AVA AVL	AI AIA	A AA
16	....	....	22	....	....	....
14	15	15	25†	30	30	30
12	20	20	30†	35	40	40
10	30	30	40†	45	50	55
8	40	45	50	60	65	70
6	55	65	70	80	85	95
4	70	85	90	105	115	120
3	80	100	105	120	130	145
2	95	115	120	135	145	165
1	110	130	140	160	170	190
1/0	125	150	155	190	200	225
2/0	145	175	185	215	230	250
3/0	165	200	210	245	265	285
4/0	195	230	235	275	310	340
250	215	255	270	315	335	....
300	240	285	300	345	380	....
350	260	310	325	390	420	....
400	280	335	360	420	450	....
500	320	380	405	470	500	....
600	355	420	455	525	545	....
700	385	460	490	560	600	....
750	400	475	500	580	620	....
800	410	490	515	600	640	....
900	435	520	555	....	....	....
1000	455	545	585	680	730	....
1250	495	590	645	....	....	....
1500	520	625	700	785	....	....
1750	545	650	735	....	....	....
2000	560	665	775	840	....	....

Correction factors for room temperatures over 30°C						
°C	°F					
40	104	0.82	0.88	0.80	0.94	0.95
45	113	0.71	0.82	0.85	0.90	0.92
50	122	0.58	0.75	0.80	0.87	0.89

Condensed from National Electrical Code—Tables 310-16 and 310-13.

General Effect of Voltage and Frequency Variation on Induction Motor Characteristics*

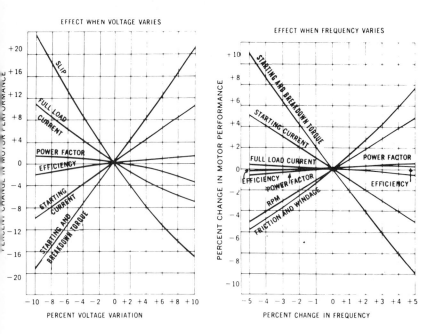

EFFECT WHEN VOLTAGE VARIES

EFFECT WHEN FREQUENCY VARIES

PERCENT VOLTAGE VARIATION

PERCENT CHANGE IN FREQUENCY

Allowable Variations from Rated Voltage and Frequency

6

Motors will operate successfully under the following conditions of voltage and frequency variations, but not necessarily in accordance with the standards established for operation at normal rating.

Where the variation in voltage does not exceed 10 percent above or below normal (6 percent for small power universal motors).

Where the frequency variation does not exceed 5 percent above or below normal.

Where the sum of the voltage and frequency variation does not exceed 10 percent (provided the variation in frequency does not exceed 5 percent) above or below normal ratings as stamped on motor nameplate.

The charts show the approximate effects of variations in voltage and frequency on motor characteristics. These values should in no way be considered as guarantees.

* The reference point for voltage variation and frequency variation of the power supply is understood to be the rated voltage and frequency as given on the motor nameplate. This data shows general effects which will vary somewhat for specific ratings.

Motor Speeds

A-C Motors. The synchronous speed of a-c motors is determined by the number of poles and frequency.

$$\text{Synchronous speed} = \frac{120 \times f}{p}$$

where f = frequency in Hertz (Hz) (cycles)
p = number of poles of the motor

Full-Load Speeds of Synchronous Motors

No. of poles	Full-Load Speeds of Synchronous Motors						
	Hertz (Hz)						
	25	30	40	45	50	60	100
2	1500	1800	2400	2700	3000	3600	....
4	750	900	1200	1350	1500	1800	3000
6	500	600	800	900	1000	1200	2000
8	375	450	600	675	750	900	1500
10	300	360	480	540	600	720	1200
12	250	300	400	450	500	600	1000
14	214.3	257	343	386	428.6	514.2	853.2
16	187.5	225	300	337.5	375	450	750
18	166.6	200	266.6	300	333.3	400	666.4
20	150	180	240	270	300	360	600

Induction motors will have full-load speeds of from 2 to 6% less than the above, average 4% less.

D-C Motors will have standard full-load speeds, when hot, of: 575, 850, 1150, 1750, and 3500 rev per min (rpm)

At normal temperature, rated load and voltage the variation above or below the above full-load motor speeds may not exceed 7½% in motors up to 7½ hp at 1150 rpm, and 5% in motors larger than 7½ hp at 1150 rpm.

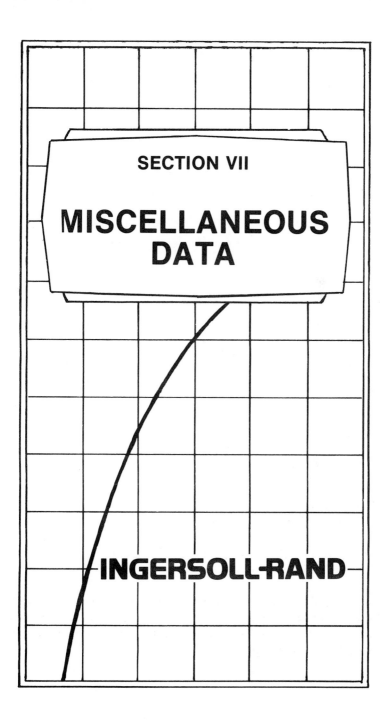

SECTION VII

MISCELLANEOUS DATA

INGERSOLL-RAND

CONTENTS OF SECTION 7

Miscellaneous Data

Page

Decimal and Millimeter Equivalents

Fraction			Decimal equivalent	Millimeter equivalent of fractional inches	Fraction			Decimal equivalent	Millimeter equivalent of fractional inches
		1/64	0.015625	0.397			33/64	0.515625	13.097
	1/32		0.03125	0.794		17/32		0.53125	13.494
		3/64	0.046875	1.191			35/64	0.546875	13.891
1/16			0.0625	1.588	9/16			0.5625	14.288
		5/64	0.078125	1.984			37/64	0.578125	14.684
	3/32		0.09375	2.381		19/32		0.59375	15.081
		7/64	0.109375	2.778			39/64	0.609375	15.478
1/8			0.125	3.175	5/8			0.625	15.875
		9/64	0.140625	3.572			41/64	0.640625	16.272
	5/32		0.15625	3.969		21/32		0.65625	16.669
		11/64	0.171875	4.366			43/64	0.671875	17.066
3/16			0.1875	4.763	11/16			0.6875	17.463
		13/64	0.203125	5.159			45/64	0.703125	17.859
	7/32		0.21875	5.556		23/32		0.71875	18.256
		15/64	0.234375	5.953			47/64	0.734375	18.653
1/4			0.250	6.350	3/4			0.750	19.050
		17/64	0.265625	6.747			49/64	0.765625	19.447
	9/32		0.28125	7.144		25/32		0.78125	19.844
		19/64	0.296875	7.541			51/64	0.796875	20.241
5/16			0.3125	7.938	13/16			0.8125	20.638
		21/64	0.328125	8.334			53/64	0.828125	21.034
	11/32		0.34375	8.731		27/32		0.84375	21.431
		23/64	0.359375	9.128			55/64	0.859375	21.828
3/8			0.375	9.525	7/8			0.875	22.225
		25/64	0.390625	9.922			57/64	0.890625	22.622
	13/32		0.40625	10.319		29/32		0.90625	23.019
		27/64	0.421875	10.716			59.64	0.921875	23.416
7/16			0.4375	11.113	15/16			0.9375	23.813
		29/64	0.453125	11.509			61/64	0.953125	24.209
	15/32		0.46875	11.906		31/32		0.96875	24.606
		31/64	0.484375	12.303			63/64	0.984375	25.003
1/2			0.500	12.700	1			1.000	25.400

Arithmetical and Geometrical Formulas:

Circumference of Circle = 3.1416 x dia = 6.2832 x radius

Area of Circle = .7854 x $(dia)^2$ = 3.1416 x $(radius)^2$

Area of Sphere = 3.1416 x $(dia)^2$

Volume of Sphere = 0.5236 x $(dia)^3$

Area of triangle = 0.5 x base x height

Area of a trapezoid = 0.5 x sum of the two parallel sides x height

Area of a square, a rectangle or parallelogram = base x height

Volume of a pyramid = area of base x 1.3 height

Volume of a cone = 0.2618 x (dia of base)^2 x height

Volume of a cylinder = 0.7854 x height x dia^2

7

Approximate Atmospheric Pressures and Barometer
Readings at Different Altitudes

Altitude		Barometer		Atmospheric pressure lb/in²	Equivalent head of water (75°F) Feet	Boiling point of water	
Feet	Meters	Inches of mercury	Mm of mercury			°F	°C
−1000	−304.8	31.02	787.9	15.2	35.2	213.8	101.0
−500	−152.4	30.47	773.9	15.0	34.7	212.9	100.5
0	0	29.921	760.0	14.7	34.0	212.0	100.0
500	152.4	29.38	746.3	14.4	33.4	211.1	99.5
1000	304.8	28.86	733.1	14.2	32.8	210.2	99.0
1500	457.2	28.33	719.6	13.9	32.2	209.3	98.5
2000	609.6	27.82	706.6	13.7	31.6	208.4	98.0
2500	762.0	27.31	693.7	13.4	31.0	207.4	97.4
3000	914.4	26.81	681.0	13.2	30.5	206.5	96.9
3500	1066.8	26.32	668.5	12.9	29.9	205.6	96.4
4000	1219.2	25.84	656.3	12.7	29.4	204.7	95.9
4500	1371.6	25.36	644.1	12.4	28.8	203.8	95.4
5000	1524.0	24.89	632.2	12.2	28.3	202.9	94.9
5500	1676.4	24.43	620.5	12.0	27.8	201.9	94.4
6000	1828.8	23.98	609.1	11.8	27.3	201.0	93.9
6500	1981.2	23.53	597.7	11.5	26.7	200.1	93.4
7000	2133.6	23.09	586.5	11.3	26.2	199.2	92.9
7500	2286.0	22.65	575.3	11.1	25.7	198.3	92.4
8000	2438.4	22.22	564.4	10.9	25.2	197.4	91.9
8500	2590.8	21.80	553.7	10.7	24.8	196.5	91.4
9000	2743.2	21.38	543.1	10.5	24.3	195.5	90.8
9500	2895.6	20.98	532.9	10.3	23.8	194.6	90.3
10000	3048.0	20.58	522.7	10.1	23.4	193.7	89.8
15000	4572.0	16.88	428.8	8.3	19.1	184	84.4
20000	6096	13.75	349.3	6.7	15.2	—	
30000	9144	8.88	225.6	4.4	10.2	—	
40000	12192	5.54	140.7	2.7	6.3	—	
50000	15240	3.44	87.4	1.7	3.9	—	

Barometer Corrections

Miscellaneous

Other barometer corrections include those for latitude, altitude and difference in elevation between barometer and datum plane. These are given on the following page.

Table I, III, IV and V apply to mercurial barometers.

Table V applies to aneroid barometers.

Table II applies to small-bore, single-tube mercury columns. U-tubes and manometers, in which both legs have approximately the same bore, and large-bore, single-tube columns do not require capillarity correction. The temperature correction from Table I applies to any mercury column when brass scales calibrated in inches at 62°F and a density factor for mercury based on 32°F are used.

Tables III and IV apply to all mercury columns in which a density factor based on 45° latitude and sea level altitude is used. The corrections are small and are usually ignored or taken into account by using a density factor based on the latitude and altitude of the datum point.

In general, aneroid barometers are not satisfactory for accurate testing. If one is used, it should be compensated for temperature and frequently calibrated against a standard mercurial barometer, as a violent knock or shaking may introduce a substantial error.

Example of use of Tables III, IV and V.

Assume a barometer reading of 20.013″ Hg at 70°F. 1000 ft altitude, 45° latitude and 30 ft above the datum plane for which a reading is desired.

Barometer reading . . . . 29.013″
Latitude correction (Table III) . . . . −.048″
Altitude correction (Table IV) . . . . −.002″
Elevation correction (Table V) (.3 × .102) . . . . +.031″
Temperature correction (Table I) . . . . −.019″
Corrected barometer (to 32°F, 970 ft altitude,
    and 45° latitude) . . . . 28.885″

Correction for Relative Expansion of Mercury and Brass Scale to 32°F Standard

Table I

Temp hg col °F	Observed reading of the barometer, in inches												
	25	25.5	26	26.5	27	27.5	28	28.5	29	29.5	30	30.5	31.0
	Correction to be subtracted from observed reading												
40	.026	.026	.027	.027	.028	.028	.029	.029	.030	.030	.031	.031	.032
42	.030	.031	.032	.032	.033	.033	.034	.035	.035	.036	.036	.037	.038
44	.035	.036	.036	.037	.038	.038	.039	.040	.040	.041	.041	.042	.043
46	.039	.040	.041	.042	.043	.043	.044	.045	.046	.046	.047	.048	.049
48	.044	.045	.046	.047	.047	.048	.049	.050	.051	.052	.053	.054	.054
50	.048	.049	.050	.051	.052	.053	.054	.055	.056	.057	.058	.059	.060
52	.053	.054	.055	.056	.057	.058	.059	.060	.061	.062	.064	.065	.066
54	.057	.059	.060	.061	.062	.063	.064	.066	.067	.068	.069	.070	.071
56	.062	.063	.064	.066	.067	.068	.069	.071	.072	.073	.074	.076	.077
58	.066	.068	.069	.070	.072	.073	.074	.076	.077	.078	.080	.081	.082
60	.071	.072	.074	.075	.077	.078	.080	.081	.082	.084	.085	.087	.088
62	.076	.077	.079	.080	.082	.083	.085	.086	.088	.089	.091	.092	.094
64	.080	.082	.083	.085	.086	.088	.090	.091	.093	.094	.096	.098	.099
66	.085	.086	.088	.090	.091	.093	.095	.096	.098	.100	.101	.103	.105
68	.089	.091	.093	.094	.096	.098	.100	.102	.103	.105	.107	.109	.110
70	.094	.095	.097	.099	.101	.103	.105	.107	.109	.110	.112	.114	.116
71	.096	.098	.100	.102	.103	.105	.107	.109	.111	.113	.115	.117	.119
72	.098	.100	.102	.104	.106	.108	.110	.112	.114	.116	.118	.120	.122
73	.100	.102	.104	.106	.108	.110	.112	.115	.116	.118	.120	.122	.124
74	.103	.105	.107	.109	.111	.113	.115	.117	.119	.121	.123	.125	.127
75	.105	.107	.109	.111	.113	.115	.117	.119	.122	.124	.126	.128	.130
76	.107	.109	.111	.113	.116	.118	.120	.122	.124	.126	.128	.131	.133
77	.109	.112	.114	.116	.118	.120	.122	.125	.127	.129	.131	.133	.136
78	.112	.114	.116	.118	.120	.123	.125	.127	.129	.132	.134	.136	.138
79	.114	.116	.118	.121	.123	.125	.127	.130	.132	.134	.137	.139	.141
80	.116	.118	.121	.123	.125	.128	.130	.132	.135	.137	.139	.142	.144
81	.118	.121	.123	.125	.128	.130	.132	.135	.137	.140	.142	.144	.147
82	.121	.123	.125	.128	.130	.133	.135	.137	.140	.142	.145	.147	.149
83	.123	.125	.128	.130	.133	.135	.138	.140	.142	.145	.147	.150	.152
84	.125	.128	.130	.133	.135	.138	.140	.143	.145	.148	.150	.153	.155
85	.127	.130	.132	.135	.137	.140	.143	.145	.148	.150	.153	.155	.158
86	.130	.132	.135	.137	.140	.142	.145	.148	.150	.153	.155	.158	.161
87	.132	.134	.137	.140	.142	.145	.148	.150	.153	.155	.158	.161	.163
88	.134	.137	.139	.142	.145	.147	.150	.153	.155	.158	.161	.163	.166
89	.136	.139	.142	.144	.147	.150	.153	.155	.158	.161	.164	.166	.169
90	.138	.141	.144	.147	.150	.152	.155	.158	.161	.163	.166	.169	.172
92	.143	.146	.149	.152	.154	.157	.160	.163	.166	.169	.172	.174	.177
94	.147	.150	.153	.156	.159	.162	.165	.168	.171	.174	.177	.180	.183
96	.152	.155	.158	.161	.164	.167	.170	.173	.176	.179	.182	.185	.188
98	.156	.160	.163	.166	.169	.172	.175	.178	.181	.185	.188	.191	.194
100	.161	.164	.167	.171	.174	.177	.180	.183	.187	.190	.193	.196	.200

Condensed from circular F, U.S. Weather Bureau.

Correction of Small Bore Single-tube Mercury Columns for Capillarity

Table II

I D tube inches	Height of meniscus—inches							
	.01	.02	.03	.04	.05	.06	.07	.08
	Correction to be added to hg column reading—inches							
.15	.024	.047	.069	.092	.116			
.20	.011	.022	.033	.045	.059	.078		
.25	.006	.012	.019	.028	.037	.047	.059	
.30	.004	.008	.013	.018	.023	.029	.035	.042
.40		.004	.006	.008	.010	.012	.014	.016
.50			.002	.004	.005	.006	.006	.007

(From Smithsonian Physical Tables—1933)

Explanation of Correction Tables for Mercurial Barometers

Table I—Examples of use

Reading of barometer at 75°F .... 29.964″

Temperature correction (Table I) .... −.126″

Barometer corrected to 32°F .... 29.838″

Reading of Mercury column at 97°F .... 28.120″

Temperature correction (Table I) .... −.173″

Vacuum corrected to 32°F.............................. 27.947″

Absolute pressure (29.838 − 27.947) .... 1.891″

Table II—Example of Use

Suppose above mercury column had a single tube of 5/32″ bore and the estimated height of meniscus was .05″

Correction for capillarity (Table II) .... +.102″

Vacuum corrected for capillarity (27.947 + .102) .... 28.049″

Absolute pressure (29.838 − 28.049) .... 1.789″

NOTE:—Always read the top of the meniscus and add the capillarity correction to this vacuum column reading. There is no correction on double tube mercury columns or manometers.

Correction of Mercurial Barometer for Latitude in Inches Hg to Reduce to 45° Latitude

To be added to barometer reading for latitudes above 45°. To be subtracted from barometer reading for latitudes below 45°

Table III

Latitude		Reading of the barometer, in inches												
		18	19	20	21	22	23	24	25	26	27	28	29	30
°	°													
0	90	0.047	0.049	0.052	0.054	0.057	0.060	0.062	0.065	0.067	0.070	0.073	0.075	0.078
5	85	.046	.048	.051	.054	.056	.059	.061	.064	.066	.069	.071	.074	.077
6	84	.046	.048	.051	.053	.056	.058	.061	.063	.066	.068	.071	.073	.076
7	83	.045	.048	.050	.053	.055	.058	.060	.063	.065	.068	.070	.073	.075
8	82	.045	.047	.050	.052	.055	.057	.060	.062	.065	.067	.070	.072	.075
9	81	.044	.047	.049	.052	.054	.057	.059	.062	.064	.067	.069	.071	.074
10	80	.044	.046	.049	.051	.054	.056	.058	.061	.063	.066	.068	.071	.073
11	79	.043	.046	.048	.050	.053	.055	.058	.060	.062	.065	.067	.070	.072
12	78	.043	.045	.047	.050	.052	.054	.057	.059	.062	.064	.066	.069	.071
13	77	.042	.044	.047	.049	.051	.054	.056	.058	.061	.063	.065	.068	.070
14	76	.041	.043	.046	.048	.050	.053	.055	.057	.059	.062	.064	.066	.069
15	75	.040	.043	.045	.047	.049	.052	.054	.056	.058	.061	.063	.065	.067
16	74	.040	.042	.044	.046	.048	.051	.053	.055	.057	.059	.061	.064	.066
17	73	.039	.041	.043	.045	.047	.049	.052	.054	.056	.058	.060	.062	.064
18	72	.038	.040	.042	.044	.046	.048	.050	.052	.054	.057	.059	.061	.063
19	71	.037	.039	.041	.043	.045	.047	.049	.051	.053	.055	.057	.059	.061
20	70	.036	.038	.040	.042	.044	.046	.048	.050	.052	.054	.056	.058	.060
21	69	.035	.037	.038	.040	.042	.044	.046	.048	.050	.052	.054	.056	.058
22	68	.034	.035	.037	.039	.041	.043	.045	.047	.048	.050	.052	.054	.056
23	67	.032	.034	.036	.038	.040	.041	.043	.045	.047	.049	.050	.052	.054
24	66	.031	.033	.035	.036	.038	.040	.042	.043	.045	.047	.049	.050	.052
25	65	.030	.032	.033	.035	.037	.038	.040	.042	.043	.045	.047	.048	.050
26	64	.029	.030	.032	.033	.035	.037	.038	.040	.041	.043	.045	.046	.048
27	63	.027	.029	.030	.032	.033	.035	.037	.038	.040	.041	.043	.044	.046
28	62	.026	.028	.029	.030	.032	.033	.035	.036	.038	.039	.041	.042	.043
29	61	.025	.026	.027	.029	.030	.032	.033	.034	.036	.037	.038	.040	.041
30	60	.023	.025	.026	.027	.028	.030	.031	.032	.034	.035	.036	.038	.039
31	59	.022	.023	.024	.026	.027	.028	.029	.030	.032	.033	.034	.035	.036
32	58	.020	.022	.023	.024	.025	.026	.027	.028	.030	.031	.032	.033	.034
33	57	.019	.020	.021	.022	.023	.024	.025	.026	.027	.028	.029	.031	.032
34	56	.017	.018	.019	.020	.021	.022	.023	.024	.025	.026	.027	.028	.029
35	55	.016	.017	.018	.019	.019	.020	.021	.022	.023	.024	.025	.026	.027
36	54	.014	.015	.016	.017	.018	.018	.019	.020	.021	.022	.022	.023	.024
37	53	.013	.014	.014	.015	.016	.016	.017	.018	.019	.019	.020	.021	.021
38	52	.011	.012	.013	.013	.014	.014	.015	.016	.016	.017	.018	.018	.019
39	51	.010	.010	.011	.011	.012	.012	.013	.013	.014	.015	.015	.016	.016
40	50	.008	.009	.009	.009	.010	.010	.011	.011	.012	.012	.013	.013	.013
41	49	.006	.007	.07	.008	.008	.008	.009	.009	.009	.010	.010	.010	.011
42	48	.005	.005	.005	.006	.006	.006	.006	.007	.007	.007	.008	.008	.008
43	47	.003	.003	.004	.004	.004	.004	.004	.005	.005	.005	.005	.005	.005
44	46	.002	.002	.002	.002	.002	.002	.002	.002	.002	.002	.003	.003	.003
45	45	.000	.000	.000	.000	.000	.000	.000	.000	.000	.000	.000	.000	.000

Correction of Mercurial Barometer for Altitude

Inches Hg to be subtracted from barometer reading

Table IV

Altitude ft	Reading of barometer, inches						
	25	26	27	28	29	30	31
0	....	....	.000	.000	.000	.000	.000
500	....	....	.001	.001	.001	.001	.001
1000	....	....	.002	.002	.002	.002	.002
1500	....	.002	.002	.003	.003	.003	
2000	....	.003	.003	.003	.003	.004	
2500	.004	.004	.004	.004	.004		
3000	.004	.005	.005	.005	.005		
3500	.005	.005	.006	.006			
4000	.006	.006	.006	.007			
4500	.007	.007	.007				
5000	.007	.008	.008				
5500	.008	.009					
6000	.009	.009					
6500	.010						
7000	.010						

Elevation Correction for Barometer

In inches Hg per 100 ft difference in elevation. To be added to barometer reading when barometer is above datum plane. To be subtracted from barometer reading when barometer is below datum plane.

Table V

Altitude ft	Temperature, °F									
	0	10	20	30	40	50	60	70	80	90
0	.122	.119	.117	.114	.112	.110	.108	.106	.104	.102
1000	.118	.115	.113	.110	.108	.106	.104	.102	.100	.098
2000	.113	.110	.108	.106	.104	.102	.100	.098	.096	.094
3000	.108	.106	.104	.102	.100	.098	.096	.094	.092	.090
4000	.104	.102	.100	.098	.096	.094	.092	.090	.088	.086
5000	.100	.098	.096	.094	.092	.090	.088	.086	.084	.082
6000	.096	.094	.092	.090	.088	.086	.084	.082	.081	.080
7000	.093	.091	.089	.087	.085	.084	.082	.080	.079	.078

7

Approx. Weights—Cast Iron Flanged Pipe

Approx Weights of Cast Iron Flanged Pipe

Nominal size inches	Class A 43 lb per sq in press Thickness inches	Wt lb per foot	single flange	Class B 86 lb per sq in press Thickness inches	Wt lb per foot	single flange	Class C 130 lb per sq in press Thickness inches	Wt lb per foot	single flange	Class D 173 lb per sq in press Thickness inches	Wt lb per foot	single flange	Class F 260 lb per sq in press Thickness inches	Wt lb per foot	single flange	Class H 347 lb per sq in press Thickness inches	Wt lb per foot	single flange
3	.39	13.0	6.4	.42	14.6	6.2	.45	15.5	6.2	.48	16.4	6.2						
4	.42	18.0	11.1	.45	20.1	10.7	.48	21.3	10.7	.52	22.8	10.7						
6	.44	27.9	15.0	.48	31.1	14.4	.51	32.9	14.4	.55	35.3	14.4	.61	39.5	30.6	.69	45.2	29.9
8	.46	38.7	23.1	.51	42.7	23.1	.56	48.0	22.0	.60	51.2	22.0	.71	60.6	45.3	.80	69.0	44.1
10	.50	51.9	32.2	.57	58.8	32.2	.62	65.5	30.6	.68	71.4	30.6	.80	84.7	65.7	.92	98.5	63.6
12	.54	67.0	47.7	.62	76.4	47.7	.68	85.4	45.6	.75	93.7	45.6	.89	112.5	94.1	1.04	132.9	90.7
14	.57	82.3	58.1	.66	94.7	58.1	.74	108.1	55.1	.82	119.2	55.1	.99	145.5	118.8	1.16	172.4	114.0
16	.60	98.8	73.2	.70	114.6	73.2	.80	113.3	69.1	.89	147.5	69.1	1.08	180.8	147.3	1.27	215.0	140.8
18	.64	118.3	78.1	.75	137.8	78.1	.87	162.4	72.8	.96	178.4	72.8	1.17	219.8	179.6	1.39	264.2	170.8
20	.67	137.4	98.8	.80	163.1	99.8	.92	190.6	92.9	1.03	212.3	92.9	1.27	264.8	215.5	1.51	318.4	204.4
24	.76	186.5	137.2	.89	217.3	137.2	1.04	257.6	126.8	1.16	286.0	126.8	1.45	361.7	321.4			
30	.88	266.1	214.4	1.03	312.6	207.2	1.26	366.9	196.0	1.37	421.2	186.4	1.73	538.0	446.9			
36	.99	358.7	327.4	1.15	418.7	314.8	1.36	497.7	299.9	1.58	581.9	282.5						
42	1.10	464.6	458.5	1.28	542.2	444.2	1.54	657.4	415.4	1.78	764.1	392.1						
48	1.26	608.0	555.9	1.42	687.2	538.9	1.71	832.7	504.4	1.96	960.8	470.8						

Approximate Weights 125 lb Standard
Cast Iron Flanged Fittings

All weights given in pounds

Nominal pipe size	45° ells	90° ells	90° L R ells	Tees	Crosses	Laterals	Red ells	Re-ducers	Com-panion flanges	Std gate valves
1	4	5	7	9	11	10			2	19
1¼	6	7	9	11	15	13			2	23
1½	8	9	11	15	19	17			3	27
2	12	14	16	21	28	25			5	31
2½	17	19	23	30	39	36			7	40
3	20	24	28	37	48	44	22	19	8	54
3½	27	31	37	49	63	59	28	24	11	67
4	36	41	48	64	82	75	37	31	14	84
5	45	52	62	81	105	96	48	39	17	110
6	60	68	85	105	135	125	60	50	22	140
8	94	110	145	165	210	210	90	77	31	240
10	145	175	230	270	330	340	150	120	45	380
12	220	250	350	380	470	520	220	180	63	590
14	270	350	470	530	650	680	320	250	82	770
16	360	470	670	700	850	950	420	340	105	1100
18	420	580	840	860	1040	1150	540	430	120	1300
20	540	740	1080	1100	1330	1480	680	520	150	1900
24	800	1160	1640	1730	2080	2080	1010	760	220	2800
30	1430	1850	2800	2710	3210	3680				4950
36	2280	2800	4450	4050	4750					8700
42	3380	4010	6610	5790	6710					
48	4680	5400	9250	7620	8740					

7

Dimensions of Cast Iron Pipe Flanges

American National Standard
dimensions in inches

Nominal pipe sizes	Dia of flange	Dia of bolt circle	No of bolts	25 lb standard			125 lb standard		
				Flange thickness	Bolt size	Bolt length	Flange thickness	Bolt size	Bolt length
1	4.25	3.12	4				0.44	0.50	1.75
1¼	4.62	3.50	4				0.50	0.50	2.00
1½	5.00	3.88	4				0.56	0.50	2.00
2	6.00	4.75	4				0.62	0.62	2.25
2½	7.00	5.50	4				0.69	0.62	2.50
3	7.50	6.00	4				0.75	0.62	2.50
3½	8.50	7.00	8				0.81	0.62	2.75
4	9.00	7.50	8	0.75	0.62	2.50	0.94	0.62	3.00
5	10.00	8.50	8	0.75	0.62	2.50	0.94	0.75	3.00
6	11.00	9.50	8	0.75	0.62	2.50	1.00	0.75	3.25
8	13.50	11.75	8	0.75	0.62	2.50	1.12	0.75	3.50
10	16.00	14.25	12	0.88	0.62	2.75	1.19	0.88	3.75
12	19.00	17.00	12	1.00	0.62	3.00	1.25	0.88	3.75
14	21.00	18.75	12	1.12	0.75	3.50	1.38	1.00	4.25
16	23.50	21.25	16	1.12	0.75	3.50	1.44	1.00	4.50
18	25.00	22.75	16	1.25	0.75	3.75	1.56	1.12	4.75
20	27.50	25.00	20	1.25	0.75	3.75	1.69	1.12	5.00
24	32.00	29.50	20	1.38	0.75	4.00	1.88	1.25	5.50
30	38.75	36.00	28	1.50	0.88	4.50	2.12	1.25	6.25
36	46.00	42.75	32	1.62	0.88	4.75	2.38	1.50	7.00
42	53.00	49.50	36	1.75	1.00	5.25	2.62	1.50	7.50
48	59.50	56.00	44	2.00	1.00	5.75	2.75	1.50	7.75
54	66.25	62.75	44	2.25	1.00	6.25	3.00	1.75	8.50
60	73.00	69.25	52	2.25	1.12	6.25	3.12	1.75	8.75
72	86.50	82.50	60	2.50	1.12	6.75	3.50	1.75	9.50
84	99.75	95.50	64	2.75	1.25	7.50	3.88	2.00	10.50
96	113.25	108.50	68	3.00	1.25	8.00	4.25	2.25	11.50

25 lb flanges have 45 psi non-shock pressure rating in 4 to 36" sizes and 25 lb in 42–96" sizes up to 150°F.
125 lb flanges (Class B) have non-shock working pressure rating of 200 psi in 1 to 12" sizes, 150 psi in 14 to 48" sizes up to 150°F.
From American National Standard—ANSI B 16.1—1975.

Dimensions of Cast Iron Pipe Flanges (Continued)

American National Standard
dimensions in inches

Nominal pipe size	250 lb standard					800 lb standard				
	Flange		Bolt circle dia	Bolts		Flange		Bolt circle dia	Bolts	
	dia	thick-ness		no	size	dia	thick-ness		no	size
1	4.88	0.69	3.50	4	0.62					
1¼	5.25	0.75	3.88	4	0.62					
1½	6.12	0.81	4.50	4	0.75					
2	6.50	0.88	5.00	8	0.62	6.50	1.50	5.00	8	0.62
2½	7.50	1.00	5.88	8	0.75	7.50	1.62	5.88	8	0.75
3	8.25	1.12	6.62	8	0.75	8.25	1.75	6.62	8	0.75
3½	9.00	1.19	7.25	8	0.75	9.00	1.88	7.25	8	0.88
4	10.00	1.25	7.88	8	0.75	10.75	2.12	8.50	8	0.88
5	11.00	1.38	9.25	8	0.75	13.00	2.38	10.50	8	1.00
6	12.50	1.44	10.62	12	0.75	14.00	2.50	11.50	12	1.00
8	15.00	1.62	13.00	12	0.88	16.50	2.75	13.75	12	1.12
10	17.50	1.88	15.25	16	1.00	20.00	3.12	17.00	16	1.25
12	20.50	2.00	17.75	16	1.12	22.00	3.25	19.25	20	1.25
14	23.00	2.12	20.25	20	1.12					
16	25.50	2.25	22.50	20	1.25					
18	28.00	2.38	24.75	24	1.25					
20	30.50	2.50	27.00	24	1.25					
24	36.00	2.75	32.00	24	1.50					
30	43.00	3.00	39.25	28	1.75					
36	50.00	3.38	46.00	32	2.00					
42	57.00	3.69	52.75	36	2.00					
48	65.00	4.00	60.75	40	2.00					

250 lb flanges (Class B) have non-shock pressure rating of 500 psi in 1 to 12" sizes, 300 psi in 14 to 48" sizes up to 150°F.
800 lb flanges have non-shock hydraulic pressure rating (not steam) of 800 psi up to 150°F.
American National Standard—ANSI B 16.1—1975.

Pressure—Temperature Ratings

Temperature of	25 lb		125 lb			250 lb			800 lb
	ASTM A126 Class A		ASTM A126			ASTM A126			ASTM A126 Class B
			Class A	Class B		Class A	Class B		
	Sizes 4–36	Sizes 42–96	Sizes 1–12	Sizes 14–24	Sizes 30–48	Sizes 1–12	Sizes 14–24	Sizes 30–48	Sizes 2–12
−20 to 150	45	25	175	150	150	400	300	300	800
200	40	25	165	135	115	370	280	250	
225	35	25	155	130	100	355	270	225	
250	30	25	150	125	85	340	260	200	
275	25	25	145	120	65	325	250	175	
300			140	110	50	310	240	150	
325			130	105		295	230	125	
350[1]			125	100		280	220	100	
375						265	210		
400[2]						250	200		

All pressure ratings given in PSIG. Allowable pressures may be interpolated between temperatures.
[1] 353 F (Max) to reflect the temperature of saturated steam at 125 psig.
[2] 406 F (Max) to reflect the temperature of saturated steam at 250 psig.

Limitations:
25 lb: When 25 lb cast iron flanges and flanged fittings are used for gaseous service, the maximum pressure shall be limited to 25 psig. Tabulated pressure-temperature ratings above 25 psig for 25 lb cast iron flanges and flanged fittings are applicable for non-shock hydraulic service only.
250 lb: When used for liquid service the tabulated pressure-temperature ratings in sizes 14 in. and larger are applicable to 250 lb flanges only and not to 250 lb fittings.
800 lb: The tabulated rating is *not a steam rating* and applies to non-shock hydraulic pressure only.
From ANSI B 16.1.

7

Dimensions of Cast Iron Flanged Fittings

**25 lb and 125 lb American National Standard
dimensions in inches**

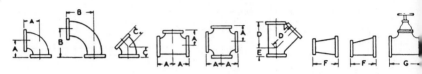

Nominal size*	A Elbows, tees, crosses	B Long radius elbows	C 45° elbows c to f	D* 45° Laterals† c to f	E* 45° Laterals† short c to f	F Reducers f to f	G‡ Gate valve f to f
1	3.50	5.00	1.75	5.75	1.75		
1¼	3.75	5.50	2.00	6.25	1.75		
1½	4.00	6.00	2.25	7.00	2.00		
2	4.50	6.50	2.50	8.00	2.50	5.0	7.0
2½	5.00	7.00	3.00	9.50	2.50	5.5	7.5
3	5.50	7.75	3.00	10.00	3.00	6.0	8.0
3½	6.00	8.50	3.50	11.50	3.00	6.5	8.5
4	6.50	9.00	4.00	12.00	3.00	7.0	9.0
5	7.50	10.25	4.50	13.50	3.50	8.0	10.0
6	8.00	11.50	5.00	14.50	3.50	9.0	10.5
8	9.00	14.00	5.50	17.50	4.50	11.0	11.5
10	11.00	16.50	6.50	20.50	5.00	12.0	13.0
12	12.00	19.00	7.50	24.50	5.50	14.0	14.0
14	14.00	21.50	7.50	27.00	6.00	16.0	11.5
16	15.00	24.00	8.00	30.00	6.50	18.0	12.0
18	16.50	26.50	8.50	32.00	7.00	19.0	12.5
20	18.00	29.00	9.50	35.00	8.00	20.0	13.0
24	22.00	34.00	11.00	40.50	9.00	24.0	13.5
30	25.00	41.50	15.00	49.00	10.00	30.0	15.0
36	28.00	49.00	18.00			36.0	16.0
42	31.00	56.50	21.00			42.0	17.5
48	34.00	64.00	24.00			48.0	19.5
54	39.0	71.50	27.0				21.0
60	44.0	79.00	30.0				25.0
72	53.0	94.00	36.0				28.5

* No 25 lb fittings 1″ to 3½″.—54, 60 and 72″ fittings are 25 lb only.
  † No lateral fittings are listed in 25 lb standard American National Standard—ANSI B 16.1—1975.
  ‡ Typical—not listed in ANSI standards.

Welded and Seamless Wrought Steel Pipe

Size	Schedule no	Diameter External (in)	Diameter Internal (in)	Thickness (in)	Circumference External (in)	Circumference Internal (in)	Transverse area External (sq in)	Transverse area Internal (sq in)	Length External surface (feet)	Length Internal surface (feet)	Weight per ft of length (lbs)	Allowable working pressure at 100°F (lb/sq in)	Water hammer factor
1/8	40 S	0.405	0.269	0.068	1.272	0.845	0.129	0.057	9.431	14.199	0.24	3500	338
	80 X		0.215	0.095	1.272	0.675	0.129	0.036	9.431	17.766	0.31	4800	535
1/4	40 S	0.540	0.364	0.088	1.696	1.144	0.229	0.104	7.073	10.493	0.42	2100	185
	80 X		0.302	0.119	1.696	0.949	0.229	0.072	7.073	12.648	0.54	4350	268
3/8	40 S	0.675	0.493	0.091	2.121	1.549	0.358	0.191	5.658	7.748	0.57	1700	101
	80 X		0.423	0.126	2.121	1.329	0.358	0.141	5.658	9.030	0.74	3800	137
1/2	40 S	0.840	0.622	0.109	2.639	1.954	0.554	0.304	4.547	6.141	0.85	2300	63.4
	80 X		0.546	0.147	2.639	1.715	0.554	0.234	4.547	6.99	1.09	4100	82.3
	160		0.464	0.188	2.639	1.458	0.554	0.169	4.547	8.23	1.31	7300	114
	XX		0.252	0.294	2.639	0.792	0.554	0.050	4.547	15.15	1.71	12300	385
3/4	40 S	1.050	0.824	0.113	3.299	2.589	0.866	0.533	3.637	4.635	1.13	2000	36.1
	80 X		0.742	0.154	3.299	2.331	0.866	0.433	3.637	5.15	1.47	3500	44.5
	160		0.612	0.219	3.299	1.923	0.866	0.294	3.637	6.24	1.94	8500	65.5
	XX		0.434	0.308	3.299	1.363	0.866	0.148	3.637	8.80	2.44	10000	130
1	40 S	1.315	1.049	0.133	4.131	3.296	1.358	0.864	2.904	3.641	1.68	2100	22.3
	80 X		0.957	0.179	4.131	3.007	1.358	0.719	2.904	3.99	2.17	3500	26.8
	160		0.815	0.250	4.131	2.560	1.358	0.522	2.904	4.69	2.84	5700	36.9
	XX		0.599	0.358	4.131	1.882	1.358	0.282	2.904	6.38	3.66	9500	68.3
1 1/4	40 S	1.660	1.380	0.140	5.215	4.335	2.164	1.495	2.301	2.768	2.27	1800	12.9
	80 X		1.278	0.191	5.215	4.015	2.164	1.283	2.301	2.99	3.00	3000	15.0
	160		1.160	0.250	5.215	3.645	2.164	1.057	2.301	3.29	3.76	4400	18.2
	XX		0.896	0.382	5.215	2.815	2.164	0.631	2.301	4.26	5.21	7900	30.5
1 1/2	40 S	1.900	1.610	0.145	5.969	5.058	2.835	2.036	2.010	2.372	2.72	1700	9.46
	80 X		1.500	0.200	5.969	4.712	2.835	1.767	2.010	2.55	3.63	2800	10.9
	160		1.338	0.281	5.969	4.205	2.835	1.406	2.010	2.86	4.86	4500	13.7
	XX		1.100	0.400	5.969	3.456	2.835	0.950	2.010	3.47	6.41	7200	20.3
2	40 S	2.375	2.067	0.154	7.461	6.494	4.430	3.555	1.608	1.847	3.65	1500	5.74
	80 X		1.939	0.218	7.461	6.092	4.430	2.953	1.608	1.97	5.02	2500	6.52
	160		1.687	0.344	7.461	5.300	4.430	2.235	1.608	2.26	7.46	4600	8.60
	XX		1.503	0.436	7.461	4.722	4.430	1.774	1.608	2.54	9.03	6300	10.9
2 1/2	40 S	2.875	2.469	0.203	9.032	7.757	6.492	4.788	1.328	1.547	5.79	1900	4.02
	80 X		2.323	0.276	9.032	7.298	6.492	4.238	1.328	1.64	7.66	2800	4.54
	160		2.125	0.375	9.032	6.676	6.492	3.545	1.328	1.80	10.01	4200	5.43
	XX		1.771	0.552	9.032	5.564	6.492	1.391	1.328	2.16	13.69	6900	7.82

Selected from ANSI B 36.10—1975. See notes, page 7-19.

Welded and Seamless Wrought Steel Pipe (Continued)

Welded and Seamless Wrought Steel Pipe

Size	Sched ule no	Diameter External (inches)	Diameter Internal (inches)	Thick- ness (inches)	Circumference External (inches)	Circumference Internal (inches)	Transverse area External (sq in)	Transverse area Internal (sq in)	Length of pipe per sq ft surface area — External surface (feet)	Length of pipe per sq ft surface area — Internal surface (feet)	Weight per ft of length (lbs)	Allowable working pressure at 100°F* (lb/sq in)	Water hammer factor
3	40 -S	3.500	3.068	0.216	10.996	9.638	9.621	7.393	1.091	1.245	7.58	1600	2.60
	80 -X		2.900	0.300	10.996	9.111	9.621	6.605	1.091	1.32	10.25	2600	2.92
	160		2.624	0.438	10.996	8.244	9.621	5.408	1.091	1.46	14.32	4100	3.56
	XX		2.300	0.600	10.996	7.226	9.621	4.155	1.091	1.66	18.58	6100	4.64
3½	40 -S	4.000	3.548	0.226	12.566	11.146	12.566	9.886	0.954	1.076	9.11	1500	1.94
	80 -X		3.364	0.318	12.566	10.57	12.566	8.888	0.954	1.14	12.50	2400	2.17
	XX		2.728	0.636	12.566	8.57	12.566	5.845	0.954	1.40		5600	3.29
4	40 -S	4.500	4.026	0.237	14.137	12.648	15.904	12.703	0.848	0.948	10.79	1400	1.51
	80 -X		3.826	0.337	14.137	12.020	15.904	11.497	0.848	0.998	14.98	2300	1.67
	120		3.624	0.438	14.137	11.39	15.904	10.315	0.848	1.05	19.00	3350	1.87
	160		3.438	0.531	14.137	10.80	15.904	9.282	0.848	1.11	22.51	4000	2.08
	XX		3.152	0.674	14.137	9.90	15.904	7.803	0.848	1.21	27.54	5300	2.47
5	40 -S	5.563	5.047	0.258	17.477	15.856	24.306	20.006	0.686	0.756	14.62	1300	0.960
	80 -X		4.813	0.375	17.477	15.120	24.306	18.19	0.686	0.793	20.78	2090	1.06
	120		4.563	0.500	17.477	14.34	24.306	16.35	0.686	0.837	27.04	2950	1.18
	160		4.313	0.625	17.477	13.55	24.306	14.61	0.686	0.897	32.96	3850	1.32
	XX		4.063	0.750	17.477	12.76	24.306	12.97	0.686	0.940	38.55	4780	1.49
6	40 -S	6.625	6.065	0.280	20.813	19.054	34.472	28.891	0.756	0.629	18.97	1210	0.666
	80 -X		5.761	0.432	20.813	18.099	34.472	26.07	0.756	0.663	28.57	2070	0.738
	120		5.501	0.562	20.813	17.29	34.472	23.77	0.756	0.695	36.39	2850	0.810
	160		5.187	0.719	20.813	16.30	34.472	21.13	0.756	0.736	45.35	3760	0.912
	XX		4.897	0.864	20.813	15.38	34.472	18.83	0.756	0.780	53.16	4660	1.02
8	20	8.625	8.125	0.250	27.096	25.53	58.43	51.87	0.443	0.470	22.36	795	0.371
	30		8.071	0.277	27.096	25.39	58.43	51.30	0.443	0.473	24.70	910	0.375
	40 S		7.981	0.322	27.096	25.07	58.43	50.03	0.443	0.478	28.55	1100	0.385
	60		7.813	0.406	27.096	24.54	58.43	47.94	0.443	0.489	35.64	1460	0.402
	80 X		7.625	0.500	27.096	23.955	58.43	45.66	0.443	0.500	43.39	1870	0.422
	100		7.437	0.594	27.096	23.36	58.43	43.44	0.443	0.514	50.95	2280	0.443
	120		7.187	0.719	27.096	22.58	58.43	40.56	0.443	0.532	60.71	2840	0.475
	140		7.001	0.812	27.096	21.99	58.43	38.50	0.443	0.546	67.76	3260	0.500
	XX		6.875	0.875	27.096	21.60	58.43	37.12	0.443	0.556	72.42	3560	0.519
	160		6.813	0.906	27.096	21.40	58.43	36.44	0.443	0.561	74.69	3700	0.529

Selected from ANSI B 36.10—1975. See notes, page 7-19.

Welded and Seamless Wrought Steel Pipe (*Continued*)

Welded and Seamless Wrought Steel Pipe

Size	Schedule no	Diameter External (in)	Diameter Internal (in)	Thickness (in)	Circumference External (in)	Circumference Internal (in)	Transverse area External (sq in)	Transverse area Internal (sq in)	Length of pipe per sq ft — External surface (feet)	Length of pipe per sq ft — Internal surface (feet)	Weight per ft of length (lbs)	Allowable working pressure at 100°F (lb/sq in)	Water hammer factor
10	20	10.750	10.250	0.250	33.77	32.20	90.76	82.52	0.355	0.373	28.04	636	233
	30		10.136	0.307	33.77	31.84	90.76	80.69	0.355	0.377	34.24	827	239
	40 S		10.020	0.365	33.77	31.48	90.76	78.85	0.355	0.381	40.48	1030	244
	60 X		9.750	0.500	33.77	30.63	90.76	74.66	0.355	0.392	54.74	1490	258
	80		9.562	0.594	33.77	30.04	90.76	71.81	0.355	0.399	64.43	1800	268
	100		9.312	0.719	33.77	29.25	90.76	68.10	0.355	0.410	77.03	2250	283
	120		9.062	0.844	33.77	28.48	90.76	64.50	0.355	0.421	89.29	2700	299
	140 XX		8.750	1.000	33.77	27.49	90.76	60.13	0.355	0.437	104.13	3310	320
	160		8.500	1.125	33.77	26.70	90.76	56.75	0.355	0.449	115.64	3740	340
12	20	12.750	12.250	0.250	40.06	38.48	127.68	117.86	0.299	0.312	33.38	535	163
	30		12.090	0.330	40.06	37.98	127.68	114.80	0.299	0.316	43.77	760	168
	S		12.000	0.375	40.06	37.70	127.68	113.10	0.299	0.318	49.56	890	170
	40		11.938	0.406	40.06	37.50	127.68	111.93	0.299	0.320	53.52	1000	172
	X		11.750	0.500	40.06	36.91	127.68	108.43	0.299	0.325	65.42	1250	178
	60		11.626	0.562	40.06	36.52	127.68	106.16	0.299	0.329	73.15	1425	181
	80		11.374	0.688	40.06	35.73	127.68	101.61	0.299	0.336	88.63	1800	190
	100		11.062	0.844	40.06	34.75	127.68	96.11	0.299	0.345	107.32	2255	200
	120 XX		10.750	1.000	40.06	33.77	127.68	90.76	0.299	0.355	125.49	2700	212
	140		10.500	1.125	40.06	32.99	127.68	86.59	0.299	0.364	139.67	3115	222
	160		10.126	1.312	40.06	31.81	127.68	80.53	0.299	0.377	160.27	3700	239
14	10	14.000	13.500	0.250	43.98	42.41	153.94	143.14	0.272	0.283	36.71	485	134
	20		13.376	0.312	43.98	42.02	153.94	140.52	0.272	0.286	45.61	645	137
	30 S		13.250	0.375	43.98	41.63	153.94	137.89	0.272	0.288	54.57	810	138
	40		13.124	0.438	43.98	41.23	153.94	135.28	0.272	0.291	63.44	970	142
	X		13.000	0.500	43.98	40.84	153.94	132.73	0.272	0.294	72.09	1140	145
	60		12.812	0.594	43.98	40.25	153.94	128.92	0.272	0.298	85.05	1380	149
	80		12.500	0.750	43.98	39.26	153.94	122.72	0.272	0.306	106.13	1795	157
	100		12.124	0.938	43.98	38.09	153.94	115.45	0.272	0.315	130.85	2300	167
	120		11.876	1.062	43.98	37.31	153.94	110.77	0.272	0.322	150.79	2645	174
	140		11.500	1.250	43.98	36.13	153.94	103.87	0.272	0.332	170.21	3170	185
	160		11.188	1.406	43.98	35.15	153.94	93.31	0.272	0.341	189.11	3615	206

Selected from ANSI B 36.10—1975. See notes, page 7-19

7

Welded and Seamless Wrought Steel Pipe (Continued)

Welded and Seamless Wrought Steel Pipe

Size	Schedule no	Diameter External inches	Diameter Internal inches	Thickness inches	Circumference External inches	Circumference Internal inches	Transverse area External sq in	Transverse area Internal sq in	Length per sq ft External surface feet	Length per sq ft Internal surface feet	Weight per ft of length lbs	Allowable working pressure at 100°F lb/sq in	Water hammer factor
16	10	16.000	15.500	0.250	50.27	48.69	201.06	188.69	.239	.246	42.05	425	.102
	20	16.000	15.376	0.312	50.27	48.31	201.06	185.68	.239	.248	52.27	565	.104
	30 S	16.000	15.250	0.375	50.27	47.91	201.06	182.65	.239	.250	62.58	710	.105
	40 X	16.000	15.000	0.500	50.27	47.12	201.06	176.71	.239	.255	82.77	990	.109
	60	16.000	14.688	0.656	50.27	46.14	201.06	169.44	.239	.260	107.50	1345	.114
	80	16.000	14.312	0.844	50.27	44.96	201.06	160.88	.239	.267	136.61	1785	.120
	100	16.000	13.938	1.031	50.27	43.79	201.06	152.58	.239	.274	164.82	2225	.126
	120	16.000	13.562	1.219	50.27	42.61	201.06	144.64	.239	.282	192.43	2660	.133
	140	16.000	13.124	1.438	50.27	41.23	201.06	135.28	.239	.291	223.64	3215	.142
	160	16.000	12.812	1.594	50.27	40.25	201.06	128.92	.239	.298	245.25	3600	.149
18	10	18.000	17.500	0.250	56.55	54.98	254.47	240.53	.212	.218	47.39	380	.080
	20	18.000	17.376	0.312	56.55	54.59	254.47	237.13	.212	.220	58.94	500	.081
	S	18.000	17.250	0.375	56.55	54.19	254.47	233.71	.212	.221	70.59	630	.082
	30	18.000	17.124	0.438	56.55	53.80	254.47	230.30	.212	.223	82.15	750	.084
	X	18.000	17.000	0.500	56.55	53.41	254.47	226.98	.212	.225	93.45	880	.085
	40	18.000	16.876	0.562	56.55	53.02	254.47	223.68	.212	.226	104.67	1000	.086
	60	18.000	16.500	0.750	56.55	51.84	254.47	213.82	.212	.231	138.17	1385	.090
	80	18.000	16.124	0.938	56.55	50.66	254.47	204.19	.212	.237	170.92	1775	.094
	100	18.000	15.688	1.156	56.55	49.29	254.47	193.30	.212	.243	207.96	2230	.100
	120	18.000	15.250	1.375	56.55	47.92	254.47	182.77	.212	.250	244.14	2700	.105
	140	18.000	14.876	1.562	56.55	46.73	254.47	173.80	.212	.257	274.22	3110	.111
	160	18.000	14.438	1.781	56.55	45.36	254.47	163.72	.212	.265	308.50	3590	.118
20	10	20.000	19.500	0.250	62.83	61.26	314.16	298.65	.191	.196	52.73	340	.064
	20 S	20.000	19.250	0.375	62.83	60.48	314.16	291.04	.191	.198	78.60	570	.066
	30 X	20.000	19.000	0.500	62.83	59.69	314.16	283.53	.191	.201	104.13	790	.068
	40	20.000	18.812	0.594	62.83	59.10	314.16	277.95	.191	.203	123.11	955	.069
	60	20.000	18.376	0.812	62.83	57.73	314.16	265.21	.191	.208	166.40	1355	.073
	80	20.000	17.938	1.031	62.83	56.35	314.16	252.72	.191	.213	208.87	1765	.076
	100	20.000	17.438	1.281	62.83	54.78	314.16	238.83	.191	.219	256.10	2240	.081
	120	20.000	17.000	1.500	62.83	53.41	314.16	226.98	.191	.225	296.37	2660	.085
	140	20.000	16.500	1.750	62.83	51.84	314.16	213.82	.191	.231	341.09	3150	.090
	160	20.000	16.062	1.969	62.83	50.46	314.16	202.62	.191	.238	379.17	3585	.095

Selected from ANSI B 36.10—1975. See notes, page 7-19.

Welded and Seamless Wrought Steel Pipe (Continued)

Size	Schedule no	Diameter External (inches)	Diameter Internal (inches)	Thickness (inches)	Circumference External (inches)	Circumference Internal (inches)	Transverse area External (sq in)	Transverse area Internal (sq in)	Length of pipe per sq ft of surface area — External surface (feet)	Length of pipe per sq ft of surface area — Internal surface (feet)	Weight per ft of length (lbs)	Allowable working pressure at 100 F* (lb sq in)	Water hammer factor
24	10	24.000	23.500	0.250	75.40	73.83	452.4	433.7	159	163	63.41	280	.044
	10	24.000	23.438	0.281	75.40	73.63	452.4	431.5	159	163	71.18	329	.045
	20 S	24.000	23.250	0.375	75.40	73.04	452.4	424.6	159	164	94.62	470	.045
	X	24.000	23.000	0.500	75.40	72.26	452.4	415.5	159	166	125.49	660	.046
	30	24.000	22.876	0.562	75.40	71.87	452.4	411.0	159	167	140.68	747	.047
	40	24.000	22.624	0.688	75.40	71.08	452.4	402.0	159	169	171.29	937	.048
	60	24.000	22.062	0.969	75.40	69.31	452.4	382.3	159	173	238.45	1365	.050
	80	24.000	21.562	1.219	75.40	67.74	452.4	365.1	159	177	296.58	1755	.053
	100	24.000	20.938	1.531	75.40	65.78	452.4	344.3	159	182	367.39	2245	.056
	120	24.000	20.376	1.812	75.40	64.01	452.4	326.1	159	187	429.39	2695	.059
	140	24.000	19.876	2.062	75.40	62.44	452.4	310.3	159	192	483.12	3105	.062
	160	24.000	19.312	2.344	75.40	60.67	452.4	292.9	159	197	542.13	3575	.066
30	10	30.000	29.376	0.312	94.25	92.29	706.9	677.8	127	130	98.93	299	.028
	S	30.000	29.250	0.375	94.25	91.89	706.9	672.0	127	131	118.65	375	.029
	20 X	30.000	29.000	0.500	94.25	91.11	706.9	660.5	127	132	157.33	530	.029
	30	30.000	28.750	0.625	94.25	90.32	706.9	649.2	127	133	196.08	674	.030
36	10	36.000	35.376	0.312	113.10	111.14	1017.9	982.9	106	108	118.92	249	.020
	S	36.000	35.250	0.375	113.10	110.74	1017.9	975.9	106	108	142.68	311	.020
	20 X	36.000	35.000	0.500	113.10	109.96	1017.9	962.1	106	109	189.57	434	.020
	30	36.000	34.750	0.625	113.10	109.17	1017.9	948.4	106	110	236.13	560	.020
	40	36.000	34.500	0.750	113.10	108.38	1017.9	934.8	106	111	282.35	683	.021
42	S	42.000	41.250	0.375	131.95	129.59	1385.4	1336.4	091	093	166.71	266	.014
	X	42.000	41.000	0.500	131.95	128.81	1385.4	1320.3	091	093	221.61	372	.015
48	S	48.000	47.250	0.375	150.80	148.44	1809.6	1753.5	080	081	190.74	233	.011
	X	48.000	47.000	0.500	150.80	147.65	1809.6	1734.9	080	081	253.65	325	.011

Selected from ANSI B 36.10—1975.
S = Standard. X = Extra strong. XX = Double extra strong.
* Allowable working pressures based on Grade B pipe: tensile strength 60,000 psi; 35,000 psi yield point.
Allowable working pressures at 400°F are 86.3% of those at 100°F.
Allowable working pressures of Grade A pipe at 100°F are 80% of Grade B pipe at 100°F.
Water hammer factors should be used to reduce allowable working pressure by the amount of flow in gal per min times water hammer factor.

7

Steel Pipe Flanges   American National Standard

Nominal pipe size	Flange rating psi	Outside flange dia in	Flange thickness (min) in	Diameter bolt circle	Threaded slip-on socket welding	Lapped	Welding neck
½	150	3.50	0.44	2.375	0.62	0.62	1.88
	300	3.75	0.56	2.625	0.88	0.88	2.06
	400	3.75	0.56	2.625	0.88	0.88	2.06
	600	3.75	0.56	2.625	0.88	0.88	2.06
	900	4.75	0.88	3.25	1.25	1.25	2.38
	1500	4.75	0.88	3.25	1.25	1.25	2.38
	2500	5.25	1.19	3.5	1.56	1.56	2.88
¾	150	3.88	0.50	2.75	0.62	0.62	2.06
	300	4.62	0.62	3.25	1.00	1.00	2.25
	400	4.62	0.62	3.25	1.00	1.00	2.25
	600	4.62	0.62	3.25	1.00	1.00	2.25
	900	5.12	1.00	3.5	1.38	1.38	2.75
	1500	5.12	1.00	3.5	1.38	1.38	2.75
	2500	5.50	1.25	3.75	1.69	1.69	3.12
1	150	4.25	0.56	3.125	0.69	0.69	2.19
	300	4.88	0.69	3.5	1.06	1.06	2.44
	400	4.88	0.69	3.5	1.06	1.06	2.44
	600	4.88	0.69	3.5	1.06	1.06	2.44
	900	5.88	1.12	4.0	1.62	1.62	2.88
	1500	5.88	1.12	4.0	1.62	1.62	2.88
	2500	6.25	1.38	4.25	1.88	1.88	3.50
1¼	150	4.62	0.62	3.5	0.81	0.81	2.25
	300	5.25	0.75	3.875	1.06	1.06	2.56
	400	5.25	0.81	3.875	1.12	1.12	2.62
	600	5.25	0.81	3.875	1.12	1.12	2.62
	900	6.25	1.12	4.375	1.62	1.62	2.88
	1500	6.25	1.12	4.375	1.62	1.62	2.88
	2500	7.25	1.50	5.125	2.06	2.06	3.75
1½	150	5.00	0.69	3.875	0.88	0.88	2.44
	300	6.12	0.81	4.5	1.19	1.19	2.69
	400	6.12	0.88	4.5	1.25	1.25	2.75
	600	6.12	0.88	4.5	1.25	1.25	2.75
	900	7.00	1.25	4.875	1.75	1.75	3.25
	1500	7.00	1.25	4.875	1.75	1.75	3.25
	2500	8.00	1.75	5.75	2.38	2.38	4.38
2	150	6.00	0.75	4.75	1.00	1.00	2.50
	300	6.50	0.88	5.0	1.31	1.31	2.75
	400	6.50	1.00	5.0	1.44	1.44	2.88
	600	6.50	1.00	5.0	1.44	1.44	2.88
	900	8.50	1.50	6.5	2.25	2.25	4.00
	1500	8.50	1.50	6.5	2.25	2.25	4.00
	2500	9.25	2.00	6.75	2.75	2.75	5.00
2½	150	7.00	0.88	5.5	1.12	1.12	2.75
	300	7.50	1.00	5.875	1.50	1.50	3.00
	400	7.50	1.12	5.875	1.62	1.62	3.12
	600	7.50	1.12	5.875	1.62	1.62	3.12
	900	9.62	1.62	7.5	2.50	2.50	4.12
	1500	9.62	1.62	7.5	2.50	2.50	4.12
	2500	10.50	2.25	7.75	3.12	3.12	5.62

From ANSI B 16.5.
Slip-on welding not in 2500 lb rating, and only in 1½ to 2½ sizes for 1500 lb rating and 1½ to 3 in sizes for 150 lb rating.
Socket welding not in 400, 900 and 2500 lb ratings and only in ½ to 2½ sizes for 1500 lb rating and ½ to 3 sizes in 300 lb rating.
Threaded in 1500 lb rating from ½ to 12 in sizes only.

Steel Pipe Flanges — American National Standard (cont.)

Nominal pipe size	Flange rating psi	Outside flanage dia in	Flange thickness (min) in	Diameter bolt circle	Length thru hub in		
					Threaded slip-on socket welding	Lapped	Welding neck
3	150	7.50	0.94	6	1.19	1.19	2.75
	300	8.25	1.12	6.625	1.69	1.69	3.12
	400	8.25	1.25	6.625	1.81	1.81	3.25
	600	8.25	1.25	6.625	1.81	1.81	3.25
	900	9.50	1.50	7.5	2.12	2.12	4.00
	1500	10.50	1.88	8.0	2.88	2.88	4.62
	2500	12.00	2.62	9.0	3.62	3.62	6.62
3½	150	8.50	0.94	7	1.25	1.25	2.81
	300	9.00	1.19	7.25	1.75	1.75	3.19
	400	9.00	1.38	7.25	1.94	1.94	3.38
	600	9.00	1.38	7.25	1.94	1.94	3.38
	900	—	—	—	—	—	—
	1500	—	—	—	—	—	—
	2500	—	—	—	—	—	—
4	150	9.00	0.94	7.25	1.31	1.31	3.00
	300	10.00	1.25	7.875	1.88	1.88	3.38
	400	10.00	1.38	7.875	2.00	2.00	3.50
	600	10.75	1.50	8.5	2.12	2.12	4.00
	900	11.50	1.75	9.25	2.75	2.75	4.50
	1500	12.25	2.12	9.5	3.56	3.56	4.88
	2500	14.00	3.00	10.75	4.25	4.25	7.50
5	150	10.00	0.94	8.5	1.44	1.44	3.50
	300	11.00	1.38	9.25	2.00	2.00	3.88
	400	11.00	1.50	9.25	2.12	2.12	4.00
	600	13.00	1.75	10.5	2.38	2.38	4.50
	900	13.75	2.00	11.0	3.12	3.12	5.00
	1500	14.75	2.88	11.5	4.12	4.12	6.12
	2500	16.50	3.62	12.75	5.12	5.12	9.00
6	150	11.00	1.00	9.5	1.56	1.56	3.50
	300	12.50	1.44	10.625	2.06	2.06	3.88
	400	12.50	1.62	10.625	2.25	2.25	4.06
	600	14.00	1.88	11.5	2.62	2.62	4.62
	900	15.00	2.19	12.5	3.38	3.38	5.50
	1500	15.50	3.25	12.5	4.69	4.69	6.75
	2500	19.00	4.25	14.5	6.00	6.00	10.75
8	150	13.50	1.12	11.75	1.75	1.75	4.00
	300	15.00	1.62	13.0	2.44	2.44	4.38
	400	15.00	1.88	13.0	2.69	2.69	4.62
	600	16.50	2.19	13.75	3.00	3.00	5.25
	900	18.50	2.50	15.5	4.00	4.50	6.38
	1500	19.00	3.62	15.5	5.62	5.62	8.38
	2500	21.75	5.00	17.25	7.00	7.00	12.50
10	150	16.00	1.19	14.25	1.94	1.94	4.00
	300	17.50	1.88	15.25	2.62	3.75	4.62
	400	17.50	2.12	15.25	2.88	4.00	4.88
	600	20.00	2.50	17.0	3.38	4.38	6.00
	900	21.50	2.75	18.5	4.25	5.00	7.25
	1500	23.00	4.25	19.0	6.25	7.00	10.00
	2500	26.50	6.50	21.25	9.00	9.00	16.50

From ANSI B 16.5.

Slip-on welding not in 2500 lb rating, and only in 1½ to 2½ sizes for 1500 lb rating and 1½ to 3 in sizes for 150 lb rating.

Socket welding not in 400, 900 and 2500 lb ratings and only in ½ to 2½ sizes for 1500 lb rating and ½ to 3″ sizes in 300 lb rating.

Threaded in 1500 lb rating from ½ to 12 in sizes only.

7

Steel Pipe Flanges — American National Standard (cont.)

Nom- inal pipe size	Flange rating psi	Out- side flanage dia in	Flange thick- ness (min) in	Diameter bolt circle	Length thru hub in		
					Threaded slip-on socket welding	Lapped	Welding neck
12	150	19.00	1.25	17.0	2.19	2.19	4.50
	300	20.50	2.00	17.75	2.88	4.00	5.12
	400	20.50	2.25	17.75	3.12	4.25	5.38
	600	22.00	2.62	19.25	3.62	4.62	6.12
	900	24.00	3.12	21.0	4.62	5.62	7.88
	1500	26.50	4.88	22.5	7.12	8.62	11.12
	2500	30.00	7.25	24.375	10.00	10.00	18.25
14	150	21.00	1.38	18.75	2.25	3.12	5.00
	300	23.00	2.12	20.25	3.00	4.38	5.62
	400	23.00	2.38	20.25	3.31	4.62	5.88
	600	23.75	2.75	20.75	3.69	5.00	6.50
	900	25.25	3.38	22.0	5.12	6.12	8.38
	1500	29.50	5.25	25.0	—	9.50	11.75
16	150	23.50	1.44	21.25	2.50	3.44	5.00
	300	25.50	2.25	22.5	3.25	4.75	5.75
	400	25.50	2.50	22.5	3.69	5.00	6.00
	600	27.00	3.00	23.75	4.19	5.50	7.00
	900	27.75	3.50	24.25	5.25	6.50	8.50
	1500	32.50	5.75	27.75	—	10.25	12.25
18	150	25.00	1.56	22.75	2.69	3.81	5.50
	300	28.00	2.38	24.75	3.50	5.12	6.25
	400	28.00	2.62	24.75	3.88	5.38	6.50
	600	29.25	3.25	25.75	4.62	6.00	7.25
	900	31.00	4.00	27.0	6.00	7.50	9.00
	1500	36.00	6.38	30.5	—	10.88	12.88
20	150	27.50	1.69	25.0	2.88	4.06	5.69
	300	30.50	2.50	27.0	3.75	5.50	6.38
	400	30.50	2.75	27.0	4.00	5.75	6.62
	600	32.00	3.50	28.5	5.00	6.50	7.50
	900	33.75	4.25	29.5	6.25	8.25	9.75
	1500	38.75	7.00	32.75	—	11.50	14.00
24	150	32.00	1.88	29.5	3.25	4.38	6.00
	300	36.00	2.75	32.0	4.19	6.00	6.62
	400	36.00	3.00	32.0	4.50	6.25	6.88
	600	37.00	4.00	33.0	5.50	7.25	8.00
	900	41.00	5.50	35.5	8.00	10.50	11.50
	1500	46.00	8.00	39.0	—	13.00	16.00

From ANSI B 16.5.
Slip-on welding not in 2500 lb rating, and only in 1½ to 2½ sizes for 1500 lb rating and 1½ to 3 in sizes for 150 lb rating.
Socket welding not in 400, 900 and 2500 lb ratings and only in ½ to 2½ sizes for 1500 lb rating and ½ to 3 sizes in 300 lb rating.
Threaded in 1500 lb rating from ½ to 12 in sizes only.

MISCELLANEOUS

Weights and Dimensions of Copper and Brass Pipe and Tubes

Nominal size in	Outside diam in	Type K Inside diam in	Type K Wt per ft lb	Type L Inside diam in	Type L Wt per ft lb	Type M Inside diam in	Type M Wt per ft lb	Outside diam in	Inside diam in	67% Copper	85% Copper	100% Copper
⅛	.250	.186	.085	.200	.068	.20	.068	.405	.281	.246	.253	.259
¼	.375	.311	.134	.315	.126	.325	.106	.540	.375	.437	.450	.460
⅜	.500	.402	.269	.430	.198	.450	.144	.675	.494	.612	.630	.643
½	.625	.527	.344	.545	.284	.569	.203	.840	.625	.911	.938	.957
⅝	.750	.652	.418	.666	.362	.690	.263					
¾	.875	.745	.641	.785	.454	.811	.328	1.050	.822	1.24	1.27	1.30
1	1.125	.995	.839	1.025	.653	1.055	.464	1.315	1.062	1.74	1.79	1.83
1¼	1.375	1.245	1.04	1.265	.882	1.291	.681	1.660	1.368	2.56	2.63	2.69
1½	1.625	1.481	1.36	1.505	1.14	1.571	.940	1.900	1.600	3.04	3.13	3.20
2	2.125	1.959	2.06	1.985	1.75	2.009	1.46	2.375	2.062	4.02	4.14	4.23
2½	2.625	2.435	2.92	2.465	2.48	2.495	2.03	2.875	2.500	5.83	6.00	6.14
3	3.125	2.907	4.00	2.945	3.33	2.981	2.68	3.500	3.062	8.31	8.56	8.75
3½	3.625	3.385	5.12	3.425	4.29	3.459	3.58	4.000	3.500	10.85	11.17	11.41
4	4.125	3.857	6.51	3.905	5.38	3.935	4.66	4.500	4.000	12.29	12.66	12.94
4½								5.000	4.500	13.74	14.15	14.46
5	5.125	4.805	9.67	4.875	7.61	4.907	6.66	5.563	5.063	15.40	15.85	16.21
6	6.125	5.741	13.87	5.845	10.20	5.881	8.91	6.625	6.125	18.44	18.99	19.41
7								7.625	7.062	23.92	24.63	25.17
8	8.125	7.583	25.90	7.725	19.29	7.785	16.46	8.625	8.000	30.05	30.95	31.63

The National Bureau of Standards has recommended the elimination of the 3½″ and 4½″ pipe sizes.

Volume of Horizontal Tanks in Gallons per Foot of Length

Dia of cylindrical tank ft	0.1	0.2	0.3	0.4	0.5	0.6	0.7	0.8	0.9	full
0.5	0.08	0.21	0.31	0.55	0.73	0.92	1.10	1.26	1.39	1.47
1.0	0.31	0.84	1.48	2.19	2.94	3.68	4.39	5.0	5.6	5.88
1.5	0.69	1.88	3.34	4.94	6.6	8.3	9.9	11.3	12.5	13.22
2.0	1.22	3.35	5.9	8.8	11.8	14.7	17.6	20.2	22.3	23.50
2.5	1.91	5.2	9.3	13.7	18.4	22.5	27.5	31.5	34.8	36.72
3.0	2.75	7.5	13.3	19.8	26.4	33.1	39.5	45.4	50.1	52.88
3.5	3.74	10.2	18.2	26.9	36.0	45.1	53.8	61.7	68.2	71.97
4.0	4.89	13.4	23.7	35.1	47.0	58.9	70.3	80.6	89.1	94.00
4.5	6.2	16.9	30.0	44.4	59.5	74.5	89.0	102	113	119.0
5.0	7.6	20.9	37.1	54.9	73.4	92.0	110	126	139	146.9
6	11.0	30.1	53.4	79.0	106	133	158	181	200	211.5
7	15.0	41.0	72.6	108	144	180	215	247	273	287.9
8	19.6	53.5	94.9	140	188	236	281	322	356	376.0
9	24.8	67.8	120	178	238	298	356	408	451	475.9
10	30.6	83.7	148	219	294	368	439	504	557	587.5
11	37.0	101	179	266	335	445	532	610	674	710.9
12	44.0	120	213	316	423	530	633	726	802	846.0
13	51.7	141	251	371	496	622	742	852	941	992.9
14	59.9	164	291	430	576	721	861	988	1092	1152
15	68.8	188	334	494	661	828	988	1134	1253	1322

Volume in tank (gals)* = $7.4805 \left[\dfrac{\pi D^2 \times \theta}{720} - \dfrac{D^2}{2} (\sin \theta)(0.5 - \text{portion filled}) \right] \times \text{length}; \sin \theta = \sqrt{1 - \cos^2\theta}$

Cos θ = 2(0.5 − portion filled); D = tank dia (ft); vol of full tank (gals) = $7.4805 \dfrac{\pi D^2}{4} \times \text{length}$

* Applies to tanks up to 50% filled. When tank is over 50% filled, calculate portion *not* filled and subtract from full tank.

7-23

Capacities—Cylinders and Tanks

Capacities, in U.S. Gallons, of Cylinders and Tanks of Various Diameters and Lengths

Length of cylinder

Diam inches	1"	1'	5'	6'	7'	8'	9'	10'	11'	12'	13'	14'	15'	16'	17'	18'	20'	22'	24'
1	0.01	0.04	0.20	0.24	0.28	0.32	0.36	0.40	0.44	0.48	0.52	0.56	0.60	0.64	0.68	0.72	0.80	0.88	0.96
2	0.03	0.16	0.80	0.96	1.12	1.28	1.44	1.60	1.76	1.92	2.08	2.24	2.40	2.56	2.72	2.88	3.20	3.52	3.84
3	0.05	0.37	1.84	2.20	2.56	2.92	3.30	3.68	4.04	4.40	4.76	5.12	5.48	5.84	6.22	6.60	7.36	8.08	8.80
4	0.05	0.65	3.26	3.92	4.58	5.24	5.88	6.52	7.18	7.84	8.50	9.16	9.82	10.5	11.1	11.8	13.0	14.4	15.7
5	0.08	1.02	5.10	6.12	7.14	8.16	9.18	10.2	11.2	12.2	13.3	14.3	15.3	16.3	17.3	18.4	20.4	22.4	24.4
6	0.12	1.47	7.34	8.80	10.3	11.8	13.2	14.7	16.1	17.6	19.1	20.6	22.0	23.6	25.0	26.4	29.4	32.2	35.2
7	0.17	2.00	10.0	12.0	14.0	16.0	18.0	20.0	22.0	24.0	26.0	28.0	30.0	32.0	34.0	36.0	40.0	44.0	48.0
8	0.22	2.61	13.0	15.6	18.2	20.8	23.4	26.0	28.6	31.2	33.8	36.4	39.0	41.6	44.2	46.8	52.0	57.2	62.4
9	0.28	3.31	16.5	19.8	23.1	26.4	29.8	33.0	36.4	39.6	43.0	46.2	49.6	52.8	56.2	60.0	66.0	72.4	79.2
10	0.34	4.08	20.4	24.4	28.4	32.6	36.8	40.8	44.8	48.8	52.8	56.8	61.0	65.2	69.4	73.6	81.6	89.6	97.6
11	0.41	4.94	24.6	29.6	34.6	39.4	44.4	49.2	54.2	59.2	64.2	69.2	74.0	78.8	83.8	88.8	98.4	104.	118.
12	0.49	5.88	29.4	35.2	41.0	46.8	52.8	58.8	64.6	70.4	76.2	82.0	87.8	93.6	99.6	106.	118.	129.	141.
13	0.57	6.90	34.6	41.6	48.6	55.2	62.2	69.2	76.2	83.2	90.2	97.2	104.	110.	117.	124.	138.	152.	166.
14	0.67	8.00	40.0	48.0	56.0	64.0	72.0	80.0	88.0	96.0	104.	112.	120.	128.	136.	144.	160.	176.	192.
15	0.77	9.18	46.0	55.2	64.4	73.6	82.8	92.0	101.	110.	120.	129.	138.	147.	156.	166.	184.	202.	220.
16	0.87	10.4	52.0	62.4	72.8	83.2	93.6	104.	114.	125.	135.	146.	156.	166.	177.	187.	208.	229.	250.
17	0.98	11.8	59.0	70.8	81.6	94.4	106.	118.	130.	142.	153.	163.	177.	189.	201.	212.	236.	260.	283.
18	1.10	13.2	66.0	79.2	92.4	106.	119.	132.	145.	158.	172.	185.	198.	211.	224.	240.	264.	290.	317.
19	1.23	14.7	73.6	88.4	103.	118.	132.	147.	162.	177.	192.	206.	221.	235.	250.	265.	294.	324.	354.
20	1.36	16.3	81.6	98.0	114.	130.	147.	163.	180.	196.	212.	229.	245.	261.	277.	294.	326.	359.	392.
21	1.50	18.0	90.0	108.	126.	144.	162.	180.	198.	216.	238.	252.	270.	288.	306.	324.	360.	396.	432.
22	1.65	19.8	99.0	119.	139.	158.	178.	198.	218.	238.	257.	277.	297.	317.	337.	356.	396.	436.	476.
23	1.80	21.6	108.	130.	151.	173.	194.	216.	238.	259.	281.	302.	324.	346.	367.	389.	432.	476.	518.
24	1.96	23.5	118.	141.	165.	188.	212.	235.	259.	282.	306.	330.	353.	376.	400.	424.	470.	518.	564.
25	2.12	25.5	128.	153.	179.	204.	230.	255.	281.	306.	332.	358.	383.	408.	434.	460.	510.	562.	612.
26	2.30	27.6	138.	166.	193.	221.	248.	276.	304.	331.	359.	386.	414.	442.	470.	496.	552.	608.	662.
27	2.48	29.7	148.	178.	208.	238.	267.	297.	326.	356.	386.	416.	446.	476.	504.	534.	594.	652.	712.
28	2.67	32.0	160.	192.	224.	256.	288.	320.	352.	384.	416.	448.	480.	512.	544.	576.	640.	704.	768.
29	2.86	34.3	171.	206.	240.	274.	309.	343.	377.	412.	446.	480.	514.	548.	584.	618.	686.	754.	824.
30	3.06	36.7	183.	220.	257.	294.	330.	367.	404.	440.	476.	514.	550.	588.	624.	660.	734.	808.	880.
32	3.48	41.8	209.	251.	293.	334.	376.	418.	460.	502.	544.	586.	628.	668.	710.	752.	836.	920.	1004.
34	3.93	47.2	236.	283.	330.	378.	424.	472.	520.	566.	614.	660.	708.	756.	802.	848.	944.	1040.	1132.
36	4.41	52.9	264.	317.	370.	422.	476.	528.	582.	634.	687.	740.	792.	844.	898.	952.	1056.	1164.	1268.

MISCELLANEOUS

Displacement per Stroke—In U.S. Gallons
For Various Diameter Plungers

Stroke lengths in inches

Plunger diam in inches	1	1½	2	2½	3	3½	4	5	6	7	8
.8125	.00224	.00336	.00448	.00560	.00672	.00785	.00896	.01120	.01345	.01570	.01792
.875	.00261	.00392	.00522	.00652	.00783	.00914	.01044	.01305	.01565	.01830	.02090
.9375	.00299	.00448	.00598	.00748	.00897	.01046	.01196	.01495	.01795	.02093	.02329
1.000	.00340	.00510	.00680	.00850	.01020	.01190	.01360	.0170	.0204	.0238	.0272
1.0625	.00383	.00574	.00770	.00959	.01151	.01343	.01535	.01915	.02298	.02681	.03064
1.125	.0043	.00645	.0086	.01076	.0129	.01506	.01721	.0215	.0258	.0301	.0344
1.1875	.00479	.00718	.00957	.01196	.01435	.01674	.01916	.02395	.02874	.03353	.03832
1.250	.00532	.00797	.0106	.0133	.0159	.0186	.0213	.0266	.0319	.0372	.0425
1.3125	.00586	.00879	.01172	.01465	.01758	.02051	.02344	.02930	.03516	.04102	.04688
1.375	.00643	.00965	.0129	.0161	.0193	.0225	.0257	.0322	.0386	.0451	.0514
1.4375	.00703	.01054	.01405	.01756	.02108	.02459	.02810	.03513	.04216	.04920	.05621
1.500	.00765	.01148	.0153	.0191	.02295	.0268	.0306	.0383	.0458	.0536	.0612
1.5625	.0083	.01245	.01660	.02075	.02490	.02905	.03320	.04150	.04980	.05810	.06640
1.625	.00898	.01348	.01798	.0225	.0270	.0360	.0360	.0450	.0538	.0628	.0718
1.6875	.00968	.01452	.01936	.02420	.02904	.03389	.03873	.04841	.05809	.06777	.07745
1.750	.01041	.01561	.02082	.02610	.0312	.0364	.0417	.0521	.0624	.0728	.0832
1.8125	.01117	.01675	.02234	.02792	.03351	.03909	.04468	.05585	.06702	.07819	.08936
1.875	.01196	.01794	.0239	.0299	.0359	.0418	.0478	.0598	.0718	.0837	.0957
1.9375	.01276	.01914	.02552	.03190	.03828	.04466	.05104	.06380	.07656	.08932	.10208
2.000	.01360	.0241	.0272	.0340	.0408	.0477	.0544	.0680	.0817	.0953	.1088
2.0625	.01446	.02169	.02892	.03615	.04338	.05061	.05784	.07230	.08676	.10122	.11568
2.125	.01536	.0230	.0307	.0384	.0461	.0537	.0614	.0768	.0922	.1075	.1228
2.1875	.01627	.02440	.03254	.04067	.04881	.05694	.06508	.08135	.09762	.11389	.13016
2.250	.01720	.0258	.0344	.0430	.0516	.0602	.0688	.0860	.1033	.1205	.1376
2.3125	.01818	.02727	.03646	.04545	.05454	.06363	.07272	.09090	.10908	.12726	.14528
2.375	.01917	.0287	.0383	.0478	.0575	.0671	.0767	.0958	.1148	.1340	.1532
2.500	.02125	.0319	.0425	.0532	.0637	.0744	.0850	.1063	.1274	.1488	.1700
2.625	.02347	.0352	.0469	.0587	.0704	.0822	.0939	.1173	.1409	.1643	.1878
2.750	.02573	.0386	.0514	.0643	.0772	.0900	.1029	.1287	.1544	.1802	.2058
2.875	.02810	.0421	.0562	.0702	.0843	.0983	.1124	.1405	.1686	.1967	.2248
3.000	.03060	.0459	.0612	.0765	.0918	.1071	.1224	.1530	.1836	.2142	.2448
3.125	.03320	.0498	.0664	.0830	.0996	.1162	.1328	.1660	.1992	.2324	.2656
3.250	.03590	.0538	.0718	.0897	.1077	.1256	.1436	.1795	.2154	.2513	.2872
3.375	.03872	.0581	.0714	.0968	.1162	.1355	.1549	.1936	.2323	.2710	.3097
3.500	.04165	.0624	.0833	.1042	.1249	.1458	.1666	.2083	.2499	.2916	.3332
3.625	.04470	.0670	.0894	.1117	.1341	.1565	.1788	.2235	.2682	.3129	.3576
3.750	.04780	.0717	.0956	.1195	.1434	.1673	.1912	.2390	.2868	.3346	.3824
3.875	.05110	.0766	.1022	.1277	.1533	.1788	.2044	.2555	.3066	.3577	.4088
4.000	.0542	.0813	.1084	.1360	.1626	.1897	.2168	.2710	.3252	.3794	.4336
4.125	.0578	.0867	.1156	.1445	.1734	.2023	.2312	.2890	.3468	.4046	.4624
4.250	.0614	.0921	.1228	.1535	.1842	.2149	.2456	.3070	.3684	.4298	.4912
4.375	.06508	.0976	.1302	.1627	.1952	.2278	.2603	.3254	.3905	.4556	.5207
4.500	.06885	.1033	.1378	.1722	.2066	.2410	.2755	.3444	.4131	.4820	.5508
4.625	.07273	.1091	.1454	.1818	.2182	.2545	.2909	.3636	.4364	.5091	.5818
4.750	.07672	.1151	.1534	.1918	.2302	.2685	.3069	.3836	.4603	.5370	.6138
4.875	.0808	.1212	.1616	.2020	.2424	.2828	.3232	.4040	.4848	.5656	.6464
5.000	.0850	.1275	.1700	.2125	.2550	.2975	.3400	.4250	.5100	.5950	.6800
5.250	.09371	.1405	.1874	.2343	.2811	.3279	.3748	.4685	.5622	.6560	.7497
5.500	.10286	.1542	.2057	.2571	.3086	.3600	.4114	.5143	.6171	.7200	.8228
5.790	.11242	.1686	.2248	.2810	.3372	.3934	.4496	.5621	.6745	.7869	.8993
6.000	.12241	.1836	.2448	.3061	.3672	.4284	.4896	.6121	.7345	.8569	.9793
6.250	.13282	.1992	.2656	.3321	.3984	.4648	.5313	.6641	.7969	.9297	1.0625
6.500	.14366	.2155	.2873	.3593	.4310	.5028	.5746	.7183	.8620	1.0056	1.1493
6.750	.15492	.2324	.3098	.3873	.4647	.5422	.6197	.7746	.9295	1.0845	1.2393
7.000	.16660	.2499	.3333	.4166	.4998	.5831	.6666	.8333	.9998	1.1662	1.3328
7.250	.17872	.2681	.3574	.4468	.5361	.6255	.7148	.8935	1.0723	1.2510	1.4297
7.500	.19125	.2867	.3825	.4781	.5737	.6694	.7650	.9562	1.1475	1.3387	1.5300
7.750	.20423	.3063	.4084	.5106	.6127	.7148	.8169	1.0212	1.2254	1.4297	1.6337
8.000	.21760	.3264	.4352	.5440	.6538	.7616	.8704	1.0880	1.3056	1.5232	1.7408
8.500	.24566	.3685	.4913	.6141	.7370	.8598	.9826	1.2283	1.4738	1.7196	1.9653
9.000	.27450	.4131	.5508	.6885	.8262	.9639	1.1016	1.3770	1.6525	1.9278	2.2033

$$\text{Displacement} = \frac{\text{Plunger area} \times \text{stroke}}{231}$$

Areas of Circles

Diameters in Inches and Areas in Square Inches*

Dia	Area	Dia	Area	Dia	Area	Dia	Area	Dia	Area
1/8	.012272	1/2	44.1787	7/8	173.782	1/2	471.436	1/4	1209.958
1/4	.049087	5/8	45.6636	15	176.715	3/4	481.107	1/2	1225.42
3/8	.110447	3/4	47.1731	1/8	179.673	25	490.875	3/4	1240.981
1/2	.19635	7/8	48.7071	1/4	182.655	1/4	500.742	40	1256.64
5/8	.306796	8	50.2656	3/8	185.661	1/2	510.706	1/4	1272.397
3/4	.441787	1/8	51.8487	1/2	188.692	3/4	520.769	1/2	1288.252
7/8	.601322	1/4	53.4563	5/8	191.748	26	530.93	3/4	1304.206
1	.7854	3/8	55.0884	3/4	194.828	1/4	541.19	41	1320.257
1/8	.99402	1/2	56.7451	7/8	197.933	1/2	551.547	1/4	1336.407
1/4	1.2272	5/8	58.4264	16	201.062	3/4	562.003	1/2	1352.655
3/8	1.4849	3/4	60.1322	1/8	204.216	27	572.557	3/4	1369.001
1/2	1.7671	7/8	61.8625	1/4	207.395	1/4	583.209	42	1385.45
5/8	2.0739	9	63.6174	3/8	210.598	1/2	593.959	1/4	1401.99
3/4	2.4053	1/8	65.3968	1/2	213.825	3/4	604.807	1/2	1418.63
7/8	2.7612	1/4	67.2008	5/8	217.077	28	615.754	3/4	1435.37
2	3.1416	3/8	69.0293	3/4	220.354	1/4	626.798	43	1452.2
1/8	3.5466	1/2	70.8823	7/8	223.655	1/2	637.941	1/4	1469.14
1/4	3.9761	5/8	72.7599	17	226.981	3/4	649.182	1/2	1486.17
3/8	4.4301	3/4	74.6621	1/8	230.331	29	660.521	3/4	1503.3
1/2	4.9087	7/8	76.5888	1/4	233.706	1/4	671.959	44	1520.53
5/8	5.4119	10	78.54	3/8	237.105	1/2	683.494	1/2	1555.29
3/4	5.9396	1/8	80.5158	1/2	240.529	3/4	695.128	45	1590.43
7/8	6.4918	1/4	82.5161	5/8	243.977	30	706.86	1/2	1625.97
3	7.0686	3/8	84.5409	3/4	247.45	1/4	718.69	46	1661.91
1/8	7.6699	1/2	86.5903	7/8	250.948	1/2	730.618	1/2	1698.23
1/4	8.2958	5/8	88.6643	18	254.47	3/4	742.645	47	1734.95
3/8	8.9462	3/4	90.7628	1/8	258.016	31	754.769	1/2	1772.06
1/2	9.6211	7/8	92.8858	1/4	261.587	1/4	766.990	48	1809.56
5/8	10.3206	11	95.0334	3/8	265.183	1/2	779.313	1/2	1847.46
3/4	11.0447	1/8	97.2055	1/2	268.803	3/4	791.732	49	1885.75
7/8	11.7933	1/4	99.4022	5/8	272.448	32	804.25	1/2	1924.43
4	12.5664	3/8	101.6234	3/4	276.117	1/4	816.865	50	1963.5
1/8	13.3641	1/2	103.8691	7/8	279.811	1/2	829.579	1/2	2002.97
1/4	14.1863	5/8	106.1394	19	283.529	3/4	842.391	51	2042.83
3/8	15.033	3/4	108.4343	1/8	287.272	33	855.301	1/2	2083.08
1/2	15.9043	7/8	110.7537	1/4	291.04	1/4	868.309	52	2123.72
5/8	16.8002	12	113.098	3/8	294.832	1/2	881.415	1/2	2164.76
3/4	17.7206	1/8	115.466	1/2	298.648	3/4	894.62	53	2206.19
7/8	18.6655	1/4	117.859	5/8	302.489	34	907.922	1/2	2248.01
5	19.635	3/8	120.277	3/4	306.355	1/4	921.323	54	2290.1
1/8	20.629	1/2	122.719	7/8	310.245	1/2	934.822	1/2	2332.9
1/4	21.6476	5/8	125.185	20	314.16	3/4	948.42	55	2376.4
3/8	22.6907	3/4	127.677	1/4	322.063	35	962.115	56	2463.4
1/2	23.7583	7/8	130.192	1/2	330.064	1/4	975.909	57	2551.8
5/8	24.8505	13	132.733	3/4	338.164	1/2	989.9	58	2641
3/4	25.9673	1/8	135.297	21	346.361	3/4	1003.79	59	2734.
7/8	27.1086	1/4	137.887	1/4	354.657	36	1017.878	60	2834.
6	28.2744	3/8	140.501	1/2	363.051	1/4	1032.065	61	2921
1/8	29.4648	1/2	143.139	3/4	371.543	1/2	1046.349	62	3019
1/4	30.6797	5/8	145.802	22	380.134	3/4	1060.732	63	3117
3/8	31.9191	3/4	148.49	1/4	388.822	37	1075.213	64	3217
1/2	33.1831	7/8	151.202	1/2	397.609	1/4	1089.792	65	3318
5/8	34.4717	14	153.938	3/4	406.494	1/2	1104.469	66	3421
3/4	35.7848	1/8	156.7	23	415.477	3/4	1119.244	67	3527
7/8	37.1224	1/4	159.485	1/4	424.558	38	1134.118	68	3632
7	38.4846	3/8	162.296	1/2	433.737	1/4	1149.089	69	3739
1/8	39.8713	1/2	165.13	3/4	443.015	1/2	1164.159	70	3849
1/4	41.2826	5/8	167.99	24	452.39	3/4	1179.327	71	3960
3/8	42.7184	3/4	170.874	1/4	461.864	39	1194.593	72	4071

* Also applies to any consistent system; i.e. ft-sq ft, yd-sq yd, meters-sq meters, etc.

Standard Hardness Conversion Tables for Steel

Rockwell			Brinell	Vickers
Diamond Cone Penetrator			10 mm Standard Ball 3000 kg load	
C Scale 150 kg load	D Scale 100 kg load	A Scale 60 kg load		Diamond Pyramid
68	76.9	85.6	—	940
67	76.1	85.0	—	900
66	75.4	84.5	—	865
65	74.5	83.9	—	832
64	73.8	83.4	—	800
63	73.0	82.8	—	772
62	72.2	82.3	—	746
61	71.5	81.8	—	720
60	70.7	81.2	—	697
59	69.9	80.7	—	674
58	69.2	80.1	—	653
57	68.5	79.6	—	633
56	67.7	79.0	—	613
55	66.9	78.5	—	595
54	66.1	78.0	—	577
53	65.4	77.4	—	560
52	64.6	76.8	500	544
51	63.8	76.3	487	528
50	63.1	75.9	475	513
49	62.1	75.2	464	498
48	61.4	74.7	451	484
47	60.8	74.1	442	471
46	60.0	73.6	432	458
45	59.2	73.1	421	446
44	58.5	72.5	409	434
43	57.7	72.0	400	423
42	56.9	71.5	390	412
41	56.2	70.9	381	402
40	55.4	70.4	371	392
39	54.6	69.9	362	382
38	53.8	69.4	353	372
37	53.1	68.9	344	363
36	52.3	68.4	336	354
35	51.5	67.9	327	345
34	50.8	67.4	319	336
33	50.0	66.8	311	327
32	49.2	66.3	301	318
31	48.4	65.8	294	310
30	47.7	65.3	286	302
29	47.0	64.7	279	294
28	46.1	64.3	271	286
27	45.2	63.8	264	279
26	44.6	63.3	258	272
25	43.8	62.8	253	266
24	43.1	62.4	247	260
23	42.1	62.0	243	254
22	41.6	61.5	237	248
21	40.9	61.0	231	243
20	40.1	60.5	226	238

Data from ASTM E 140.
Conversion of hardness values must be considered as somewhat approximate.

MEASUREMENT OF HEAD WITH VARIOUS TYPES OF GAGES*

Symbols

(The following symbols apply to Figs. A to H)

h_{dg} = Discharge gage reading in feet of water

h_{sg} = Suction gage reading in feet of water

Z_d = Elevation of discharge gage zero above datum elevation in feet

Z_s = Elevation of suction gage zero above datum elevation in feet

(Z_d and Z_s are negative if the gage zero is below the datum elevation)

Y_d = Elevation of discharge gage connection to discharge pipe above datum elevation in feet

Y_s = Elevation of suction gage connection to suction pipe above datum elevation in feet

(Y_d and Y_s are negative if the gage connection to the pipe lies below the datum elevation)

V_d = Average water velocity in discharge pipe at discharge gage connection in ft/sec

V_s = Average water velocity in suction pipe at suction gage connection in ft/sec

h_d = Total discharge head in feet above atmospheric pressure at datum elevation

h_g = Suction or discharge gage reading in feet of mercury

h_s = Total suction head in feet above atmospheric pressure at datum elevation

H = Total pump head in feet

$H = h_d - h_s$

(h_d and h_s are negative if the corresponding pressures at the datum elevation are below the atmospheric pressure)

W_m = Specific weight of mercury, lbs/cu ft = 848.699 lb/ft³ at 0°C (32°F) or 845.622 lb/ft³ at 20°C (68°F)

w = Specific weight of liquid pumped, lbs/cu ft

h, Z and V without subscripts apply equally to suction and discharge head measurements.

Datum elevation is at the centerline of horizontal pumps and at the entrance eye of the suction impeller on vertical shaft pumps.

Note:—The word "Water" is used in the following text to represent the liquid being pumped. The provisions are applicable to the pumping of other liquids, such as oil, the gages except mercury gages, containing the same liquid as that being pumped.

Pages 7-28 to 7-33 reprinted from Standards of the Hydraulic Institute.

Connecting pipe air-filled, to be drained before reading. Water cannot be used in U tube if either h_{dg} or h_{sg} exceeds height of rising loop.

In particular installations, either h_d or h_s may be measured by various types of gages. Figs. D to H illustrate various examples, h_g representing generally the gage reading, applicable to either the discharge gage reading h_{dg} or the suction heading h_{sg}.

Measurement of Head by Means of Water Gages

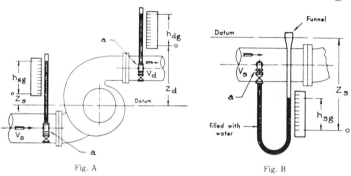

Fig. A   Fig. B

If the pressure at the gage connection "a" is above the atmospheric pressure use arrangement shown in Fig. A with line between discharge or suction pipe and the corresponding gage filled completely with water.

In this case

$$h_d = h_{dg} + Z_d + \frac{V_d^2}{2g} \qquad\qquad h_s = h_{sg} + Z_s + \frac{V_s^2}{2g}$$

If pressure at gage connection "a" is below atmospheric pressure use arrangement shown in Fig. B showing suction gage.

In this case

$$h_s = h_{sg} - Z_s + \frac{V_s^2}{2g}$$

The negative sign of Z_s indicates that the gage zero is located below the datum.

If the pressure at the gage connection "a" is below the atmospheric pressure, use arrangement shown in Fig. C with line between the discharge or suction pipe and the corresponding gage filled completely with air.

In this case

$$h_d = -h_{dg} + Y_d + \frac{V_d^2}{2g}$$

$$h_s = -h_{sg} + Y_s + \frac{V_s^2}{2g}$$

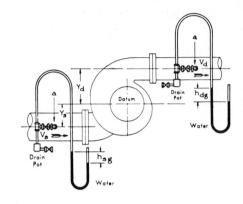

Fig. C

Signs of Y_d and Y_s apply to positions shown in Fig. C.

Measurement of Head by Means of Mercury Gages

The gage pressure is above the atmospheric pressure and the connection line is filled with liquid pumped. *Arrangement per Fig. D*

In this case

$$h = \frac{W_m}{w}h_g + Z + \frac{V^2}{2_g}$$

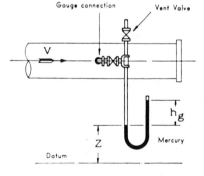

Fig. D.

When the gage pressure is below the atmospheric pressure, and the connecting line is completely filled with air, with a rising loop to prevent water from passing to mercury column. *Arrangement per Fig. E.*

In this case

$$h = \frac{W_m}{w} h_g + Y + \frac{V^2}{2_g}$$

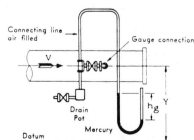

Fig. E.

Measurement of Total Pump Head by Means of Differential Mercury Gage

In this case

$$H = \left(\frac{W_m}{w} - 1 \right) h_g + \frac{V_d^2}{2_g} - \frac{V_s^2}{2_g}$$

Fig. F

hg — Reading of differential mercury gage in feet of mercury. Connecting lines are completely filled with water.

Besides the differential gage, use a separate suction gage as shown in Figs. B and E.

$$h_s = - \frac{W_m}{w} h_{sg} - Z + \frac{V_s^2}{2_g}$$

Measurement of Head by Means of Calibrated Bourdon Gages

The relation between the pressure expressed in pounds per square inch (psi) and that expressed in feet of head is:

P_g = Gage reading, psi

w = Specific weight of the liquid in lbs/cu ft

Z is measured to the center of the gage and is negative if the center of the gage lies below the datum line.

Gage pressure above the atmospheric pressure and the connecting line completely filled with water.

In this case

$$h = \frac{144 P_g}{w} + Z + \frac{V^2}{2_g}$$

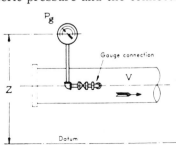

Fig. G

(Continued, next page)

Measurement of Head on Vertical Suction Pumps in Sumps and Channels

In installations of vertical shaft pumps drawing water from large open sumps and having short inlet passages of a length not exceeding about three diameters of the inlet opening, such inlet pieces having been furnished as part of the pump, the total head shall be the reading of the discharge gauge in feet, plus the velocity head at the gauge connection in feet, plus the vertical distance from the gauge center to the free water level in the sump in ft. $(Z_{ws} - Z_s)$.

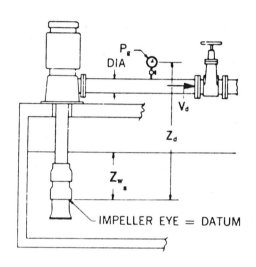

Fig. H

Data Required by Pump Manufacturers For
Proper Selection of Material

1. SOLUTION TO BE PUMPED (Give common name, where possible such as "spinning bath," "black liquor," "spent pickle," etc.) ....
2. PRINCIPAL CORROSIVES (H_2SO_4, HCl, etc.) ....%
   by weight (In cases of mixtures, state definite percentages by weight. For example: mixture contains 2% acid, in terms of 96.5% H_2SO_4.
3. pH (if aqueous solution).................. at ....F
4. IMPURITIES OR OTHER CONSTITUENTS NOT GIVEN IN "2" (List amounts of any metallic salts, such as chlorides, sulphates, sulphides, chromates, and any organic materials which may be present, even though in percentages as low as .01%. Indicate, where practical, whether they act as accelerators or inhibitors on the pump material.) ....
   ....
5. SPECIFIC GRAVITY (solution pumped).............. at..............................F
6. TEMPERATURE OF SOLUTION: Maximum...F,
   Minimum..........F, Normal..........F
7. VAPOR PRESSURES AT ABOVE TEMPERATURES: Maximum ....
   Minimum ....Normal ....(Indicate units used, such as pounds gauge, inches water, millimeters mercury.)
8. VISCOSITY ....SSU; or ....centistokes; at..............................F
9. AERATION: Air-Free ....Partial ....Saturated ....
   Does liquid have tendency to foam? ....
10. OTHER GASES IN SOLUTION ....ppm, or ....cc per liter ....
    ....
11. SOLIDS IN SUSPENSION: (state types) ....
    ....
    Specific gravity of solids ....
    Quantity of solids ....% by weight
    Particle size..........mesh ....% by weight
    ....mesh ....% by weight
    ....mesh ....% by weight
    Character of solids: Pulpy .... Gritty........ Hard ....Soft ....
12. CONTINUOUS OR INTERMITTENT SERVICE..
    Will pump be used for circulation closed system or transfer? ....
    Will pump be operated at times against closed discharge? ....
    If intermittent, how often is pump started?.........times per ....
    Will pump be flushed and drained when not in service? ....
13. TYPE OF MATERIAL IN PIPE LINES TO BE CONNECTED TO PUMP ....
    If desirable, are insulated joints practical? ....
    If so, what percentage of element (Fe, Ni, Cu, etc.) is objectionable? ....
14. IS METAL CONTAMINATION UNDESIRABLE? ....
15. PREVIOUS EXPERIENCE: Have you pumped this solution? ....
    If so, of what material or materials was pump made? ....
    ....
    Service life in months?...
    In case of trouble, what parts were affected? ....
    Was trouble primarily due to corrosion?.........erosion?.........galvanic action? ....
    stray current? ....
    Was attack uniform?.........If localized, what parts were involved? ....
    ....
    If galvanic action, name materials involved ....
    ....
    If pitted, describe size, shape and location (A sketch will be helpful in an analysis of problem..
    ....
16. WHAT IS CONSIDERED AN ECONOMIC LIFE? ....
    (If replacement does not become too frequent, the use of inexpensive pump materials may be the most economical.)

Reprinted from Standards of the Hydraulic Institute.

7

Pump Materials

The accompanying tables are printed as a guide to pump users, indicating the materials commonly used in the manufacture of pumps for the liquid services listed. It must be recognized, however, that temperature, abrasive qualities of the liquid, concentration, purity, and structural design problems are factors that will seriously affect selection of the materials for a pump.

The letter symbols and numerical selections as used in Column 5 "Material Selection" are summarized below.

A — designates an all bronze pump
B — designates a bronze fitted pump
C — designates an all iron pump

Summary of Materials Selections and National Society Standards Designations

Institute selection no.	Corresponding National Society* Standards Designation			Remarks
	ASTM	ACI	AISI	
1	A48, Classes 20, 25, 30, 35, 40 & 50	......	....	Gray Iron—six grades
2	B143, 1B & 2A; B144, 3A; B145, 4A	......	....	Tin Bronze—six grades (includes two grades not covered by ASTM Specifications as explained above under Selection No. 2)
3	A216, WCB	......	1030	Carbon Steel
4	A217, C5	......	501	5% Chromium Steel
5	A296, CA15	CA15	410	13% Chromium Steel
6	A296, CB30	CB30	....	20% Chromium Steel
7	A296, CC50	CC50	446	28% Chromium Steel
8	A296, CF-8	CF-8	304	18-8 Austenitic Steel
9	A296, CF-8M	CF-8M	316	18-8 Molybdenum Austenitic Steel
10	....	CN-7M	....	A series of highly-alloyed steels normally used where the corrosive conditions are severe
11	....	......	....	A series of nickel-base alloys
12	....	......	....	High-silicon cast iron
13	....	......	....	Austenitic cast iron
14	....	......	....	Monel metal
15	....	......	.....	Nickel

* ASTM—denotes American Society for Testing Materials.
ACI—denotes Alloy Casting Institute.
AISI—denotes American Iron and Steel Institute.
Tables reprinted from the Standards of the Hydraulic Institute. Copyright by the Hydrauliuc Institute.

WARNING

Some of the liquids covered in the following tables are extremely corrosive, toxic or volatile, and can be hazardous if mishandled or misused. Improper handling or usage could result in severe damage to equipment or property and/or serious personal injury or death.

Pump Materials
*Materials of Construction For Pumping Various Liquids

Column 1 Liquid	Column 2 Condition of liquid	Column 3 Chemical symbol	Column 4 Specific gravity	Column 5 Material selection
Acetaldehyde	....	C_2H_4O	0.78	C
Acetate Solvents	....			A, B, C, 8, 9, 10, 11
Acetone	....	C_3H_6O	0.79	B, C
Acetic Anhydride	....	$C_4H_6O_3$	1.08	8, 9, 10, 11, 12
Acid, Acetic	Conc. Cold	$C_2H_4O_2$	1.05	8, 9, 10, 11, 12
Acid, Acetic	Dil. Cold	....	....	A, 8, 9, 10, 11, 12
Acid, Acetic	Conc. Boiling	....	....	9, 10, 11, 12
Acid, Acetic	Dil. Boiling	....	....	9, 10, 11, 12
Acid, Arsenic, Ortho-	....	$H_3AsO_4 \cdot \frac{1}{2}H_2O$	2.0–2.5	8, 9, 10, 11, 12
Acid, Benzoic	....	$C_7H_6O_2$	1.27	8, 9, 10, 11
Acid, Boric	Aqueous Sol.	H_3BO_3		A, 8, 9, 10, 11, 12
Acid, Butyric	Conc.	$C_4H_8O_2$	0.96	8, 9, 10, 11
Acid, Carbolic	Conc. (M. P. 106 F)	C_6H_6O	1.07	C, 8, 9, 10, 11
Acid, Carbolic	(See Phenol)	....	....	B, 8, 9, 10, 11
Acid, Carbonic	Aqueous Sol.	$CO_2 + H_2O$	....	A
Acid, Chromic	Aqueous Sol.	$Cr_2O_3 + H_2O$	....	8, 9, 10, 11, 12
Acid, Citric	Aqueous Sol.	$C_6H_8O_7 + H_2O$	....	A, 8, 9, 10, 11, 12
Acids, Fatty (Oleic, Palmitic, Stearic, etc.)	....	....	....	A, 8, 9, 10, 11
Acid, Formic	....	CH_2O_2	1.22	9, 10, 11
Acid, Fruit	....	....	....	A, 8, 9, 10, 11, 14
Acid, Hydrochloric	Coml. Conc.	HCl	1.19 (38%)	11, 12
Acid, Hydrochloric	Dil. Cold	....	....	10, 11, 12, 14, 15
Acid, Hydrochloric	Dil. Hot	....	....	11, 12
Acid, Hydrocyanic	....	HCN	0.70	C, 8, 9, 10, 11
Acid, Hydrofluoric	Anhydrous, with Hydro Carbon	HF + HxCx	....	3, 14
Acid, Hydrofluoric	Aqueous Sol.	HF	....	A, 14
Acid, Hydrofluosilicic	....	$H SiF_6$	1.30	A, 14
Acid, Lactic	....	$C_3H_6O_3$	1.25	A, 8, 9, 10, 11, 12
Acid, Mine Water	....	....	....	A, 8, 9, 10, 11
Acid, Mixed	Sulfuric—Nitric	....	....	C, 3, 8, 9, 10, 11, 12
Acid, Muriatic	(See Acid, Hydrochloric)	....	....	
Acid, Naphthenic	....	....	....	C, 5, 8, 9, 10, 11
Acid, Nitric	Conc. Boiling	HNO_3	1.50	6, 7, 10, 12
Acid, Nitric	Dilute	....	....	5, 6, 7, 8, 9, 10, 12
Acid, Oxalic	Cold	$C_2H_2O_4 \cdot 2H_2O$	1.65	8, 9, 10, 11, 12
Acid, Oxalic	Hot	$C_2H_2O_4 \cdot 2H_2O$	....	10, 11, 12
Acid, Ortho-Phosphoric		H_3PO_4	1.87	9, 10, 11
Acid, Pictric	....	$C_6H_3N_3O_7$	1.76	8, 9, 10, 11, 12
Acid, Pyrogallic	....	$C_6H_6O_3$	1.45	8, 9, 10, 11
Acid, Pyroligneous	....			A, 8, 9, 10, 11
Acid, Sulfuric	>77% Cold	H_2SO_4	1.69–1.84	C, 10, 11, 12
Acid, Sulfuric	65/93% > 175F	....	....	11, 12
Acid, Sulfuric	65/93% < 175F	....	....	10, 11, 12
Acid, Sulfuric	10–65%	....	....	10, 11, 12
Acid, Sulfuric	<10%	....	....	A, 10, 11, 12, 14
Acid, Sulfuric (Oleum)	Fuming	$H_2SO_4 + SO_3$	1.92–1.94	3, 10, 11
Acid, Sulfurous	....	H_2SO_3	....	A, 8, 9, 10, 11
Acid, Tannic	....	$C_{14}H_{10}O_9$	....	A, 8, 9, 10, 11, 14
Acid, Tartaric	Aqueous Sol.	$C_4H_6O_6 \cdot H_2O$	....	A, 8, 9, 10, 11, 14
Alcohols	....	....	....	A, B
Alum	See Aluminum Sulphate and Potash Alum)	....	....	....
Aluminum Sulphate	Aqueous Sol.	$Al_2(SO_4)_3$	....	10, 11, 12, 14
Ammonium, Aqua	....	NH_4OH	....	C

*Materials of Construction For Pumping Various Liquids (cont.)

Column 1 Liquid	Column 2 Condition of liquid	Column 3 Chemical symbol	Column 4 Specific gravity	Column 5 Material selection
Ammonium Bicarbonate	Aqueous Sol.	NH_4HCO_3	....	C
Ammonium Chloride	Aqueous Sol.	NH_4Cl	....	9, 10, 11, 12, 14
Ammonium Nitrate	Aqueous Sol.	NH_4NO_3	....	C, 8, 9, 10, 11, 14
Ammonium Phosphate, Dibasic	Aqueous Sol.	$(NH_4)_2HPO_4$	....	C, 8, 9, 10, 11, 14
Aluminum Sulfate	Aqueous Sol.	$(NH_4)_2SO_4$	....	C, 8, 9, 10, 11
Ammonium Sulfate	With sulfuric acid	....	....	A, 9, 10, 11, 12
Aniline	....	C_6H_7N	1.02	B, C
Aniline Hydrochloride	Aqueous Sol.	$C_6H_5NH_2HC_1$	....	11, 12
Asphalt	Hot	....	0.98–1.4	C, 5
Barium Chloride	Aqueous Sol.	$BaCl_2$	....	C, 8, 9, 10, 11
Barium Nitrate	Aqueous Sol.	$Ba(NO_3)_2$	....	C, 8, 9, 10, 11
Beer	....	....	....	A, 8
Beer Wort	....	....	....	A, 8
Beet Juice	....	....	....	A, 8
Beet Pulp	....	....	....	A, B, 8, 9, 10, 11
Benzene	....	C_6H_6	0.88	....
Benzine	(See Petroleum ether)	....	....	....
Benzol	(See Benzene)	....	....	B, C
Bichloride of Mercury	(See Mercuric Chloride)	....	....	....
Black Liquor	(See Liquor, Pulp Mill)	....	....	....
Bleach Solutions	(See type)	....	....	....
Blood	....	....	....	A, B
Boiled Feedwater	(See Water, Boiler Feed)	....	....	....
Brine, Calcium Chloride	pH > 8	$CaCl_2$	....	C
Brine, Calcium Chloride	pH < 8	....	....	A, 10, 11, 13, 14
Brine, Calcium & Magnesium Chlorides	Aqueous Sol.	....	....	A, 10, 11, 13, 14
Brine, Calcium & Sodium Chloride	Aqueous Sol.	....	....	A, 10, 11, 13, 14
Brine Sodium Chloride	Under 3% Salt, Cold	NaCl	....	A, C, 13
Brine, Sodium Chloride	Over 3% Salt, Cold	....	1.02–1.20	A, 8, 9, 10, 11, 13, 14
Brine, Sodium Chloride	Over 3% Salt, Hot	....	....	9, 10, 11, 12, 14
Brine, Sea Water	....	....	1.03	A, B, C
Butane	....	C_4H_{10}	0.60 @ 32F	B, C, 3
Calcium Bisulfite	Paper Mill	$Ca(HSO)_2$	1.06	9, 10, 11
Calcium Chlorate	Aqueous Sol.	$Ca(ClO_3)_2H_2O$	....	10, 11, 12
Calcium Hypochlorite	....	$Ca(OCl)_2$	....	C, 10, 11, 12
Calcium Magnesium Chloride	(See Brines)	....	....	....
Cane Juice	....	....	....	A, B, 13
Carbon Bisulfide	....	CS_2	1.26	C
Carbonate of Soda	(See Soda Ash)	....	....	....
Carbon Tetrachloride	Anhydrous	CCl_4	1.50	B, C
Carbon Tetrachloride	Plus Water	....	....	A, 8
Catsup	....	....	....	A, 8, 9, 10, 11
Caustic Potash	(See Potassium Hydroxide)	....	....	....
Caustic Soda	(See Sodium Hydroxide)	....	....	....
Cellulose Acetate	....	....	....	9, 10, 11
Chlorate of Lime	(See Calcium Chlorate)	....	....	....

* Courtesy of Hydraulic Institute.

*Materials of Construction For Pumping Various Liquids (cont.)

Column 1 Liquid	Column 2 Condition of liquid	Column 3 Chemical symbol	Column 4 Specific gravity	Column 5 Material selection
Chloride of Lime	(See Calcium Hypochlorite)	. . . .	. . . .	. . . .
Chlorine Water	(Depending on conc.)	. . . .	. . . .	9, 10, 11, 12
Chlorobenzene	. . . .	C_6H_5Cl	1.1	A, B, 8
Chloroform		$CHCl_3$	1.5	A, 8, 9, 10, 11, 14
Chrome Alum	Aqueous Sol.	$CrK(SO_4)_2 \cdot 12H_2O$		10, 11, 12
Condensate	(See Water, Distilled)	. . . .	. . . .	. . . .
Copperas, Green	(See Ferrous Sulfate)	. . . .	. . . .	
Copper Ammonium Acetate	Aqueous Sol.	. . . .	. . . .	C, 8, 9, 10, 11
Copper Chloride (Cupric)	Aqueous Sol.	$CuCl_2$	. . . .	11, 12
Copper Nitrate	. . . .	$Cu(NO_3)_2$	. . . .	8, 9, 10, 11
Copper Sulfate, Blue Vitriol	Aqueous Sol.	$CuSO_4$	. . . .	8, 9, 10, 11, 12
Creosote	(See Oil, Creosote)	. . . .	. . . .	. . . .
Cresol, Meta	. . . .	C_7H_8O	1.03	C, 5
Cyanide	(See Sodium Cyanide and Potassium Cyanide)	. . . .	. . . .	. . . .
Cyanogen	In Water	$(CN)_2$ Gas	. . . .	C
Diphenyl	. . . .	$C_6H_5 \cdot C_6H_5$	.99	C, 3
Enamel	. . . .	. . . .	. . . .	C
Ethanol	(See Alcohols)	. . . .	. . . .	. . . .
Ethylene Chloride (di-chloride)	Cold	$C_2H_4Cl_2$	1.28	A, 8, 9, 10, 11, 14
Ferric Chloride	Aqueous Sol.	$FeCl_3$	. . . .	11, 12
Ferric Sulphate	Aqueous Sol.	$Fe_2(SO_4)_3$	. . . .	8, 9, 10, 11, 12
Ferrous Chloride	Cold, Aqueous	$FeCl_2$	. . . .	11, 12
Ferrous Sulphate (Green Copperas)	Aqueous Sol.	$FeSO_4$	. . . .	9, 10, 11, 12, 14
Formaldehyde	. . . .	CH_2O	1.08	A, 8, 9, 10, 11
Fruit Juices	. . . .	. . . .	. . . .	A, 8, 9, 10, 11, 14
Furfural	. . . .	$C_5H_4O_2$	1.16	A, C, 8, 9, 10, 11
Gasoline		. . . .	0.68–0.75	B, C
Glaubers Salt	(See Sodium Sulfate)	. . . .	. . . .	
Glucose	. . . .	. . . .	. . . .	A, B
Glue	Hot	. . . .	. . . .	B, C
Glue Sizing	. . . .	. . . .	. . . .	A
Glycerol (Glycerin)	. . . .	$C_3H_8O_3$	1.26	A, B, C
Green Liquor	(See Liquor, Pulp Mill)			
Heptane	. . . .	C_7H_{16}	0.69	B, C
Hydrogen Peroxide	Aqueous Sol.	H_2O_2	. . . .	8, 9, 10, 11
Hydrogen Sulfide	Aqueous Sol.	H_2S	. . . .	8, 9, 10, 11
Hydrosulfite of Soda	(See Sodium Hydrosulfite)	. . . .	. . . .	. . . .
Hyposulfite of Soda	(See Sodium Thiosulfate)	. . . .	. . . .	. . . .
Kaolin Slip	Suspension in Water	. . . .	. . . .	C, 3
Kaolin Slip	Suspension in Acid	. . . .	. . . .	10, 11, 12
Kerosene	(See Oil, Kerosene)	. . . .	. . . .	. . . .
Lard	Hot	. . . .	. . . .	B, C
Lead Acetate (Sugar of Lead)	Aqueous Sol.	$Pb(C_2H_3O_2)_2 \cdot 3H_2O$	. . . .	9, 10, 11, 14
Lead	Molten	. . . .	. . . .	C, 3
Lime Water (Milk of Lime)	. . . .	$Ca(OH)_2$	. . . .	C
Liquor—Pulp Mill: Black	. . . .	. . . .	. . . .	C, 3, 9, 10, 11, 12, 14

* Courtesy of Hydraulic Institute.

7

*Materials of Construction For Pumping Various Liquids (cont.)

Column 1 Liquid	Column 2 Condition of liquid	Column 3 Chemical symbol	Column 4 Specific gravity	Column 5 Material selection
Liquor—Pulp Mill: Green	....		....	C, 3, 9, 10, 11, 12, 14
Liquor—Pulp Mill: White	....		....	C, 3, 9, 10, 11, 12, 14
Liquor—Pulp Mill: Pink	....		....	C, 3, 9, 10, 11, 12, 14
Liquor—Pulp Mill: Sulfite	....		....	9, 10, 11
Lithium Chloride	Aqueous Sol.	$LiCl$	....	C
Lye, Caustic	(See Potassium & Sodium Hydroxide)			
Magnesium Chloride	Aqueous Sol.	$MgCl_2$	....	10, 11, 12
Magnesium Sulfate (Epsom Salts)	Aqueous Sol.	$MgSO_4$	....	C, 8, 9, 10, 11
Manganese Chloride	Aqueous Sol.	$MnCl_2 \cdot {}_4H_2O$	....	A, 8, 9, 10, 11, 12
Manganous Sulfate	Aqueous Sol.	$MnSO_4 \cdot 4H_2O$	....	A, C, 8, 9, 10, 11
Mash	....		....	A, B, 8
Mercuric Chloride	Very Dilute Aqueous Sol.	$HgCl_2$	....	9, 10, 11, 12
Mercuric Chloride	Coml. Conc. Aqueous Sol.	$HgCl_2$	....	11, 12
Mercuric Sulfate	In Sulfuric Acid	$HgSO_4 + H_2SO_4$	....	10, 11, 12
Mercurous Sulfate	In Sulfuric Acid	$Hg_2 SO_4 + H_2SO_4$	....	10, 11, 12
Methyl Chloride	....	CH_3Cl	0.52	C
Methylene Chloride	....	CH_2Cl_2	1.34	C, 8
Milk	....		1.03–1.04	8
Milk of Lime	(See Lime Water)		....	....
Mine Water	(See Acid, Mine Water)		....	....
Miscella	(20% Soyabean Oil & Solvent)		0.75	C
Molasses	....		....	A, B
Mustard	....		....	A, 8, 9, 10, 11, 12
Naphtha	....		0.78–0.88	B, C
Naphtha, Crude	....		0.92–0.95	B, C
Nicotine Sulfate	....	$(C_{10}H_{11}N_2)2H_2SO_4$	....	10, 11, 12, 14
Nitre	(See Potassium Nitrate)		....	....
Nitre Cake	(See Sodium Bi-sulphate		....	....
Nitre Ethane		$C_2H_3NO_2$	1.04	B, C
Nitro Methane	....	CH_3NO_2	1.14	B, C
Oil Coal Tar	....		....	B, C, 8, 9, 10, 11
Oil, Coconut	....		0.91	A, B, C, 8, 9, 10, 11, 14
Oil, Creosote	....		1.04–1.10	B, C
Oil, Crude	Cold		....	B, C
Oil, Crude	Hot		....	3
Oil, Essential	....		....	A, B, C
Oil, Fuel	....		....	B, C
Oil, Kerosene	....		....	B, C
Oil, Linseed	....		0.94	A, B, C, 8, 9, 10, 11, 14
Oil, Lubricating	....		....	B, C
Oil, Mineral	....		....	B, C
Oil, Olive	....		0.90	B, C
Oil, Palm	....		0.90	A, B, C, 8, 9, 10, 11, 14
Oil, Quenching	....		0.91	B, C
Oil, Rapeseed	....		0.92	A, 8, 9, 10, 11, 14
Oil, Soya Bean	....		....	A, B, C, 8, 9, 10, 11, 14
Oil, Turpentine	....		0.87	B, C

* Courtesy of Hydraulic Institute.

*Materials of Construction For Pumping Various Liquids (cont.)

Column 1 Liquid	Column 2 Condition of liquid	Column 3 Chemical symbol	Column 4 Specific gravity	Column 5 Material selection
Paraffin	Hot	....	....	B, C
Perhydrol	(See Hydrogen Peroxide)	....	....	....
Peroxide of Hydrogen	(See Hydrogen Peroxide	....	....	....
Petroleum Ether	....			B, C
Phenol	....	C_6H_6O	1.07	....
Pink Liquor	(See Liquor, Pulp Mill)	....	....	....
Photographic Developers	....	....	....	8, 9, 10, 11
Plating Solutions	(Varied and complicated, consult pump mfgrs.)	....	....	....
Potash	Plant Liquor	....	....	A, 8, 9, 10, 11, 13, 14
Potash Alum	Aqueous Sol.	$Al_2(SO_4)_3K_2SO_4 \cdot 24H_2O$	....	A, 9, 10, 11, 12, 13, 14
Potassium Bichromate	Aqueous Sol.	$K_2Cr_2O_7$	....	C
Potassium Carbonate	Aqueous Sol.	K_2CO_3	....	C
Potassium Chlorate	Aqueous Sol.	$KClO_3$	....	8, 9, 10, 11, 12
Potassium Chloride	Aqueous Sol.	KCl	....	A, 8, 9, 10, 11, 14
Potassium Cyanide	Aqueous Sol.	KCN	....	C
Potassium Hydroxide	Aqueous Sol.	KOH	....	C, 5, 8, 9, 10, 11, 13, 14, 15
Potassium Nitrate	Aqueous Sol.	KNO_3	....	C, 5, 8, 9, 10, 11
Potassium Sulfate	Aqueous Sol.	K_2SO_4	....	A, 8, 9, 10, 11
Propane	....	C_3H_8	0.59 @ 48F	B, C, 3
Pyridine	....	C_5H_5N	0.98	C
Pyridine Sulphate	....	....	....	10, 12
Rhidolene	....	....	....	B
Rosin (Colophony)	Paper Mill	....	....	C
Sal Ammoniac	(See Ammonium Chloride)	....	....	....
Salt Lake	Aqueous Sol.	Na_2SO_4 — impurities	....	A, 8, 9, 10, 11, 12
Salt Water	(See Brines)	....	....	....
Sea Water	(See Brines)	....	....	....
Sewage	....		....	A, B, C
Shellac	....	....	....	A
Silver Nitrate	Aqueous Sol.	$AgNO_3$	....	8, 9, 10, 11, 12
Slop, Brewery	....	....	....	A, B, C
Slop, Distillers	....	....	....	A, 8, 9, 10, 11
Soap Liquor	....	....	....	C
Soda Ash	Cold	Na_2CO_3	....	C
Soda Ash	Hot	....	....	8, 9, 10, 11, 13, 14
Sodium Bicarbonate	Aqueous Sol.	$NaHCO_3$	....	C, 8, 9, 10, 11, 13
Sodium Bisulfate	Aqueous Sol.	$NaHSO_4$	....	10, 11, 12
Sodium Carbonate	(See Soda Ash)	....	....	....
Sodium Chlorate	Aqueous Sol.	$NaClO_3$	....	8, 9, 10, 11, 12
Sodium Chloride	(See Brines)	....	....	....
Sodium Cyanide	Aqueous Sol.	NaCN	....	C
Sodium Hydroxide	Aqueous Sol.	NaOH	....	C, 5, 8, 9, 10, 11, 13, 14, 15
Sodium Hydrosulfite	Aqueous Sol.	$Na_2S_2O_4 \cdot 2H_2O$	....	8, 9, 10, 11
Sodium Hypochlorite	....	NaOCl	....	10, 11, 12
Sodium Hyposulfite	(See Sodium Thiosulfate)	....	....	....
Sodium Meta Silicate	....	....	....	C
Sodium Nitrate	Aqueous Sol.	$NaNO_3$	....	C, 5, 8, 9, 10, 11
Sodium Phosphate: Monobasic	Aqueous Sol.	$NaH_2PO_4H_2O$	....	A, 8, 9, 10, 11

* Courtesy of Hydraulic Institute.

*Materials of Construction For Pumping Various Liquids (cont.)

Column 1	Column 2	Column 3	Column 4	Column 5
Liquid	Condition of liquid	Chemical symbol	Specific gravity	Material selection
Sodium Phosphate: Dibasic	Aqueous Sol.	$Na_2HPO_4 \cdot 7H_2O$	....	A, C, 8, 9, 10, 11
Sodium Phosphate: Tribasic	Aqueous Sol.	$Na_4P_1 \cdot 2H_2O$	....	C
Sodium Phosphate: Meta	Aqueous Sol.	$Na_4P_4O_{12}$	....	A, 8, 9, 10, 11
Sodium Phosphate: Hexameta	Aqueous Sol.	$(NaPO_3)_6$	....	8, 9, 10, 11
Sodium Plumbite	Aqueous Sol.	....	....	C
Sodium Sulfate	Aqueous Sol.	Na_2SO_4	....	A, 8, 9, 10, 11
Sodium Sulfide	Aqueous Sol.	Na_2S	....	C, 8, 9, 10, 11
Sodium Sulfite	Aqueous Sol.	Na_2SO_3	....	A, 8, 9, 10, 11
Sodium Thiosulfate	Aqueous Sol.	$Na_2S_2O_3 \cdot 5H_2O$	....	8, 9, 10, 11
Stannic Chloride	Aqueous Sol.	$SnCl_4$	....	11, 12
Stannous Chloride	Aqueous Sol.	$SnCl_2$	....	11, 12
Starch	....	$(C_6H_{10}O_5)x$	....	A, B
Strontium Nitrate	Aqueous Sol.	$Sr(NO_3)_2$	....	C, 8
Sugar	Aqueous Sol.	....	....	A, 8, 9, 10, 11, 13
Sulfite Liquor	(See Liquor, Pulp Mill)	....	....	....
Sulfur	In Water	S	....	A, C, 8, 9, 10, 11
Sulfur	Molten	S	....	C
Sulfur Chloride	Cold	S_2Cl_2	....	C
Syrup	(See Sugar)			
Tallow	Hot	....	0.90	C
Tanning Liquors	....	....	....	A, 8, 9, 10, 11, 12, 14
Tar	Hot	....	....	C, 3
Tar & Ammonia	In Water	....	....	C
Tetrachloride of Tin	(See Stannic Chloride)			
Tetraethyl Lead	....	$Pb(C_2H_5)_4$	1.66	B, C
Toluene (Toluol)	....	C_7H_8	0.87	B, C
Trichloroethylene	....	$C2HCl_3$	1.47	A, B, C, 8
Urine	....	....	....	A, 8, 9, 10, 11
Varnish	....	....	....	A, B, C, 8, 14
Vegetable Juices	....	....	....	A, 8, 9, 10, 11, 14
Vinegar	....	....	....	A, 8, 9, 10, 11, 12
Vitriol, Blue	(See Copper Sulfate)	....	....	....
Vitriol, Green	(See Ferrous Sulfate)	....	....	....
Vitriol, Oil of	(See Acid, Sulfuric)	....		
Vitriol, White	(See Zinc Sulfate)	....		
Water, Boiler Feed High Makeup	Not evaporated pH > 8.5		1.00	C
	pH < 8.5			B
Low Makeup	Evaporated, any pH		1.66	4, 5, 8, 14
Water, Distilled	High Purity	....	0.87	A, 8
Water, Distilled	Condensate	....	....	A, B
Water, Fresh	....	....	1.00	B
Water, Mine	(See Acid, Mine Water)	....	....	....
Water, Salt & Sea	(See Brines)	....	....	....
Whiskey	....	....	....	A, 8
White Liquor	(See Liquor, Pulp Mill)	....	....	....
White Water	Paper Mill	....	....	A, B, C
Wine	....	....	....	A, 8
Wood Pulp (Stock)	....	....	....	A, B, C
Wood Vinegar	(See Acid Pyroligneous)	....	....	....
Wort	(See Beer Wort)	....		
Xylol (Xylene)	....	C_8H_{10}	0.87	B, C, 8, 9, 10, 11
Yeast	....	....	....	A, B
Zinc Chloride	Aqueous Sol.	$ZnCl_2$	....	9, 10, 11, 12
Zinc Sulfate	Aqueous Sol.	$ZnSO_4$	....	A, 9, 10, 11

* Courtesy of Hydraulic Institute.

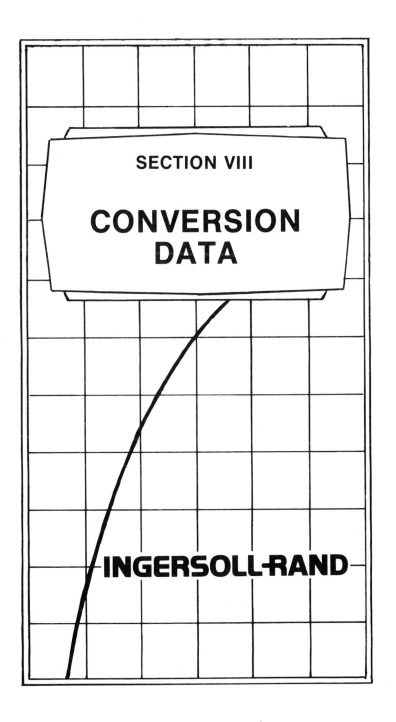

SECTION VIII

CONVERSION DATA

INGERSOLL-RAND

8

CONTENTS OF SECTION 8

Conversion Factors

CONVERSION FACTOR DATA

General Notes

Since the British Gravitational System (English System) of units is still the system in practical use in the United States today and will continue to be so for sometime in the future and is the basis on which the data in this book is printed, the proper understanding of certain fundamental terms in this system is essential and therefore the following review is offered:

The pound (lb) is the unit applying to force or weight and also to mass, but with a different meaning. It is therefore ambiguous, and confusion in its use may result. Force is a "quantity" (of something rather undefinable, a primary cause known only by its effects) which will change the velocity of—accelerate or decelerate—a particle of matter. Weight of a body means the force required to support it against the action of gravity (in that locality). Mass is defined by the relation; Force = mass × acceleration = weight × acceleration of gravity. To avoid confusion we should really speak of "lb force" and "lb mass".

The foot (ft) is the "arbitrarily selected" unit of length.

The foot-pound (ft-lb) is the unit of work, or of mechanical energy which is the capacity to do work. 1 ft-lb is the work performed by a force of 1 lb acting through a distance of 1 ft; or the work required to lift a weight of 1 lb vertically by 1 ft; or the potential energy of the weight after being raised, in reference to its former level. Standard conversions of ft-lb to other units are based on the acceleration of gravity at sea level, 45° latitude.

The horsepower (hp) is a unit for measuring power, or work performed in unit time. It is a rate of doing work or expending mechanical energy

1 hp = 550 ft-lb per sec = 33,000 ft-lb per min = 0.7067 Btu per sec.

1 hp = 0.7457 kW

The horsepower-hour (hp·h) is a unit of work; so is the **kilowatt-hour (kW·h).** The time consumed may be anything, say a fraction of a second or a million years, depending on the rate at which the work is performed. It is one hour only if the rate of work is 1 hp or 1 kW.

1 hp·h = 1,980,000 ft-lb = 2544.17 Btu = 0.7457 kW·h.

1 kW·h = 1.341 hp·h = 3412.14 Btu = 2,655,000 ft-lb

Torque is turning effort caused by a force acting normal to a radius at a set distance from the axis of rotation, and is expressed in pound-feet (lb at a radius of 1 ft).

$$\text{Torque (lb-ft)} = \text{force (lb)} \times \text{lever arm (ft)} = \frac{5250 \ (\text{hp})}{\text{rpm}}$$

Conversions . . . Equations involving units of measure are of two types: (1) equations of equivalent physical quantities, such as 12 in. = 1 ft; and, (2) equations of equivalent numerical value, such as (no. of in.) = 12 × (no. of ft). In making conversions or in substituting terms in a formula the second type is usually more convenient.

English Conversion Table

To Convert From	To	Multiply By	To Convert From	To	Multiply By
Length			**Volume**		
inches	feet	0.0833	cu inches	cu feet	0.0005787
inches	yards	0.0278	cu inches	cu yards	0.00002143
feet	inches	12	cu inches	U S gal	0.004329
feet	yards	0.3333	cu feet	cu inches	1728
feet	miles	0.0001894	cu feet	cu yards	0.03704
yards	feet	3	cu feet	U S gal	7.481
yards	miles	0.0005682	cu yards	cu inches	46,656
			cu yards	cu feet	27
Area			**Weight (Avoirdupois)**		
sq inches	sq feet	0.00694	grains	ounces	0.002286
sq inches	sq yards	0.000772	ounces	grains	437.5
sq feet	sq inches	144	ounces	pounds	0.0625
sq feet	sq yards	0.11111	pounds	ounces	16
sq yards	sq inches	1296	pounds	U S tons	0.0005
sq yards	sq feet	9	pounds	long tons	0.000446
sq yards	acres	0.000207	U S tons	pounds	2000
acres	sq feet	43,560	long tons	pounds	2240
acres	sq yards	4840			

Circumference of Circle = 3.1416 × dia = 6.2832 × radius
Area of Circle = .7854 × (dia)^2 = 3.1416 × (radius)^2
Area of Sphere = 3.1416 × (dia)^2
Volume of Sphere = 0.5236 × (dia)^3
Area of triangle = 0.5 × base × height
Area of a trapezoid = 0.5 × sum of the two parallel sides × height
Area of a square, a rectangle or parallelogram = base × height
Volume of a pyramid = area of base × 1/3 height
Volume of a cone = 0.2618 × (dia of base)^2 × height
Volume of a cylinder = 0.7854 × height × dia^2

International System of Units (Metric)

General Notes

The International System of Units, generally known as "SI", has been adopted by the International Standards Organization. Recognizing the worldwide trend to the use of this modernized metric system this edition is providing these guidelines for the use of SI in its practical applications to hydraulic engineering. These guidelines include most units which are likely to be used in handling of hydraulic fluids.

This system is known as SI and consists of seven base units and other units which are coherently derived from them. The fact that it is coherent is one of the main advantages claimed for SI. It means that the product or quotient of any two unit quantities in the system results in another unit quantity.

SI Base and Supplementary Units

Quantity	Unit	Symbol
Length	meter	m
Mass	kilogram	kg
Time	second	s
Electric current	ampere	A
Thermodynamic temperature	kelvin	K
Luminous intensity	candela	cd
Molecular substance	mole	mol
Plane angle	radian	rad
Solid angle	steradian	sr

Derived Units

Quantity	Unit	Symbol

SPACE AND TIME

Quantity	Unit	Symbol
Area	square meter	m^2
Volume	cubic meter	m^3
Velocity	meter per second	m/s
Acceleration	meter per second squared	m/s^2
Angular velocity	radian per second	rad/s
Angular acceleration	radian per second squared	rad/s^2
Frequency	hertz	Hz = cycle/s
Rotational speed	revolution per second	r/s
	revolution per minute	r/min

Quantity	Unit	Symbol

MECHANICS

Quantity	Unit	Symbol
Density	kilogram per cubic meter	kg/m^3
Momentum	kilogram meter per second	$kg \cdot m/s$
Moment of inertia	kilogram meter squared	$kg \cdot m^2$
Force	newton	$N = kg \cdot m/s^2$
Torque, moment of force	newton meter	$N \cdot m$
Energy, work, heat quantity	joule	$J = N \cdot m$
Power	watt	$W = J/s$
Pressure, stress	pascal	$Pa = N/m^2$

LIGHT

Quantity	Unit	Symbol
Customary temperature	degree Celsius	°C
Thermal conductivity	watt per meter kelvin	$W/(m \cdot K)$
Entropy	joule per kelvin	J/K
Specific heat	joule per kilogram kelvin	$J/(kg \cdot K)$

ELECTRICITY AND MAGNETISM

Quantity	Unit	Symbol
Electric charge	coulomb	$C = A \cdot s$
Electric potential, voltage, electromotive force	volt	$V = W/A$
Electric field strength	volt per meter	V/m
Capacitance	farad	$F = A \cdot s/V$
Current density	ampere per square meter	A/m^2
Magnetic field strength	ampere per meter	A/m
Magnetic flux	weber	$Wb = V \cdot s$
Magnetic flux density	tesla	$T = Wb/m^2$
Inductance	henry	$H = V \cdot s/A$
Permeability	henry per meter	H/m
Resistance	ohm	$\Omega = V/A$
Conductance	siemens	$S = A/V$
Magnetomotive force	ampere	A

LIGHT

Quantity	Unit	Symbol
Lumonous flux	lumen	$lm = cd \cdot sr$
Illumination	lux	$lx = lm/m^2$
Luminance	candela per square meter	cd/m^2

Quantity	Unit	Symbol
VISCOSITY		
Kinemetic viscosity	square meter per second	m^2/s
Dynamic (absolute) viscosity	pascal second	$Pa \cdot s$

Explanation of Some of the Units

The principal departure of SI from the gravimetric form of metric engineering units is the separate and distinct units for mass and force.

Kilogram (kg) is restricted to the unit of mass. Mass is the property of matter to which it owes its inertia.

Newton (N) is a unit of force and should be used in place of kilogramforce, poundforce, etc. The first law of motion, force is equal to mass times acceleration, defines the newton in terms of base units. $1 \text{ N} = 1 \text{ kg} \cdot m/s^2$

Joule (J) is a unit of energy and is the work done when the point of application of a force of one newton is displaced a distance of one meter in the direction of the force. $1 \text{ J} = 1 \text{ N} \cdot m$

Watt (W) is a unit of power which gives rise to the production of energy at the rate of one joule per second. $1 \text{ W} = 1 \text{ J/s}$

Pascal (Pa) is a unit for pressure or stress of one newton per square meter. $1 \text{ Pa} = 1 \text{ N}/m^2$

Kelvin (K) is the unit for Thermodynamic Temperature and should be used as the preferred unit to express temperature and temperature intervals. However, wide use is made of the degree Celsius in non-scientific areas, and it is permissible to use the Celsius scale where considered necessary. The Celsius scale is what was formerly called the centigrade scale. The temperature interval one degree Celsius equals one Kelvin exactly: $1°C = 1K$.

Celsius temperature is related to thermodynamic temperature by the equation: $°C = K - 273.15$.

8

SI Units and Conversion Factors

Units underlined are those selected for common use

To Convert from	to		Multiply by
LENGTH			
Feet	meter	m	0.304 8
Inch	millimeter	mm	25.4
Microinches	micrometer	μm	0.025 4
Statute miles	kilometer	km	1.609
AREA			
Square inches	square millimeter	mm²	645.2
Square inches	square centimeter	cm²	6.452
Square inches	square meter	m²	0.000 645
Square feet	square meter	m²	0.092 90
Acres	hectare	ha	0.404 7
VOLUME			
Cubic inches	cubic millimeter	mm³	16387.
Cubic inches	cubic centimeter	cm³	16.387
Cubic inches	cubic meter	m³	0.000 016 3!
Cubic feet	cubic meter	m³	0.028 32
Fluid ounce	milliliter	mL	29.57
Quarts (U.S.)	liter	L	0.946 4
Gallons (U.S.)	liter	L	3.785
MASS			
Pounds	kilogram	kg	0.453 59
Ton (short)	metric ton (†)	t	0.907 2
Ton (long)	metric ton (†)	t	1.016
FORCE			
Pound force	newton	N	4.448
Kilogram force	newton	N	9.807

† Note: The unit tonne is used in place of metric ton in other countries using ISO symbols.

CONVERSION FACTOR DATA

SI Units and Conversion Factors (*Continued*)

Units underlined are those selected for common use

To Convert from	to		Multiply by
PRESSURE, STRESS			
Pounds/square inch	pascal	Pa	6895.
Pounds/square inch	kilopascal	kPa	6.895
Pounds/square inch	megapascal	MPa	0.006 895
Kilogram/square meter	pascal	Pa	9.807
Bar*	kilopascal	kPa	100.
Millibar*	pascal	Pa	100.
SPEED, VELOCITY			
Feet/second	meter per second	m/s	0.304 8
Feet/minute	meter per second	m/s	0.005 08
Miles/hour	kilometer per hour	km/h	1.609
ENERGY, WORK			
British Thermal Units BTU	joule	J	1055.
Foot pound force	joule	J	1.356
Calorie	joule	J	4.186 8
POWER			
BTU/hour	watt	W	0.293 1
BTU/second	watt	W	1055.
Horsepower	kilowatt	kW	0.746
TORQUE; BENDING MOMENT			
Pound feet	newton meter	N·m	1.356
Kilogram meter	newton meter	N·m	9.807
DENSITY, MASS/VOLUME			
Pound-mass/cubic foot	kilogram per cubic meter	kg/m³	16.018
FLOW RATE VOLUME**			
Cubic feet/minute	cubic meter per minute	m³/min	0.028 32
Gallons (U.S.)/minute	liter per minute	L/min	3.785
FLOW RATE MASS			
Pounds/minute	kilogram per minute	kg/min	0.453 6

* Note: Some European countries have adopted the Bar for pressure units for its practical value and/or use in specialized fields.

** For other flow conversions see **pages 2-6 and 2-7**.

SI Units and Conversion Factors (*Continued*)

Units underlined are those selected for common use

To Convert from	to		Multiply by
WATER HARDNESS			
Grains/gallon (U.S.) (GPG)	grams per liter	g/L	0.017 12
ACCELERATION			
Feet/second²	meter per second²	m/s²	0.304 8
Free fall, standard	meter per second²	m/s²	9.806 7
ENERGY/AREA TIME			
BTU/feet² second	watt per meter²	W/m²	11348
BTU/feet² hour	watt per meter²	W/m²	3.152 5
THERMAL CONDUCTIVITY			
BTU·inch/hour·feet²·deg F	watt per meter— kelvin	W/(m·K)	0.144 2
THERMAL CONDUCTANCE			
BTU/hour·feet²·deg F	watt per meter²— kelvin	W/(m²·K)	5.678
CAPACITY, DISPLACEMENT			
inches³/revolution	liter per revolution	L/r	0.016 39
inches³/revolution	milliliter per revolution	mL/r	16.39
SPECIFIC ENERGY, LATENT HEAT			
BTU/pound	joule/kilogram	J/kg	2326
ENERGY DENSITY			
BTU/cubic foot	kilojoule/meter³	kJ/m³	37.25
SPECIFIC HEAT, SPECIFIC ENTROPY			
BTU/pound-deg F	joules/kilogram— kelvin	J/(Kg·K)	4184

Equivalent Temperature Readings for Fahrenheit and Celsius Scales

°F = 9/5 °C + 32 | °C = 5/9 (°F-32)

°Fahrenheit	°Celsius	°Fahrenheit	°Celsius	°Fahrenheit	°Celsius	°Fahrenheit	°Celsius
−459.4	−273.	−21.	−29.4	17.6	−8.	56.	13.3
−436.	−260.	−20.2	−29.	18.	−7.8	57.	13.9
−418.	−250.	−20.	−28.9	19.	−7.2	57.2	14.
−400.	−240.	−19.	−28.3	19.4	−7.	58.	14.4
−382.	−230.	−18.4	−28.	20.	−6.7	59.	15.
−364.	−220.	−18.	−27.8	21.	−6.1	60.	15.6
−346.	−210.	−17.	−27.2	21.2	−6.	60.8	16.
−328.	−200.	−16.6	−27.	22.	−5.6	61.	16.1
−310.	−190.	−16.	−26.7	23.	−5.	62.	16.7
−292.	−180.	−15.	−26.1	24.	−4.4	62.6	17.
−274.	−170.	−14.8	−26.	24.8	−4.	63.	17.2
−256.	−160.	−14.	−25.6	25.	−3.9	64.	17.8
−238.	−150.	−13.	−25.	26.	−3.3	64.4	18.
−220.	−140.	−12.0	−24.4	26.6	−3.	65.	18.3
−202.	−130.	−11.2	−24.	27.	−2.8	66.	18.9
−184.	−120.	−11.	−23.9	28.	−2.2	66.2	19.
−166.	−110.	−10.0	−23.3	28.4	−2.	67.	19.4
−148.	−100.	−9.4	−23.	29.	−1.7	68.	20.
−139.	−95.	−9.	−22.8	30.	−1.1	69.	20.6
−130.	−90.	−8.	−22.2	30.2	−1.	69.8	21.
−121.	−85.	−7.6	−22.	31.	−0.6	70.	21.1
−112.	−80.	−7.	−21.7	32.	0.	71.	21.7
−103.	−75.	−6.	−21.1	33.	+0.6	71.6	22.
−94.	−70.	−5.8	−21.	33.8	1.	72.	22.2
−85.	−65.	−5.	−20.6	34.	1.1	73.	22.8
−76.	−60.	−4.	−20.	35.	1.7	73.4	23.
−67.	−55.	−3.	−19.4	35.6	2.	74.	23.3
−58.	−50.	−2.2	−19.	36.	2.2	75.	23.9
−49.	−45.	−2.	−18.9	37.	2.8	75.2	24.
−40.	−40.	−1.	−18.3	37.4	3.	76.	24.4
−39.	−39.4	−0.4	−18.	38.	3.3	77.	25.
−38.2	−39.	0.	−17.8	39.	3.9	78.	25.6
−38.	−38.9	+1.	−17.2	39.2	4.	78.8	26.
−37.	−38.3	1.4	−17.	40.	4.4	79.	26.1
−36.4	−38.	2.	−16.7	41.	5.	80.	26.7
−36.	−37.8	3.	−16.1	42.	5.6	80.6	27.
−35.	−37.2	3.2	−16.	42.8	6.	81.	27.2
−34.6	−37.	4.	−15.6	43.	6.1	82.	27.8
−34.	−36.7	5.	−15.	44.	6.7	82.4	28.
−33.	−36.1	6.	−14.4	44.6	7.	83.	28.3
−32.8	−36.	6.8	−14.	45.	7.2	84.	28.9
−32.	−35.6	7.	−13.9	46.	7.8	84.2	29.
−31.	−35.	8.	−13.3	46.4	8.	85.	29.4
−30.	−34.4	8.6	−13.	47.	8.3	86.	30.
−29.2	−34.	9.	−12.8	48.	8.9	87.	30.6
−29.	−33.9	10.	−12.2	48.2	9.	87.8	31.
−28.	−33.3	10.4	−12.	49.	9.4	88.0	31.1
−27.4	−33.	11.	−11.7	50.	10.0	89.	31.7
−27.	−32.8	12.	−11.1	51.	10.6	89.6	32.
−26.	−32.2	12.2	−11.	51.8	11.	90.	32.2
−25.6	−32.	13.	−10.6	52.	11.1	91.	32.8
−25.	−32.9	14.	−10.	53.	11.7	91.4	33.
−24.	−31.7	15.	−9.4	53.6	12.	92.	33.3
−23.8	−31.1	15.8	−9.	54.	12.2	93.	33.9
−23.	−30.5	16.	−8.9	55.	12.8	93.2	34.
−22.	−30.	17.	−8.3	55.4	13.	94.	34.4

8

Equivalent Temperature Readings for Fahrenheit and Celsius Scales (*Continued*)

$°F = 9/5 °C + 32$ $°C = 5/9 (°F-32)$

°Fahr-enheit	°Celsius	°Fahr-enheit	°Celsius	°Fahr-enheit	°Celsius	°Fahr-enheit	°Celsius
95.	35.	134.	56.7	172.4	78.	211.	99.4
96.	35.6	134.6	57.0	173.	78.3	212.	100.
96.8	36.	135.	57.2	174.	78.9	213.	100.6
97.	36.1	136.	57.8	174.2	79.	213.8	101.
98.	36.7	136.4	58.	175.	79.4	214.	101.1
98.6	37.	137.	58.3	176.	80.	215.	101.7
99.	37.2	138.	58.9	177.	80.6	215.6	102.
100.	37.8	138.2	59.0	177.8	81.	216.	102.2
100.4	38.	139.	59.4	178.	81.1	217.	102.8
101.	38.3	140.	60.	179.	81.7	217.4	103.
102.	38.9	141.	60.6	179.6	82.	218.	103.3
102.2	39.	141.8	61.	180.	82.2	219.	103.9
103.	39.4	142.	61.1	181.	82.8	219.2	104.
104.	40.	143.	61.7	181.4	83.	220.	104.4
105.	40.6	143.6	62.	182.	83.3	221.	105.
105.8	41.	144.	62.2	183.	83.9	222.	105.6
106.	41.1	145.	62.8	183.2	84.	222.8	106.
107.	41.7	145.4	63.	184.	84.4	223.	106.1
107.6	42.	146.	63.3	185.	85.	224.	106.7
108.	42.2	147.	63.9	186.	85.6	224.6	107.
109.	42.8	147.2	64.	186.8	86.	225.	107.2
109.4	43.	148.	64.4	187.	86.1	226.	107.8
110.	43.3	149.	65.	188.	86.7	226.4	108.
111.	43.9	150.	65.6	188.6	87.	227.	108.3
111.2	44.	150.8	66.	189.	87.2	228.	108.9
112.	44.4	151.	66.1	190.	87.8	228.2	109.
113.	45.	152.	66.7	190.4	88.	229.	109.4
114.	45.6	152.6	67.	191.	88.3	230.	110.
114.8	46.	153.	67.2	192.	88.9	231.	110.6
115.	46.1	154.	67.8	192.2	89.	231.8	111.
116.	46.7	154.4	68.	193.	89.4	232.	111.1
116.6	47.	155.	68.3	194.	90.	233.	111.7
117.	47.2	156.	68.9	195.	90.6	233.6	112.
118.	47.8	156.2	69.	195.8	91.	234.	112.3
118.4	48.	157.	69.4	196.	91.1	235.	112.8
119.	48.3	158.	70.	197.	91.7	235.4	113.
120.	48.9	159.	70.6	197.6	92.	236.	113.3
120.2	49.	159.8	71.	198.	92.2	237.	113.9
121.	49.4	160.	71.1	199.	92.8	237.2	114.
122	50.	161.	71.7	199.4	93.	238.	114.4
123.	50.6	161.6	72.	200.	93.3	239.	115.
123.8	51.	162.	72.2	201.	93.9	240.	115.6
124.	51.1	163.	72.8	201.2	94.	240.8	116.
125.	51.7	163.4	73.	202.	94.4	241.	116.1
125.6	52.	164.	73.3	203.	95.	242.	116.7
126.	52.2	165.	73.9	204.	95.6	242.6	117.
127.	52.8	165.2	74.	204.8	96.	243.	117.2
127.4	53.	166.	74.4	205.	96.1	244.	117.8
128.	53.3	167.	75.	206.	96.7	244.4	118.
129.	53.9	168.	75.6	206.6	97.	245.	118.3
129.2	54.	168.8	76.	207.	97.2	246.	118.9
130.	54.4	169.	76.1	208.	97.8	246.2	119.
131.	55.	170.	76.7	208.4	98.	247.	119.4
132.	55.6	170.6	77.	209.	98.3	248.	120.
132.8	56.	171.	77.2	210.	98.9	249.	120.6
133.	56.1	172.	77.8	210.2	99.	249.8	121.

Equivalent Temperature Readings for Fahrenheit and Celsius Scales (Continued)

$°F = 9/5 °C + 32$ $°C = 5/9 (°F-32)$

°Fahren-heit	°Celsius	°Fahren-heit	°Celsius	°Fahren-heit	°Celsius	°Fahren-heit	°Celsius
250.	121.1	281.	138.3	312.8	156.	343.4	173.
251.	121.7	282.	138.9	313.	156.1	344.	173.3
251.6	122.	282.2	139.	314.	156.7	345.	173.9
252.	122.4	283.	139.4	314.6	157.	345.2	174.
253.	122.8	284.	140.	315.	157.2	346.	174.4
253.4	123.	285.	140.6	316.	157.8	347.	175.
254.	123.3	285.8	141.	316.4	158.	348.	175.6
255.	123.9	286.	141.1	317.	153.3	348.8	176.
255.2	124.	287.	141.7	318.	158.9	349.	176.1
256.	124.4	287.6	142.	318.2	159.	350.	176.7
257.	125.	288.	142.2	319.	159.4	350.6	177.
258.	125.5	289.	142.8	320.	160.	351.	177.2
258.8	126.	289.4	143.	321.	160.6	352.	177.8
259.	126.1	290.	143.3	321.8	161.	352.4	178.
260.	126.7	291.	143.9	322.	161.1	353.	178.3
260.6	127.	291.2	144.	323.	161.7	354.	178.9
261.	127.2	292.	144.4	323.6	162.	354.2	179.
262.	127.8	293.	145.	324.	162.2	355.	179.4
262.4	128.	294.	145.6	325.	162.8	356.	180.
263.	128.3	294.8	146.	325.4	163.	357.	180.6
264.	128.9	295.	146.1	326.	163.3	357.8	181.
264.2	129.	296.	146.7	327.	163.9	358.	181.1
265.	129.4	296.6	147.	327.2	164.	359.	181.6
266.	130.	297.	147.2	328.	164.4	359.6	182.
267.	130.6	298.	147.8	329.	165.	360.	182.2
267.8	131.	298.4	148.	330.	165.6	361.	182.8
268.	131.3	299.	148.3	330.8	166.	361.4	183.
269.	131.7	300.	148.9	331.	166.1	362.	183.3
269.6	132.	300.2	149.	332.	166.7	363.	183.9
270.	132.2	301.	149.4	332.6	167.	363.2	184.
271.	132.8	302.	150.	333.	167.2	364.	184.4
271.4	133.	303.	150.6	334.	167.8	365.	185.
272.	133.3	303.8	151.	334.4	168.	366.	185.6
273.	133.9	304.	151.1	335.	168.3	366.8	186.
273.2	134.	305.	151.7	336.	168.9	367.	186.1
274.	134.4	305.6	152.	336.2	169.	368.	186.7
275.	135.	306.	152.2	337.	169.4	368.6	187.
276.	135.6	307.	152.8	338.	170.	369.	187.2
276.8	136.	307.4	153.	339.	170.6	370.	187.8
277.	136.1	308.	153.3	339.8	171.	370.4	188.
278.	136.7	309.	153.9	340.	171.1	371.	188.3
278.6	137.	309.2	154.	341.	171.7	372.	188.9
279.	137.2	310.	154.4	341.6	172.	372.2	189.
280.	137.8	311.	155.	342.	172.2	373.	189.4
280.4	138.	312.	155.6	343.	172.8	374.	190..

8

General Conversion Factors

*Indicates preferred SI system units

To convert from	To	Multiply by
absolute (dynamic) viscosity	(refer to viscosity tables—pages 4-25 to page 4-28)	
acres	square feet (ft²)	43 560
	*square meters (m²)	4 046.9
	*hectares (ha)	0.404 69
acre-feet	cubic feet (ft³)	43 560
	gallons (U.S.)	325 851
	*cubic meters (m³)	1 233.5
atmospheres (standard)	bars (bar)	1.013 25
	centimeters of mercury (cmHg) at 32°F (0°C)	76.0
	feet of water (ftH₂O) at 68°F (20°C)	33.96
	inches of mercury at 32°F (0°C)	29.921
	kilograms-force per square centimeter (kgf/cm²)	1.033 2
	kilograms-force per square meter (kgf/m²)	10 332
	*kilopascals (kPa)	101.325
	pounds-force per square inch (lbf/in²) (psi)	14.696
	tons-force (short) per square foot (tonf/ft²)	1.058 1
	torr (torr) (= mmHg at 0°C)	760
barrels (U.S. liquid)	gallons (U.S.)	31.5
	*cubic meters (m³)	0.119 24
barrels (oil)	gallons of oil (U.S.)	42
	*cubic meters (m³)	0.158 99
bars	atmospheres (atm) (standard)	0.986 92
	feet of water (ftH₂O at 68°F) (20°C)	33.52
	inches of mercury (inHg) at 0°C	29.53
	kilograms-force per square centimeter (kgf/cm²)	1.019 7
	kilograms-force per square meter (kgf/m²)	10 197
	*kilopascals (kPa)	100
	pounds-force per square inch (lbf/in²) (psi)	14.504
	torr (torr) (= mmHg at 0°C)	750.06
boiler horsepower	British thermal units per hour (Btu/h) (see note)	33 479
	*kilowatts (kW)	9.809 5
	pounds of water evaporated per hour at 212°F (100°C)	34.5
British thermal units (Btu) (see note)	calories (cal)	252.0
	foot-pounds (ftlb)	778.2
	horsepower hours (hp·h)	0.000 393
	*joules (J)	1 055
	kilowatt-hours (kW·h)	0.000 293
	kilo-calories (kcal)	0.252
	kilogram-force-meters (kgf·m)	107.6

General Conversion Factors (*Continued*)

*Indicates preferred SI system units

To convert from	To	Multiply by
British thermal units (Btu) per second (see note)	*watts (W)	1 055
British thermal units (Btu) per minute (see note)	horsepower (hp) *watts (W)	0.023 58 17.58
British thermal units (Btu) per hour (see note)	*watts (W)	0.293 1
calories	British thermal units (Btu) foot-pounds (ft·lb) *joules (J) kilogram-meters (kg·m) watt hours (W·h)	0.003 968 3 3.088 4.186 8 0.426 5 0.001 163
Celsius (centigrade)	degrees F—see pages 8-11 to 8-14 also see temperature page 8-26	
*centimeters (cm)	inches (in)	0.393 7
centimeters of mercury (cmHg at 0°C)	atmospheres (standard) (atm) bars feet of water (ftH$_2$O) at 68°F inches of water (inH$_2$O) at 68°F kilograms-force per square centimeter (kgf/cm^2) *kilopascals (kPa) pounds-force per square inch (lbf/in^2) (psi) pounds-force per square foot (lbf/ft^2) torr (= mmHg at 0°C)	0.013 158 0.013 33 0.446 8 5.362 0.013 595 1.333 2 0.193 37 27.85 10
centimeters per second (cm/s)	feet per second (ft/s) feet per minute (ft/min) miles per hour (mph) kilometers per hour (km/h) meters per minute (m/min)	0.032 81 1.968 5 0.022 37 0.036 00 0.600 00
centipoises centistokes	(see pages 4-25 to 4-28) (see pages 4-25 to 4-28)	
circumference circular mils	radians (rad) square inches (in^2)	6.283 0.000 000 785 4

8

General Conversion Factors (*Continued*)
*Indicates preferred SI system units

To convert from	To	Multiply by
cubic centimeters (cm³)	cubic inches (in³)	0.061 02
	cubic feet (ft³)	0.000 035 315
	cubic yards (yd³)	0.000 001 308
	gallons (U.S.) (U.S. gal)	0.000 264 2
	gallons (Imperial) (imp gal)	0.000 22
	*liters (L)	0.001
cubic feet (ft³)	cubic centimeters (cm³)	28 317
	*cubic meters (m³)	0.028 317
	cubic inches (in³)	1 728
	cubic yards (yd³)	0.037 04
	gallons—U.S. (U.S. gal)	7.480 5
	gallons—Imperial (imp gal)	6.229
	*liters (L)	28.32
cubic feet per minute (ft³/min)	cubic centimeters per second (cm³/s)	471.9
	*cubic meters per second (m³/s)	0.000 471 9
	cubic meters per hour (m³/h)	1.699
	liters per second (L/s)	0.471 9
	gallons—U.S. per second (U.S. gps)	0.124 7
	pounds of water per minute (lbH₂O/min) at 68°F	62.32
cubic feet per second (ft³/s)	*cubic meters per second (m³/s)	0.028 317
	cubic meters per minute (m³/min)	1.699
	cubic meters per hour (m³/h)	101.9
	gallons—U.S. per minute (U.S. gal/min)	448.8
	gallons—U.S. per 24 hours (U.S. gpd) (see table—pages 2-6 and 2-7)	646 315
	liters per second (L/s)	28.32
cubic inches (in³)	cubic centimeters (cm³)	16.387
	cubic feet (ft³)	0.000 578 7
	*cubic meters (m³)	0.000 016 387
	cubic yards (yd³)	0.000 021 43
	gallons—U.S. (U.S. gal)	0.004 329
	gallons—Imperial (imp gal)	0.003 605
	*liters (L)	0.016 387
*cubic meters (m³)	cubic inches (in³)	61 024
	cubic feet (ft³)	35.315
	cubic yards (yd³)	1.308 0
	gallons—U.S. (U.S. gal)	264.17
	gallons—Imperial (imp gal)	219.97
	liters (L)	1 000
*cubic meters per hour (m³/h)	cubic meters per minute (m³/min)	0.016 667
	*cubic meters per second (m³/s)	0.000 277 78
	gallons U.S. per minute (U.S. g/min)	4.403 3
	liters per second (L/s)	0.277 78
*cubic meters per second (m³/s)	*cubic meters per hour (m³/h)	3 600
	gallons U.S. per minute (U.S. gpm)	15 850

General Conversion Factors (*Continued*)

*Indicates preferred SI system units

To convert from	To	Multiply by
cubic yards (yd³)	cubic centimeters (cm³)	764 550
	cubic feet (ft³)	27
	cubic inches (in³)	46 656
	*cubic meters (m³)	0.764 55
	gallons—Imperial (imp gal)	168.17
	gallons—U.S. (U.S. gal)	201.97
	liters (L)	764.55
degrees angular	grade (gon)	1.111
	radians (rad)	0.017 453
degrees per second (angular)	radians per second (rad/s)	0.017 453
	revolutions per minute (r/min)	0.166 67
	revolutions per second (r/s)	0.002 777 8
degrees (temperature)	(see temperature—page 8-26)	
drams—avoir	grains (gr)	27.344
	*grams (g)	1.771 8
	ounces (oz)	0.062 5
dynes	*newtons (N)	0.000 01
ergs	*joules (J)	0.000 000 1
fathoms	feet (ft)	6
	*meters (m)	1.828 8
feet (ft)	centimeters (cm)	30.480
	inches (in)	12
	*meters (m)	0.304 80
	yards (yd)	0.333 3
feet of water (ftH₂O) at 68°F	atmosphere (standard) (atm)	0.029 45
	bars (bar)	0.029 84
	inches of mercury at 0°C (inHg)	0.881 1
	kilograms-force per square centimeter (kgf/cm²)	0.030 42
	*kilopascals (kPa)	2.984
	pounds-force per square inch (lbf/in²) (psi)	0.432 8
	pounds-force per square foot (lbf/ft²)	62.32
feet per minute (ft/min)	centimeters per second (cm/s)	0.508 0
	kilometers per hour (km/h)	0.018 29
	meters per minute (m/min)	0.304 80
	*meters per second (m/s)	0.005 08
	miles per hour (mph)	0.011 36
feet per second (ft/s)	centimeters per second (cm/s)	30.480
	kilometers per hour (km/h)	1.097.
	meters per minute (m/min)	18.29
	*meters per second (m/s)	0.304 80
	miles per hour (mph)	0.681 8

8

General Conversion Factors (*Continued*)

*Indicates preferred SI system units

To convert from	To	Multiply by
feet per second squared (ft/s²)	centimeters per second squared (cm/s²)	30.480
	*meters per second squared (m/s²)	0.304 80
foot-pounds-force (ft·lbf)	British thermal units (Btu) (see note)	0.001 285
	calories	0.323 8
	horsepower hours (hp·h)	0.000 000 505 0
	*joules (J)	1.355 8
	kilocalories (kcal)	0.000 323 8
	kilogram-force meters (kgf·m)	0.138 25
	kilowatt hours (kW·h)	0.000 000 376 6
foot candle	*lumen per square meter (lux)	10.764
gallons (U.S.) (gal)	cubic centimeters (cm³)	3 785.4
	*cubic meters (m³)	0.003 785 4
	cubic inches (in³)	231
	cubic feet (ft³)	0.133 68
	cubic yards (yd³)	0.004 951 5
	pints—liquid (pt)	8
	quarts—liquid (qt)	4
	gallons—Imperial (imp gal)	0.832 7
	*liters (L)	3.785 4
	pounds of water at 60°F	8.338
gallons (Imperial)	cubic centimeters (cm³)	4 546.1
	*cubic meters (m³)	0.004 546 1
	cubic feet (ft³)	0.160 54
	cubic yards (yd³)	0.005 946
	gallons U.S. (U.S. gal)	1.200 94
	*liters (L)	4.546 1
	pounds of water at 62°F	10.000
gallons (U.S.) per minute (U.S. gpm)	*cubic meters per second (m³/s)	0.000 063 090
	*cubic meters per minute (m³/min)	0.003 785 4
	*cubic meters per hour (m³/h)	0.227 1
	cubic feet per second (ft³/s)	0.002 228
	cubic feet per hour (ft³/h)	8.021
	*liters per second (L/s)	0.063 09
grains (gr)	*grams (g)	0.064 8
	ounces—avoir (oz)	0.002 285 7
grains per gallon (U.S.) (gr/U.S. gal)	grams per cubic meter (g/m³)	17.118
	*kilograms per cubic meter (kg/m³)	0.017 118
	parts per million by weight in water (ppm)	17.118
	pounds per million gallons	142.9
grains per gallon (Imperial)	grams per cubic meter (g/m³)	14.25
	*kilograms per cubic meter (kg/m³)	0.014 25
	parts per million by weight in water (ppm)	14.25

CONVERSION FACTOR DATA

General Conversion Factors (*Continued*)

*Indicates preferred SI system units

To convert from	To	Multiply by
grams (g)	grains (gr)	15.432
	ounces-avoir (oz)	0.035 274
	pounds-avoir (lb)	0.002 204 6
grams-force (gf)	*newtons (N)	0.009 806 6
grams-force per centimeter (gf/cm)	*newtons per meter (N/m)	98.07
	pounds-force per inch (lbf/in)	0.005 600
grams per cubic centimeter (g/cm³)	*kilograms per cubic meter (kg/m³)	0.001
	pounds per cubic inch (lb/in³)	0.036 13
	pounds per cubic foot (lb/ft³)	62.427
*grams per liter (g/L)	grains per U.S. gallon (gr/U.S. gal)	58.417
	parts per million (ppm) by mass weight in water	1 000
	pounds per cubic foot (lb/ft³)	0.062 242 7
	pounds per 1000 U.S. gallons	8.354 4
hectares (ha)	acres	2.471 0
	square feet (ft²)	107 639
	*square meters (m²)	10 000
horsepower (hp)	British thermal units per minute (see note) (Btu)/min)	42.43
	foot-pounds force per minute (ft·lbf/min)	33 000
	foot-pounds force per second (ft·lbf/s)	550
	kilocalories per minute (kcal/min)	10.69
	*kilowatts (kW)	0.745 7
	horsepower-metric	1.013 9
	*watts (W)	745.7
horsepower-boiler	British thermal units per hour (see note) (Btu/h)	33 479
	kilowatts (kW)	9.809 5
	pounds of water evaporated per hour at 212°F	34.5
horsepower hours (hp·h)	British thermal units (Btu)	2 545
	foot-pounds-force (ft·lbf)	1 980 000
	*joules (J)	2 684 500
	kilocalories (kcal)	641.5
	kilogram-force-meters (kgf·m)	273 200
	*kilowatt-hours (kW·h)	0.745 7
inches (in)	centimeters (cm)	2.540
	*meters (m)	0.025 40
	*millimeters (mm)	25.40

8

General Conversion Factors (*Continued*)

*Indicates preferred SI system units

To convert from	To	Multiply by
inches of mercury (inHg) at 0°C	atmospheres (standard) (atm)	0.033 42
	bars (bar)	0.033 864
	feet of water (ftH$_2$O) at 68°F	1.135
	inches of water (inH$_2$O) at 68°F	13.62
	kilograms-force per square centimeter (kgf/cm^2)	0.034 532
	kilograms-force per square meter (kgf/m^2)	345.32
	*kilopascals (kPa)	3.386 4
	millimeters of mercury (mmHg)	25.40
	pounds-force per square foot (lbf/ft^2)	70.73
	pounds-force per square inch (lbf/in^2) (psi)	0.491 2
inches of water (inH$_2$O) at 68°F	atmosphere (standard) (atm)	0.002 454
	bars (bar)	0.002 487
	inches of mercury (inHg) at 0°C	0.073 42
	kilograms-force per square centimeter (kgf/cm^2)	0.002 535
	*kilopascals (kPa)	0.248 7
	ounces-force per square inch (ozf/in^2)	0.577 0
	pounds-force per square foot (lbf/ft^2)	5.193
	pounds-force per square inch (lbf/in) (psi)	0.036 06
*joules (J)	British thermal units (see note)	0.000 948 4
	calories (cal) (thermochemical)	0.239 0
	foot-pounds-force (ft·lbf)	0.737 56
	watt-hours (W·h)	0.000 277 78
kelvin (K)	(see temperature—page 8-26)	
*kilograms (kg)	pounds (lb)	2.204 6
	tons (ton) short	0.001 102 3
kilograms-force (kgf)	*newtons (N)	9.806 6
	pounds-force (lbf)	2.204 6
kilograms-force per meter (kgf/m)	*newtons per meter (N/m)	9.806 6
	pounds-force per foot (lbf/ft)	0.672 1
kilograms-force per square centimeter (kgf/cm^2)	atmospheres (standard) (atm)	0.967 8
	bars (bar)	0.980 66
	feet of water (ftH$_2$O) at 68°F	32.87
	inches of mercury (inHg) at 0°C	28.96
	*kilopascals (kPa)	98.066
	pounds-force per square foot (lbf/ft^2)	2 048
	pounds-force per square inch (lbf/in^2) (psi)	14.223
kilograms-force per square millimeter (kgf/mm^2)	kilograms-force per square meter (kgf/m^2)	1 000 000
	*megapascals (MPa)	9.806 6

General Conversion Factors (*Continued*)

*Indicates preferred SI system units

To convert from	To	Multiply by
*kilometers (km)	feet (ft)	3 280.8
	miles (mi)	0.621 37
kilometers per	centimeters per second (cm/s)	27.778
hour (km/h)	feet per second (ft/s)	0.911 3
	feet per minute (ft/min)	54.68
	international knots (kn)	0.539 96
	meters per minute (m/min)	16.667
	*meters per second (m/s)	0.277 78
	miles per hour (mph)	0.621 4
kilometers per	centimeters per second squared (cm/s^2)	27.778
hour per second	feet per second squared (ft/s^2)	0.911 3
(km/h·s)	*meters per second squared (m/s^2)	0.277 78
kilometers per	miles per minute (mi/min)	37.28
second (km/s)		
*kilopascals (kPa)	dynes per square centimeter (dy/cm^2)	10 000
	feet of water (ftH$_2$O) at 68°F	0.335 1
	inches of mercury (inHg) at 32°F	0.295 3
	inches of water (inH$_2$O) at 68°F	4.021
	kilograms-force per square centimeter (kgf/cm^2)	0.010 197
	pascals (Pa) (or newtons per square meter (N/m^2)	1 000
	pounds-force per square inch (lbf/in^2) (psi)	0.145 0
kiloponds	*newton (N)	9.807
	kilograms-force (kgf)	1
	pounds-force (lbf)	2.204 6
	poundals	70.932
	kips	0.002 205
kips (1000 lbf)	*newton (N)	4 448
	kilogram-force (kgf)	453.6
	pounds-force (lbf)	1 000
	poundal	32 174
	kilopond	453.6
kips per square	*kilopascals	6 894.8
inch (ksi)	kilograms-force per square centimeter (kgf/cm^2)	70.307
	bars (bar)	68.94
	pounds per square inch (psi)	1 000
*kilowatts (kW)	British thermal units per minute (Btu/min)	56.92
	foot-pounds-force per minute (ft·lbf/min)	44 254
	foot-pounds-force per second (ft·lb/s)	737.6
	horsepower (hp)	1.341 0
	kilocalories per minute (kcal/min)	14.34

8

General Conversion Factors (*Continued*)

*Indicates preferred SI system units

To convert from	To	Multiply by
kilowatt hours (kW·h)	British thermal units (Btu) (see note)	3 413
	foot-pounds-force (ft·lbf)	2 655 000
	horsepower hours (hp·h)	1.341 0
	*joules (J)	3.600 000
	kilocalories (kcal)	860
	kilogram-force meters (kgf·m)	367 100
knots (international)	*meters per second (m/s)	0.514 4
	miles per hour (mph)	1.151 6
*liters (L)	cubic centimeters (cm³)	1 000
	cubic feet (ft³)	0.035 315
	cubic inches (in³)	61.024
	cubic meters (m³)	0.001
	cubic yards (yd³)	0.001 308
	gallons U.S. (U.S. gal)	0.264 18
	gallons Imperial (imp gal)	0.220 0
*liters per minute (L/min)	cubic feet per second (ft³/s)	0.000 588 5
	*liters per second (L/s)	0.016 67
	gallons (U.S.) per second (U.S. gal/s)	0.004 403
	gallons (U.S.) per minute (U.S. gal/min)	0.264 18
	gallons (Imperial) per min (imp gal/min)	0.003 666
*liters per second (L/s)	cubic meters per second (m³/s)	0.001
	cubic meters per minute (m³/min)	0.06
	cubic meters per hour (m³/h)	3.600
	liters per minute (L/min)	60
	gallons (U.S.) per minute (U.S. gal/min)	15.85
	gallons (Imperial) per minute (imp gal)	13.20
*megapascals (MPa)	kilograms-force per square millimeter (kgf/mm²)	0.101 97
	kilograms-force per square centimeter (kgf/cm²)	10.197
	*kilopascals (kPa)	1 000
	*pascals (Pa)	1 000 000
	pounds-force per square inch (lbf/in²) (psi)	145.0
*meters (m)	feet (ft)	3.280 8
	inches (in)	39.370
	yards (yd)	1.093 6
*meters per minute (m/min)	centimeters per second (cm/s)	1.666 7
	feet per minute (ft/min)	3.280 8
	feet per second (ft/s)	0.054 68
	kilometers per hour (km/h)	0.060 0
	miles per hour (mph)	0.037 28

General Conversion Factors (*Continued*)

*Indicates preferred SI system units

To convert from	To	Multiply by
*meters per second (m/s)	feet per minute (ft/min)	196.8
	feet per second (ft/s)	3.281
	kilometers per hour (km/h)	3.600
	kilometers per minute (km/min)	0.060 0
	miles per hour (mph)	2.237
	miles per minute (mi/min)	0.037 28
*micrometers (formerly microns)	*meters (m)	0.000 001
mills (0.001 inches)	*millimeters (mm)	0.025 4
miles	feet (ft)	5 280
	*kilometers (km)	1.609 3
	*meters (m)	1 609.3
	yards (yd)	1 760
miles per hour (mph)	centimeters per second (cm/s)	44.70
	feet per minute (ft/min)	88
	feet per second (ft/s)	1.466 7
	international knots (kn)	0.869 0
	*kilometers per hour (km/h)	1.609 3
	*meters per minute (m/min)	26.82
milligrams per liter (mg/L)	parts per million (ppm)	1.0
*millimeters (mm)	inches (in)	0.039 370
millimeters of mercury at 0°C (mmHg)	bars (bar)	0.001 333 2
	feet of water at 68°F	0.004 680
	inches of mercury (inHg)	0.039 37
	inches of water (68°F)	0.536 16
	kilograms per square centimeter (kg/cm²)	0.001 359 5
	*pascals (Pa)	133.32
	pounds per square inch (psi)	0.019 336 8
million gallons per day	(see table pages 2-6 and 2-7)	
miner's inch	(see page 2-6)	
minutes, angular (')	radians (rad)	0.000 290 9
*newtons (N)	dynes (dyn)	100 000
	kilograms-force (kgf)	0.101 97
	poundals	7.233 0
	pounds-force (lbf)	0.224 8

8

General Conversion Factors (*Continued*)
*Indicates preferred SI system units

To convert from	To	Multiply by
ounces-avoir (oz)	drams-avoir (dr)	16
	grains (gr)	437.5
	*grams (g)	28.349 5
	*kilograms (kg)	0.028 350
	pounds-avoir (lb)	0.062 50
	tons (ton) long	0.000 027 90
	*tonnes (t) metric ton	0.000 028 350
ounces—U.S. fluid	cubic inches (in³)	1.804 6
	*liters (L)	0.029 57
ounces-force per square inch (ozf/in²)	grams-force per square centimeter (gf/cm²)	4.395
	*pascals (Pa)	43.1
	pounds-force per square inch (lbf/in²) (psi)	0.062 50
parts per million by mass (ppm)	grains per U.S. gallon at 60°F (gr/U.S. gal)	0.058 3
	grains per imperial gallon at 62°F (gr/imp gal)	0.070 0
	grams per cubic meter (g/m³) at 15°C	0.999 1
	*milligrams per liter (mg/L)	1.0
	pounds per million U.S. gallons at 60°F	8.328
*pascals (Pa)	bars (bar)	0.000 01
	dynes per square centimeters (dyn/cm²)	10.0
	grams-force per square centimeter (gf/cm²)	0.010 197
	kilograms-force per square centimeter (kg/cm²)	0.000 010 197
	kilograms-force per square meter (kg/m²)	0.101 97
	*kilopascals (kPa)	0.001
	*newtons per square meter (N/m²)	1.0
	pounds-force per square inch (lbf/in²) (psi)	0.000 145 0
poise	(see viscosity tables—page 4-25 to 4-28)	
	centipoises (CP)	100
	*pascal second (Pa·s)	0.100 0
	pound-force-seconds per square foot (lbf·s/ft²)	0.002 088 6
	pounds per foot second (lb/ft·s)	0.067 21
poundals	*newtons (N) (joules per meter)	0.138 26
pounds-force (lbf)	kilograms-force (kgf)	0.453 59
	*newtons (N)	4.448 2
pounds-avoir (lb)	drams-avoir (dr)	256
	grains (gr)	7 000
	*grams (g)	453.59
	*kilograms (kg)	0.453 59
	ounces-avoir (oz)	16
	*tonnes-metric tons (t)	0.000 453 59
	tons—long	0.000 446 43
	tons—short	0.000 5

General Conversion Factors (*Continued*)

*Indicates preferred SI system units

To convert from	To	Multiply by
pounds per foot (lb/ft)	*kilograms per meter (kg/m)	1.488 2
pounds per square foot (lb/ft²)	*kilograms per square meter (kg/m²)	4.882 4
pounds-mass of water at 60°F	cubic centimeters (cm³)	454.00
	cubic feet (ft³)	0.016 03
	cubic inches (in³)	27.70
	gallons (U.S.) (U.S. gal)	0.119 93
	liters (L)	0.453 98
pounds of water per minute at 60°F	cubic centimeters per second (cm³/s)	7.566 7
	cubic feet per second (ft³/s) (cfs)	0.000 267 5
	*cubic meters per minute (m³/min)	0.000 453 98
	*kilograms per second (kg/s)	0.007 559 9
pounds per cubic foot (lb/ft³)	grams per cubic centimeter (g/cm³)	0.016 018
	*kilograms per cubic meter (kg/m³)	16.018
	pounds per cubic inch (lb/in³)	0.000 578 7
pounds per cubic inch (lb/in³)	grams per cubic centimeter (g/cm³)	27.68
	*kilograms per cubic meter (kg/m³)	27 680
	pounds per cubic foot (lb/ft³)	1 728
pounds-force per foot (lbf/ft)	grams-force per centimeter (gf/cm)	14.882
	kilograms-force per meter (kgf/m)	1.488 2
	*newtons per meter (N/m)	14.594
pounds-force per square foot (lbf/ft²)	feet of water (ftH₂O) at 68°F	0.016 05
	kilograms-force per square centimeter (Kgf/cm²)	0.000 488 2
	*kilopascals (kPa)	0.004 788 0
	*pascals (Pa)	47.880
	pounds-force per square inch (lbf/in²) (psi)	0.006 944 4
pounds-force per square inch (lbf/in²) (psi)	atmospheres (standard) (atm)	0.068 05
	feet of water (ftH₂O) at 68°F	2.311
	inches of water (inH₂O) at 68°F	27.73
	inches of mercury (inHg) at 0°C	2.036
	kilograms-force per square centimeter (kgf/cm²)	0.070 31
	*kilopascals (kPa)	6.894 8
quarts—dry (qt dry)	cubic centimeters (cm³)	1 101.2
	cubic inches (in³)	67.20
	*cubic meters (m³)	0.001 101 2
quarts—liquid (qt liquid)	cubic centimeters (cm³)	946.35
	cubic inches (in³)	57.75
	*liters (L)	0.946 35
radians (rad)	degrees (°) angular	57.296

8

General Conversion Factors (*Continued*)

*Indicates preferred SI system units

To convert from	To	Multiply by
radians per second (rad/s)	degrees per second (°/s) angular revolutions per minute (r/min)	57.296 9.549
revolutions per minute (r/min)	degrees per second radians per second (rad/s)	6 0.014 72
square centimeters (cm²)	square inches (in²)	0.155 0
square feet (ft²)	acres *square meters (m²)	0.000 022 956 0.092 903
square inches (in²)	square centimeters (cm²)	6.451 6
square kilometers (km²)	acres square miles	247.10 0.386 10
*square meters (m²)	acres square feet (ft²)	0.000 247 10 10.764
square miles	acres square kilometers (km²)	640 2.590
square yards (yd²)	acres *square meters (m²)	0.000 206 61 0.836 13
standard cubic feet per minute (scfm) (at 14.696 psia and 60°F)	cubic meters per hour (m³/h) at standard conditions (15°C and 101.325 kPa) liters per second (L/s) at standard conditions (15°C and 101.325 kPa)	1.695 7 0.471 03
stokes	square feet per second (ft²/s) *square meters per second (m²/s) (see viscosity tables—pages 4-25 to 4-28)	0.001 076 0.000 1
temperatures degrees Fahrenheit (°F)	*degrees Celsius (°C); °C = 5/9 (°F - 32)	
*degrees Celsius (°C)	degrees Fahrenheit (°F); °F = 9/5°C + 32	
degrees Fahrenheit (°F)	*kelvin (K) K = 5/9 (°F + 459.67)	
*degrees Celsius (°C)	*kelvin (K) K = °C + 273.15	
degrees Rankine (°R)	*kelvin (K) K = °R/1.8	
degrees Fahrenheit (°F)	degrees Rankine (°R); °R = °F + 459.67	

for temperature conversion tables; i.e. °F to °C and vice versa refer to pages 8-11 to 8-14

tons—long	*kilograms (kg) metric tons (t) pounds-avoir (lb) tons—short	1 016.0 1.016 0 2 240 1.120

General Conversion Factors (*Continued*)

*Indicates preferred SI system units

To convert from	To	Multiply by
*tonnes-metric ton	*kilograms (kg)	1 000
	pounds (lb)	2 204.6
tons—short	*kilograms (kg)	907.18
	pounds-avoir (lb)	2 000
	tons—long	0.892 86
	tonnes (metric ton) (t)	0.907 2
tons (short) of water per 24 hours (at 60°F)	cubic feet per hour (ft³/h)	1.338
	cubic meters per hour (m³/h)	0.037 89
	gallons (U.S.) (U.S. gal/min)	0.166 8
	pounds of water per hour (lbH₂O/h) at 60°F	83.333
tons of refrigeration	British thermal units (Btu) (see note) per hour	12 000
	British thermal units (Btu) (see note) per 24 hours	288 000
*watts (W)	British thermal units (Btu) per minute (Btu/min)	0.056 91
	foot-pounds-force per second (ft·lbf/s)	0.737 56
	foot-pounds-force per minute (ft·lbf/min)	44.254
	horsepower (hp)	0.001 341 0
	joules per second (J/s)	1.0
	kilocalories per minute (kcal/min)	0.014 340
watt-hours (W·h)	British thermal units (Btu)	3.413
	foot-pounds-force (ft·lbf)	2 655
	horsepower hours (hp·h)	0.001 341 0
	*joules (J)	3 600
	kilocalories (kcal)	0.860 4
	kilograms-force-meters (kgf·m)	367.10
yards (yd)	*meters (m)	0.914 40

NOTE: BRITISH THERMAL UNITS (Btu)—since there are several definitions of the Btu, the values of applicable and/or equivalent factors may vary slightly depending on the definition used. In the accompanying tables of conversion factors, the first three or four significant figures given, in most cases, are common to most definitions of the Btu; if greater accuracy is required for certain calculations then reference to the appropriate handbooks and standards should be made.

8

Metric Flow Formulas

Velocity: $V = \dfrac{Q}{A} = \dfrac{4\,Q}{\pi\,D^2} = \dfrac{1{,}273{,}240\,Q}{d^2} = \dfrac{21.22\,q}{d^2}$

velocity head: $h_v = \dfrac{V^2}{2\,g_c} = 0.050\ 99\,V^2 = \dfrac{0.082\ 66\,Q^2}{D^4} = \dfrac{22.958\,q^2}{d^4}$

head: $H = \dfrac{0.102\ kPa}{sp\ gr} = \dfrac{10.2\ B}{sp\ gr}$

power required: $P = \dfrac{Q(kPa)}{eff} = \dfrac{q(kPa)}{60{,}000 \times (eff)}$

$$= \dfrac{q(B)}{600(eff)} = \dfrac{q(H)\ sp\ gr}{6118(eff)}$$

Reynolds no.: $R = \dfrac{VD}{v} = \dfrac{1000\ Vd}{k} = \dfrac{1{,}273{,}240\,Q}{Dk} = \dfrac{21{,}221\,q}{dk}$

Darcy friction formula: $H_f = \dfrac{fLV^2}{2\,g_cD} - \dfrac{0.082\ 66\ fLQ^2}{D^5} = \dfrac{22{,}965\ fLq^2}{d^5}$

Hazen & Williams friction formula:

$$H_f = 0.002\ 126\ L\left(\dfrac{100}{C}\right)^{1.85} \dfrac{Q^{1.85}}{D^{4.8655}} = 1214.6\ L\left(\dfrac{100}{C}\right)^{1.85} \dfrac{q^{1.85}}{d^{4.8655}}$$

Symbols
To be used only with formulas above on this page

A = cross sectional area of pipe—m^2
B = pressure—bars = 100 kPa
C = Hazen and Williams friction factor (see page 3-8)
D = internal diameter of pipe—m
d = internal diameter of pipe—mm
eff = efficiency expressed as a decimal
f = friction factor for Darcy formula (see page 3-11)
g_c = acceleration due to gravity = 9.806 65 m/sec^2
H = head in meters of liquid—m
H_f = friction loss in meters of liquid—m
h_v = velocity head in meters—m
k = kinematic viscosity—centistokes = 0.000 001 m^2/sec
kPa = pressure—kilopascals
L = length of pipe—meters—m
P = power for pumping—kilowatts—kW
Q = flow—m^3/sec
q = flow—liters per minute—L/min
R = Reynolds number
$sp\ gr$ = density—kg/L—kg/dm^3—g/cm^3
V = velocity of flow—m/sec
v = kinematic viscosity—m^2/sec = 1,000,000 centistokes

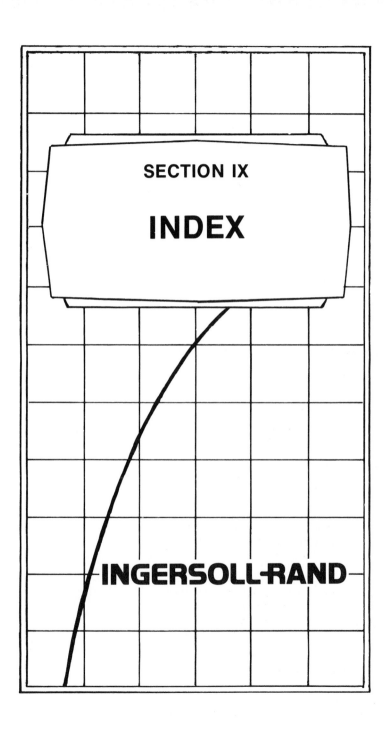

SECTION IX

INDEX

INGERSOLL-RAND

9

*General Index (A to Z)

Page

*General Index (A to Z)—(Continued)

*Index of Liquids pages 9-11 to 9-15

*Index of Liquids pages 9-11 to 9-15

9

*Index of Liquids pages 9-11 to 9-15

9

*Index of Liquids pages 9-11 to 9-15

*General Index (A to Z)—(Continued)

*Index of Liquids pages 9-11 to 9-15

9

*Index of Liquids pages 9-11 to 9-15

INGERSOLL-RAND CAMERON HYDRAULIC DATA

INDEX OF LIQUIDS

Key	Liquid Information	Page No.s
1	Boiling points	4-37 to 4-46
2	Specific gravities	4-6 to 4-19 and 4-37 to 4-46
3	Vapor pressures	4-19 to 4-23
4	Viscosities	4-23 to 4-35 and 4-37 to 4-46
*	Pump construction materials	7-34 to 7-41

9

Index of Liquids (Continued)

Key	Liquid Information	Page No.s
1	Boiling points	4-37 to 4-46
2	Specific gravities	4-6 to 4-19 and 4-37 to 4-46
3	Vapor pressures	4-19 to 4-23
4	Viscosities	4-28 to 4-35 and 4-37 to 4-46
*	Pump construction materials	7-34 to 7-41

Copper am acetate—*
Copper chloride—*
Copper nitrate—*
Copper sulfate—*
Corn oil—2, 4
Corn starch sol—2, 4
Cotton seed oil—2, 4
Creosote—2, 4, *
Cresol, meta—*
Crude oil—2, 4, *
Cyanide—*
Cyanogen—*

Decane—1, 2, 3, 4
Diethylene glycol—2, 4
Diethyl ether—1, 2, 4
Diesel fuel—2, 4, *
Diphenol—*

Enamel—*
Ethane—2, 3
Ethanol—*
Ether—2, 3
Ethyl acetate—1, 2, 4
Ethyl bromide—1, 2, 4
Ethylene—1, 2, 3
Ethylene bromide—1, 2, 4
Ethylene chloride—1, 2, 4, *
Ethylene glycol—2, 4

Ferric chloride—*
Ferric sulphate—*
Ferrous chloride—*
Ferrous sulphate—*
Formaldehyde—*
Formic acid—2, 4

Freon—2, 3, 4
Fruit juices—*
Fuel oils—2, 4
Furfural—1, 2, 4, *

Gas oils—2, 4
Gasoline—2, 3, 4, *
Glaubers salt—*
Glucose—2, 4, *
Glue—*
Glue sizing—*
Glycerine—1, 2, 4, *
Green liquor—*

Heavy water—2
Heptane—1, 2, 3, 4, *
Hexane—1, 2, 3, 4
Honey—4
Hydrocarbons—2, 3
Hydrogen peroxide—*
Hydrogen sulfide—*
Hydrosulfite of soda—*

Industrial lubricants—4
Ink—2, 4
Iso-butane—2, 3
Iso-pentane—2, 3
Insulating oil—4

Jet fuel—2, 4

Kaolin slip—*
Kerosene—2, 4, *

Lard—2, 4, *
Lard oil—2, 4

9

INGERSOLL-RAND CAMERON HYDRAULIC DATA

Index of Liquids (Continued)

Key	Liquid Information	Page No.s
1	Boiling points	4-37 to 4-46
2	Specific gravities	4-6 to 4-19 and 4-37 to 4-46
3	Vapor pressures	4-19 to 4-23
4	Viscosities	4-23 to 4-35 and 4-37 to 4-46
*	Pump construction materials	7-34 to 7-41

Sodium chlorate—*
Sodium chloride—4-9, 2, 4, *
Sodium cyanide—*
Sodium hydroxide—2, 4, *
Sodium hydrosulfite—*
Sodium hypochlorite—*
Sodium hyposulfite—*
Sodium meta silicate—*
Sodium nitrate—*
Sodium phosphate—*
Sodium plumbite—*
Sodium sulfate—*
Sodium sulfide—*
Sodium sulfite—*
Sodium thiosulfate—*
Soya bean oil—2, 4, *
Sperm oil—2, 4
Stannic chloride—*
Stannous chloride—*
Starch—*
Strontium nitrate—*
Sugar solutions, 4-12, 2, 4, *
Sulfite liquor—*
Sulfur—1, *
Sulfur chloride—*
Sulfur dioxide—2, 3, 4
Sulfuric acid—2, 4
Sulfurous acid—2, 3

Tallow—*
Tanning liquors—*
Tar—2, 4, *
Tar & ammonia—*
Tetrachloride of tin—*
Tetraethyl of lead—*

Toluene—1, 2, 3, 4, *
Trichloroethylene—*
Triethylene glycol—2, 4
Turbine oils—4
Turpentine—1, 2, 3, 4, *

Urine—*

Varnish—2, 4 *
Vegetable juice—*
Vinegar—*
Vitriol—*

Water, 4-3, 3
Water, boiler feed—*
Water, make up—*
Water, distilled—2, 4, *
Water, fresh—2, 4, *
Water, heavy—2
Water, mine—*
Water, salt & sea—2, 4, *
Whale oil—*
Whiskey—*
White liquor—*
White water—*
Wine—*
Wood pulp—stock—*
Wood vinegar—*
Wort—*

Xylol (xylene)—1, 2, 4, *

Yeast—*

Zinc chloride—*
Zinc sulfate—*

9-14

WORLD-WIDE CAPABILITIES

in pump design and application
pump manufacture
pump technical service

INGERSOLL-RAND

9

WORLD WIDE

Here's where Ingersoll-Rand pumps are manufactured, sold and serviced

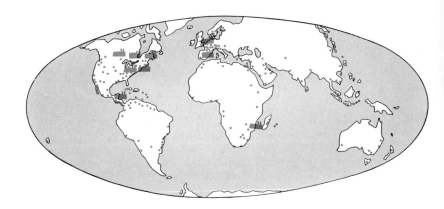

![factory] Pump Manufacturing Plants

Phillipsburg, N.J., U.S.A.
Allentown, Pa., U.S.A.
Hastings, Neb., U.S.A.
Gateshead, Co. Durham, England
Sherbrooke, Que., Canada
Kitchner/Cambridge, Ontario, Canada
Naucalpan de Juarez, Mexico
Alberton, Transvaal, So. Africa
Coslada, Madrid, Spain

● Pump Sales & Services Offices

For addresses of offices that can best serve you see pages following plant illustrations.

ILLUSTRATION (Preceding page)
Map of the world showing the two Hemispheres. Engraving by Honduis, mid 17th century. Courtesy The Bettman Archive, Inc., 136 E. 57th St., New York, N.Y. 10022

Ingersoll-Rand executive office at Woodcliff Lake, N.J., U.S.A.

Ingersoll-Rand has world-wide capabilities to supply your pump requirements with factories in strategic world-wide locations, sales offices in 29 countries and distributors in 80 countries. You are never far from a reliable source of supply and service.

Proven product designs, with extensive field experience, are available from these well-distributed production facilities. Ingersoll-Rand offices in all major capitals provide technical application service to insure proper selection followed by technical field service after the sale.

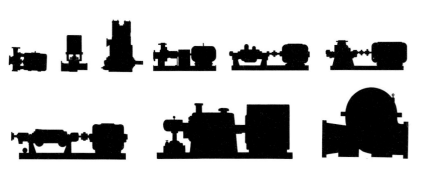

9

Engineered Pump Division
Phillipsburg, N.J., U.S.A.

Standard Pump Division
Allentown, Pa., U.S.A.

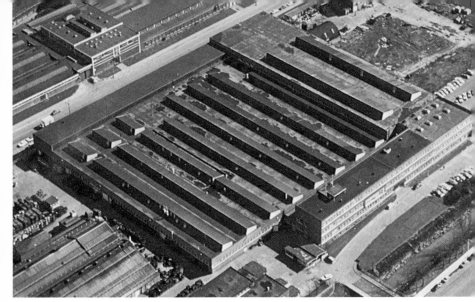

Ingersoll-Rand Pumps Ltd.
Gateshead Co. Durham, England

Ingersoll-Rand, S.A. de C.V.
Naucalpan de Juarez, Mexico

Canadian Machinery Corporation
(subsidiary of Canadian Ingersoll-Rand Company, Limited)
Cambridge, Ontario, Canada

CIA Ingersoll-Rand S.A.
Coslada (Madrid) Spain

Ingersoll-Rand Co. S.A. (Proprietary) Ltd.
Alberton (Johannesburg) Transvaal, South Africa

Ingersoll-Rand Pumps
Serve International Industrial
Activity In:

Electric Utilities (fossil & nuclear)

Marine	Pollution Control
Iron & Steel	General Industrial
Building Trades	Pulp & Paper
Chemical	Water Supply
Mining	Rubber
Petroleum	

Western Landroller
Hastings, Neb., U.S.A.

Addresses of sales and service offices on next page

INGERSOLL-RAND ADDRESSES
UNITED STATES

Atlanta
111 Ingersoll-Rand Dr.
Chamblee, GA 30341

Boston
65 Williams St.
Wellesley, MASS. 02181

Chicago
888 Industrial Dr.
Elmhurst, ILL. 60126

Cleveland
9257 Midwest Ave.
Cleveland, OH. 44125

Dallas
P.O. Box 47204 (F.C. Mail)
8901 Directors Row
Dallas TX. 75247

Denver
5805 East 39th Ave.
Denver, COL. 80207

Detroit
P.O. Box 209 (F.C. Mail)
22122 Telegraph Rd.
Southfield, MICH. 48037

Houston
P.O. Box 1455
6800 Sands Point Dr.
Houston, TX. 77001

Kansas City
8900 Ward Pkwy.
Kansas City, MO. 64114

Los Angeles
5533 East Olympic Blvd.
Commerce, CA. 90022

Minneapolis
Cr. Franklin & Cedar Aves.
Minneapolis, MINN. 55404

Newark
222 Old New Brunswick Rd.
Piscataway, N.J. 08854

New Orleans
P.O. Box 9426 (F.C. Mail)
939 Lake Ave.
Metairie, LA. 70055

New York
277 Park Ave.
New York, N.Y. 10017

Philadelphia
P.O. Box 425
651 Park Ave.
King of Prussia, PA. 19406

Pittsburgh
Six Parkway Cntr.
Pittsburgh, PA. 15220

Richmond
2715A Enterprice Pkwy.
Richmond, VA. 23229

St. Louis
1515 Page Industrial Blvd.
St. Louis, MO. 63132

San Francisco
101 Howard St.
San Francisco, CA. 94105

Tulsa
P.O. Box 3167 (mail)
6106 E. 32 Pl.
Tulsa, OKLA. 74101

CANADA
Canadian Ingersoll-Rand Co., Limited

611 11th Avenue, S.W.
Calgary, Alberta T2R 0E1 Canada

P.O. Box 1148 Station B
Montreal, Quebec H3B 3K9
Canada

P.O. Box 2220
Sudbury, Ontario P3A 3T3
Canada

255 Lesmill Rd., Don Mills
Toronto, Ontario M3B 2V1
Canada

1234 Border St.
Winnipeg, Manitoba R3H 0M6
Canada

1695 Main Street
Vancouver, B.C. V6A 2W7
Canada

AUTONOMOUS COMPANIES

Argentina
Ingersoll-Rand Argentina
   S.A.I. y C.
Casilla 2412
Correo Central
Buenos Aires, Argentina

Australia
Ingersoll-Rand (Australia) Ltd.
P.O. Box 219
South Melbourne 3205 Victoria
Australia

Austria
Ingersoll-Rand Gesmb H
Schoenbrunnerstrasse
   213-215/2/5
A2110 Vienna, Austria

Bahrain
Ingersoll-Rand Bahrain (Manama)
P.O. Box 5797
Manama, Bahrain

Belgium
Ingersoll-Rand Benelux S.A.
Kouterveldstraat 10-12 B1920
Machelen, Belgium

Brazil
Ingersoll-Rand S.A. Industria e
Comercio
Caixa Postal 911
Sao Bernardo do Campo
Est. Sao Paulo, Brazil

Colombia
Maquinarias Ingersoll-Rand de
Colombia, S.A.
Apartado Aereo 7451
Bogotá, Columbia

Egypt
Ingersoll-Rand North East Africa
P.O. Box 820
Cairo, Egypt

France
Compagnie Ingersoll-Rand
Avenue Albert Einstein
Zone Industrielle
78 190 Trappes, France

Germany
Ingersoll-Rand GmbH
403 Ratingen
Postfach 1380
Ratingen, Germany

Hong Kong
Ingersoll-Rand Far East
19th Floor, Lap Heng House
50, Gloucester Rd.
Hong Kong

India
Ingersoll-Rand (India) Ltd.
P.O. Box 9138
Bombay 400025 India

Ireland
Ingersoll-Rand Company
(Ireland) Ltd.
John F. Kennedy Dr.
Bluebell, Dublin 12, Ireland

Italy
Ingersoll-Rand Italiana S.p.A.
Casella Postale 1232
20100—Milan, Italy

Japan
Ingersoll-Rand Japan, Ltd.
Kowa Bldg., No. 17
2-7 Nishi-Azabu 1-Chome
Minato-Ku
Tokyo, 106, Japan

Latin America
Latin American Distributor
Operations
3651 N.W. 79 Avenue
Miami Springs, Fla. 33166

Malaysia
Ingersoll-Rand Malaysia,
Sdn, Bhd.
P.O. Box 125
Petaling Jaya
Selangor, Malaysia

Mexico
Ingersoll-Rand S.A. de C.V.
Apartado 41-666
Mexico 10, D.F., Mexico

Mid Africa
Ingersoll-Rand Co. Ltd.
Bowater House, Knightsbridge
London, SW1X 7LU England

Middle East
Ingersoll-Rand Middle East
Mesogion 2-4
Athens, 610, Greece

Netherlands
Ingersoll-Rand Nederland N.V.
P.O. Box 33
Zoeterwoude, Netherlands

Norway
Ingersoll-Rand AB
P.O. Box 143—Sentrum
Oslo, 11, Norway

Peru
Ingersoll-Rand Co. of Peru, S.A.
Casilla 2261
Lima, Peru

Philippines
Ingersoll-Rand Philippines, Inc.
P.O. Box 445 MCC
Makati, Rizal 3117
Philippines

Portugal
Ingersoll-Rand Lda.
Apartado 2933
Lisbon, Portugal

Singapore
Ingersoll-Rand South East Asia
(Pte.) Ltd.
G.P.O Box 2062, Singapore 1

South Africa
Ingersoll-Rand Co. S.A.
(Proprietary) Ltd.
P.O. Box 3720
Alrode, 1451
Alberton, South Africa

Spain
Cia Ingersoll-Rand S.A.
Apartado 518
Madrid, Spain

Sweden
Ingersoll-Rand A.B.
Fack
S-16125 Bromma 1 Sweden

United Kingdom
Ingersoll-Rand Co., Ltd.
Bowater House, Knightsbridge
London, SW1X 7LU England

Venezuela
Ingersoll-Rand de Venezuela
S.A.
Apartado 70588, Los Ruices
Caracas, 1071, Venezuela

Offices or distributors in principal cities the world over

INGERSOLL-RAND

WOODCLIFF LAKE, NEW JERSEY 07675

9

9